PROPERTY of A. BISCHOFF

BETZ HANDBOOK
OF INDUSTRIAL WATER CONDITIONING

SIXTH EDITION

BETZ HANDBOOK

OF INDUSTRIAL

WATER CONDITIONING

SIXTH EDITION

1962

Published by

TREVOSE, PENNSYLVANIA 19047

SIXTH EDITION - 1962
Third Printing—July, 1967

Library of Congress Catalog Card Number: 62-21097

•

Copyright 1962

BETZ LABORATORIES, INC.

TREVOSE, PENNSYLVANIA 19047

•

Printed in U. S. A.

Acknowledgment

This book was prepared by the engineering and technical staff of Betz Laboratories, Inc. Many individuals contributed to this edition and previous editions. We particularly wish to thank the following for their editorial contributions to this Sixth Edition.

H. L. Boyer
A. B. Cherry
R. B. Conlan
J. M. Donohue
C. M. Frova
P. J. Gaughan
H. B. Haldeman
R. H. Hayman
J. B. Lord
J. J. Maguire
S. O. Meyer
W. L. Nieland
C. A. Noll

A. J. Piluso
O. H. Preis
M. U. Priester
L. F. Probst
R. L. Reed
J. H. Richards
C. J. Schafer
J. R. Schieber
B. F. Shema
W. A. Tanzola
J. G. Weidman
G. A. Wilhelm

TABLE OF CONTENTS

INDUSTRIAL WATER TREATMENT PROBLEMS AND PROCESSES

CONTROL WATER ANALYSES AND THEIR INTERPRETATION

1

Industrial Water Conditioning

Water, used directly or indirectly in an industrial process, is classed as industrial water. The use of water in boilers for steam generation is an obvious industrial use. Cooling water, either on a once-through basis or with cooling towers, is a prominent industrial use. Water is essential to large air conditioning systems. But, water has a multitude of industrial uses—some as commonplace as washing of equipment—others specific to an individual industry or plant, such as use in a high pressure spray for debarking logs. Water is incorporated in many products and foods. Water is used as a carrier in industrial processes and as a convenient means of disposing of wastes.

Figure 1-1 · External Treatment by Hot Process Softening

WHAT IS
INDUSTRIAL WATER CONDITIONING?

To many people, industrial water conditioning is shrouded in an air of mystery. Much of this confusion is due to a lack of understanding of what industrial water conditioning is . . . and what it is supposed to accomplish.

Basically, industrial water conditioning embraces the broad field of *fitting water to the job*. Its purpose is twofold. One—it involves *removing* or minimizing undesirable characteristics of water, such as removing hardness by softening to avoid boiler scale. Two—it involves *adding* desirable properties to water, such as adding chromate ion to give corrosion inhibitory properties.

Industrial water conditioning may be grouped into two major parts or spheres of operation—external treatment and internal treatment.

EXTERNAL TREATMENT

This phase of industrial water conditioning has many names: preliminary treatment, pre-treatment, indirect treatment, primary purification, etc. Whatever it is called, it means doing something to a water to make it more suitable for its intended application *before it reaches the point of use.*

External treatment usually requires the use of equipment, which may include hot or cold process lime-soda softeners, zeolite and other ion exchange systems; deaerators, filters, clarifiers, etc. Such equipment is used for the purpose of reducing hardness and alkalinity, eliminating dissolved oxygen and for the removal of suspended solids.

The use of external treatment should be as complete as can be justified by the severity of the water problem and engineering economies.

Regardless of the purity of the water provided by the use of such equipment, additional internal chemical treatments normally are required for complete protection against scale, corrosion, and a host of other potential sources of trouble.

There are often cases where an investment in external treatment equipment is not warranted because of non-critical requirements, a good water supply, small size of the plant, or a combination of these reasons. In such cases, internal chemical treatment alone, will produce successful operating results.

INTERNAL CHEMICAL TREATMENT

Like external treatment, this phase of industrial water conditioning is known by several names: secondary treatment, after-treatment, direct treatment, etc. In this case, it means doing something to a water *at the point of use* to make it suitable for its intended application.

In boiler water systems, the objective of internal treatment is to make possible the control of scale formation and corrosive action. Steam purity and caustic embrittlement must be controlled. It also may be necessary to use internal chemical treatment to prevent return line corrosion due to dissolved gases liberated in the boiler system.

Internal chemical treatment is used also in cooling water systems for the prevention of scale and corrosion, as well as conditions brought about by biological growths. Proper application of internal chemical treatment results in improved heat transfer by eliminating these insulating deposits.

There are cases, too, where internal chemical treatment is used in the solution of specific water problems other than in boiler and cool-

ing systems. These cases include the use of chemicals at various points in process applications to impart desirable properties to a water.

Water conditioning is in many respects unlike any other field of engineering. It demands an unusual variety of talents including those of the chemical, mechanical, corrosion and sanitary engineer, microbiologist, physical chemist and bacteriologist.

WATER CONDITIONING CONTROL

Control water analyses are an essential part of any industrial water conditioning program. The processes of corrosion, scaling, slime formation and the like are dynamic, not static. The treatment measures employed for their control must be adjusted frequently on the basis of control water analyses. Such analyses need not determine every ion or substance present in the water, but only those required for control of treatment process. For example, in sodium zeolite softening the important tests for control purposes are hardness and chloride. The hardness test is employed to determine the end of the softening cycle and the chloride test to determine the end of the rinse cycle.

INDUSTRIAL WATER PROBLEMS

Following is a list of the more common water problems that plague industry. Each industry has its individual problems. This list is not intended to be complete, but only to indicate the great variety of problems common to most industries.

Figure 1-2 · Internal Treatment Chemical Tanks and Pumps

Boiler Water Problems

Scale Deposits
Excessive Sludge
General Corrosion
Pitting
Carryover
Embrittlement
Feedline and Heater Deposits
High Blowdown Rate
Carbonized Oil

Steam and Condensate Problems

Carbon Dioxide Grooving
Oxygen Pitting
Turbine Blade Deposits
Superheater Fouling
Oil Contamination
Condenser Leakage
Process Contamination

Cooling and Process Water Problems

Deposition of Scale
General Corrosion
Fungus Attack of Cooling Tower Wood
Product Contamination
Pitting and Tuberculation
Slime and Algae Deposits
Red Water

*Figure 1-3 · Plant Operator
Conducting Control Analyses*

Preliminary Treatment Problems
(removal of impurities)

Turbidity, Mud, Silt
Excessive Color
Iron and Manganese
Soluble Silica
High Hardness
Acidity or Alkalinity
Objectionable Gases—CO_2, H_2S, NH_3
High Solids
Microorganisms

General Problems

Poor Quality Water Supply
Waste of Water—Lack of Re-use
Inadequate Pretreatment Equipment
Improper Control of Existing Equipment
Unsatisfactory Chemical Feeding
Stream Pollution
Waste Disposal
High Costs
Improper Over-all
    Water Conditioning Program

2

Water and its Impurities

IF water as it occurs in nature were "pure" water and nothing else there would be no need for water analyses and water conditioning. Whatever the source, water always contains impurities in solution or suspension. It is the determination of these impurities that makes water analyses necessary and the control of these impurities that makes water conditioning essential.

Pure water is tasteless, colorless and odorless and is one of the most universal solvents. The chemical formula for water is H_2O (or HOH) and it is composed of two volumes of hydrogen and one volume of oxygen, chemically combined.

SOURCES

The various sources of water can be conveniently classified as:

Rain water.

Surface water (streams, ponds, lakes and impounded reservoirs).

Ground water (from springs, shallow wells and deep wells).

Water is evaporated from the surface of the

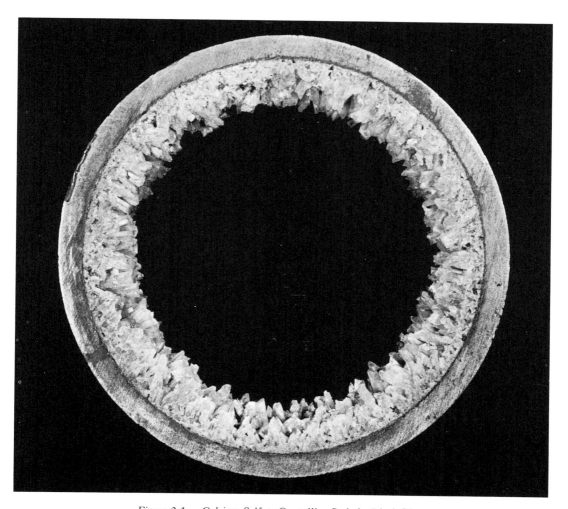

Figure 2-1 • Calcium Sulfate Crystalline Scale in 5 inch Line

Figure 2-2 • Pipe Section Pitted from Dissolved Oxygen

earth by heat furnished from the sun. Water precipitated from the atmosphere, high above the earth's surface, is chemically pure. As water descends through the air oxygen, nitrogen and carbon dioxide (the normal gases present in the atmosphere) are dissolved in the falling water in proportion to their partial pressure in the atmosphere. Rain water also encounters dust, smoke and fumes which are dissolved or retained in suspension. Bacteria and the spores of microscopic organisms may be picked up.

RAIN WATER. Rain water in descending through the air and in percolating through the upper layers of soil absorbs carbon dioxide with which it forms carbonic acid. This action increases the solvent power of the water so that it dissolves a certain amount of the mineral matter of the soil or rock with which it comes in contact. Water obtained from surface streams may be rendered turbid by the presence of clay and silt. Agricultural land may contribute to the

organic matter and may pollute the water with animal waste. Swamps may discharge their waters during floods and carry decay and vegetable matter, color and microscopic organisms into the stream. In addition, surface waters are exposed to pollution by animals and humans, the sewage of cities, and the wastes of industry.

SURFACE WATERS. Surface waters obtained from ponds, lakes and impounded reservoirs are similar to those from flowing streams. However, within these large bodies of water considerable self-purification may take place and the water quality may change to a large extent.

GROUND WATER. Ground water obtained from shallow wells may be hard or soft depending upon the mineral characteristics of the surrounding area. Natural filtration through the sand will usually provide a water relatively free of turbidity and with low organic matter. The water from shallow wells is usually softer than deep wells.

The water from deep wells usually contains relatively high concentrations of dissolved minerals. These waters are usually clear and colorless due to the filtration taking place through the layers of sand.

Spring water is usually similar in characteristics to water obtained from shallow or deep wells in the surrounding area. However, springs are more likely to be affected by the normal surface pollution due to their relatively shallow origin.

IMPURITIES

The impurities that may be present in a water supply can be divided into suspended and dissolved solids. Suspended solids are those which do not dissolve in water and which can be removed or separated by filtration. Examples of suspended solids are mud, clay or silt. Dissolved solids are those which naturally dissolve in the water and which therefore cannot be removed by filtration. The presence of hardness or chloride in a water supply is an example of dissolved solids. Gases may also dissolve in water, but unless they combine chemically with other impurities also in solution, these gases will be expelled from the water on boiling and are not considered as dissolved solids.

Fig. 2-4 is a listing of the analytical determinations made in the examination of most natural waters. Illustrated are the chemical formula, if one can be given, the difficulties commonly caused by the presence of that constituent and the usual means of treatment to prevent these difficulties. This listing covers the usual determinations made in the analysis of a water prior to treatment. Of course, for certain special water uses, additional analyses are necessary. For example, boron is of importance in irrigation waters because of its effect on the growth of certain crops. Boron possesses little significance industrially and usually is not determined in a water analysis. Similarly, water analyses are made for certain constituents that are added to water as a method of treatment. For example, chromate is employed as a corrosion inhibitor in cooling

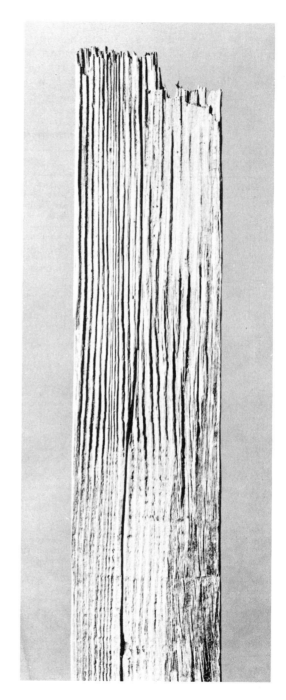

Figure 2-3 • Delignification of Cooling Tower Wood

water systems, phosphate as a precipitating agent in boiler water and sulfite is used to control oxygen corrosion. Analyses must be made of such treating agents for control purposes. Figure 2-4, however, deals only with the constituents that normally are present naturally in untreated water supplies and is not intended as a complete listing of all of the analytical determinations that should be made where specific problems are involved.

Fig. 2-4—Common Impurities Found in Water

CONSTITUENT	CHEMICAL FORMULA	DIFFICULTIES CAUSED	MEANS OF TREATMENT
TURBIDITY	None—expressed in analysis as units.	Imparts unsightly appearance to water. Deposits in water lines, process equipment, boilers, etc. Interferes with most process uses.	Coagulation, settling and filtration.
COLOR	None—expressed in analysis as units.	May cause foaming in boilers. Hinders precipitation methods such as iron removal, hot phosphate softening. Can stain product in process use.	Coagulation and filtration. Chlorination. Adsorption by activated carbon.
HARDNESS	Calcium and magnesium salts expressed as $CaCO_3$.	Chief source of scale in heat exchange equipment, boilers, pipe lines, etc. Forms curds with soap, interferes with dyeing, etc.	Softening. Distillation. Internal boiler water treatment. Surface active agents.
ALKALINITY	Bicarbonate (HCO_3), carbonate (CO_3), and hydrate (OH), expressed as $CaCO_3$.	Foaming and carryover of solids with steam. Embrittlement of boiler steel. Bicarbonate and carbonate produce CO_2 in steam, a source of corrosion.	Lime and lime-soda softening. Acid treatment. Hydrogen zeolite softening. Demineralization. Dealkalization by anion exchange. Distillation.
FREE MINERAL ACID	H_2SO_4, HCl, etc. expressed as $CaCO_3$.	Corrosion	Neutralization with alkalies.
CARBON DIOXIDE	CO_2	Corrosion in water lines and particularly steam and condensate lines.	Aeration. Deaeration. Neutralization with alkalies. Filming and neutralizing amines.
pH	Hydrogen ion concentration defined as: $$pH = \log \frac{1}{(H^+)}$$	pH varies according to acidic or alkaline solids in water. Most natural waters have a pH of 6.0-8.0.	pH can be increased by alkalies and decreased by acids.
SULFATE	$(SO_4)^{--}$	Adds to solids content of water, but, in itself, is not usually significant. Combines with calcium to form calcium sulfate scale.	Demineralization. Distillation.
CHLORIDE	Cl^-	Adds to solids content and increases corrosive character of water.	Demineralization. Distillation.
NITRATE	$(NO_3)^-$	Adds to solids content, but is not usually significant industrially. High concentrations cause methemoglobinemia in infants. Useful for control of boiler metal embrittlement.	Demineralization. Distillation.
FLUORIDE	F^-	Cause of mottled enamel in teeth. Also used for control of dental decay. Not usually significant industrially.	Adsorption with mangnesium hydroxide, calcium phosphate, or bone black. Alum coagulation.

Fig. 2-4—Common Impurities Found in Water (cont.)

CONSTITUENT	CHEMICAL FORMULA	DIFFICULTIES CAUSED	MEANS OF TREATMENT
SILICA	SiO_2	Scale in boilers and cooling water systems. Insoluble turbine blade deposits due to silica vaporization.	Hot process removal with magnesium salts. Adsorption by highly basic anion exchange resins, in conjunction with demineralization. Distillation.
IRON	Fe^{++} (ferrous) Fe^{+++} (ferric)	Discolors water on precipitation. Source of deposits in water lines, boilers, etc. Interferes with dyeing, tanning, paper mfr., etc.	Aeration. Coagulation and filtration. Lime softening. Cation exchange. Contact filtration. Surface active agents for iron retention.
MANGANESE ...	Mn^{++}	Same as iron.	Same as iron.
OIL	Expressed as oil or chloroform extractable matter.	Scale, sludge and foaming in boilers. Impedes heat exchange. Undesirable in most processes.	Baffle separators. Strainers. Coagulation and filtration. Diatomaceous earth filtration.
OXYGEN	O_2	Corrosion of water lines, heat exchange equipment, boilers, return lines, etc.	Deaeration. Sodium sulfite. Corrosion inhibitors.
HYDROGEN SULFIDE	H_2S	Cause of "rotten egg" odor. Corrosion.	Aeration. Chlorination. Highly basic anion exchange.
AMMONIA	NH_3	Corrosion of copper and zinc alloys by formation of complex soluble ion.	Cation exchange with hydrogen zeolite. Chlorination. Deaeration.
CONDUCTIVITY	Expressed as micromhos, specific conductance.	Conductivity is the result of ionizable solids in solution. High conductivity can increase the corrosive characteristics of a water.	Any process which decreases dissolved solids content will decrease conductivity. Examples are demineralization, lime softening.
DISSOLVED SOLIDS	None	"Dissolved solids" is measure of total amount of dissolved matter, determined by evaporation. High concentrations of dissolved solids are objectionable because of process interference and as a cause of foaming in boilers.	Various softening process, such as lime softening and cation exchange by hydrogen zeolite, will reduce dissolved solids. Demineralization. Distillation.
SUSPENDED SOLIDS	None	"Suspended Solids" is the measure of undissolved matter, determined gravimetrically. Suspended solids plug lines, cause deposits in heat exchange equipment, boilers, etc.	Subsidence. Filtration, usually preceded by coagulation and settling.
TOTAL SOLIDS ..	None	"Total Solids" is the sum of dissolved and suspended solids, determined gravimetrically.	See "Dissolved Solids" and "Suspended Solids."

3

Aeration

Aeration is a process which consists of intimately admixing water and air in some manner. This mixing may be accomplished in the form of a thin film, drops or spray. Aeration is based on the establishment of a state of equilibrium between the gases present in the water and those present in the atmosphere.

Aeration is employed primarily for the removal of undesirable gases from water. Carbon dioxide and hydrogen sulfide are corrosive gases and, when present in appreciable quantities, must be removed to avoid corrosion of lines, pumps and equipment. Although aeration results in saturating water with another corrosive gas — oxygen — this process is the one most commonly used for the elimination of carbon dioxide and hydrogen sulfide.

In some cases, the purpose in removing carbon dioxide by aeration is simply to reduce chemical treatment requirements where the water is subsequently lime softened. Carbon dioxide can be removed more economically by aeration than by chemical precipitation with lime.

In the removal of iron and manganese from water, aeration is frequently employed. The oxygen introduced by aeration encourages the chemical oxidation of iron and manganese, thus aiding in their precipitation as the insoluble hydroxides.

Aeration may be employed in potable water treatment for the removal of certain tastes and odors, such as those resulting from the decomposition of algae. In sewage treatment, aeration is used to promote the biochemical oxidation of organic matter.

THEORY INVOLVED

The removal of gases from water by aeration follows Henry's Law which, in brief, states that the solubility of a gas in water is directly proportional to its partial pressure in the surrounding atmosphere. At 20 C and at sea level, water in equilibrium with the atmosphere will contain approximately 15.8 ppm nitrogen, 9.4 ppm oxygen, 0.5 ppm carbon dioxide and no measurable amount of hydrogen sulfide.

Both carbon dioxide and hydrogen sulfide are relatively soluble in water. At 20 C and sea level, carbon dioxide is soluble to the extent of approximately 1700 ppm while hydrogen sulfide solubility is approximately 3900 ppm. The partial pressure of each of these gases in a normal atmosphere, however, is practically "zero." Consequently, the establishment of a state of equilibrium between water and air by means of aeration will result in saturation of the water with nitrogen and oxygen and the practically complete elimination of carbon dioxide and hydrogen sulfide from the water.

The basic requirement in securing removal of gases by aeration is the establishment of a state of equilibrium between the gases in the water and those present in the surrounding atmosphere. The removal of gases by aeration is favored by increase in temperature, increase in aeration time, increase in the volume of air in contact with the water and increase in the surface area of water exposed to the air. The efficiency of aeration is greater where the concentration of the gas to be removed is high in the water and low in the atmosphere. For example, aeration efficiency is higher with a water containing 100 ppm carbon dioxide, than with one containing only 10 ppm.

BASIC AERATION METHODS

Aeration is primarily a mechanical process for which two general methods are employed. The first method is that where the water falls through the air as with the use of spray nozzles, cascade devices and forced draft type aerators. This method of aeration is the most common in industrial water conditioning.

The second general method of aeration is where air is bubbled up through a solid body of water, as in a tank, and is known as the air diffusion method. In industrial water conditioning this method is usually confined to the treatment of relatively low flows.

WATER FALL AERATORS. Many variations of the water fall principle are in use. The simplest is the use of vertical risers to discharge the water by free fall into a basin. The risers can operate on the available head of water and efficiency of aeration is increased by making the fall as great as practical. The addition of steps or shelves to break up the fall and to spread the water into thin sheets or films increases contact time and acts as a further refinement. Spray nozzles are another variation of this principle and can provide efficient removal of dissolved gases. However, space requirements frequently limit the usefulness of this type aeration in industrial water conditioning.

Coke tray aerators and wood slat aerators are relatively similar in design and possess the advantage of smaller space requirements. Coke tray aerators are widely used in iron and manganese removal since a catalytic effect is secured by contact of the iron-bearing water with freshly precipitated iron sludge. As shown by Figure 3-1, these units consist of a series of coke filled trays through which the water percolates with additional aeration supplied during the free fall from one tray to the next. Wood slat tray aerators are similar to small atmospheric cooling towers. The tray slats are staggered so as to break up the free fall of water and to spread out the water surface before finally dropping into a basin.

Forced draft aerators, as illustrated by Figure 3-2, are favored for many industrial water conditioning purposes. These units

Courtesy Infilco, Incorporated

Figure 3-1 • Coke Tray Aerator

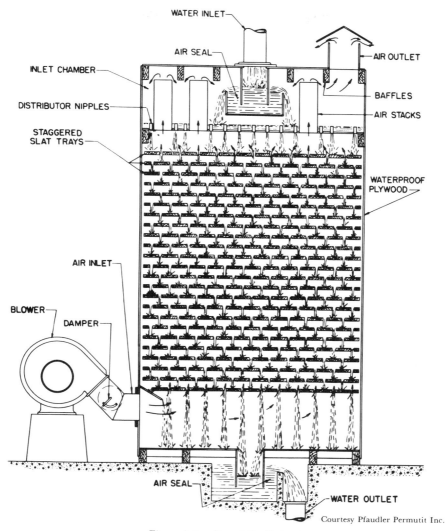

WATER INLET

AIR SEAL

INLET CHAMBER

DISTRIBUTOR NIPPLES

STAGGERED SLAT TRAYS

AIR INLET

BLOWER

DAMPER

AIR OUTLET

BAFFLES

AIR STACKS

WATERPROOF PLYWOOD

AIR SEAL

WATER OUTLET

Courtesy Pfaudler Permutit Inc.

Figure 3-2 • Forced Draft Aerator

provide horizontal wood slat trays which divide the falling water into small streams. Air is forced up through the unit by a blower with uniform air distribution across the entire cross section. Air flow is counter-current to the fall of water and positive air circulation prevents any stagnant areas. Because of these features, forced draft aerators are more efficient for gas removal and require less space for a given capacity.

AIR DIFFUSION. Air diffusion is accomplished by pumping air into water through perforated pipes, strainers, porous plates or tubes. Aeration by diffusion is theoretically superior to water fall aeration inasmuch as a fine bubble of air rising through water will continually be exposed to fresh liquid surfaces, providing maximum water surface per unit of air. Also, the velocity of bubbles ascending through the water is much slower than the velocity of free falling drops of water, providing longer contact. However, for gas removal, air requirements by the diffusion method are higher than for odor removal and the cost of the air supply is a factor restricting application of this type of aeration in industrial water conditioning.

APPLICATIONS

In industrial water conditioning one of the major applications of aeration is in the removal of the corrosive characteristics imparted to water by the presence of carbon dioxide and hydrogen sulfide. On many occasions aeration is used to remove the carbon dioxide liberated by a treatment process. For example, in boiler feedwater conditioning, it is common practice to acid treat the effluent from a sodium zeolite softener in order to reduce the alkalinity of the boiler feedwater. Carbon dioxide is produced as a result of the acid treatment and aeration is employed to rid the water of this corrosive gas. Similarly, when the effluents of hydrogen and sodium zeolite units are blended, the carbon dioxide formed is eliminated by aeration. In anion-cation exchange, aeration is similarly used. Forced draft aerators are usually employed in these applications.

Aeration is also applied for the removal of methane from certain ground waters. Since methane constitutes an explosion hazard on release in confined spaces, aeration is employed for its removal. Electric motors in the vicinity are undesirable and forced draft aerators are not employed in this application.

Iron and manganese removal can be secured with a variety of methods. In all but a few of the processes used, aeration plays a part since it is a convenient method of supplying the oxygen required for the oxidation of iron and manganese. However, aeration alone should not be considered a universally effective method for the removal of iron and manganese, but rather only as a part of the treatment steps required.

In municipal water treatment practice, aeration has been employed primarily for the removal of odors due to volatile materials.

Aeration has also been applied as an aid in rapid mixing of chemicals, and in backwashing filters as well as for the esthetic effect in water works plants.

LIMITATIONS

Theoretically, at 20 C it is possible to reduce the carbon dioxide content of the water to 0.5 ppm by means of aeration to equilibrium conditions. Practically, it is not economical to attempt such complete gas removal and reduction of carbon dioxide to 10 ppm is normally considered satisfactory.

Although removal of free carbon dioxide increases the pH of a water and renders it less corrosive from this standpoint, aeration also results in the saturation of the water with dissolved oxygen. In some cases, where the original oxygen content is already quite high, no undesirable effect is thus produced. However, in the case of a well supply, high in carbon dioxide but devoid of oxygen, aeration may simply exchange one corrosive gas for another.

The efficiency of aeration is greatest where the initial concentration of the gas to be removed is considerably above its equilibrium value. Therefore, with waters containing only a small amount of carbon dioxide, lime treatment is usually more efficient.

Aeration alone will not secure the complete removal of hydrogen sulfide, but must be combined with pH reduction or chlorination.

Where odors are not due to the gases of decomposition or to volatile oils, aeration will not remove these odors. Tastes and odors due to industrial wastes, phenols and cresols are unaffected by aeration. The medicinal taste imparted to water by the chlorination of water containing phenols and cresols is not removed by aeration.

REFERENCES

"Aeration of Water", *Journal*, Am. Water Works Assoc., Vol. 47, pp. 873-885 (1955)
M. L. Riehl, "Hoover's Water Supply and Treatment", 8th Ed., pp. 18-19, National Lime Assoc., Washington, D.C. (1957)

4

Subsidence

SUBSIDENCE is the process which permits the settling of suspended substances from water.

The main purpose of subsidence is to effect clarification of a water by permitting the settling of suspended matter and consequent reduction in turbidity. Subsidence is of value chiefly in the removal of coarse particles which settle rapidly and which can be more economically removed in this fashion than by coagulation. A secondary result of subsidence is removal of bacteria. Percentage bacteria removal generally closely parallels turbidity removal. While dependent on many factors, turbidity and bacteria removal by subsidence may vary from 30% to 80%.

THEORY INVOLVED

All particles heavier than water possess a tendency to settle due to the influence of gravity. The time required for settling is dependent on a number of factors such as the weight, shape and size of the particle together with the viscosity and frictional resistance of the water.

To illustrate the effect of particle size, the following tabulation is presented:

VELOCITIES AT WHICH PARTICLES OF
SAND AND SILT WILL SUBSIDE IN STILL WATER

10C (50F)
Specific Gravity = 2.65

Diameter of Particle, in mm	Order of Magnitude	Time Required to Settle 1 Foot
10.0	Gravel	0.3 seconds
1.0	Coarse Sand	3 seconds
0.1	Fine Sand	38 seconds
0.01	Silt	33 minutes
0.001	Bacteria	35 hours
0.0001	Clay Particles	230 days
0.00001	Colloidal Particles	63 years

The specific gravity of suspended particles is one of the main factors governing the rate of settling. Particles of high specific gravity will naturally settle at a faster rate than those of a specific gravity only slightly greater than that of water.

The viscosity of the water is also a major factor influencing settling velocity and the water viscosity is, in turn, dependent on the temperature. For example, the rate of settling at 0 C is only 43% of the settling rate at 30 C. It is for this reason that greater efficiency in turbidity removal by subsidence may be obtained during the summer months when water temperatures are higher. During the winter months, with normally lower water temperatures, the rate of settling will be reduced and lower efficiency results or else it may be necessary to increase the time permitted for subsidence.

Settling velocities may be calculated from Stoke's Law.

$$V = \frac{18.5 \, D^2 \, (S_1 - S_2)}{Z}$$

Where:

V = Velocity of fall in feet per second.

D = Diameter in inches of particle.

S_1 = Density of particle in pounds per cubic foot.

S_2 = Density of fluid in pounds per cubic foot.

Z = Viscosity in centipoises.

In employing this equation it is assumed that the particles are spherical, falling under viscous resistance in an infinitely large body of fluid.

The use of Stoke's Law and tabulation of settling velocity is based on still water. Theoretically, velocity of flow in a horizontal plane will not affect settling velocity of the suspended particles because their downward movement is caused by gravity. However, velocity of flow in a vertical plane and convection currents directly tend to prevent settling. Design of subsidence basins is therefore such as to keep such interferences to a minimum and to assure continued quiescence of the water.

A study of the tabulation of settling velocities will indicate that for industrial purposes the practical limit on solids removal by subsidence is for particles of a diameter of

0.01 mm or more. Smaller particles have such a low rate of settling that the time required is greater than can be practically allowed. In large storage reservoirs having a retention period of weeks and months, it is possible to effect removals of particles of less than 0.01 mm diameter.

EQUIPMENT EMPLOYED

Subsidence may be employed by using a simple tank which is filled with the turbid water and allowed to stand. After the sediment has settled, the clarified water may be decanted off and the settled solids removed from the bottom. The tank is then ready to be refilled for another cycle. This method is designated as a "fill and draw" system, and the settling rates will correspond to those previously tabulated.

Continuous methods of subsidence are in greater use in plants of recent design. This is accomplished by passing the water through a basin or tank of such size, shape and design that the velocity of the water is reduced to a point sufficiently low to permit settling of the readily settleable solids. Clarified water is removed from the tank continuously from an overflow, the settled solids remaining in the bottom of the tank.

In smaller plants of less than 1 million gallons per day, usually only one settling basin is employed. In larger plants, two or three basins in series are used. The use of three basins is favored to permit the removal of one basin from service for cleaning, while two basins remain on line. Where continuous sludge removal is used, one basin is adequate even in plants of greater capacity.

Basins are usually rectangular and if only one basin is employed, the use of a square layout provides the most economical construction. However, in many cases the basin dimensions must be made to fit the space available. Sloping bottoms are provided to facilitate sludge removal by flushing with high pressure jets. Depth of settling basins will vary usually over the range of 12 to 20 feet with an average of 16 feet.

It is necessary in basin design to make allowance for the sludge accumulated between cleanings. Twenty-five per cent of the tank volume is usually provided for this purpose. When proper settling is no longer obtained, due to sludge accumulation, the tank is drained and flushed.

In the larger tanks and particularly where there is a considerable amount of sludge, mechanical means are provided frequently for continuous sludge removal. Mechanically operated rakes and scrapers travel just above the floor and collect sludge to the draw off point for continuous removal. The design and speed of operation of the scrapers must be such that a minimum of disturbance is presented to the desired settling of the suspended solids.

APPLICATIONS AND LIMITATIONS

Waters containing turbidity due to relatively large size or high density suspended solids may be clarified to a substantial degree by subsidence. This applies to natural waters, sewage and industrial trade wastes. Subsidence is an economical method of obtaining clarification where it is applicable and in such cases is employed prior to coagulation.

Suspended solids of low specific gravity or those of fine particle size cannot be removed by subsidence within a reasonable period of time. Increase in basin size or retention period may not be feasible. In such cases, chemical coagulation is necessary to increase the size of the particles and render them more easily settleable.

REFERENCES

H. E. Babbitt and J. J. Doland, "Water Supply Engineering", 3rd Ed., pp. 499-509, McGraw-Hill Book Co., Inc., New York, N.Y. (1939)

M. N. Baker, "The Quest for Pure Water", pp. 286-298, Am. Water Works Assoc., New York, N.Y. (1948)

M. L. Riehl, "Hoover's Water Supply and Treatment", 8th Ed., pp. 37-39, National Lime Assoc., Washington, D.C. (1957)

"Water Quality and Treatment", 2nd Ed., pp. 131-162, Am. Water Works Assoc., New York, N.Y. (1950)

5

Coagulation

COAGULATION is that process whereby finely divided particles of turbidity and color, capable of remaining in suspension indefinitely, are combined by chemical means into masses sufficiently large to effect rapid settling.

Ordinary subsidence usually will not produce a water sufficiently low in turbidity to be suitable for domestic purposes or for most industrial requirements. Additional settling time is not usually of benefit because of the small size of the suspended particles and their slow settling rate. Filtration, without coagulation, will not remove the fine particles of turbidity if a filter medium sufficiently coarse for modern filtration rates is employed. Coagulation is required to agglomerate the suspended particles, thus making the water more readily filtered and also causing much of the coagulated matter to settle out prior to filtration.

THEORY OF COAGULATION

Coagulation reactions can be written very simply showing the use of aluminum or iron salts precipitating to form a floc of aluminum hydroxide or iron hydroxide. While these reactions will be shown for the sake of simplicity, coagulation is a much more complex phenomenon than thus illustrated.

It is thought that the precipitation of an aluminum or iron coagulant produces finely divided precipitates of the hydrous oxide. These precipitates are positively charged and thus repel each other. Neutralization of the positive charges by negative ions such as sulfate and chloride in the water causes coalescence of the fine particles, thus forming a gelatinous porous precipitate of large volume.

Flocculation, as practiced in water treatment, is the further increase in size and volume of the precipitate caused by bringing together by gentle agitation of the water a number of the individual precipitated hydrous oxide particles together with enmeshed turbidity to form larger and more readily settleable masses.

In the flocculation of the hydrous oxide particles into larger masses, the suspended turbidity particles, bacteria, microorganisms, etc., become enmeshed by the floc. Any suspended particles carrying a negative charge are more easily enmeshed by the floc and it is believed that color is removed in this fashion.

For each coagulant there is an optimum pH zone for best coagulation. It is desirable to control the pH to the point of maximum precipitation of the coagulant, equivalent to the minimum solubility of the floc. The best pH for this precipitation is dependent not only on the coagulant, however, but also upon the mineral characteristics of the water. For example, while alum will coagulate best at a pH of approximately 5.5 for pure distilled water, for most natural waters the ideal pH is higher and may range from pH 5.5 to 8.0.

The temperature of the water also affects the process of coagulation and at temperatures near the freezing point increased mixing time as well as increased coagulant doses may be required.

In general, successful coagulation involves three main factors:

1. The presence of a minimum quantity of aluminum or iron ions to form an insoluble floc.
2. The presence of a strong anion such as sulfate or chloride.
3. The pH of the water must be controlled within a definite range.

It is not possible to predict from the analysis of a water which will be the best coagulant to use, the quantities that will be required or the optimum pH for control of the process. For most efficient and economical coagulation it is necessary that laboratory tests be made with different coagulants at varied concentrations and varied pH levels. Laboratory stirring devices should be used in these tests to provide uniform test conditions. While previous practical experience with a given water will aid in selecting coagulant dosage and optimum pH, in order to consistently secure the desired results it is necessary to change coagulant dosage and pH control to compensate for varying raw water characteristics.

Coagulation problems vary greatly not only because of varying raw water characteristics, but also because of the ultimate use of the water. For potable systems the removal of bacteria and microorganisms is quite important and these requirements may affect coagulation control. For example, a slight excess of coagulant may be used over and above that necessary to produce a relatively clear water in order that bacteria removal may be increased in the sedimentation basin, thus reducing the residual chlorine concentration required in the finished water and minimizing taste and odor problems. These considerations would not be important in the preparation of boiler feedwater where clarity of the filter effluent at minimum coagulant dosage would be the controlling factor. In boiler feedwater conditioning, however, softening is usually important and coagulation may be combined with softening to achieve a finished water of the most desirable characteristics. The presence of iron and manganese in the raw supply introduces additional factors affecting coagulant choice and dosage. Industrial wastes present in the raw water also may complicate the coagulation problem.

TYPES OF EQUIPMENT

Three essential steps in the proper control of coagulation processes prior to filtration are:

1—Mixing
2—Flocculation
3—Sedimentation

It is important that the coagulant be mixed rapidly with the water to be treated in order to secure efficient coagulation at minimum chemical dosage. By rapid or "flash" mixing the coagulant is uniformly distributed throughout the water before precipitation is

Courtesy Graver Water Conditioning Co.

Figure 5-1 • Sludge Contact Clarifier

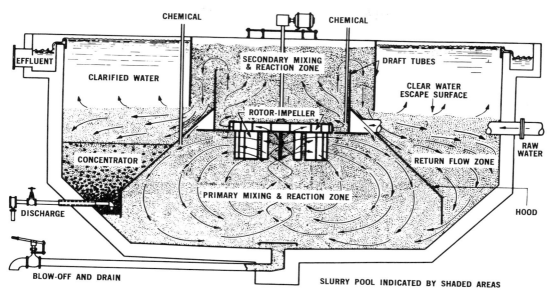

Figure 5-2 • Upflow Clarifier

Courtesy Infilco, Incorporated

completed. Mixing is secured usually by motor-driven propellers placed in small basins where the coagulant is introduced or by adding the coagulant at some point of turbulence.

Following mixing, the next step is to secure flocculation by bringing the small particles together under the influence of gentle mixing, thus permitting them to increase in size and therefore to settle more rapidly in the sedimentation basin. Flocculation may be achieved by the use of baffled basins where change in the direction of flow will produce the desired agitation. Lack of flexibility is inherent in this method since the agitation secured will vary with the rate of flow. Mechanical drive paddles or mixers are generally preferred for this purpose since their speed can be controlled to conform with the rate of flow and floc characteristics. With proper flocculation a uniform dense floc can usually be produced.

After mixing and floc formation, the treated water is passed to a sedimentation basin which provides the retention time for the floc particles to settle. Retention periods of two to six hours are usually provided. It is important to so design the basins as to avoid short-circuiting and to keep the velocity of flow quite low. Modern basins are usually designed for continuous mechanical desludging rather than the periodic draining and manual desludging employed in older designs.

Upflow clarifiers which combine in one unit the functions of mixing, flocculation and sedimentation have been installed in large numbers in recent years. Particularly in industrial practice, these units are favored because of the marked reduction in space requirements and installation cost. These units are designed for only one or two hours retention in comparison with two to six hours for conventional sedimentation basins.

Figure 5-2 illustrates one design of an upflow clarifier. In this unit the coagulant precipitates in the presence of a recirculated slurry of previously formed precipitates. Floc formation is encouraged by this slurry recirculation and finely divided precipitates are avoided. In the secondary mixing and reaction zone the raw water is circulated in contact with three to five volumes of recirculated slurry, aiding in bringing treatment reactions to equilibrium. Clarified water separates from the top of the slurry pool and sludge is automatically blown from the concentrator compartments. Units of this type provide efficient clarification of water in a single compact unit.

COAGULANTS

ALUM $Al_2(SO_4)_3.18H_2O$. The most widely used coagulant is aluminum sulfate or filter alum. Commercial filter alum contains slightly less water of crystallization than indicated by the above formula and corresponds to $Al_2(SO_4)_3.14H_2O$. This material is specified on the basis of 17% Al_2O_3 content. Alum is applicable as a coagulant over a pH range of approximately 5.5 to 8.0 and reacts with either natural or added alkalinity to produce a floc of aluminum hydroxide as illustrated below.

$Al_2(SO_4)_3$ + $3Ca(HCO_3)_2$ = $2Al(OH)_3$ +
aluminum + calcium = aluminum +
sulfate bicarbonate hydroxide

$3CaSO_4$ + $6CO_2$
calcium + carbon
sulfate dioxide

$Al_2(SO_4)_3$ + $3Na_2CO_3$ + $3H_2O$ =
aluminum + sodium + water =
sulfate carbonate

$2Al(OH)_3$ + $3Na_2SO_4$ + $3CO_2$
aluminum + sodium + carbon
hydroxide sulfate dioxide

$Al_2(SO_4)_3$ + $3Ca(OH)_2$ = $2Al(OH)_3$ +
aluminum + calcium = aluminum +
sulfate hydroxide hydroxide

$3CaSO_4$
calcium
sulfate

SODIUM ALUMINATE $Na_2Al_2O_4$. Sodium aluminate is actually aluminum oxide stabilized with caustic soda. A good commercial grade of sodium aluminate contains approximately 55% aluminum oxide, 35% combined sodium hydroxide and 6% excess sodium hydroxide. This material may be used in place of an alkali in water which must be coagulated with aluminum in a higher pH zone.

The use of sodium aluminate is advantageous under certain conditions because there is no need for additional alkali.

Sodium aluminate may be used in conjunction with alum, particularly for color removal. Alum alone, or in conjunction with acid, may be used to coagulate color at a relatively low pH with sodium aluminate added after primary color removal for pH adjustment and secondary coagulation.

Sodium aluminate is employed frequently as a coagulant in conjunction with both hot and cold lime-soda softening. In addition to providing a lower turbidity of the softener effluent, sodium aluminate assists in more complete precipitation of magnesium, thus reducing the magnesium content of the softened water. This effect on magnesium reduction is obtained to a greater extent in cold process softening, but is also of value in hot process softening.

Ammonium alum is not widely used in coagulation processes, but is useful in some special applications. In lump or crystal form ammonium alum dissolves slowly and is employed where alum pots are used for coagulant feed in small installations as in swimming pool practice. Truly proportional feeding is not achieved. On the basis of aluminum content, ammonium alum costs approximately three times as much as filter alum. The ammonia content may be of value where chlorine-ammonia treatment is used by eliminating the need of a separate source of ammonia.

Activated alum is a commercial brand of alum containing insoluble silicates to aid in the coagulation and to produce a tougher floc. This material contains less water of crystallization than the usual filter alum. Black alum is a commercial filter alum containing powdered activated carbon. Black alum is employed where it is desired to obtain both coagulation and a degree of taste and odor removal with a single material.

COPPERAS (Ferrous Sulfate—$FeSO_4.7H_2O$). The natural alkalinity of most waters is not sufficient to react with copperas to form the desired ferric hydroxide floc. Lime or another alkali must be added to produce this result. The first reaction with lime produces ferrous hydroxide which in turn is oxidized by the dissolved oxygen in the water to form ferric hydroxide. This oxidation occurs only at higher pH values and copperas is a suitable coagulant only in the alkaline pH range of 8.5 to 11.0.

$$FeSO_4 + Ca(OH)_2 = Fe(OH)_2 +$$
ferrous + calcium = ferrous +
sulfate   hydroxide   hydroxide

$$CaSO_4$$
calcium
sulfate

$$4Fe(OH)_2 + O_2 + 2H_2O = 4Fe(OH)_3$$
ferrous + oxygen + water = ferric
hydroxide   hydroxide

An advantage of both ferrous and ferric coagulants in comparison with aluminum coagulants is that the floc produced will not redissolve at higher alkalinities. However, the need for coagulating at a higher pH and the consequent use of larger amounts of alkalies restricts the general use of this material for coagulation purposes except in conjunction with lime softening.

FERRIC COAGULANTS. The ferric coagulants, ferric sulfate—$Fe_2(SO_4)_3$ and ferric chloride —$FeCl_3$, act to precipitate ferric hydroxide as is the case with copperas. However, since the iron is already in the ferric state, dissolved oxygen is not required for oxidation.

Ferric chloride is available either in the anhydrous form, or as $FeCl_3.6H_2O$ or as a water solution containing 35-40% $FeCl_3$. Ferric chloride is quite corrosive in the presence of moisture. Reactions with natural or added alkalinity can be illustrated as follows:

$$2FeCl_3 + 3Ca(HCO_3)_2 = 2Fe(OH)_3 +$$
ferric + calcium = ferric +
chloride   bicarbonate   hydroxide

$$3CaCl_2 + 6CO_2$$
calcium + carbon
chloride   dioxide

$$2FeCl_3 + 3Ca(OH)_2 = 2Fe(OH)_3 + 3CaCl_2$$
ferric + calcium = ferric + calcium
chloride hydroxide hydroxide chloride

Ferric sulfate is available as the anhydrous material and as $Fe_2(SO_4)_3.9H_2O$. Ferric sulfate is corrosive, but not to the same extent as ferric chloride. Reactions with ferric sulfate can be shown as follows:

$$Fe_2(SO_4)_3 + 3Ca(HCO_3)_2 = 2Fe(OH)_3 +$$
ferric + calcium = ferric +
sulfate   bicarbonate   hydroxide

$$3CaSO_4 + 6CO_2$$
calcium + carbon
sulfate   dioxide

$$Fe_2(SO_4)_3 + 3Ca(OH)_2 = 2Fe(OH)_3 +$$
ferric + calcium = ferric +
sulfate   hydroxide   hydroxide

$$3CaSO_4$$
calcium
sulfate

In general, the ferric coagulants will coagulate at much lower pH values than the aluminum salts and can be employed over the wide pH range of 4.0-11.0. Ferric coagulants have been employed successfully in color removal at low pH values. At high pH values, ferric coagulants are also useful in combining color removal with oxidation and precipitation of iron and manganese. The ferric hydroxide floc is heavier than alum and settles more rapidly. Chlorinated copperas is also classed as a ferric coagulant. Chlorine will oxidize copperas and form a mixture of ferric chloride and ferric sulfate.

$$6Fe(SO_4) + 3Cl_2 = 2Fe_2(SO_4)_3 +$$
ferrous + chlorine = ferric +
sulfate   sulfate

$$2FeCl_3$$
ferric
chloride

In practice, the copperas solution is mixed with the chlorinator discharge prior to the entry of the mixed solution into the coagulation system. Theoretical chlorine requirements are 1 part of chlorine for each 7.8 parts of copperas. Since this reaction produces both ferric chloride and ferric sulfate, chlorinated copperas has the same field of usefulness as these materials. Because of the comparative ease of feeding copperas as compared with the ferric coagulants, chlorinated copperas is sometimes preferred.

MAGNESIUM OXIDE (MgO). Activated magnesium oxide was developed as an efficient

Fig. 5-3—Data on Coagulants and Coagulant Aids

Name	Formula	Commercial Strength	Grades Available	Weight, lb/cu ft	Suitable Handling Materials	Miscellaneous
Aluminum Sulfate	$Al_2(SO_4)_3.18H_2O$	17% Al_2O_3	Lump Powder Granules	Powder, 38-45 Other, 57-67	Lead Rubber Silicon Iron	pH (1% solution) = 3.4
Sodium Aluminate	$Na_2Al_2O_4$	55% Al_2O_3	Crystals	60	Iron Steel Rubber Plastics	Stabilized with approx. 6% excess NaOH
Ammonium Alum	$Al_2(SO_4)_3.$ $(NH_4)_2SO_4.24H_2O$	11% Al_2O_3	Lump Powder	60-68	Lead Rubber Silicon Iron Stoneware	pH (1% solution) = 3.5
Copperas	$FeSO_4.7H_2O$	55% $FeSO_4$	Crystals Granules	63-68	Lead Tin Wood	Efflorescent
Ferric Sulfate	$Fe_2(SO_4)_3$	90% $Fe_2(SO_4)_3$	Powder Granules	60-70	Lead Rubber Stainless Steel Plastics	Hygroscopic
Ferric Chloride	$FeCl_3.6H_2O$	60% $FeCl_3$	Crystals	45-55	Rubber Glass Stoneware	Hygroscopic
Magnesium Oxide	MgO	95% MgO	Powder	25-35	Iron Steel	Essentially insoluble, fed in slurry form
Bentonite	. . . .	. . . .	Powder	60	Iron Steel	Essentially insoluble, fed in slurry form
Sodium Silicate	$Na_2O.3.22SiO_2$	41° Bé	Solution	87	Iron Steel Rubber	Solid grades are available with varied Na_2O—SiO_2 ratios

means for the removal of soluble silica from water. Magnesium oxide is also an efficient coagulant in the alkaline pH range of 9.5 and above. Magnesium oxide provides excellent coagulation properties in conjunction with hot and cold process lime-soda softening and can be considered as a coagulant specific to the lime-soda softening process. A unique and useful advantage is that no soluble salts are added to the water with its use and no lime or soda ash is required for its precipitation. The additional advantage of silica removal is secured with this coagulant and unlike aluminum coagulants, no ions are introduced into the water which may result in complex boiler scales.

Figure 5-4 • Jar Test Coagulation Studies

COAGULANT AIDS

Polyelectrolyte coagulant aids are being used in increasing quantities in water clarification processes. The increase in use far exceeds the increasing demands for water as a raw material indicating that the synthetic polymers have definitely proven themselves superior in many applications.

Polyelectrolytes are high molecular weight water soluble polymers that contain groups capable of undergoing electrolytic dissociation to give a highly charged, large molecular weight ion. Originally, the term was applied only to synthetic polymers or copolymers but has become more inclusive through general use. The term now includes naturally occurring organic flocculents many of which function through hydration alone rather than through electrolytic activity. In some cases, the term is applied to combination of natural organic flocculents and inorganic weighting agents.

Polyelectrolytes are further classified as an-

ionic, cationic or nonionic. Polymers whose functional groups in water solution give positively charged particles are cationic. Polymers that dissociate to form negatively charged ions are called anionic. Polymers in the nonionic group provide both positive and negative charges in solution.

The mechanisms of the aids are not completely understood but a great deal of research is being done in order to develop further knowledge of this function. Such factors relating to colloidal behavior as Zeta potential, Brownian movement, van der Waals forces and electrophoretic mobility are being studied to determine a more scientific approach to the selection of coagulants and coagulant aids. At the present time the most dependable tool for checking out a system of coagulants is the well-known jar test as illustrated in Figure 5-4.

The pH of a water to be clarified is usually a very critical factor. In actual practice, there is generally a very narrow pH range where the quickest and best results are obtained with any particular coagulant. In many cases, the application of a polyelectrolyte will not only broaden the pH range over which satisfactory flocculation will occur but also reduce the quantity of primary coagulant required.

In many cases, the use of polyelectrolyte aids has been justified on the basis of improved quality water rather than any cost saving. These polymers may also prove advantageous in permitting higher flow rates through existing clarification equipment. This factor can be very desirable to a company which would otherwise be faced with a capital investment for new clarification equipment because of an increased water demand. Increases in throughput up to 100% have been attained without sacrificing the quality of the effluent.

In many clarification installations, the aids are employed when influent conditions are such that the heaviest demand is placed on the efficiency of the unit. During the run-off period following storms and during cold weather operations, surface supplies can severely tax the effectiveness of normal clarification processes and it is here that the aids can often be of most value.

REFERENCES

A. P. Black, "Basic Mechanisms of Coagulation", *Journal,* Am. Water Works Assoc., Vol. 52, pp. 492-504 (1960)

J. M. Cohen, "Improved Jar Test Procedure", *Journal,* Am. Water Works Assoc., Vol. 49, pp. 1425-1431 (1957)

J. M. Cohen, G. A. Rourke and R. L. Woodward, "Natural and Synthetic Polyelectrolytes as Coagulant Aids", *Journal,* Am. Water Works Assoc., Vol. 50, pp. 463-478 (1958)

C. R. Cox, "Laboratory Control of Water Purification", pp. 163-190, Case-Shepperd-Mann Publishing Corp., New York, N.Y. (1946)

W. A. Hardenbergh, "Water Supply and Purification", 3rd Ed., pp. 331-367, International Textbook Co., Scranton, Pa. (1952)

A. A. Hirsch, "Manual for Water Plant Operators", pp. 56-76, Chemical Publishing Co., Brooklyn, N.Y. (1945)

"Water Quality and Treatment", 2nd Ed., pp. 131-162, Am. Water Works Assoc., New York, N.Y. (1950)

6

Filtration

FILTRATION is the process of passing a liquid containing suspended matter through a suitable porous material in such a manner as to effectively remove the suspended matter from the liquid.

Filtration is employed in the treatment of industrial water in order to remove or reduce suspended solids and turbidity. The turbidity or suspended matter may be present initially in the raw water undergoing treatment or may be the result of chemical coagulation or a precipitation process of water treatment. For example, in lime-soda softening, calcium and magnesium salts are precipitated in the softening process and final clarification by filtration must be done prior to use. In general, most water treatment processes involving coagulation and precipitation are followed by filtration in order to complete the removal of undesirable impurities from the finished water.

Filtration as such does not provide removal of dissolved solids although it may be used in conjunction with a softening process that does reduce the dissolved solids content of the water treated.

THEORY INVOLVED

With proper sedimentation following chemical treatment, the heavier coagulated particles will have been removed prior to filtration. Only the smaller and lighter particles of floc reach the filters. When a freshly backwashed filter is first placed in operation, many of the finely coagulated particles penetrate into the filter bed through the many voids in the bed surface. As the particles lodge between grains of filter medium, flow is restricted. Coagulated particles then build up on the surface of the filter bed. With continued filtration, the rate of flow increases through the larger unclogged passages and decreases through the smaller and partially clogged passages. As the flow penetrates the bed further, the water spreads out and velocity decreases with lodging of coagulated particles again at points of low velocity.

Penetration of the filter medium by coagulated particles normally does not extend deeper than 2-4 inches and most of the filtration is secured at the surface or in the first one or two inches of the bed. This coagulated mat acts as a fine filter for smaller particles. It is necessary in selecting the size of filter medium to have sufficient coarseness so that some penetration of the top few inches of the bed takes place. With no penetration of the bed by coagulated material, the loss of head would increase rapidly and filter runs would be short.

It is desirable from the standpoint of filtration to provide a size of filter medium which will prevent floc from passing through the filters, hold the floc as loosely as possible in order to permit easy washing and hold as large a volume of floc as possible without clogging. The removal of turbidity is affected not only by the sand grain size, but by the particle shape. Sharp, angular particles produce larger voids and do not remove as much fine material as rounded particles of the same equivalent diameter. From the standpoint of backwashing the filter medium should be of such size that backwashing will free it of adhering floc without it being lost during backwash.

Sand and anthracite coal are the materials usually used as filter media. Bed depths of 15-30 inches are employed depending on the type of filter used.

Quartz sand, silica sand and anthracite coal used in most gravity and pressure filters must meet definite standards, namely effective size and uniformity coefficient. The effective size is that size such that 10% of the sand grains by weight are smaller and 90% coarser. Thus, the effective size is the minimum size of the bulk of the sand particles. However, this does not indicate either the coarseness limits nor the degree of variation. To assure that the variation is not too great the second measurement must be made. This is the size of the sand grains of which 60% by weight of the sand is finer and 40% coarser. This size divided by the effective size is the uniformity coefficient. For example: if a screen analysis showed 10% of a sand was finer than 0.40 mm, and 60% was finer than 0.64 mm, the effective size would be 0.40 mm and the uniformity coefficient would be 0.64 divided by 0.40 or 1.6.

The most desirable effective size and uniformity coefficient depends on conditions of operation and effluent quality requirements. Modern practice usually calls for two grades of filter sand; for gravity filters the effective size of from 0.35 to 0.50 mm, as conditions warrant, and a uniformity coefficient of not over 1.75. Pressure filters are generally provided with filter sand with effective size of 0.50 to 0.60 mm and the uniformity coefficient of 1.7 maximum. Experiments made at the Chicago Water Department concluded good results can be obtained with coarser sand, with an effective size range of 0.60 to

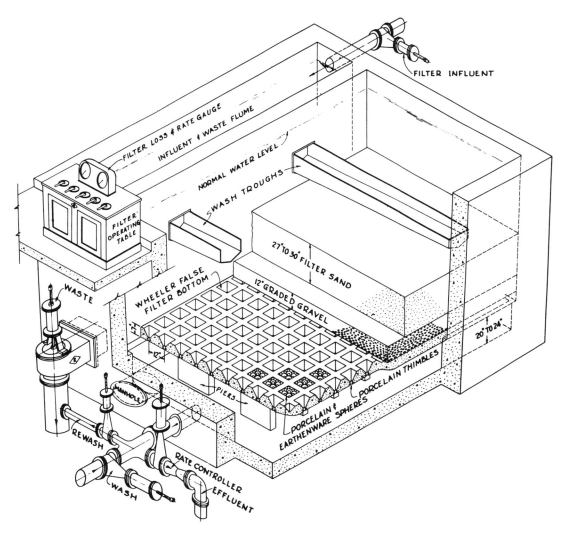

Courtesy Roberts Filter Mfg. Co.

Figure 6-1 • Cutaway of Gravity Filter

0.72 mm, with a uniformity coefficient of 1.3 to 1.5. This work indicated a 26 inch bed depth optimum.

Anthracite coal prepared in similar sizes is equally effective and may be used in place of sand and gravel in filters. Extended filter runs, less backwash water requirements and higher filtration rates have been experienced with anthracite coal filters. In many industrial filtration applications, the anthracite medium is preferred because no silica is added to the water due to high alkalinities and heat. The lower specific gravity permits a lesser backwash rate.

Other materials such as quartz, calcite and magnetite are sometimes used as filter media for special purposes.

TYPES OF FILTERS

Filters are divided into two types—gravity filters and pressure filters.

GRAVITY FILTERS. As the name implies, the flow of water through these filters is obtained by gravity.

"Slow sand filters" or "English" filters are mentioned in passing because of their historical significance. These were the first form of filtration employed. These filters, now essentially obsolete, use beds of fine sand. The water is filtered at very low rates, usually in the range of 2-10 million gallons per day per acre (0.032-0.160 gpm per sq ft). The removal of suspended solids is secured by straining through the pores in the surface of the sand layer and by adherence of the solid particles to the sand grains. Biological action in these beds accounts for the good results obtained. As backwashing of such large areas is impractical, at intervals the accumulated growth and suspended matter with some of the sand from the top of the bed are removed by rakes.

In rapid sand or coal filters, the water is passed downward by gravity at a relatively high velocity, usually at rates between 2-4 gpm per square foot. Pretreatment by coagulation and sedimentation is necessary in order to permit these higher rates of filtration. Re-

moval of accumulated suspended matter is secured by backwashing up through the filter bed, expanding the bed and washing the solids to waste.

The essential parts of a gravity filter, in addition to the filter medium, can be briefly outlined as follows:

1. The filter shell itself may be of concrete, steel or wood and may be square, rectangular or circular in shape. However, rectangular units of reinforced concrete are most widely used.

2. The filter medium is supported by a gravel bed which serves the purpose of preventing the fine sand or anthracite from passing down into the underdrain system and also acts to distribute the backwash water. The supporting bed may vary in depth usually from 12 to 24 inches and consists of several layers varying from $1\frac{1}{2}$ inches to $\frac{1}{8}$ inch in diameter.

3. The underdrain system is provided for two purposes—the collection of the filtered water after passing down through the filter medium and supporting gravel and also for the distribution of backwash water to the underside of the filter medium. It is essential that the underdrain system act uniformly in both operations otherwise filtering and backwashing rates in one part of a filter would exceed those in another and result in inefficient operation. The underdrain system may consist of header and laterals with perforations or strainers suitably spaced. False bottom type underdrain systems are also popular.

4. Wash water troughs are provided to collect backwash water. These troughs may be of steel, cast iron or concrete with the newer plants employing aluminum, asbestos-cement and fiberglass for greater resistance to corrosion. They must be of adequate size to handle maximum backwash rates without flooding. Troughs are spaced so that the horizontal travel of backwash water will not exceed 3 to $3\frac{1}{2}$ feet. Wash troughs are placed approximately 24 inches above the top of the filter surface although where high backwash

Courtesy Infilco, Incorporated

Figure 6-2 • Battery of Pressure Filters with Pilot Operated Diaphragm Valves

rates are employed, the freeboard above the filter surface should equal the inches of vertical rise per minute.

5. Certain control devices are required to insure maximum efficiency in filter operation. Rate-of-flow controllers automatically maintain uniform delivery of filtered water, operating from Venturi tubes in the effluent line. Backwash rate-of-flow controllers are used similarly to provide proper wash conditions. Rate-of-flow and loss-of-head gages are also considered necessary for most efficient operation. It is possible to group most gages, together with the operating controls, on operating tables for convenience for either manual or automatic operation.

New concepts in automatic gravity filtration are offered by several manufacturers that reduce the need for various controllers and manual operations previously required on standard gravity filters. Their application to industrial water filtration problems is increasing.

PRESSURE FILTERS. Pressure filters are somewhat more widely used than gravity filters in industrial water conditioning. Pressure filters possess the advantage that they may be placed in the line under pressure and thus eliminate double pumping. The use of pressure filters is required in conjunction with hot process softening to permit high temperature operation and to avoid thermal loss. The general design of pressure filters is essentially the same as gravity filters with respect to filter medium, supporting bed, underdrain system and control devices. The filter shell, of course, differs from a gravity filter and wash water troughs are not employed.

Pressure filters may be of the vertical or

horizontal type. The filter shells are steel, cylindrical in shape, with dished heads. Vertical filters range in diameter from 1 to 10 feet with capacities from 2.4 gpm to 235 gpm at a filter rate of 3 gal per sq ft per minute. Horizontal filters, usually 8 feet in diameter, may be 10 to 25 feet long with capacities from 218 gpm to 570 gpm. The general trend is away from horizontal pressure filters because certain areas of the filter bed adjacent to the shell are inactive during filtration and backwashing. One vendor has redesigned the horizontal unit with cells thereby improving operations.

Figure 6-3

Filter and Backwash Rates for Vertical Pressure Filters

Diameter, ft	Area Sq Ft	Filter Rate* gpm	Backwash Rate† gpm
3	7.1	21	106
4	12.6	38	189
5	19.6	59	295
6	28.3	85	425
7	38.5	116	578
8	50.3	150	755
9	63.6	190	954
10	78.5	235	1180

* Filter rate of 3 gal per sq ft per minute
† Backwash rate of 15 gal per sq ft per minute

Figure 6-4

Typical Filter Bed Layers and Sizes For Pressure Filters

SAND . . . . . 12" layer—sand, 0.45-0.50 mm effective size
10" layer—sand, 0.80-1.20 mm effective size
4" layer—gravel, 1/4"-1/8"
4" layer—gravel, 1/2"-1/4"
8" layer—gravel, 1"-1/2"
4" layer—gravel, 1 1/2"-1"
ANTHRAFILT 18" layer—No. 1 Anthrafilt, 0.6-0.8 mm
9" layer—No. 2 Anthrafilt, 3/32"-3/16"
9" layer—No. 4 Anthrafilt, 5/16"-9/16"
4" layer—No. 6 Anthrafilt, 13/16"-1 5/8"

FILTER OPERATION

After backwashing, and placing a filter in operation, the water is filtered to waste for the first few minutes. This procedure rids the system of possible suspended solids remaining in the underdrain system after backwashing and also permits a small amount of suspended matter to accumulate on the bed. As soon as the filter produces clear water, the unit is returned to service.

During operation, the suspended matter removed by the filter accumulates on the surface and the increased frictional resistance is shown by the loss-of-head gage. When loss-of-head reaches 5 psi, it is advisable to backwash the filter to remove the mat on the bed surface. While industrial filtration rates are usually 3 gal per sq ft of filter area per minute, backwash rates are much higher in order to lift the suspended matter from the surface and expand the filter bed. Backwash rates of 12-15 gals per sq ft per minute are employed for sand and rates of 8-12 gals per sq ft per minute for anthracite. The backwashing is continued for 5 to 10 minutes, then the filter is returned to service, following filtering to waste until the water is clear.

Surface washers are of assistance in maintaining maximum filter efficiency. These units consist of horizontal arms, equipped with nozzles, supported just above the surface of the filter bed. High pressure backwash water supplied to the washer causes rotation of the arms and water leaving the nozzles impinges on the media, and loosens the accumulated suspended matter.

APPLICATIONS

Filtration is a requirement in the clarification of turbid waters for most industrial uses. In the preparation of domestic supplies, process water, boiler feedwater and, in fact, for almost every use it is necessary that the water be freed of objectionable suspended solids. While both coagulation and sedimentation may be employed for the removal of a portion of the suspended matter, filtration normally also is required to complete the production of a water of satisfactory quality.

Filtration is also employed as a part of other water treatment processes. For example, all of the precipitation methods of softening employ filtration as a final step in the process. Filtration is employed following hot phosphate softening as well as both hot and cold lime and lime-soda softening, except in some special cases.

Filtration ahead of exchange softeners and demineralizers is standard practice. Filtration is also a final step in certain iron removal methods and in the removal of oil from condensate.

LIMITATIONS

Filtration, without coagulation and sedimentation, is usually an unsatisfactory method for completely removing turbidity and suspended solids. In such an application, the filter provides only the removal of the larger particles.

Pressure filters are favored where double pumping can be avoided by placing the filter under line pressure. Pressure filters also usually require less space for installation. Pressure filters are required with hot process operation and prevent thermal loss in filtration and backwashing. Oxygen pickup is also prevented by the use of pressure filters.

Disadvantages in pressure filtration are that the appearance of the filter effluent and the filter medium are not under observation, backwashing effectiveness cannot be observed and loss of filter medium cannot be noted. Wash water troughs cannot be provided in pressure filters for as effective removal of backwash

solids as in gravity filters. Pressure filters are more difficult to inspect and clean. The replacement of filter medium, gravel and underdrain systems presents more of a problem.

However, the most pertinent criticism of pressure filters in comparison with gravity filters is the inability of the operator to observe the effectiveness of the filtering and backwashing operations. While pressure filters are capable of providing an effluent of as high quality as gravity filters, this inability to maintain constant observation of the process may result in the production of an effluent of poorer quality than is obtained with gravity filters. Consequently, gravity filters are preferred where the conditions of the installation permit their use and where a water of highest quality is desired. Any malfunctioning of a gravity filter may be quickly observed and corrected. The selection between the two types must be made after a study of the conditions and problems involved in the particular installation.

REFERENCES

G. D. Dickey, "Filtration", Reinhold Publishing Corp., New York, N.Y. (1961)

"Filtration", The Public Works Manual and Catalog File, Public Works Publications, Ridgewood, N.J. (1961)

E. Nordell, "Water Treatment for Industrial and Other Uses", 2nd Ed., pp. 363-387, Reinhold Publishing Corp., New York, N.Y. (1961)

7

Precoat Filtration

Diatomaceous earth filtration is a process in which a filter cake or precoat of diatomaceous earth is used as a filter medium. The precoat of diatomaceous earth is formed over a permeable base or septum, by adding a slurry of diatomite to the filter shell and either filtering to waste or recirculating the slurry until the precoat is formed. The unit is then ready for the filtering operation.

Diatomaceous earth filtration is a special form of filtration that is employed basically where the utmost clarity of the effluent is required or where space and weight limitations are quite stringent.

Diatomite filtration achieved prominence during World War II, primarily because of the need of the armed forces for filter units for potable water that would conserve space and weight, which would be portable and relatively simple to operate. During the war, these filter units were also applied to the removal of oil from condensate on shipboard, where space and weight requirements must also be kept at a minimum.

EQUIPMENT EMPLOYED

The principle of diatomaceous earth filtration is relatively simple. A permeable base or septum of some type is required to support the diatomite filter cake. The septum must be of such a nature that it will prevent the passage of the filter aid, must be permeable to the flow of filtered water and must be of sufficient strength to withstand the pressure drop. Among the materials used as a supporting base are filter cloths, porous stone tubes, wire screens, wire-wound tubes, and porous paper filter pads. This supporting medium is first coated with a slurry of diatomaceous earth which then acts as the filter medium. The water is filtered in passing through the diatomite coating. During the filter run, additional diatomite slurry is usually added. When a high back pressure drop develops, due to the accumulation of suspended matter removed in filtration, the filter coating is sloughed off by backwash, and the filter returned to service after again precoating. Coagulants, with attendant pH control, are not required.

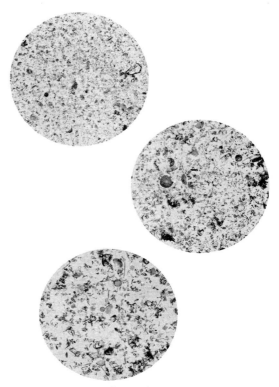

Courtesy Johns Manville Products Corp.

Figure 7-1 • Photomicrographs (X100) of Fine, Medium and Coarse Particle Size Filter Aids

THEORY INVOLVED

Chemically, diatomaceous earth is silica (SiO_2). It is produced from mineral deposits formed by diatoms (a form of plant life related to algae). Diatomaceous earth is really composed of billions of tiny fossils, resulting from the silica "skeletons" left by diatoms in prehistoric times. Diatomaceous earth deposits have been found as much as 1400 feet in thickness.

The structure of diatomaceous earth is due to the shape of the tiny plants from which it originated. These plants, or diatoms, are so small that they must be examined under a microscope. Individual figures are of many shapes such as flowers, discs and needles. Over 10,000 types have been identified. Commercial filter aids are produced from the crude material by a gentle milling process which separates the diatoms from one another. The finished product is a fine powder, consisting of rigid particles so tiny that hundreds could be placed on a pinpoint.

When a precoat of diatomaceous earth is formed on the septum, the irregular, but symmetrical, shape of each diatom forms an incompressible filter medium consisting of approximately 10% solids and 90% voids. In effect, a screen is formed with extremely tiny openings—so fine, in fact, that even most types of bacteria are strained out. The object of the septum is to provide support for the precoat. The openings in the septum are not sufficiently small in size to prevent the passage of individual diatomite particles. Instead, the septum supports the mat or filter cake formed by the interlacing of thousands of diatomite particles over each opening. Some diatomite particles pass through the septum during the precoat operation, but once formation of the precoat is complete, the interlocked mass of diatomite particles prevents further passage.

Commercial diatomite filter-aids are produced in several different grades offering a range of filtration rates and clarity of filter effluents. In addition to applications for water filtration, diatomaceous earth filter-aids are employed widely in the filtration of process liquids.

While diatomite is the filter aid primarily employed with filters of this type, there are also available various grades of purified wood cellulose which find application in the filtration of high pH solutions where silica pickup is to be avoided. Other media used include perlite, asbestos and carbon.

FILTER OPERATION

The primary difference among the several different types of precoat filters lies in the construction of the filter element. These construction differences affect the manner of filter operation.

In filters where wire-wound tubes are employed, these are usually mounted vertically on a removable plate and inserted as a unit in the filter shell. In the larger sizes, the filter shell is usually of steel. Diatomite for the precoat is added as a slurry and the raw water pumped through the filter to waste or recirculated until the diatomite evenly precoats the filter elements. Only a few minutes are required for this operation and the filter is then ready for service.

As suspended matter is removed during the filtering cycle, the pressure drop across the filter element increases and rate of flow decreases. The filter is then backwashed by reversing the flow through the unit, removing the filter cake from the elements by the reverse flow of water. Spent diatomite is drained from the filter shell.

One system uses a variation of this procedure in that the elements are backwashed from filtered water storage to waste, ending with the unit filled with filtered water.

Other designs may employ compressed air to remove the filter cake from the elements at conclusion of a filter run. In another method, the air trapped and compressed in the filter dome is utilized to remove the filter cake from the elements, in conjunction with backwash by filtered water.

Leaf type filters, which are employed frequently in the removal of oil from condensate, employ no backwash water. At the conclusion of the filter run, the unit is drained and the filter cake is manually peeled off the filter leaves.

In some operations, the precoat is the only filter aid employed. More frequently, however, additional diatomite is continuously added to the raw water during the entire filter run. It has been found that where a precoat only is employed relatively short filter runs will be experienced. Suspended matter will tend to plug the openings in the precoat, acting to form an impervious mat. Pressure drop increases rapidly resulting in short filter runs. By adding additional diatomite continuously during filtration, the filter cake is maintained in a more porous condition. Lesser pressure drop and longer filter runs result. The diatomite added during filtration is referred to as body feed to distinguish it from the initial precoat.

Because diatomaceous earth is an abrasive material, some special designs of feeding apparatus have been developed. The specific gravity of the material is high and the material will settle out of suspension and tend to pack at points of low velocity. Feeding equipment must be designed with these considerations in mind.

The amount of diatomite required to form the precoat and also the amount necessary for body feed will vary widely. Factors influencing the diatomite requirements include the grade of media employed, the characteristics of the influent water and the design of the filter. However, experience has indicated precoat requirements in the range of 1.0-2.0 ounces per square foot of filter area. Body dosages are directly influenced by influent turbidity and filtration rates and consequently are subject to wide variation. Values varying from 5-50 ounces per thousand gallons of filter effluent have been reported.

APPLICATIONS

Because of the savings in both space and weight of diatomite filters compared with conventional sand filters, diatomite filters are obviously favored for mobile use by the armed forces. Figure 7-3 illustrates the comparison of the U. S. Army pack and mobile units with conventional pressure and sand filters.

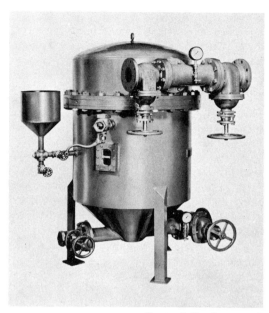

Courtesy Infilco, Incorporated

Figure 7-2 • Industrial Type of Diatomaceous Earth Filter Unit

Figure 7-3
U. S. Army Pack and Mobile Units
Compared with Pressure Sand Filters

	Pack Unit	Pressure Sand Filter	Mobile Unit	Pressure Sand Filter
Rated Capacity, gpm	15	15	50	50
Filter area, sq ft	3.6	7.1	10	19.6
Weight, lbs	30	2860	350	8050
Diameter, in	8	36	18	60
Over-all Height, in	22	73	30	82
Floor Space, in	10 x 10	37 x 49	24 x 24	61 x 78

Due to the extremely fine openings in a diatomite filter cake, a greater clarity of effluent can be obtained. Army tests showed that diatomite filters can be expected to provide filtered water approximating U. S. Public Health Service Standards, even without chlorination. Diatomite filters will remove cysts of amoebic dysentery and the cercariae of schistosomia (blood flukes), prevalent in Philippine waters. Consequently, the armed forces favor diatomite filters for mobile purification units.

Diatomite filtration is also applied to certain process industries where rigid water requirements exist with respect to clarity and bacteriological quality. In such applications, the diatomite filter is frequently applied as a "polishing" filter after conventional coagulation, sedimentation and sand filtration.

In the removal of oil from contaminated condensate, diatomite filters possess an advantage over conventional coagulation and filtration methods. No control of coagulant and alkali feed is required since neither coagulant nor pH adjustment is employed with diatomite filters. In addition, no increase results in the solids content of the filtered condensate, due to the coagulant.

Diatomite filtration is being widely applied

to swimming pools where advantages are experienced in the somewhat simpler operating control and lesser need for coagulating chemicals.

LIMITATIONS

The major factors limiting the use of diatomite filtration are the need for a relatively low turbidity influent water, and the high operating costs compared with conventional sand filtration.

In general, it is not advisable to employ diatomite filters where raw water turbidities exceed 200 ppm. Uneconomically short filter runs result from high turbidity influent waters.

The purchase price of diatomite filters may exceed the cost of pressure sand filters although installation cost may be less because of the smaller space requirements. The operating cost of diatomite filters will generally exceed the cost of coagulation and pressure sand filtration, due primarily to the cost of the diatomaceous earth.

Diatomite filters operate with a high pressure drop across the unit, as much as 25-50 psi. Pumping costs are increased and the installation of diatomite filters may be limited by the available pressure.

Continuity of operation is generally considered a requirement for diatomite filters. If the filters are operated intermittently, the filter cake will slough off when flow is stopped. To avoid a turbid effluent, when flow is resumed, it is necessary to again precoat the filter. Intermittent operation is unsuitable to diatomaceous earth filtration. In boiler feedwater conditioning particularly, it is necessary to guard against careless operation which permits high turbidity in the filter effluent from disturbance of the precoat. The silica thus introduced would tend to be solubilized under boiler temperature and pH conditions, possibly resulting in the formation of siliceous boiler scales. For these applications, nonsiliceous media must be employed.

Some types of filter elements have shown susceptibility to clogging with iron, manganese and other materials and require removal of the elements for chemical cleaning.

REFERENCES

"Diatomite Filter Aids", Technical Bulletin D10, Great Lakes Carbon Corp., Los Angeles, Calif. (1961)
"The Filtration of Water", Johns-Manville Corp., New York, N.Y. (1961)

8

Chlorination

CHLORINATION is the process in which chlorine gas or chlorine compounds such as hypochlorites are added to water or sewage, usually for the purpose of disinfection.

The principal use of chlorination is to safeguard water supplies by killing disease producing organisms. For this purpose chlorination is standard practice and is one of the major reasons for the bacterial safety of our public water supplies.

In addition to its bactericidal qualities, chlorine and chlorine compounds are used in the reduction and removal of objectionable tastes and odors from drinking water, the oxidation of iron, manganese and hydrogen sulfide present in waters thereby aiding in their removal, and the oxidation, decolorization and destruction of organic matter. It has been stated that chlorine is probably the most powerful and flexible tool that chemical science has provided the sanitary engineer. Further uses to which it has become essential include its injection into sewage and industrial wastes prior to their discharge to streams not only for the bacterial reduction in these waste waters, but for the destruction of chemicals that may react directly with oxygen, such as sulfides, sulfites, ferrous iron and others. Chlorine is widely used for the control of slime and algae in cooling waters in both once-through and recirculating systems.

In the clarification process of water treatment, chlorine is often applied to the raw water along with the coagulant. Included in the benefits derived from prechlorination practices are improved coagulation probably due to the action of chlorine on the organic material in the water; reduction in taste, odor and color producing materials by oxidation; reduction of biological loading by longer contact with the water thereby providing a safety factor; and oxidation of iron and manganese for removal by settling and filtration.

Chlorine has been used successfully as the activating agent for sodium silicate in the preparation of the coagulant aid, activated silica. The advantage claimed by this process is that the chlorine used for the activating process continues to be available for sterilization and oxidation.

The addition of chlorine to treated sewage is widely used for bacterial control and sterilization. Further, substantial reduction in apparent BOD has been experienced where reasonably high dosages of chlorine were applied to sewage, either in the partially treated or completely treated stage.

In the industrial waste field, chlorine has been generally adopted for cyanide destruction in the presence of an alkaline salt. Other uses in industrial wastes have included the destruction of hydrogen sulfide and phenol. Here, approximately 8.5 parts of chlorine are required for each part of hydrogen sulfide present and approximately 20 ppm chlorine for each ppm of phenol. The pH of reaction is important to obtain maximum efficiency.

CHEMISTRY OF CHLORINATION

THEORY OF DISINFECTING ACTION. Chlorine hydrolyzes in dilute water solution as follows:

$$Cl_2 + H_2O = HOCl$$
$$chlorine + water = hypochlorous\ acid$$
$$+ HCl$$
$$+ hydrochloric\ acid$$

It is the hypochlorous acid produced in this hydrolysis that provides the disinfecting and oxidizing properties of chlorine solutions.

Early theories that the sterilizing properties of chlorine were due to nascent oxygen liberated from hypochlorous acid or to complete oxidation of organic matter have been disproved. Later work has led to the theory that the destruction of organisms results from the chemical reaction between hypochlorous acid formed when chlorine is mixed with water and an enzyme in the organism cell. The amount of HOCl is dependent on the pH of the solution. At pH below 6.5, the HOCl constitutes almost 100% of the free available chlorine. At a pH of 9.0 and above, the ionized hypochlorite ion accounts for practically all of the free available chlorine. Since it is hypochlorous acid and not the hypochlorite ion that is the principal disinfectant in chlorine solutions, the efficiency of disinfection will be substantially greater at low pH values where the hypochlorous acid content is greater. The free available residual chlorine of a treated water is considered to be that portion of the total residual chlorine existing in the water as the hypochlorous acid.

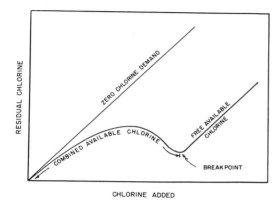

Figure 8-1 • Breakpoint Chlorination

The disinfecting ability of chlorine is reduced when hypochlorous acid reacts with ammonia or amines to form chloramines. Formation of chloramines may be shown as follows:

$$HOCl + NH_3$$
hypochlorous acid + ammonia
$$= NH_2Cl + H_2O$$
= monochloramine + water

$$2HOCl + NH_3$$
hypochlorous acid + ammonia
$$= NHCl_2 + 2H_2O$$
= dichloramine + water

The pH of the treated water determines which product will be formed. At pH 8.5 monochloramine is the major product. At about pH 4.5 dichloramine is the major product. Mixtures of the two prevail between these two values. Below pH 4.5 nitrogen trichloride predominates.

Where chloramines exist, it is necessary to provide longer contact time or increased chlorine residual for comparable bacterial reduction. With the oxidizing properties of chlorine being substantially reduced when in such com-

bination and the resulting retarded action of chlorine with organic matter, the maintenance of a stable residual in outlying water distribution systems is facilitated. Although this combined residual is ordinarily more stable than a free chlorine residual, due to its decreased bactericidal qualities it is essential to maintain higher residuals.

The combined available residual chlorine of a treated water is considered to be that portion of the total residual existing in chemical combination with ammonia or organic nitrogen compounds. Studies on the bactericidal properties of free and combined available chlorine residuals have indicated that for complete kill with similar contact periods, approximately 25 times as much combined available residual chlorine is required as is necessary with free available residual chlorine. By the same studies it was apparent that to obtain complete bacteria kill when using combined available residual equal to the free residual, approximately 100 times as long contact period was required.

CHLORINE REQUIREMENTS. In addition to its bactericidal action chlorine displays its strong oxidizing properties in other ways. Chlorine will react with and oxidize ferrous iron (Fe^{++}), manganous manganese (Mn^{++}), nitrite (NO_2^-) and hydrogen sulfide. Reaction with such inorganic constituents present in the water being chlorinated increases the quantity of chlorine required and adds to the chlorine demand of the water. In this oxidation process chlorine is reduced to the chloride ion which possesses no further oxidizing properties or disinfecting power. The reaction between hydrogen sulfide and chlorine illustrates this point.

$$H_2S + 4Cl_2 + 4H_2O$$
hydrogen sulfide + chlorine + water
$$= H_2SO_4 + 8HCl$$
= sulfuric acid + hydrochloric acid

Chlorine will also react with and be consumed by organic matter present in the water. In some cases chlorine is consumed in direct chlorination of organic compounds present in sewage or industrial waste pollution with the formation of chlorinated compounds such as chlorphenols. Products of this type may possess undesirable tastes and odors. Chlorine may also oxidize and bleach organic matter with the extent of oxidation dependent on time of contact and the residual chlorine present. In either case, this oxidation of inorganic and organic compounds requires the use of higher amounts of chlorine to satisfy the chlorine demand before a chlorine residual for disinfection can be established.

Chlorine demand may be described as the difference between the amount of chlorine applied to a water and the amount of free, combined or total residual chlorine remaining at the end of a specified contact period. The chlorine demand will vary on any water with contact time, water quality, temperature and pH. The chlorine requirement is the amount of chlorine that must be added to accomplish a specific objective, i.e., bacterial kill, hydrogen sulfide removal or oxidation of iron and manganese.

The residual chlorine requirement in treated water is usually established by bacteriological testing to determine the amount necessary for effective disinfection. Normally, a residual of 0.2 to 0.5 ppm is satisfactory after a minimum 10 minute contact period at or above 20 C. Higher residual values may be required if the chlorine exists as combined residual and the pH of the water exceeds 7.0. The need for higher combined available chlorine residuals is markedly increased in colder water.

CHLORINE-AMMONIA PROCESS. Ammonia or ammonium salts are employed in conjunction with chlorine to produce a combined available chlorine residual that is useful for certain specific problems. This process was originally developed for taste and odor control where free chlorine reacted with organic matter in the water. Further, some minimizing of phenolic and other type tastes by chloramines is sometimes accomplished over conditions resulting from normal marginal chlorination. The lower bacterial efficiency of this combined residual limits the usefulness of the process. Actually, this process has been superseded to a large extent by the more positive breakpoint process for taste as well as bacterial control.

BREAKPOINT PROCESS. Normal chlorination of water is generally described as marginal. Breakpoint chlorination is the application of chlorine to water to maintain free available chlorine residuals. The addition of chlorine to water containing ammonia or organic matter will first produce an increased combined chlorine residual. After reaching a maximum value, increased chlorine doses result in decreased residual values. This decrease is caused by the decomposition of the combined available chlorine residuals, formed when chlorine is first added. This decrease in chlorine residual will not start until the chlorine applied amounts to at least 8 times or more the amount of free ammonia present. If this chlorine-ammonia ratio is materially less than 8 to 1, say 4 to 1, chloramines will be formed and the breakpoint reactions will not take place. The ammonia will have been essentially removed when the chlorine dosage amounts to 10 times the amount of ammonia present. When the instantaneous chlorine demand is high, the chlorine requirements to obtain free available chlorine residuals may be 20 or more times the amount of ammonia present.

After the minimum chlorine residual or breakpoint is reached, the chlorine is present as free available residual and increases in direct proportion to the chlorine applied. In developing the free available residual, destruction of taste and odors is usually achieved; practically all of the bacteria have been killed, organic matter oxidized and the free residual is quite stable and not readily dissipated.

Breakpoint chlorination may also be used to control slime and algal growths, to aid coagulation, oxidize iron and manganese, to remove ammonia from boiler makeup water and to generally improve water quality in the treatment cycles or in the distribution system.

The object of breakpoint chlorination is to produce and maintain a free available chlorine residual. Since a stable free chlorine residual can exist only beyond the breakpoint, the process is controlled by making certain that a definite free chlorine residual has been produced and that it is adequate to carry throughout a plant or into the distribution system as required.

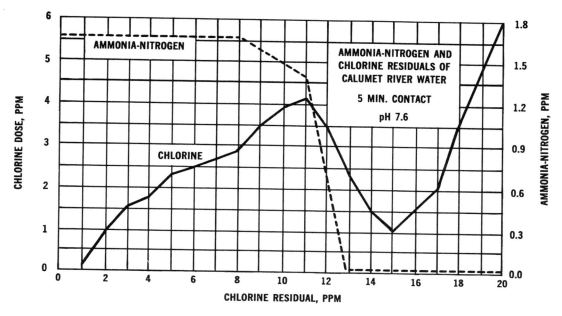

Figure 8-2 • Ammonia Removal by Chlorination

The breakpoint process is of specific application in the removal of ammonia from boiler makeup water. Figure 8-2 illustrates results obtained in applying this process to Calumet River water. In these experiments it was found that greatest ammonia removal efficiency was obtained with a chlorine to ammonia ratio of 8:1 and it was possible to reduce the undesirable ammonia concentration of the steam from the boilers to a negligible value.

CHLORINE DIOXIDE

Another satisfactory and proven method for using chlorine in the treatment of water, sewage and industrial wastes is in combination with sodium chlorite to form chlorine dioxide. This process was introduced in 1944 and is now used in more than 150 water works plants. It has also found wide industrial application for various applications of oxidation, bleaching and sterilization.

Chlorine dioxide is used in public water supplies for taste and odor control as well as for sterilization. It has high oxidizing powers and reportedly does not form reaction products that cause taste intensification. The costs for feeding chlorine dioxide are higher than for straight chlorine with the result that in order to justify its use there must be definite improvements obtained. Fortunately, the method for determining residual chlorine is applicable for chlorine dioxide. Chlorine dioxide reacts with acid orthotolidine rapidly and therefore can be measured by the flash test and the OTA modification.

EFFECTS OF CHLORINE

Many industrial waters are chlorinated for the control of bacteria and slime producing organisms. However, in food processing industries, the chlorine may cause tastes in canned and frozen foods or may cause corrosion of the metal containers. Also, it has been determined that excessive chlorine affects smoothness and brightness of metals in the plating industry. Paper mills producing fine paper usually establish very critical limits for chlorine residuals.

In normal concentrations, chlorine does

not render water abnormally corrosive to zinc nor does it increase the solubility of lead salts.

Reports on irrigation water and subsequent studies indicate no injury to land plants when the irrigation water contains less than 50 ppm combined residual chlorine. Aquatic plants are reportedly harmed by concentrations of 3 ppm or more.

The concentration of chlorine required to control plankton in reservoirs varies from 0.2 to 3.0 ppm depending on the sensitivity and type of organisms present. There are some types that may require as high as 50 ppm for destruction. Normally, free available chlorine in water may be toxic to fish and other aquatic life at low concentrations, and in combination with cyanide, phenols and with other substances may be even more detrimental.

There are no specific data concerning the limiting physiological tolerance for chlorine in potable water, but it is generally agreed that the small amounts of chlorine present in chlorinated waters are dissipated by the reaction with saliva and gastric juices as soon as the water is swallowed. It is reported that chlorinated drinking water may, in rare cases, cause asthma, colitis and eczema. When afflicted patients drank distilled water in place of chlorinated water, their conditions improved and when they returned to chlorinated water, the symptoms reappeared.

HYPOCHLORINATION

In addition to gaseous chlorine, there are commercially available calcium and sodium hypochlorites. The most common forms include sodium hypochlorite having approximately 15% available chlorine and high test calcium hypochlorite with 70% available chlorine. The hypochlorite salt most widely used for water treatment is the calcium hypochlorite, $Ca(OCl)_2$.

When this material is dissolved in water, ionization occurs:

$$Ca(OCl)_2 = Ca^{++}$$
calcium hypochlorite = calcium ions

$$+ \quad 2(OCl)^-$$
+ hypochlorite ions

The hypochlorite ions establish equilibrium with hydrogen ions, depending on pH, as does gaseous chlorine. The significant difference is in the effect on pH. Solutions of hypochlorite contain an excess of alkali which tends to raise the pH. In some hard waters, scale problems have been experienced due to the precipitation of calcium carbonate by hypochlorites. Usually a complex phosphate can be added to overcome this difficulty. In other cases, hypochlorite treatment, due to the high alkalinity, improves the quality of soft and highly corrosive waters.

Calcium hypochlorite is soluble in water although when dissolved in hard water, a precipitate often results. For liquid feeding of this material, the solutions should be prepared at approximately 1% to 2% available chlorine.

Sodium hypochlorite, NaOCl, is available in several forms ranging from the familiar grocery store bleaches to commercial laundry bleach solution. These products vary in available chlorine from 3% to as high as 20%. Most of them are quite unstable. Sodium hypochlorite may be satisfactorily fed in the normal 15% available chlorine strength or it may be diluted with water for feeding.

The available chlorine, on a pound for pound basis, is equally effective for disinfection and other purposes whether obtained from hypochlorites or from gaseous chlorine.

All hypochlorites are corrosive to some degree and must be carefully handled and corrosion resistant materials should be used for storage and dispensing. Satisfactory materials include wood, ceramic, glass, plastic or rubber.

DECHLORINATION

Dechlorination may be accomplished by the use of activated carbon or by chemical reducing agents such as sulfur dioxide, sodium sulfite, sodium bisulfite or sodium thiosulfate. Prolonged storage in open reservoirs is also an effective means for dechlorination. The practice of dechlorination may be desirable in

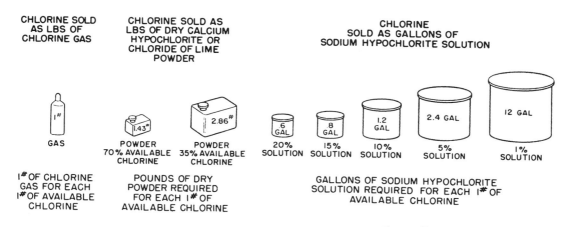

CHLORINE SOLD AS LBS OF CHLORINE GAS

CHLORINE SOLD AS LBS OF DRY CALCIUM HYPOCHLORITE OR CHLORIDE OF LIME POWDER

CHLORINE SOLD AS GALLONS OF SODIUM HYPOCHLORITE SOLUTION

GAS

POWDER 70% AVAILABLE CHLORINE

POWDER 35% AVAILABLE CHLORINE

20% SOLUTION

15% SOLUTION

10% SOLUTION

5% SOLUTION

1% SOLUTION

I# OF CHLORINE GAS FOR EACH I# OF AVAILABLE CHLORINE

POUNDS OF DRY POWDER REQUIRED FOR EACH I# OF AVAILABLE CHLORINE

GALLONS OF SODIUM HYPOCHLORITE SOLUTION REQUIRED FOR EACH I# OF AVAILABLE CHLORINE

Courtesy Chlorination Topics, Spring 1956

Figure 8-3 • Comparative Chart Showing Amounts of Material Required to Provide One Pound of Available Chlorine

either public supplies or for industrial uses. In public water supplies, the reduction or removal of chlorinous taste may be necessary. Many industrial process uses of water are adversely affected by high chlorine residuals and consequently they must be removed or reduced. Also, it has been concluded that some resins used in exchange softeners and demineralizers are adversely affected by the presence of a residual chlorine in the water to be processed and consequently dechlorination ahead of these units is required.

FEEDING EQUIPMENT

Chlorine gas or solutions or hypochlorites are in common use and are readily and accurately applied to public and industrial water or sewage and industrial wastes. These materials are applied either at a constant rate or proportional to flow, dependent upon the specific requirements. The form in which the chlorine is to be fed should be properly evaluated and the equipment supplied appropriate for the service. The tabulation (Fig. 8-3) showing comparative amounts of the various forms of chlorine should be helpful. Reliable equipment for feeding all types of chlorine and chlorine compounds is available from reputable vendors serving this specialized field.

The use of chlorine gas requires careful handling and the employment of special safety measures since chlorine is highly irritating to the eyes and to the membranes of the respiratory system. The physiological effect of various concentrations of chlorine gas are shown herewith.

	ppm chlorine by volume in air
Least detectable odor	3.5
Cause throat irritation	15
Cause coughing	30
Dangerous for 30 minutes exposure	50
Quickly fatal	1000

(From U.S. Bureau of Mines Paper 248)

LABORATORY CONTROL

The success of treating water or wastes with chlorine is dependent upon the accuracy and adequacy of the control measures practiced. A number of chemical methods have been developed for the control by measuring both free and combined residual chlorine concentrations. The iodometric titration was the initial method used. Modifications of this test have been developed which have improved the accuracy. The orthotolidine test has been very good for the purpose intended. However, the limitations of this test as well as

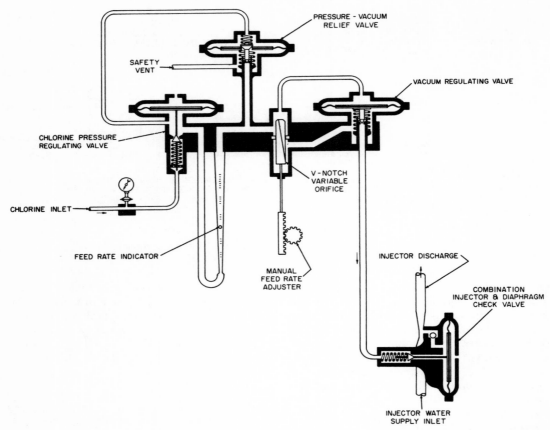

PRESSURE - VACUUM
RELIEF VALVE

SAFETY
VENT

VACUUM REGULATING VALVE

CHLORINE PRESSURE
REGULATING VALVE

V - NOTCH
VARIABLE
ORIFICE

CHLORINE INLET

FEED RATE INDICATOR

MANUAL
FEED RATE
ADJUSTER

INJECTOR DISCHARGE

COMBINATION
INJECTOR & DIAPHRAGM
CHECK VALVE

INJECTOR WATER
SUPPLY INLET

Courtesy Wallace & Tiernan Inc.

Figure 8-4 • V-notch Chlorinator

interference from various substances cause it to be used with certain caution. A modification of this test known as the OTA test has been widely used although certain inherent weaknesses continue to exist. The micro-titration of free chlorine with methyl orange or xylene cyanole has been successfully used, especially in cooling water systems. A test for titrating chlorine with a reducing agent has been developed and is generally known as the amperometric method and is gaining in application and popularity. Fortunately, residual chlorine recording can now be made with the instrumentation presently available.

Some industrial waste chlorination treatment can be controlled by the oxidation-reduction potential. Additional instruments and methods of control are continuously being developed for this very important application.

REFERENCES

"Chlorine Manual", 3rd Ed., The Chlorine Institute, Inc., New York, N.Y. (1959)

A. E. Griffin and N. S. Chamberlin, "Some Chemical Aspects of Breakpoint Chlorination", *Journal, New England Water Works Assoc.*, Vol. LV, pp. 371-383 (1941)

E. J. Laubusch, "Chlorination of Water", *Water & Sewage Works*, Vol. 105, pp. 411-417 (1958)

E. W. Moore, "Fundamentals of Chlorination of Sewage and Waste", *Water & Sewage Works*, Vol. 98, pp. 130-136 (1951)

C. N. Sawyer, "Chemistry for Sanitary Engineers", pp. 246-256, McGraw-Hill Book Company, Inc., New York, N.Y. (1960)

9

Hydrogen Sulfide Removal

HYDROGEN sulfide removal involves the use of mechanical or chemical processes to secure the elimination of this undesirable gas from solution.

Hydrogen sulfide may be present in a water supply due to purely chemical or purely biological causes. The presence of hydrogen sulfide is more common to well supplies than to surface supplies. In well waters the hydrogen sulfide results generally from the location such as Boulder clay areas or "sour gas" oil fields. In other supplies, it is generally the result of contamination due to local atmospheric conditions, the presence of some types of bacteria in the absence of oxygen, or the contamination of mine waters by sulfur.

Bacteria often encountered in industrial waters may be responsible for the presence of hydrogen sulfide. The most common of the sulfur bacteria are those that split hydrogen sulfide from organic matter containing sulfur. Most protein matter contains sulfur, therefore hydrogen sulfide will be produced when these compounds are broken down by bacteria in the absence of oxygen. One group of sulfur bacteria produces hydrogen sulfide by the reduction of inorganic sulfates, sulfites and sulfur itself.

Hydrogen sulfide possesses a definite solubility in water which is approximately three times that of carbon dioxide and imparts a characteristic taste and odor (rotten eggs) to the water. This odor becomes objectionable when present in a concentration of 1 ppm or more and can be detected when present in amounts less than 1 ppm.

If the water has a high pH, the odor may be slight, since most of the sulfide may be present as alkaline sulfides rather than as hydrogen sulfide. Figure 9-1 shows the percentage of total sulfide present as hydrogen sulfide with the difference in the total sulfide content being that present as the alkaline sulfides.

DIFFICULTIES ENCOUNTERED

Removal of hydrogen sulfide is desirable not only from the standpoint of odor, but because even small concentrations of this gas impart

Figure 9-1
Percentage of Total Sulfide Present as H_2S

pH	Percent H_2S
5.0	98
6.0	83
6.5	61
7.0	33
7.5	14
8.0	4.8
9.2	0.32

a corrosive character to the water.

Hydrogen sulfide accounts for a well occasionally yielding a water that is black due to ferrous sulfide. Ferrous sulfide is usually extremely finely divided and only a small amount is required to blacken the water. Excessive hydrogen sulfide concentrations exhibit an aggressive tendency toward iron, steel, and copper alloys, even in the absence of oxygen.

Greensand zeolites are damaged by the passage of water containing hydrogen sulfide. Cases have been reported where the mineral has been so badly attacked in a few months by water containing only 2 ppm of hydrogen sulfide that the bed could not be reconditioned. Special minerals for the catalytic removal of iron and manganese from water are also affected by the presence of hydrogen sulfide. With the use of these materials, manufacturer's guarantees are based on the absence of this gas.

Another effect of hydrogen sulfide is to react with chemicals used for the protection of systems against corrosion thus increasing the dosage required and, in some instances, increasing cost to an extent that treatment of the system with positive corrosion inhibitors is not economically feasible.

METHODS FOR REMOVAL

AERATION. The removal of hydrogen sulfide by aeration follows Henry's law. Hydrogen sulfide is relatively soluble in water while the partial pressure of this gas in the normal atmosphere is practically "zero." The establishment of a state of equilibrium between the water and the air will result in the saturation of the water with nitrogen and oxygen. The basic fundamental in securing removal of gases from water by aeration is the establishment of a state of equilibrium between the gases in the water and the gases in the surrounding atmosphere.

Reduction in hydrogen sulfide content is obtained with many different means of aeration. The absorption of oxygen by the water during aeration also assists hydrogen sulfide removal by accomplishing oxidation of a part of the hydrogen sulfide and alkaline sulfides to free sulfur. Forced draft aeration has been found desirable where there is an appreciable hydrogen sulfide concentration to be removed. Experience has indicated the desirability of considerable cross-sectional area and a tall aeration tower. With such equipment hydrogen sulfide can be reduced to 1-2 ppm. The amount of free sulfur precipitated may prove objectionable and require filtration for its removal.

Two general types of aerators are employed for hydrogen sulfide removal; one a pressure type aerator and the other a gravity type aerator. The pressure type has the advantage that line pressure is not broken. The gravity aerator requires that line pressure be broken; however, more efficient aeration is obtained. At present the tendency is toward the installation of gravity aerators.

In the use of aeration alone for the removal of hydrogen sulfide, complete removal of this gas is not obtained. At higher pH values the sulfide content will be present chiefly as alkaline sulfides which will result in incomplete removal by aeration alone. This condition results because carbon dioxide is less soluble than the hydrogen sulfide and is removed by aeration more rapidly than hydrogen sulfide. As the carbon dioxide is removed, the pH rises and the equilibrium between alkaline sulfides and hydrogen sulfide is altered so that the reaction proceeds in the wrong direction for the most complete removal of hydrogen sulfide.

AERATION WITH PH REDUCTION. Removal of hydrogen sulfide by aeration is most effective at reduced pH in the range of 4.0 to 5.0 because of the equilibrium between the alkaline sulfides and the sulfide as discussed previously. By reducing the pH of the water, the ionization constant is shifted and more of the total sulfide is converted to hydrogen sulfide in which form it is available for removal by aeration.

In recent years flue gases which are high in carbon dioxide content have been employed in reducing the pH value sufficiently to liberate hydrogen sulfide. The quantity of gas required for pH reduction will depend upon the alkalinity of the supply being treated.

One type of equipment for this process consists of a double stack with a water seal separating the upper carbonating chamber from the lower aeration chamber. The flue gas is introduced at the bottom of the carbonating chamber and mixes with the influent water flowing counter-current. Most of the hydrogen sulfide is removed at the reduced pH in the upper section. In the lower section, which is similar in design to the carbonating chamber, a counter-current of air provides additional scrubbing of the water with air alone for the removal of carbon dioxide and further removal of any residual hydrogen sulfide. Also, it is possible that any remaining alkaline sulfides will be oxidized to sulfur. This type of hydrogen sulfide degassifying apparatus is illustrated by Figure 9-2. The introduction of carbon dioxide at the bottom of the carbonating chamber permits a counter-current flow of gas and water through the entire length of the chamber, thus permitting maximum contact time between the gas and the water. The taller the tower used the greater is the contact time provided.

Reduction in pH of the water may also be obtained by the feed of a mineral acid. The feed of acid is controlled to obtain the desired pH reduction. This method provides a positive control over pH reduction.

By combining pH reduction with aeration, the size of the forced draft aerator can be considerably reduced. More effective hydrogen sulfide removal is also secured. However, with this method some precipitation of flowers of sulfur can be expected. Coagulation and filtration may be necessary if the initial total

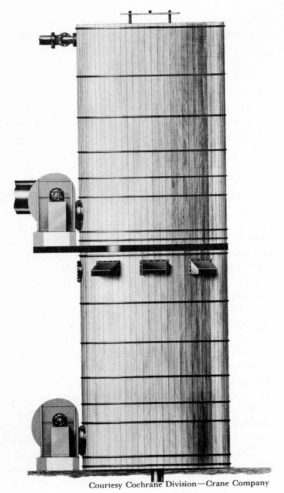

Courtesy Cochrane Division—Crane Company

Figure 9-2 • Hydrogen Sulfide Degasifier

sulfide content of the water is high.

CHLORINATION. While aeration alone and aeration combined with pH reduction will reduce the hydrogen sulfide content of a water supply to a relatively low value, depending upon the amount of gas originally present, the hydrogen sulfide content of a water can not be reduced to "zero" by either of these methods. Depending on the use of the water, complete removal of hydrogen sulfide may be required as even small quantities produce an offensive odor and result in increasing the corrosive characteristics of the water. Consequently,

aeration or aeration with pH adjustment may not provide sufficient treatment. Complete removal of hydrogen sulfide from water can be secured by means of chlorination or a combination of aeration and chlorination. One reaction with chlorine is as follows:

$$H_2S \quad + \quad Cl_2 \quad =$$
hydrogen sulfide + chlorine =
$$2HCl \quad + \quad S$$
hydrochloric acid + sulfur

In this reaction, the formation of flowers of sulfur is shown. This fine colloidal precipitate should be removed by coagulation and filtration to prevent reversion to hydrogen sulfide by the action of certain microorganisms. Theoretically, 2.1 ppm of chlorine are required for the removal of each ppm of hydrogen sulfide.

When used in greater quantities chlorine will further oxidize hydrogen sulfide to sulfuric acid without the precipitation of sulfur. This reaction is shown below:

$$H_2S \quad + \quad 4Cl_2 \quad + 4H_2O =$$
hydrogen sulfide + chlorine + water =
$$H_2SO_4 \quad + \quad 8HCl$$
sulfuric acid + hydrochloric acid

Theoretically, 8.4 ppm of chlorine are required for the removal of each ppm of hydrogen sulfide. This high chlorine consumption considerably increases the cost of this method of hydrogen sulfide removal. Consequently, it is usually the more economical procedure to remove as much hydrogen sulfide as possible by aeration with reduced pH and to use complete chlorine oxidation, if necessary, for removal of the residual hydrogen sulfide after aeration.

ANION EXCHANGE. Anion adsorbers have recently been developed which are applicable for the removal of hydrogen sulfide from water supplies. Highly basic resins have been prepared which, when regenerated with salt and/or sodium bicarbonate depending upon the pH of the water, exchange their ions for sulfides, sulfates, etc. This reaction is illustrated by the following equation in which "R" represents the resin matrix:

$$R_4N.OH \quad + \quad H_2S \quad =$$
$$\text{basic exchange resin} + \text{hydrogen sulfide} =$$
$$R_4N.HS \quad + \quad H_2O$$
$$\text{sulfide resin} + \text{water}$$

In accomplishing this removal a low cost regenerant is employed, line pressure is not broken, excess oxygen is not added to the water, and a minimum of equipment is required.

The equipment employed is a pressure type softener shell designed for counter-current flow utilizing highly basic anion exchange resins such that dealkalization will also be obtained and the chloride content of the water will be increased. By counter-current flow is meant the up flow of water during the service run and the down flow of water and regenerant for rinsing and regeneration.

At present the use of the highly basic anion resins for hydrogen sulfide removal has been limited to domestic uses though it is considered that they are satisfactory for some industrial uses. They have the limitations of low capacity, low flow rates, and iron must be absent from the water. It is preferable for the influent water to be low in hardness. However, the process can be employed with the use of a dual bed to both soften the water and remove hydrogen sulfide. It is also possible in some cases for existing zeolite softeners to be converted to perform both hydrogen sulfide removal and softening of the water.

ANALYSIS FOR SULFIDE

When dissolved gases are present in a water supply, it usually is necessary to analyze the water at the point of origin to obtain accurate results. For example, this procedure is mandatory if the gases are carbon dioxide or dissolved oxygen. The determination of hydrogen sulfide and total sulfide is a rather involved analysis which is not readily performed in the field. Fortunately, samples for sulfide can be "fixed" at the source and then transported to a laboratory for analysis.

The fixing reagents employed are 2N zinc acetate solution (220 g Zn $(C_2H_3O_2)_2.2H_2O$ per liter of distilled water) and 1N sodium hydroxide solution (40 g NaOH per liter of distilled water). To fix a sample, place 1 ml of zinc acetate in a 16 oz bottle. Collect the sample (approximately 16 oz) in this bottle with a minimum of agitation. Add 1 ml sodium hydroxide, stopper and mix. The fixed sample should be analyzed within 24 hours for maximum accuracy. The method of analysis usually employed is colorimetric, based upon the reaction between paraaminodimethylaniline, ferric chloride and the sulfide ion to produce methylene blue.

APPLICATION AND LIMITATIONS

In general, the method or combination of methods employed for hydrogen sulfide removal involves individual study. The method of removal is determined by such factors as the total sulfide content of the water, alkalinity of the water, desired effluent sulfide concentration, use or purpose for which the water will be employed, existing plant equipment, etc.

The methods discussed in detail above are the ones in general use. However, there are other methods employed in specific cases which are too limited for general application and which in general are indirect methods of hydrogen sulfide removal. Examples of these methods are the removal of sulfide by ozonation, usually accomplished as an indirect result of the sterilization of water, bacterial action on sulfides over long periods of time followed by sterilization and filtration, and slow aeration in an open reservoir followed by the use of a coagulant, sterilization, and filtration.

REFERENCES

M. E. Flentje, "Aeration", *Journal,* Am. Water Works Assoc., Vol. 29, pp. 872-880 (1937)

J. E. Foxworthy and H. K. Gray, "Removal of Hydrogen Sulfide in High Concentrations from Water", *Journal,* Am. Water Works Assoc., Vol. 50, pp. 872-878 (1958)

S. T. Powell and L. G. von Lossberg, "Removal of Hydrogen Sulfide from Well Water", *Journal,* Am. Water Works Assoc., Vol. 40, pp. 1277-1289 (1948)

S. W. Walls, "Hydrogen Sulfide Problems of Small Water Systems", *Journal,* Am. Water Works Assoc., Vol. 46, pp. 160-170 (1954)

10

Iron Removal and Iron Retention

IRON removal is the process by which objectionable amounts of iron are removed from water either in one step or a series of steps.

Iron retention is the treatment of iron-bearing water with surface active agents, capable of forming a complex with iron, thereby retaining iron in solution and preventing precipitation which would otherwise occur.

Figure 10-1 • Typical Iron Deposition in Pipe Line

Iron in water will deposit in water works distribution systems increasing the frictional resistance through pipes; water meters will become heavily coated with iron oxide and must be cleaned regularly in order to register correctly. If water containing large amounts of iron is used in the home, it will injure the color and taste of many edibles and will destroy the sanitary appearance of sinks and cooking utensils. Clothes washed with such a water will develop yellow stains. Crenothrix or "iron bacteria" frequently accompany waters of high iron content. These organisms established in a city distribution system cause clogging of service mains and are responsible for disagreeable odors.

Where well waters containing iron are used in industrial cooling water operations, deposition of iron from solution will occur. Heat ex-change surfaces become fouled with iron oxide deposits. Valves, lines, etc. will be plugged by the precipitated iron. Ferric iron present in water to be zeolite softened results in fouling of the zeolite beds and loss of efficiency. Where iron is present in boiler feedwater it constitutes another source of potential scale forming tendencies.

In many industries, the presence of iron in process water may be highly undesirable. In the paper, tanning, textile, beverage and ice manufacturing industries, for example, the presence of iron is highly detrimental to the product.

METHODS OF IRON REMOVAL

Iron can be removed from water by several different processes and combinations of processes. In fact, there are so many different methods that can be employed for iron removal that careful study is required to select a method most suitable to any individual case. Selection of an iron removal method will be influenced not only by the amount of iron in the raw water and the form in which the iron is present, but also by the ultimate use of the water and the degree of softening that may also be desired.

AERATION, SEDIMENTATION AND FILTRATION. Aeration is a process which consists of intimately admixing water and air in some manner. Where aeration is employed for iron removal, two actions occur simultaneously. First, carbon dioxide is removed by aeration, thus increasing the pH of the water. Secondly, the oxygen added to the water by aeration enters into the chemical oxidation of the iron. As a result of these two actions, precipitation of the iron occurs as ferric hydroxide, illustrated by the following equation.

$$4Fe(HCO_3)_2 \quad + \quad O_2 \quad + 2H_2O =$$
ferrous bicarbonate + oxygen + water =
$$4Fe(OH)_3 \quad + \quad 8CO_2$$
ferric hydroxide + carbon dioxide

Iron is frequently present in well waters in the ferrous or unoxidized state. Increase in pH in the absence of oxygen would precipitate ferrous hydroxide, but since ferrous hy-

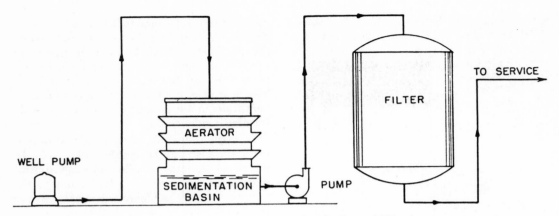

Figure 10-2 • Iron Removal by Aeration, Settling and Filtration

droxide is more soluble than ferric hydroxide, complete iron removal requires oxidation of ferrous iron to the ferric state, with precipitation of the highly insoluble ferric hydroxide.

Complete precipitation of iron by aeration is not instantaneous. For this reason, it is advisable to employ a retention and sedimentation tank following the aerator to provide time for the precipitation and settling of ferric hydroxide, prior to filtration. Sludge settled in this tank is removed periodically.

Even with an adequate supply of oxygen, the precipitation of ferric hydroxide is hindered by low pH values. For effective iron removal by aeration the pH should be increased to approximately 7.5. If aeration alone is unable to raise the pH to this point, the supplemental feed of an alkali is required, following aeration, to complete the precipitation of ferric hydroxide.

Coke-tray aerators are frequently used in the removal of iron. Other types of aerators such as cascades, cones, nozzles and towers are also employed. Provision must be made to periodically clean the unit of the precipitated iron. Figure 10-2 shows a flow sheet for iron removal by aeration, sedimentation and filtration.

To avoid re-pumping, aeration may be conducted under pressure. Carbon dioxide is not removed and an alkali feed may be required to precipitate the iron. This method of iron removal is applicable only to waters containing relatively small amounts of iron and carbon dioxide.

Under some circumstances, chlorine and other oxidants have been employed instead of aeration in order to oxidize and precipitate iron. Usually, such methods cannot compete economically with aeration.

While the insoluble ferric hydroxide precipitated from an iron-bearing water may be removed by settling alone if sufficient time is provided, it is better practice to follow with filtration in order to insure complete iron removal in a reasonable period of time. Standard pressure or gravity filters are employed for this purpose, using either sand or anthracite coal as the filter medium.

COAGULATION, SEDIMENTATION AND FILTRATION. Some waters, usually surface supplies and particularly those from swampy areas, may contain appreciable organic matter which acts to retard or prevent the precipitation of iron. Even following aeration and pH adjustment, little removal of iron may be secured. Chlorination may be of value because of its destructive action on the organic present, but may be costly and not fully effective. Where such waters are encountered, coagulation is usually the most effective measure, followed by sedimentation and filtration. The coagulant most widely employed is alum although it is necessary to conduct tests to determine the most effective and economical coagulant for each particular water.

LIME AND LIME-SODA SOFTENING. Where either lime softening or lime-soda softening is employed, the pH of the treated water is elevated sufficiently high to provide the softening reactions and iron is precipitated as ferric hydroxide. Aeration is usually provided prior to softening to supply any oxygen needed for the conversion of ferrous to ferric iron. Aeration is frequently desirable prior to cold process softening, regardless of any iron problem, in order to remove carbon dioxide and thereby decrease lime requirements.

The aerator frequently is located over the lime-soda softener. As the pH of the water is increased by the feeding of lime, oxidation of iron is rapid. Precipitation and sedimentation can take place in the same unit, followed by filtration as illustrated in Figure 10-3.

Iron removal, of course, is readily accomplished under the temperature and pH conditions existing in hot process lime or lime-soda softening. Iron, precipitated in such units, will serve to aid coagulation.

Iron removal in conjunction with cold process lime or lime-soda softening may be followed, on occasion, by acidification and zeolite softening where the use of the treated water requires low hardness.

CATION EXCHANGE. With certain waters, cation exchangers may be employed for the removal of soluble iron from water. The cation exchange process is limited essentially to well waters where the iron content is in the ferrous state.

Removal of iron by cation exchange is similar to and simultaneous with the removal of calcium and magnesium. The cation exchange material may be green sand, carbonaceous or resinous. When operated on the sodium cycle, iron removal takes place as follows:

$$\underset{\text{ferrous bicarbonate}}{Fe(HCO_3)_2} + \underset{\text{sodium zeolite}}{Na_2Z} =$$
$$\underset{\text{ferrous zeolite}}{FeZ} + \underset{\text{sodium bicarbonate}}{2NaHCO_3}$$

Regeneration reactions with salt are as follows:

$$\underset{\text{ferrous zeolite}}{FeZ} + \underset{\text{sodium chloride}}{2NaCl} =$$
$$\underset{\text{sodium zeolite}}{Na_2Z} + \underset{\text{ferrous chloride}}{FeCl_2}$$

Similar softening and regeneration reactions take place when the cation exchanger is operated on the hydrogen cycle in which case regeneration is secured with the use of sulfuric acid.

While iron removal by cation exchange possesses a field of usefulness where complete hardness removal is also necessary, it is not suited to those applications where hardness removal is not required. It is possible, however, to overrun the cation exchanger from the standpoint of hardness removal while continuing to secure iron removal.

In order to avoid fouling the exchanger bed with ferric hydroxide, it is necessary that the iron content of the influent water be present only as soluble ferrous iron. Air must be excluded from contact with the well water prior to the exchange unit.

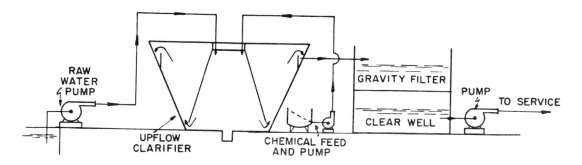

Figure 10-3 • Iron Removal by Lime Treatment

Cation exchange is applied only to waters of limited iron content and is not recommended for the removal of high iron concentrations. CONTACT FILTRATION. Contact filtration accomplishes oxidation and filtration of the iron in one step. Two types of contact filtration are employed. In one type, the material of the filter bed simply acts as a catalyst for the reaction between the iron and oxygen in the water. In the other type, the filter bed supplies the oxygen needed for oxidation of the iron, and this oxygen must be periodically replenished by use of a regenerant chemical.

Catalytic beds usually involve a filter medium containing manganese dioxide. Standard pressure or gravity filter shells are employed with the 30-36 inches catalytic bed supported on gravel. Flow rates are limited to 4 gallons per square foot per minute or less and backwash for removal of precipitated iron is at the rate of 12-15 gallons per square foot per minute. Units of this type present a simple method of iron removal since no chemical treatment is required. Proper functioning of such units, however, requires that the water be low in organic matter, free of hydrogen sulfide, possess a minimum of pH of 6.5 and contain sufficient oxygen to react with the iron present. If there is inadequate oxygen content of the raw water, oxygen must be supplied by an aerating device. This aeration can be accomplished under pressure, without need for repumping.

Manganese zeolite is an example of contact filtration where the filter bed itself supplies the needed oxygen for iron removal. Manganese zeolite is green sand which has been treated with manganous chloride to convert it to manganous zeolite. Then, treatment with potassium permanganate results in the precipitation of the higher oxides of manganese on the zeolite grains.

No removal of hardness is involved with the manganese zeolite process. The oxidation reactions occur between the natural iron content of the water and the manganese oxides on the zeolite grains. Regeneration of the unit with potassium permanganate is required, as the oxidizing ability of the bed is consumed

in the process of iron removal. Backwashing of the precipitated iron from the bed is also necessary. Filter rate is 3 gallons per square foot per minute and backwash rate is a minimum of 8 gallons per square foot per minute. Potassium permanganate is an expensive regenerant chemical and manganese zeolite installations are usually limited to waters of low iron content or employed as a polishing device, following other processes which have removed the major portion of the initial iron content of the water.

IRON RETENTION

For many industrial water uses, it is not necessary that the iron be removed, provided the water can be stabilized to prevent or retard precipitation. Well waters, high in iron content, are frequently employed for cooling purposes on a once-through basis. By stabilizing the iron content, deposits can be prevented throughout the system. The cost of stabilizing the iron is frequently less than the cost of iron removal and, in addition, the investment in equipment is avoided.

Stabilization of iron can be secured with the use of surface active agents, such as polyphosphates and organic sequestrants. A complex is formed between the iron present in the water and the surface active agent added. By this complex formation, precipitation of ferric hydroxide can be delayed or, with sufficient treatment concentration, prevented indefinitely. Usually, economic considerations limit such stabilization to once-through systems. In recirculating cooling water systems, the continuous aeration and long retention period so increases the quantity of stabilizing agent required as to make iron removal from the makeup water the more desirable practice.

The quantity of surface active agent required to retain iron in solution will vary according to such factors as the iron content, alkalinity, pH and solids content of the water. Another important factor is the temperature to which the water will be heated. For higher temperatures, increased treatment is required to overcome the increased tendency for precipitation. In general, the organic iron retention agents are more effective than the poly-phosphates. Another advantage of the organic agents is that they can be used at higher concentrations, on waters of high iron and high hardness content, without danger of pre-cipitating calcium phosphate. Under certain circumstances, a combination of organics and polyphosphates represents the most advan-tageous treatment.

The retention time of the water in the sys-tem is another important variable affecting the treatment concentrations required. If, for example, a simple system of well water pumped through a single heat exchanger and then to waste is involved, then there is little retention time in the system. Only sufficient treatment may be needed to retain iron in solution for 10-15 minutes. On the other hand, in a large plant with many varied cooling operations, and numerous smaller lines at low flow rates, it may be necessary to feed suffi-cient stabilizing agent to retain iron in solu-tion for 24 hours. The cost of iron retention treatment increases as the retention time in the system increases and all such data are re-quired for accurate treatment estimations.

The proper surface active agents are ef-fective in preventing iron precipitation re-gardless as to whether the iron is in the ferrous or ferric state. It is advisable, however, to introduce the stabilizing material to the water prior to its exposure to air and prior to chlori-nation in order to permit complex formation with the iron as quickly as possible.

Equipment for feeding iron retention agents can be relatively simple. Where the raw water is at a constant flow rate, a chemical solution tank for one day's treatment supply can be used together with a small constant rate chemical pump. If the raw water flow is vari-able, then a proportional method of chemical feed should be employed so as to permit the most economical use of treatment.

Iron retention agents are available which possess such powerful ability to form iron com-plexes that iron can be retained in solution practically indefinitely. Such agents also pos-sess the power to dissolve previously precipi-tated iron. However, for iron retention to be most economical, it is necessary that the sta-bilizing agent be fed to the water prior to a point where precipitation has already occurred and that the amount be limited to that neces-sary to retain iron in solution under the con-ditions of that individual system.

IRON BACTERIA

The iron bacteria are an unusual group of microorganisms found in industrial waters, streams, lakes, wells and in potable water supplies. These organisms may occur alone or in different combinations with other species of bacteria, fungi and algae.

Although the iron bacteria have not been studied as completely as some of the other organisms this lack of study does not indicate that they have not caused serious difficulty in industrial and fresh water systems. There are many case histories regarding the effect of these iron bacteria in city and industrial water systems. The published reports on the effect of iron bacteria in city water systems are many and are justifiably referred to as "water ca-lamities." The universal distribution of the iron bacteria is borne out by the development of these water calamities in Europe and in the United States. Recently these microorganisms have gained recognition in industry by their effect upon process equipment and on the finished product. Usually the affected water will become slightly turbid or acquire a light reddish tint and/or objectionable odor. As these microorganisms increase in number the water may become more turbid, and the color of the water will become brick-red. Hence the common reference to "red water." In addition to discoloring the water this group of micro-organisms produces undesirable accumula-tions in pipes, nozzles, spray ponds, etc. These deposits in time will slough and plug lines, foul pumps, valves and/or affect the quality of the finished product.

The growth and development of iron bac-teria may manifest itself in several different ways. For example, it has been reported that these microorganisms have reduced the ef-fective area of a 6 inch pipe to that of a 2 inch pipe in a matter of weeks. The accumulation in pipes, ponds, nozzles and so forth may be hard and crusty or it may be relatively light and spongy in appearance. Often other biological slimes may be associated with iron bacteria and thus further reduce or restrict the flow of water through pipes or entrap other debris. The association of other species of microorganisms with the iron bacteria will increase turbidity, increase color, give rise to objectionable odors and tastes in domestic water supplies and also cause sloughing of deposits in industrial systems which may affect the process or the product being produced.

The iron bacteria are usually considered as typical fresh water organisms. Recently, however, some of the iron bacteria have been isolated from high brines, which indicates the versatility of this class of organisms. These microorganisms are usually considered as aerobic, but they have also been found to grow in waters with low oxygen content. Although the iron bacteria are widely distributed in nature and are usually found in wells, cool springs and brooks they have also been isolated from marine waters, and connate waters (high brines). Although they are usually found in waters which are reasonably high in iron they may be occasionally found in waters which contain a very low amount of iron.

The prinicipal distinguishing characteristics between the iron bacteria and other types of microorganisms is that they have the capacity to absorb and to accumulate iron and/or manganese when grown in environments which contain these elements. These organisms deposit iron and manganese salts around their cells which results in the characteristic reddish brown to black color.

These autotrophic (self-sufficient) organisms oxidize iron compounds as a source of energy. However the amount of energy released by the oxidation of iron is relatively small.

On the basis of their morphological characteristics alone the iron bacteria can be placed into several different categories. The most common iron bacteria fall in the following genera: *Sphaerotilus, Leptothrix, Toxothrix,* *Crenothrix, Clonothrix, Gallionella, Siderocapsa, Siderosphaera, Sideronema, Ferribacterium, Sideromonas, Naumanniella, Ochrobium, Siderococus, Siderobacter* and *Ferrobacillus.*

In general, the iron bacteria are extremely difficult to culture in the laboratory using the usual culture media. Therefore it is not possible to evaluate or to determine the number of these microorganisms in different water supplies with the usual bacteriological procedures. A satisfactory procedure for determining the population index of these microorganisms in water supplies is a direct microscopic analysis of the water. This analysis, however, will only determine the number of the more obvious species of this group of microorganisms.

In general, the iron bacteria show preference for the lower temperatures; these organisms have been observed to grow at temperatures which range from O C to 40 C. However, their optimum temperature will range from 6 C to 25 C.

Hydrogen ion concentration has a great effect upon the growth and development of these bacteria. Although published reports show that the different species have different requirements, the pH range for growth will vary from 5.5 to 8.2. The optimum pH appears to be approximately 6.5. Much has been written regarding the sensitivity of the iron bacteria to light but their general reaction to light appears to be doubtful. These organisms have been found to grow in exposed areas, in shade and in complete darkness such as in pipes, wells, etc.

Obviously the growth and development of iron bacteria and the deposition of iron in their sheaths is influenced by the amount of dissolved iron in their immediate environment. The iron bacteria have been found in waters with as much as 30 ppm of iron and they have also been found in waters which contain as low as 0.1 ppm of iron. In the low concentrations the growth and development of the iron bacteria is dependent upon the flow of water or where the iron supply is continually renewed.

The control of iron bacteria in fresh and salt water systems is possible with the use of biocides. The selection of the most appropriate biocide will, of course, depend upon the environment in which the organism is growing, the general conditions of use of the water, and whether the water is for industrial or domestic use. Obviously the use of control agents in domestic systems must be limited to those which have the approval of the Public Health Service. Under the usual operating conditions for city water supplies the most suitable agent is chlorine. However, in industrial systems it is possible that biocides other than chlorine will give satisfactory microorganism control. In some industrial systems, where the use of chlorine is not indicated because of precipitation of iron and manganese, it may be necessary to use a special proprietary formulation. These proprietary formulations, although usually more expensive than chlorine, will produce the desired effect. It is, of course, essential that these industrial biocides be compatible with iron retention formulations and with corrosion inhibitors. In addition, the biocides must not affect the quality or manufacture of the product.

MANGANESE REMOVAL

Manganese removal is closely associated with iron removal. Fortunately, manganese is not encountered as frequently as iron in water sources and usually is present in smaller quantities. However, the methods used for manganese removal are essentially the same as for iron removal. In most waters of appreciable manganese content, iron is also present so that the treatment must be such as to remove both undesirable constituents.

Manganese is less readily oxidized than iron by aeration and a higher pH is required for its precipitation. However, coagulation, lime and lime-soda softening, cation exchange and contact filtration are effective methods for removal of manganese, as well as iron.

APPLICATIONS AND LIMITATIONS

There are many combinations of treatment methods that can be employed for iron removal. A detailed study of each individual plant problem is necessary in order to select the particular system best suited to the individual case. An iron removal method cannot be selected solely on its efficiency with respect to iron, but must be correlated with other quality requirements of the water, such as the need also for low hardness in the treated water.

Where there are both potable and industrial uses involved, it may be desirable to employ two different methods of iron removal. Also, in some cases, iron removal may be employed for potable and process water, while the larger volume of cooling water is treated for iron retention rather than iron removal. A careful study, relating all treatment methods to the individual plant needs, is highly advisable because of the many different methods that can be employed both for iron removal and iron retention.

REFERENCES

S. B. Applebaum, "Iron and Manganese Removal", *Proceedings*, Engineers Soc. of Western Penna., pp. 49-57 (1955)

R. B. Conlan, "Correcting the Iron Problem in Water Systems", *Heating and Ventilating*, Vol. 48, pp. 77-79 (Dec. 1951)

"Water Quality and Treatment", 2nd Ed., pp. 359-368, Am. Water Works Assoc., New York, N.Y. (1950)

R. S. Wolfe, "Cultivation, Morphology and Classification of the Iron Bacteria", *Journal,* Am. Water Works Assoc., Vol. 50, pp. 1241-1249 (1958)

11

Lime-Soda Softening

LIME-SODA softening is the process by which the calcium and magnesium salts constituting the hardness content of a water are chemically precipitated and removed through the use of lime (calcium hydroxide) and soda ash (sodium carbonate). This process may be carried out at normal raw water temperatures, in which case it is referred to as "cold process" or at temperatures near or above the boiling point, referred to as "hot process."

The lime-soda ash process is based upon four essential factors:

Proper selection of specific reagents to efficiently precipitate part of the impurities to be removed in the form of an insoluble sludge and to convert the remainder to a soluble form.

Correct proportioning of the specific chemical reagents to the raw water.

Propagating the chemical precipitating reactions by a suitable combination of coagulation, sedimentation, heat or sludge contact.

Filtration of the chemically softened or finished water to remove traces of turbidity or suspended matter resulting from the process.

Lime-soda softening is employed for the removal of hardness in order to minimize scale and sludge in boilers, reduce calcium carbonate deposition in heat exchange systems and cooling water systems, and in general to remove hardness wherever hardness in water is a source of difficulty either in industrial process water, boiler feedwater or city water supply.

Incidental to the removal of hardness in the proper operation of lime-soda softening, iron, free carbon dioxide and turbidity are removed.

CHEMISTRY INVOLVED

Hydrated lime—$Ca(OH)_2$—of 90% purity is usually employed in hot process lime-soda softening, or in cold process softening where the quantity of water softened is not exceptionally large. In cold process systems where very large quantities of water are softened, such as a city plant, it is usually more economical to employ unslaked lime—CaO—which is first slaked to form hydrated lime at the plant in accordance with the following reaction:

(1)

$$CaO + H_2O =$$
unslaked lime (calcium oxide) + water =
$$Ca(OH)_2$$
hydrated lime (calcium hydroxide)

Soda ash—Na_2CO_3—of 98% purity is employed in lime-soda softening at the usual specification of 58% Na_2O content.

USE OF LIME AND SODA ASH. Hydrated lime reacts to chemically precipitate the carbonate hardness present in water, thereby producing insoluble precipitates of calcium carbonate—$CaCO_3$—and magnesium hydroxide—$Mg(OH)_2$—without the production of any soluble by-products. These suspended precipitates are removed by sedimentation and filtration and thus a marked reduction in solids content is obtained.

The carbonate hardness of a water is composed of the carbonates and bicarbonates of calcium and magnesium. Their precipitation by means of hydrated lime proceeds in accordance with the following reactions:

(2)

$$Ca(HCO_3)_2 + Ca(OH)_2 =$$
calcium bicarbonate + calcium hydroxide =
$$2CaCO_3 + 2H_2O$$
calcium carbonate + water

(3)

$$Mg(HCO_3)_2 + 2Ca(OH)_2$$
magnesium bicarbonate + calcium hydroxide
$$= Mg(OH)_2 + 2CaCO_3$$
= magnesium hydroxide + calcium carbonate
$$+ 2H_2O$$
+ water

Hydrated lime also reacts with the magnesium salts constituting a portion of the non-carbonate hardness of water. In these reactions, insoluble magnesium hydroxide—$Mg(OH)_2$—is produced. This precipitate is removed in softening process by sedimentation and filtration. However, a soluble by-product of calcium sulfate, calcium chloride, etc., is formed as illustrated below:

(4)

$$MgSO_4 \quad + \quad Ca(OH)_2 \quad =$$
magnesium sulfate + calcium hydroxide =

$$Mg(OH)_2 \quad + \quad CaSO_4$$
magnesium hydroxide + calcium sulfate

(5)

$$MgCl_2 \quad + \quad Ca(OH)_2 \quad =$$
magnesium chloride + calcium hydroxide =

$$Mg(OH)_2 \quad + \quad CaCl_2$$
magnesium hydroxide + calcium chloride

Such soluble by-products of calcium sulfate, calcium chloride, etc., must be removed in the softening process, since these salts, together with the calcium sulfate and the calcium chloride naturally present in a water, constitute the calcium non-carbonate hardness.

Calcium sulfate, calcium chloride, etc., whether produced as by-products in the above reactions or naturally present in a water, are chemically precipitated as calcium carbonate—$CaCO_3$—by the use of soda ash (sodium carbonate) as follows:

(6)

$$CaSO_4 \quad + \quad Na_2CO_3 \quad =$$
calcium sulfate + sodium carbonate =

$$CaCO_3 \quad + \quad Na_2SO_4$$
calcium carbonate + sodium sulfate

(7)

$$CaCl_2 \quad + \quad Na_2CO_3 \quad =$$
calcium chloride + sodium carbonate =

$$CaCO_3 \quad + \quad 2NaCl$$
calcium carbonate + sodium chloride

In the above reactions while the calcium content is precipitated as insoluble calcium carbonate, soluble by-products in the form of sodium sulfate and sodium chloride are produced. While the use of soda ash in lime-soda softening effects removal of the hardness, a decrease in solids content is not obtained because of the production of soluble sodium salts. The previously given reactions with lime, however, do result in a reduction of the solids content. In the application of lime-soda softening to a given water supply, therefore, it is evident that if the hardness content of that water is chiefly in the carbonate form, which requires lime for its precipitation, a reduction in solids content will result. If, on the other hand, the hardness content of the water is chiefly in the non-carbonate form a marked reduction in the solids content of this supply through lime-soda softening will not occur.

It will be noted that two different forms of precipitates are produced in the lime-soda process. These are calcium carbonate—$CaCO_3$—and magnesium hydroxide—$Mg(OH)_2$. In contrast with the crystalline nature of calcium carbonate, magnesium hydroxide is gelatinous in character and may serve as a coagulating agent aiding the settling of these precipitates in the sedimentation tank. Magnesium oxide is frequently employed as a coagulant in both hot and cold process lime-soda softening. In addition, the magnesium hydroxide precipitate, formed through the use of this coagulant or formed from the precipitation of magnesium naturally present in the raw supply, possesses the property of adsorbing soluble silica from solution, thereby effecting its removal.

USE OF LIME. For certain applications, complete treatment with lime and soda ash is not required since it may be advisable to reduce only the calcium or the alkalinity of the raw water. Under such circumstances, soda ash may not be needed and the use of lime alone may suffice. In the hot lime-hot ion exchange process lime only is used to reduce alkalinity and calcium content prior to the ion exchangers.

Other applications of lime softening are in city water plants where the objective is the reduction of hardness at the most economical cost, in the beverage industry where high alkalinity is a prime objection and in the treatment of cooling tower makeup water where calcium bicarbonate hardness may be the chief scale forming factor. In these applications, cold process lime softening is employed and the use of a coagulant with the lime is usually recommended.

The degree to which hardness reduction can be secured with lime alone depends on the bicarbonate and calcium content of the water. Non-carbonate calcium hardness requires soda ash for its removal and cannot be removed though the use of lime. Non-carbonate magnesium hardness, as shown by equations (4) and (5) can be reduced by lime, but only at the expense of adding additional non-carbonate calcium hardness. Therefore, in softening with lime alone, use is made only of the reactions shown in equations (2) and (3).

Lime softening and selective calcium softening are not necessarily synonymous. Selective calcium softening, as the name implies, is used where it is desired only to reduce the calcium content without using additional chemical for removal of magnesium. Lime softening will reduce the carbonate calcium hardness, but soda ash is required for removal of non-carbonate calcium hardness. Therefore, if it is desired to precipitate calcium as completely as possible, it is sometimes necessary to also employ soda ash in selective calcium softening.

Fig. 11-1
Cold Process Softening Balances

	Raw Water	Lime Softening for Calcium Removal	Selective Calcium Softening With Lime and Soda Ash	Lime-Soda Ash Softening
Total Hardness as CaCO$_3$.	160	80	69	52
Calcium as CaCO$_3$	110	35	24	24
Magnesium as CaCO$_3$ ...	50	45	45	28
"P" Alkalinity as CaCO$_3$.	0	17	22	60
"M" Alkalinity as CaCO$_3$.	130	50	60	82
Sulfate as SO$_4$	48	48	48	48
Chloride as Cl	16	16	16	16

Chemical Treatment Requirements

Lime		98	98	156
Soda Ash			22	64

All values in parts per million.

Figure 11-1 illustrates the chemical balances obtained in softening the same water with different objectives. The second column shows anticipated softener effluent balances where only lime is used in the softening process and where it is desired to remove only the calcium and not the magnesium. A small amount of magnesium will be precipitated

even under these conditions, but the objectives of the treatment have been secured. Calcium has been reduced to a relatively low value with a minimum of chemical treatment cost.

The third column illustrates still further reduction in calcium, but to secure this reduction it has been necessary to add soda ash to further force calcium precipitation. The additional calcium removal has been achieved at the expense of slightly higher softener effluent alkalinity.

Complete lime-soda softening, including reduction in magnesium, is shown by the fourth column. To secure this reduction in magnesium it has been necessary to again increase the softener effluent alkalinity and to employ a considerable increase in lime and soda ash.

Each of the chemical balances illustrated is the most desirable for certain specific uses of the treated water. Other variations are also possible. For example it may be desired to secure maximum alkalinity reduction, or to secure maximum magnesium removal even at the expense of additional alkalinity in the effluent.

Use of Caustic Soda (sodium hydroxide). Under some circumstances, caustic soda (sodium hydroxide) can be substituted in place of lime and soda ash if the carbonate and non-carbonate hardness of the raw water are in the correct proportions. The reaction of caustic soda with calcium bicarbonate hardness is illustrated below:

(8)
$$Ca(HCO_3)_2 + 2NaOH =$$
calcium bicarbonate + sodium hydroxide =
$$CaCO_3 + Na_2CO_3 +$$
calcium carbonate + sodium carbonate +
$$2H_2O$$
water

Soda ash (sodium carbonate) is produced as a by-product in this reaction which becomes available for the precipitation of calcium non-carbonate hardness as shown by equations (6) and (7). The use of caustic soda for softening is rather limited because of the necessity for a definite relationship between the carbonate and non-carbonate hardness in the raw water and the lack of flexibility in caustic soda treatment if the raw water is subject to material fluctuations. USE OF GYPSUM (CALCIUM SULFATE). Highly alkaline waters containing appreciable quantities of sodium bicarbonate—$NaHCO_3$—are characteristic of certain sections of the country. This type of water possesses a total alkalinity considerably greater than the total hardness. To condition this type of water (particularly for boiler makeup) lime and gypsum are employed. These waters do not require the use of soda ash. Lime reacts to precipitate the carbonate hardness as in equations (2) and (3). In the presence of sodium bicarbonate, lime reacts to precipitate calcium carbonate and to form sodium carbonate as shown:

(9)

$$2NaHCO_3 \quad + \quad Ca(OH)_2 \quad =$$
sodium bicarbonate + calcium hydroxide =
$$CaCO_3 \quad + \quad Na_2CO_3 \quad +$$
calcium carbonate + sodium carbonate +
$$2H_2O$$
water

For the removal of the sodium carbonate thus formed, gypsum (calcium sulfate) is employed to precipitate calcium carbonate as follows:

(10)

$$Na_2CO_3 \quad + \quad CaSO_4 \quad =$$
sodium carbonate + calcium sulfate =
$$CaCO_3 \quad + \quad Na_2SO_4$$
calcium carbonate + sodium sulfate

It will be noted that the use of gypsum for the removal of sodium bicarbonate does not decrease the solids content of the water but instead replaces the sodium bicarbonate with an equivalent amount of sodium sulfate. In most cases this sodium sulfate is less objectionable than the sodium bicarbonate.

In a few rare occasions barium salts have been employed in order to precipitate and remove sodium sulfate in the form of insoluble barium sulfate. Barium salts are relatively expensive and poisonous. Because of these limitations, this process is rarely employed.

PROPAGATING THE CHEMICAL PRECIPITATING REACTIONS

The chemical precipitating reactions are considered to be instantaneous. This fact is not evident in the practical operation of softeners because all of the insoluble reaction products (sludge) are not immediately precipitated in a form permitting rapid and efficient sedimentation or separation from the water. A portion of the sludge formed is comprised of relatively large flocs or crystals, readily separated by sedimentation. The remainder of the sludge will be of smaller particle size and will not readily settle. Some of these particles are present as colloids and are difficult to separate from the water. It is necessary to coagulate these smaller particles into agglomerates capable of producing a sludge of the required characteristics.

If a sufficient amount of magnesium is naturally present in the raw water, in most cases satisfactory coagulation results because of the coagulating properties of the magnesium hydroxide precipitated in the softening process. In the absence of sufficient natural coagulation, recirculation of softener sludge or the addition of coagulants such as magnesium oxide, sodium aluminate, or ferric sulfate should be employed.

Temperature is an important factor directly affecting the rate of sedimentation which is in turn governed by the density of the water and the time required to effect optimum particle size. At higher temperatures, the density of the water is less and more rapid settling of the sludge is permitted in the absence of convection currents. Agglomeration of smaller particles into larger size particles capable of rapid settling is accelerated by heat. For example, conventional cold process lime-soda softening usually requires a sedimentation time of 4 hours. At the temperature of hot process operation (approx. 212 F), a one hour sedimentation period is sufficient. For consistent results, however, a constant temperature must be maintained.

Recirculation of sludge provides a contact medium for proper precipitation. The use of lime and soda ash in the cold results in the formation of a super-saturated solution, or, in other words, the water contains more calcium carbonate in solution than would normally be dissolved in that water at a given temperature. If, however, particles of calcium carbonate sludge are brought into contact with water super-saturated with calcium carbonate, crystallization of calcium carbonate from solution will occur on these particles.

EQUIPMENT EMPLOYED

Lime-soda softeners may be generally classified as follows:
Cold Process Softening.
a. Intermittent or Batch.
b. Continuous—Sedimentation Type.
c. Continuous—Sludge Contact Type.
Continuous Hot Process Softening.

INTERMITTENT OR BATCH COLD PROCESS SOFTENERS. Intermittent softeners are operated by the fill and draw method. The system consists of two or more vertical tanks. One tank is employed to supply softened water while the other tank is being cleaned, filled, treated and settled. In some cases only one tank is provided if sufficient storage capacity is available to permit repeated softening cycles without interruption of a soft water supply.

The system is operated on a definite cycle. The calculated quantities of lime, soda ash and coagulant are made into a slurry in a chemical mixing tank and added to the tank while it is being filled with raw water. The full tank is agitated for a period varying from 15 minutes to one hour, agitation stopped and the water permitted to settle for as long a time as available. The clarified water is drawn off by means of a swingpipe floating at the surface and discharged to filters usually of the gravity type.

The intermittent or batch softener is normally employed for small plants. It comprises the original softener design and is rarely recommended for new construction. Advantages of this system are its low initial cost and comparatively simple operation. Its disadvantages are the long sedimentation period required, the considerable manual operations necessary and the fact that the effluent is super-saturated with calcium carbonate and is unstable, particularly with increase in temperature.

CONTINUOUS SEDIMENTATION TYPE LIME AND SODA SOFTENERS. Continuous sedimentation type units may be of basin design similar to coagulation and sedimentation basins. Units of this type are frequently employed for city water softening. The raw water is thoroughly and continuously mixed with the proportioned lime, soda ash and coagulant in a flash mixer consisting of essentially a propeller type agitator confined in a relatively small chamber. Effluent from the mixer flows through a flocculator basin, employed to insure formation of proper particle size by the action of slowly rotating paddles. The water then flows to a basin designed to permit effective sedimentation of the sludge for approximately a four hour period. Various types of sludge collection systems are employed.

Advantages of this system are its ready adaptation to any cold process softening problem, the minimum of maintenance and supervision required and the fact that the system may easily be converted to cope with taste and odor control by pre-chlorination or super-chlorination. Disadvantages are the large space requirements, relatively high construction cost and the fact that the effluent must be recarbonated to achieve stability. Chemical requirements are comparable to other cold process methods discussed.

CONTINUOUS SLUDGE CONTACT TYPE. Improved results in cold process lime-soda softening have been made possible by the development of sludge contact units. Basically, these units operate on the principle of crystallization from a super-saturated solution by providing a contact medium for proper precipitation of the sludge. The raw water is intimately mixed with previously precipitated sludge and with the lime, soda ash and coagulant. Initial precipitation of calcium and magnesium occurs and joins the slurry pool of previously formed precipitates of calcium and magnesium by contact. In this manner, precipitation and equilibrium are quickly established. The newly formed solids do not separate individually as small particles, instead the fresh precipitate deposits on the slurry already present by accretion. The nature of this sludge permits ready separation of the treated water from the slurry. A definite line of separation exists between the slurry bed and the clarified water with the treated effluent virtually filtered through a bed of its own sludge. The entire volume of the tank is slowly but constantly circulated by an agitator.

One design of sludge contact unit is shown by Figure 11-2. Softeners of the sludge contact type are rated in capacity much the same as filters. Units are available to produce from 1.0 to 3.0 gallons per square foot of surface area per minute, dependent on the design. Turbidities of the finished water of 5.0-10.0 units (without filtration) are not uncommon. This is much lower than obtained by most other methods of cold process softening. The maximum retention time of 1 hour usually

specified effects appreciable savings in equipment cost, construction and floor space when compared with other cold process methods. Chemical requirements are low and comparable to the requirements of hot process softeners. The hardness of the finished water is lower than can be obtained with other cold process units employing a given amount of chemical.

Sedimentation chambers are eliminated inasmuch as all sludge particles are kept in suspension due to velocity of upward flow. A gradual decrease in velocity permits a definite point of separation of sludge and clarified water. The sludge bed is maintained at definite density by a constant sludge bleed and therefore expensive sludge collection systems are eliminated. Another design of this type is shown in Figure 11-3.

CONTINUOUS HOT PROCESS LIME-SODA SOFTENING. The hot process softener is normally employed as a specific external treatment for boiler feedwater. The units are designed to operate at temperatures of 212 F or above and employ live or exhaust steam as the

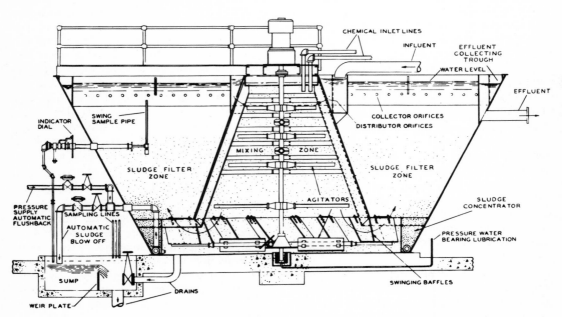

Figure 11-2 • Sludge Contact Softener

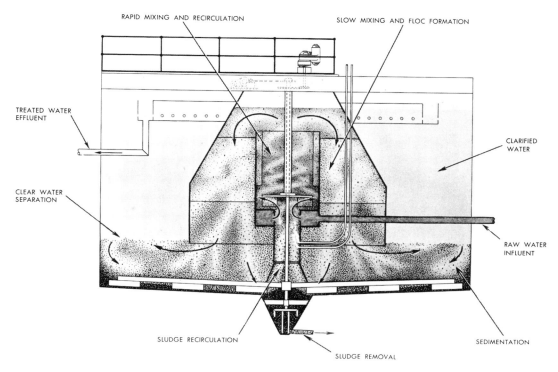

RAPID MIXING AND RECIRCULATION

SLOW MIXING AND FLOC FORMATION

TREATED WATER
EFFLUENT

CLARIFIED
WATER

CLEAR WATER
SEPARATION

RAW WATER
INFLUENT

SLUDGE RECIRCULATION

SEDIMENTATION

SLUDGE REMOVAL

Courtesy Graver Water Conditioning Co.

Figure 11-3 • Sludge Contact Softener

source of heat. The design of one type of hot process unit is shown in Figure 11-4. Other types of different design are procurable, but the softening principles are similar in all.

While varying slightly, dependent upon the particular design of different manufacturers, in a hot process softener the cold raw water enters through a float controlled regulating valve to maintain a given water level in the sedimentation tank. The flow of raw water to the softener actuates a proportioning device to continuously feed lime, soda ash and coagulant. The raw water is heated to or above 212 F in a heater which may be of a tray, jet or deaerating design. Chemical reactions to form calcium carbonate and magnesium hydroxide are practically instantaneous and due to the effect of the higher temperature sedimentation takes place rapidly. The sludge collecting cone is periodically

blown down to remove the precipitates and the clarified and softened water is drawn off through the internal take-off and subjected to pressure filtration. Since silica is quite soluble in hot alkaline solutions, anthracite or some other non-siliceous material is normally specified as a filter medium. Filters are backwashed with hot softened water from the sedimentation chamber and backwash water is returned to this chamber. No appreciable thermal loss is entailed in backwashing, therefore, and both chemicals and treated water are conserved.

Hot process softening possesses the advantage of treating large quantities of water in a relatively small compact unit. A retention time of 1 hour is normally specified. Maximum efficiency of chemical treatment is obtained by virtue of the high operating temperature. Economies in chemical treatment

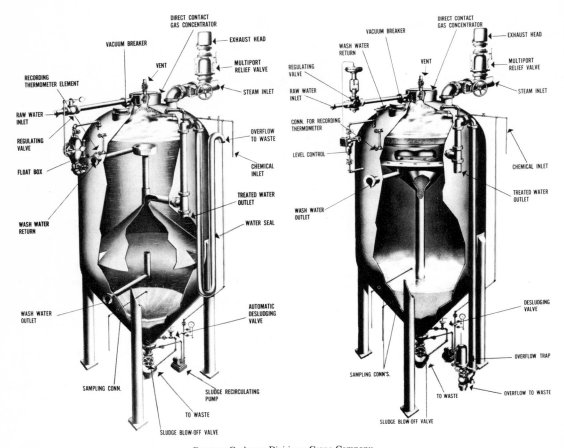

Courtesy Cochrane Division—Crane Company

Figure 11-4 • Downflow Type Hot Process Softener   *Figure 11-5 • Upflow Sludge Blanket Type Hot Process Softener*

can frequently be effected by recirculation of softener sludge.

In recent years, the sludge contact principle, originally developed in cold process work, has been applied to hot process softening. Sludge blanket hot process softeners are particularly applicable where silica reduction is required. Sludge blanket units differ from conventional designs in that, as shown by Figure 11-5, the raw water, mixed with the added chemicals, is delivered to the bottom of the tank by means of a central downtake. Flow is reversed at this point and the water rises slowly up through a blanket of previously formed sludge. The intimate contact

secured in the sludge blanket aids the efficiency of silica removal. Softening and turbidity removal are also favored by this design. The height of the sludge blanket can be determined by use of sampling cocks at different positions on the sedimentation tank. A disadvantage of the sludge blanket design is the difficulty in maintaining a uniform sludge blanket, without carryover, under varying load conditions.

The hot process lime-soda softener can be used to combine in one complete unit the functions of:

Softening by removal of calcium and magnesium salts.

Silica removal through the use of magnesium salts.

Complete deaeration of the boiler feed-water.

Filtration for the removal of suspended matter.

The effluent from the hot process softener is low in residual hardness and is relatively stable. Marked increases in temperatures such as in economizers, closed heaters, etc., will cause some after-precipitation. Under these conditions, stabilization of the softener effluent by acidification or surface active agents is necessary to prevent objectionable deposits.

APPLICATIONS

Lime-soda softening is the type of treatment most suitable to the softening of high hardness supplies, particularly those of predominately carbonate hardness. Marked reduction in solids content results where the raw water contains high carbonate hardness.

Iron or suspended matter in the raw water can be removed by lime-soda softening and pre-filtration of such supplies is not required. Where the raw water contains appreciable color and dissolved organic matter, through the use of proper coagulant it is frequently possible to effect a marked reduction in the organic content.

Lime softening alone, without the use of soda ash, can be employed advantageously where it is desired to reduce only the calcium bicarbonate content. In the cold, typical applications are in the treatment of makeup water for cooling systems, preparation of process water for the beverage industry and in the softening of city supplies. In the hot, lime softening provides an efficient method for reducing alkalinity and solids prior to hot ion exchange units.

Hot process lime-soda softening provides the ideal conditions necessary for the most economical and efficient removal of silica from boiler · feedwater. In cases where raw water hardness is relatively low, magnesium oxide and lime may be used primarily for the value in silica removal rather than for softening.

LIMITATIONS

The lime-soda softening process does not reduce the hardness of a softened water to as low a value as does the ion exchange softening process. Hardness can be reduced to approximately 10 to 30 ppm as calcium carbonate dependent upon the temperature of operation and the alkalinity maintained on the softener effluent. Consequently, where lime-soda softened makeup water is employed for boiler feedwater, internal chemical treatment requirements are higher than if ion exchange softened makeup water is employed. Because hardness can be reduced to no lower than 10 to 30 ppm this process of softening offers little value where raw water hardness is less than 50 ppm.

Particularly in cold process softening, the use of special coagulants may be required to obtain the proper softening and hardness removal and to avoid formation of complex soluble forms of hardness.

On waters of high non-carbonate hardness there will be no decrease in solids content effected by the lime and soda process and on raw waters containing only a small amount of natural alkalinity, an increase in solids may result.

Control of lime-soda softening, in general, is slightly more difficult than the control of ion exchange softening and more frequent testing of the softener effluent may be required with more frequent adjustment of control.

REFERENCES

V. J. Calise, "Factors in Hot-Process Softener Design and Operation", *Combustion*, Vol. 22, pp. 49-55 (Aug. 1950)

A. A. Kalinzke and J. M. Kahn, "Applying Steam Lift Circulation to Hot-Process Softeners", *Proceedings*, Midwest Power Conf., Vol. XII, pp. 71-78 (1950)

E. Nordell, "Water Treatment for Industrial and Other Uses", 2nd Ed., pp. 489-547, Reinhold Publishing Co., New York, N.Y. (1961)

S. T. Powell, "Water Conditioning for Industry", pp. 84-145, McGraw-Hill Book Co., Inc., New York, N.Y. (1954)

J. D. Yoder, "The Sludge Blanket Hot Process Softener", *Proceedings*, Engineers Soc. of Western Penna., pp. 65-80 (1948)

12

Hot Process
Phosphate Softening

Hot phosphate softening is a process whereby the calcium and magnesium salts constituting the hardness of water are chemically precipitated and removed through the use of phosphate, normally disodium phosphate, in conjunction with caustic soda. The calcium hardness is precipitated as tricalcium phosphate while the magnesium hardness is precipitated as magnesium hydroxide. The softening operation is carried out in the hot at temperatures of 212 F or above. Since both the calcium and magnesium precipitates formed are very insoluble, a water of practically "zero" hardness is produced by this softening process.

Hot process phosphate softening is employed as a specific form of external treatment for boiler feedwater—particularly for high pressure boilers.

This process is applicable to very soft waters of the order of hardness not exceeding 60 ppm. It is particularly well adapted to turbid waters low in hardness where coagulation and softening can be brought about in a single apparatus.

Where waters are high in hardness this system may also find application by employing two stage softening. Thus, a greater portion of the hardness may be removed economically by lime-soda softening as the first stage and the remaining hardness may be removed by subsequent phosphate softening in the second stage.

Soft waters high in silica, likewise are suited to this process. Most efficient silica reduction is accomplished in the hot phosphate softener by magnesium sulfate. It is therefore possible to decrease silica to a low value and at the same time accomplish softening to a "zero" hardness.

Where a reduction in alkalinity is desired, particularly to insure a low carbon dioxide content in the steam, phosphoric acid and/or sulfuric acid can be used prior to softening.

CHEMICAL REACTIONS

Any of the various phosphates, from the alkaline trisodium phosphate to phosphoric

acid itself may be used depending upon the characteristics of the water to be treated. For control of chemical treatment, an excess of 5-10 ppm phosphate is maintained in the softener effluent. A pH of approximately 9.7 is required for precipitation of calcium, but removal of magnesium and silica requires a slightly higher pH approximating 10.1. The softening reactions may be represented as follows:

(1)
$$3Ca(HCO_3)_2 + 6NaOH = 3CaCO_3 +$$

calcium bicarbonate $+$ sodium hydroxide $=$ calcium carbonate $+$

$$3Na_2CO_3 + 6H_2O$$

sodium carbonate $+$ water

(2)
$$3CaCO_3 + 2Na_3PO_4 = Ca_3(PO_4)_2 +$$

calcium carbonate $+$ trisodium phosphate $=$ tricalcium phosphate $+$

$$3Na_2CO_3$$

sodium carbonate

It can be noted from equation (1) that calcium bicarbonate is first converted to calcium carbonate which is fairly insoluble as discussed under lime-soda softening. In the second equation the calcium carbonate is converted to the more insoluble tricalcium phosphate. The magnesium hardness is precipitated as the hydroxide in accordance with the following equation:

(3)
$$Mg(HCO_3)_2 + 4NaOH = Mg(OH)_2 +$$

magnesium bicarbonate $+$ sodium hydroxide $=$ magnesium hydroxide $+$

$$2Na_2CO_3 + 2H_2O$$

sodium carbonate $+$ water

The tricalcium phosphate and magnesium hydroxide precipitates which form are removed in the softening process by means of sedimentation and filtration.

From the above reactions it can be noted that a soluble by-product of sodium carbonate alkalinity results, increasing the natural alkalinity from one equivalent on the untreated water to two equivalents on the treated water. Where the natural alkalinity is already high this condition is undesirable and may be offset by the use of an acid phosphate or by use of sulfuric acid. Alkalinity reduction by means of phosphoric acid is illustrated as follows:

(4)

$$Ca(HCO_3)_2 + H_3PO_4 = CaHPO_4$$

calcium bicarbonate + phosphoric acid = calcium acid phosphate

$$+ 2CO_2 + 2H_2O$$

+ carbon dioxide + water

The carbon dioxide thus formed may be removed by deaeration, thereby minimizing the carbon dioxide content of the steam. Following deaeration, the soluble calcium acid phosphate is precipitated by the addition of sodium hydroxide. This reaction is illustrated as follows:

(5)

$$3CaHPO_4 + 3NaOH = Ca_3(PO_4)_2$$

calcium acid phosphate + sodium hydroxide = tricalcium phosphate

$$+ Na_3PO_4 + 3H_2O$$

+ trisodium phosphate + water

All of the preceding reactions illustrate the removal of carbonate hardness. The removal of non-carbonate hardness proceeds in accordance with the following reactions:

(6)

$$3CaSO_4 + 2Na_3PO_4 = Ca_3(PO_4)_2 +$$

calcium sulfate + trisodium phosphate = tricalcium phosphate +

$$3Na_2SO_4$$

sodium sulfate

(7)

$$MgCl_2 + 2NaOH = Mg(OH)_2$$

magnesium chloride + sodium hydroxide = magnesium hydroxide +

$$2NaCl$$

sodium chloride

EQUIPMENT REQUIREMENTS

In general the equipment employed for hot process phosphate softening is very similar to that used in hot process lime-soda softening,

although a retention period of only 45 minutes or less has been used with phosphate softening compared with the 1 hour required for hot process lime-soda softening.

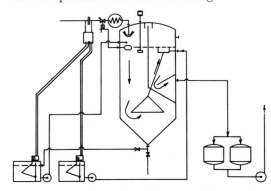

Figure 12-1 • Single Tank Two Stage Softener—Hot Lime–Soda Followed by Hot Phosphate

While a calcite filter medium can be used in conjunction with lime-soda softening, reaction of calcite with a phosphate softener effluent will result in cementing the entire filter bed. Anthracite coal is the most desirable filter medium with phosphate softening.

The two stage water softeners may take one of several forms as, for example, the incorporation of two stages in a single sedimentation tank as illustrated by Figure 12-1.

APPLICATIONS AND LIMITATIONS

Hot process phosphate softening is primarily useful in the treatment, for boiler feedwater purposes, of turbid waters that are low in hardness and alkalinity. It is possible with hot phosphate softening to combine turbidity removal, softening and deaeration in a single unit. Where silica removal is also necessary, hot phosphate softening provides a single unit to accomplish all of these objectives.

Through the use of phosphoric or sulfuric acid, reduction can be secured in potential carbon dioxide content of the steam.

The effluent from a hot process phosphate softener, while quite low in hardness, will cause after-precipitation when subjected to marked increase in temperature, such as encountered in economizers, closed heaters, etc.

Stabilization of the softener effluent by acid or the application of organic surface active agents is necessary to prevent objectionable deposits.

The fine particles of calcium phosphate formed in the sedimentation tank do not settle as rapidly as the precipitates formed in lime-soda softening. Greater difficulty is encountered in maintaining a low turbidity softener effluent with hot phosphate softening. The presence in the raw water of organic matter, which would tend to retard the precipitation reactions, may result in relatively poor hardness removal and plugged filters.

Until the development of the styrene base ion exchange resins, the combination of hot lime-soda softening, followed by hot phosphate softening, was considered the best method for producing a low hardness boiler feedwater from a hot process treatment plant. However, as discussed in the chapter on hot lime-hot ion exchange softening, this new process offers several advantages over the hot lime-soda hot phosphate process. With the hot ion exchange method, more complete hardness removal can be secured than with hot lime-soda hot phosphate softening, together with a lower carbon dioxide content of the steam.

The following is a list of the common commercial forms of phosphate that may be used for hot phosphate softening. In selecting the type of phosphate to be employed there are two important factors to consider: (a) cost per pound P_2O_5 and (b) alkalinity of the water to be treated. For example, although anhydrous monosodium phosphate has a greater P_2O_5 content than anhydrous disodium phosphate, the cost is higher and it is generally more economical to purchase the latter phosphate. However, if the alkalinity of the water to be treated is very high, it may be desirable to use anhydrous monosodium phosphate, which is acidic, in spite of its greater cost so as to reduce the alkalinity of the treated water. The general statement can be made that for the majority of cases anhydrous disodium phosphate is the most satisfactory phosphate to be employed. However, each specific application should be studied to determine this point.

Fig. 12-2
Supplementary Data—Hot Phosphate Softener

Name of Phosphate	Chemical Formula	%P_2O_5	Lbs $CaCO_3$ Removed Per 100 lbs of the Phosphate	Pounds NaOH Required to Convert 100 lbs of the Phosphate to Na_3PO_4*
Monosodium Phosphate, Anhydrous	NaH_2PO_4	58%	122 lbs.	67 lbs.
Monosodium Phosphate, Monohydrate	$NaH_2PO_4 \cdot H_2O$	51%	108 lbs.	58 lbs.
Disodium Phosphate, Anhydrous	Na_2HPO_4	48%	101 lbs.	28 lbs.
Disodium Phosphate, Crystalline	$Na_2HPO_4 \cdot 12H_2O$	19%	40 lbs.	11 lbs.
Trisodium Phosphate, Monohydrate	$Na_3PO_4 \cdot H_2O$	39%	82 lbs.	0 lbs.
Trisodium Phosphate, Crystalline	$Na_3PO_4 \cdot 12H_2O$	19%	40 lbs.	0 lbs.
Phosphoric Acid, 75% Solution	H_3PO_4	54%	114 lbs.	92 lbs.

* This value is the theoretical NaOH requirement for each phosphate used. However, the natural alkalinity or acidity of the water to be treated will vary the total NaOH requirement.

REFERENCES

E. W. Ellis and H. E. Carlson, "Lime-Soda-Phosphate Feedwater Treatment", *The Petroleum Engineer,* Vol. 26, pp. C29-32 (June 1954)

C. E. Joos, "Ramifications of the Hot Process Method of Water Conditioning", *Proceedings,* Engineers Soc. of Western Penna., pp. 79-91 (1941)

F. N. Kemmer, "Conditioning Makeup by High-Temp., Sodium Ion-Exchange Excess Calcium, Hot Lime-Zeolite Process", *Combustion,* Vol. 21, pp. 59-62 (April 1950)

13

Silica Removal By Magnesium Salts

THE removal of soluble silica from water in the hot is accomplished with the use of magnesium compounds under relatively simple controlled conditions of temperature, retention time, pH and sludge recirculation.

Hot process silica removal is carried out employing a conventional hot process lime or lime-soda softener. It is advantageous to thus combine in one unit the functions of softening and silica removal.

The magnesium compound employed may be Epsom Salt (magnesium sulfate), dolomitic lime, calcined magnesite, magnesium carbonate or magnesium oxide. Since magnesium oxide possesses the greatest silica removal efficiency and does not increase solids content, it is usually employed.

The removal of silica from boiler feed water is accomplished in order to prevent or to minimize silicate boiler scales such as calcium and magnesium silicate and also to prevent the formation of the complex sodium-alumino-silicate scales such as analcite, $Na_2O.Al_2O_3.4SiO_2.2H_2O$. For the prevention of siliceous turbine blade deposits, it may be advisable to limit the silica content of the boiler water thus involving the removal of silica from the boiler feedwater.

FACTORS CONTROLLING SILICA REMOVAL

Effect of Temperature—The higher the temperature of operation, the more efficient is the removal of silica from the solution. Figure 13-1 illustrates the increase in silica removal efficiency using magnesium oxide with increase in temperature up to 95 C, the approximate temperature of operation of hot process softeners.

Effect of Retention Time—At 95 C almost complete silica removal is accomplished by magnesium oxide in 15 minutes retention time. At lower temperatures there is a gradual increase in the quantity of silica removed with increased retention. Figure 13-2 illustrates this effect of retention. Since hot process lime-soda softeners are designed for one hour retention, it is evident that complete silica removal can readily be accomplished in this period of time.

Effect of pH—The influence of pH on silica removal by magnesium oxide is illustrated by Figure 13-3. It can be noted that the optimum pH, in each of the three cases shown, is approximately 10.1. This pH value is readily obtained with either hot or cold process lime-soda softening. The greater the percentage of silica removed the less important is the control of pH.

Effect of Sludge Recirculation—During the silica removal process, if the partially spent magnesium oxide sludge is brought back in contact with fresh incoming water high in silica, a considerable increase in silica removal efficiency can be achieved. A portion of the sludge collecting in the sludge cone of

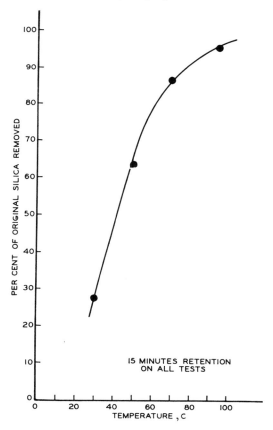

Figure 13-1 • Effect of Temperature

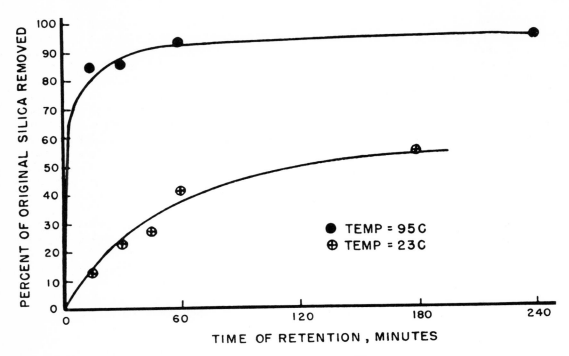

Figure 13-2 • Effect of Retention Time

the softener is recirculated by means of a small pump to the upper section of the sedimentation tank. Here it comes in contact with the raw makeup water and, through additional silica adsorption, considerably reduces the quantity of fresh magnesium oxide that must be employed. It is possible by sludge recirculation to reduce magnesium requirements by as much as 60%. The increased silica removal efficiency is shown by Figure 13-4. There is no change in the chemical balances maintained on the softener effluent and recirculation affects the characteristics of the softener effluent only with respect to a reduced silica content.

Effect of Various Magnesium Compounds —A number of different magnesium compounds have been investigated for use in the removal of silica from water. A number of these compounds such as Epsom Salt (magnesium sulfate) and dolomitic lime may considerably increase the solids content of the treated water. They may also require large increases in the quantity of lime and soda

ash needed to precipitate the magnesium or calcium compounds thus introduced. However, the major disadvantage of their use is the increase in solids content of the boiler feedwater.

Dolomitic lime can be used to provide economical silica removal where the lime requirements for softening will introduce sufficient magnesium oxide to accomplish the desired degree of silica removal. Where magnesium oxide requirements for silica removal are relatively high and lime requirements low, if sufficient dolomitic lime were fed to secure the desired silica removal, it would be necessary to feed additional soda ash to react with the excess lime thus introduced. In such cases, dolomitic lime can be used in an amount sufficient to supply lime requirements and additional magnesium oxide fed to secure the necessary silica removal.

Magnesium oxide has the advantage of causing no increase in the solids content of the treated water. In addition, no lime or soda ash is required to effect its precipitation.

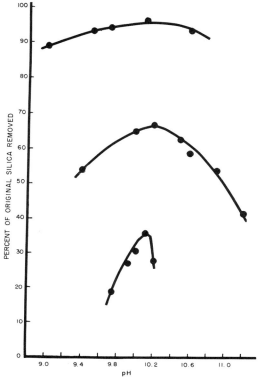

Figure 13-3 • Effect of pH

While different forms of magnesium oxide vary in their silica removal efficiencies, specially prepared adsorptive forms of magnesium oxide, have been found to possess the greatest silica removal efficiency and to be the most economically feasible reagent.

Figure 13-5 illustrates the silica removal capacity of a number of different magnesium compounds under the same conditions. Because silica removal by magnesium compounds is an adsorption reaction, those materials which effected over 80% silica removal in this test possess very high silica removal capacities.

Mechanism of Silica Removal Reactions— In the chemical reactions usually encountered in water conditioning there is a stoichiometric relation or constant reacting value. For example, a definite quantity of soda ash will always react with a definite amount of calcium sulfate in accordance with the law of combining weights. The removal of silica from the solution by magnesium compounds, however, is not a stoichiometric reaction but proceeds by adsorption from the solution.

Figure 13-6 illustrates silica removal plotted against the quantity of magnesium oxide used on a water supply high in silica. These data were obtained from actual operating results on a hot process lime-soda softening system rated at 270,000 pounds per hour and conditioning water for 450 psi boilers. It can be noted that increased quantities of magnesium oxide do not effect proportionate increases in the quantity of silica removed. In other words, as larger amounts of silica are removed, larger and larger quantities of magnesium oxide are required to effect removal of the last traces of silica. This action is characteristic of adsorption reactions.

The empirical equation of Freundlich closely fits adsorption data. This equation may be expressed as:

$$\frac{x}{m} = KC^{1/n}$$

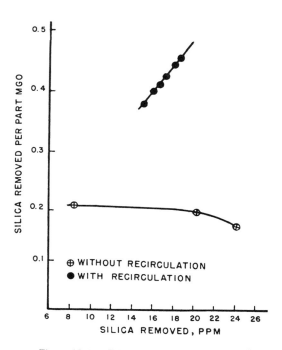

Figure 13-4 • Effect of Sludge Recirculation

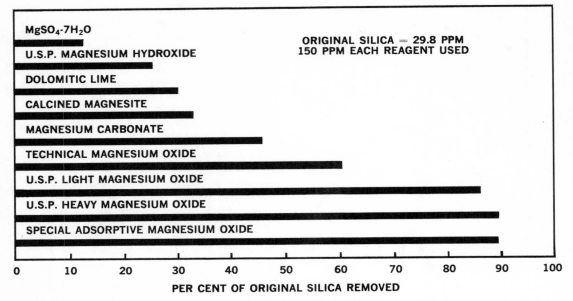

Figure 13-5 • Comparison of Various Forms of Magnesium Oxide

where K and l/n are constants.

x = quantity of silica adsorbed

m = quantity of adsorbent

C = residual concentration of adsorbed material at equilibrium.

A straight line results from plotting the logarithm of $\dfrac{x}{m}$ against the logarithm of C when the reaction proceeds by adsorption. Silica removal data thus shows the reaction to be one of adsorption similar to the removal of color by activated carbon.

EQUIPMENT REQUIRED

For the most efficient removal of silica by magnesium compounds, a combination of the following factors is required:

Temperature close to 212 F.

Retention time, 15 minutes to one hour.

pH value approximately 10.1.

Recirculation of sludge.

These conditions are most readily secured through the use of a conventional hot process softener which provides the ideal unit for the silica removal process. No special chemical

feeding equipment is required. Magnesium oxide can simply be added to the same mixing tank where the lime and soda ash are fed.

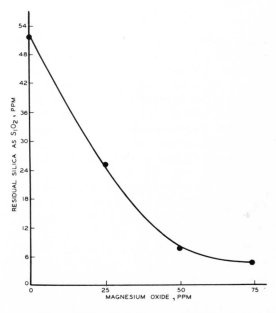

Figure 13-6 • Field Tests on Silica Removal with Sludge Recirculation

Recirculation of sludge is simply provided by tapping the sludge cone and circulating a portion of the sludge to the top of the sedimentation tank by means of a small centrifugal pump.

While silica removal can be secured in conjunction with hot lime or hot lime-soda softening, the use of lime and soda ash is not necessary for the successful operation of the silica removal process. On a water low in hardness, a conventional hot process softener can be employed for silica removal feeding only caustic soda and magnesium oxide.

APPLICATIONS

Hot process silica removal by magnesium compounds can be successfully applied to any type of water. The use of magnesium compounds is advantageous with the hot lime-hot zeolite process, providing removal of silica to as low as 1 ppm in conjunction with hardness removal to the range of 0.5-2.0 ppm. Magnesium oxide is preferred as the silica removal agent in hot lime or hot lime-soda softening, while more efficient results are secured in hot phosphate softening by the use of magnesium sulfate.

Silica removal is particularly desirable in conditioning water for use in high pressure boilers both from the standpoint of reducing scale deposits in the boilers and also to reduce siliceous deposits on turbine blading.

When the magnesium compound employed is magnesium oxide, the additional advantages secured are:

No increase in the solids content of the treated water.

More silica is removed per part of reagent employed than in any other method.

Magnesium oxide is itself an excellent coagulant and eliminates any need for other coagulants.

When magnesium oxide is employed in conjunction with hot process lime-soda softening, the additional advantages secured in addition to the above are:

No additional capital expenditure is required since both softening and silica removal are accomplished in the one operation, requiring no additional equipment.

Quantities of lime and soda ash are not increased by the use of magnesium oxide, unlike the use of Epsom Salt, dolomitic lime or iron salts which require lime and soda ash for their precipitation.

No increase in the hardness or alkalinity of the softened water is occasioned by the use of magnesium oxide.

LIMITATIONS

In order to efficiently accomplish the removal of silica by magnesium compounds and to comply with the conditions of temperature, retention time and sludge recirculation, a hot process softener complete with chemical proportioner, heater, sedimentation tank, filters and backwash facilities is required.

Where such equipment is already installed, silica removal can be very simply applied. Where a hot process softener is not already installed in a plant, its installation is necessary before silica removal by magnesium compounds can be accomplished.

REFERENCES

L. D. Betz, C. A. Noll and J. J. Maguire, "Removal of Silica from Water by Hot Process", *Ind. and Eng. Chem.*, Vol. 32, pp. 1323-1329 (1940)

L. D. Betz, C. A. Noll and J. J. Maguire, "Adsorption of Soluble Silica from Water", *Ind. and Eng. Chem.*, Vol .33, pp. 814-820 (1941)

C. A. Noll and J. J. Maguire (to Betz Laboratories, Inc.) U.S. Patent 2,307,466 (Jan. 5, 1943)

J. D. Yoder, "Removing Silica from Boiler Feed Water", *Proceedings*, Midwest Power Conf., Vol. XI, pp. 164-170 (1949)

14

Sodium Zeolite Softening

THE term zeolite is applied to insoluble, solid materials which have the property of exchanging various ions with which they come in contact. The sodium zeolite softening process, also referred to as cation exchange on the sodium cycle, exchanges sodium ions for all cations of two or more positive charges, when operating on the softening cycle. When water containing the hardness salts of calcium and magnesium is passed through the cation exchange bed, the sodium ions of the bed replace the hardness ions with a resultant effluent water of close to "zero" hardness. Sodium zeolite softening is, by far, the most common of the exchange reactions involved in water conditioning and is generally the one referred to when the term "zeolite softening" is used without further qualification.

The primary purpose of sodium zeolite softening is the removal of the scale forming ions of calcium and magnesium, replacing these ions with an equivalent amount of sodium ions. By removal of the calcium and magnesium ions, which normally constitute the hardness content of a water, this process is useful in the preparation of water for boiler feedwater, laundry use, various industrial processes and in the reduction of the hardness content of city supplies.

ZEOLITE EXCHANGE MATERIALS

Natural zeolite minerals possess a complex chemical structure and usually consist of sodium-aluminum-silicate. Other cation exchange materials are made synthetically and have as a base such chemicals as sulfonated coal (carbonaceous), phenolic resins and polystyrene resins. Regardless of how the zeolites are produced, all operating on the sodium cycle contain a complex molecule with sodium attached. Accordingly, it is possible to represent sodium zeolite in a chemical equation by using the symbol Na_2Z where Na stands for the sodium and Z for the complex zeolite radical. For simplification in the following reactions, the calcium (Ca^{++}) in solution will be considered as representing all the hardness. The following is therefore the fundamental reaction in sodium zeolite softening:

$$(1) \quad Ca^{++} + Na_2Z = CaZ + 2Na^+$$

$$\underset{\text{ion}}{\text{calcium}} + \underset{\text{zeolite}}{\text{sodium}} = \underset{\text{zeolite}}{\text{calcium}} + \underset{\text{ion}}{\text{sodium}}$$

When this reaction has proceeded to the point where the zeolite will release no more sodium in exchange for calcium, it becomes necessary to regenerate the zeolite bed. This regeneration is accomplished by washing with a strong salt solution (sodium chloride). The high concentration of the sodium ion in the salt solution reverses the above reaction resulting in regeneration of the zeolite bed. This regeneration reaction may be written as follows:

$$(2) \quad CaZ + 2NaCl = Na_2Z + CaCl_2$$

$$\underset{\text{zeolite}}{\text{calcium}} + \underset{\text{chloride}}{\text{sodium}} = \underset{\text{zeolite}}{\text{sodium}} + \underset{\text{chloride}}{\text{calcium}}$$

The calcium placed in solution by regeneration is run to waste as calcium chloride. The fundamental chemical principle of mass action determines if the reaction proceeds as in equation (1) or equation (2). In the softening cycle, where the calcium ions predominate, the reaction proceeds as in (1). In the regeneration reaction, where the sodium ions predominate, the reaction proceeds as in (2). The net result is that sodium chloride (common salt) has been consumed and hardness has been removed from solution. As it is necessary to have an excess of salt present for regeneration, an equivalent amount of hardness is not removed for a given amount of salt consumed.

The capacity of zeolites, that is the amount of hardness that can be removed before regeneration, will vary greatly. The synthetic zeolites generally have a higher exchange capacity than the natural zeolites, but are more expensive per unit volume. The capacities for synthetic zeolites range between 6000 grains per cubic foot and 32,000 grains per cubic foot. Natural zeolite capacities vary between 2500 and 5000 grains per cubic foot, depending on the processing. Greensand zeolite is more resistant to waters of low pH than the synthetic aluminum-silicate zeolites. Greensand, carbonaceous and resinous zeolites are less likely to increase the silica con-

Figure 14-1 • Microscopic View of Resin Beads (20–50 mesh) of a Sulfonated Styrene-Divinyl Benzene Cation Exchanger

Figure 14-2 • Microscopic View of Beads (20–50 mesh) of a Carboxylic Exchanger Resin

tent of the softened water and, consequently, are better applied to the softening of waters of low silica content. Synthetic zeolites of the sodium-aluminum-silicate type may impart considerable silica to waters that are low in initial silica content.

Generally, synthetic zeolites are employed in waters of high hardness where the exchange value of this material is of importance in permitting the use of a smaller unit. For low hardness waters, greensand—the natural zeolite—is still occasionally employed.

The effluent from a zeolite softener will rise quite rapidly in hardness as it approaches the limit of its capacity. In some cases, where minimum hardness is essential, the softener will be regenerated before it reaches this point. In other cases, the hardness is allowed to rise only to a predetermined level before regeneration. As the concentration of anions such as chloride and sulfate increase in the water to be softened, there is the tendency for hardness leakage to take place. With the older types of zeolite minerals and synthetics, the amount of hardness leakage could not be controlled since this leakage was a function of the influent ion concentration. However, with the advent of the polystyrene type resins, the amount of hardness leakage can be accurately controlled by adjusting the salt regeneration level. For example, in a normal water supply where the total hardness and sodium salts were in the range of 700-800 ppm, using a carbonaceous zeolite the minimum effluent hardness was found to be in the range of 15 ppm with a salt regeneration rate of 3.5 pounds of salt per pound of hardness removed. Using a polystyrene resin at the same salt rate produced an average effluent hardness of 8 ppm. By doubling the salt rate, the effluent hardness was reduced 2 ppm.

Figure 14-3 also illustrates the effect on capacity at different salt regeneration levels. From this table it can be readily understood that sodium zeolite softeners, using a polystyrene base resin, can be designed for low capital investment and high operating cost or higher capital investment with lower operating cost for the same number of gallons of water with constant characteristics. The application of this type of resin is also advantageous when used with waters having wide seasonal variations in hardness since all that is necessary is the adjustment of the salt rate to obtain softening cycles of predetermined length.

Fig. 14-3
Effect of Salt Regeneration on Exchange Capacity

Salt Requirement lbs salt/kilograin hardness removed	Polystyrene Resin Exchange Capacity grains/cu ft
0.285	18,000
0.323	21,000
0.385	24,500
0.440	27,000
0.490	29,000

EQUIPMENT EMPLOYED

Natural zeolite minerals have a sandy nature while the synthetic zeolites are in the form of small crystals or beads. A zeolite softener is, therefore, very similar in construction and appearance to a sand filter excepting that it is filled with a bed of zeolite instead of sand. Figure 14-4 illustrates one type of zeolite softener.

Although there are different modifications, in general the softener consists of a steel shell, the bottom of which contains graded sizes of gravel or anthracite. Above the graded base is located the zeolite material, usually 24 inches or more in depth. In the majority of softeners, the water enters the top of the tank and passes down through the

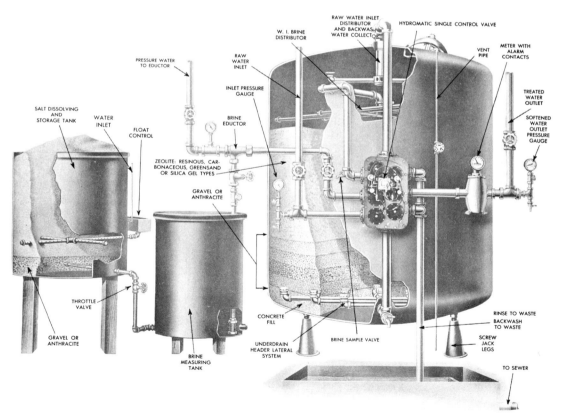

Courtesy Cochrane Division—Crane Company

Figure 14-4 • Zeolite Softener with Single Control Valve and Header Lateral Underdrain

zeolite. The size of the zeolite bed will depend upon the exchange capacity of the zeolite, the hardness of the water being treated, the amount of water to be softened between regenerations, and the flow rate. The bed must also be of sufficient size to allow proper contact time between the water and the zeolite and flow rate is usually regulated at 5-8 gallons per square foot per minute. In addition, it is necessary to provide a tank to hold the salt solution for regeneration, proper control valves and interconnecting piping.

In regenerating the unit, it is first backwashed to clean the bed. In backwashing, water is first passed up through the bed and sent to waste until it runs clear. The rate of backwash should be sufficient to lift and expand the bed to thoroughly clean it, but not high enough to wash the zeolite out of the unit. The required rate is a function of the type of zeolite, water temperature and freeboard in the tank above the zeolite bed and the usual range is between 4 and 10 gallons per square foot of bed area per minute. A clear water, free from suspended matter, should always be available for backwashing. A strong salt solution is next passed into the softener at the top. Rinse water is next added to the top of the softener to force the salt water or brine through the zeolite and out the bottom to waste. At first, this water will contain large quantities of calcium and magnesium chlorides together with unreacted sodium chloride. As the bed becomes regenerated, the calcium and magnesium chlorides in the effluent are eliminated, and the excess salt is gradually washed out by continuing to add further quantities of fresh water, which acts as a rinse. Rinsing is continued until all of the excess salt is washed from the bed and the unit is then returned to service. Many units are provided with a master valve which controls the various operations by merely turning a hand wheel in steps as indicated at points on the rim of the valve.

Softeners can be manufactured for manual, semi-automatic or completely automatic operation. In manual operation the regeneration steps are accomplished by manually turning a valve or valves. Semi-automatic operation entails pushing a button for each regeneration step to actuate motorized valves. The motive force can be electric, pneumatic or hydraulic. Completely automatic operation requires no attendance. The usual method consists of having a water meter preset so that when a certain number of gallons of water have been softened, an electrical contact is made in the meter. This electrical contact actuates a system of counters and timers which in turn actuates the valves controlling the various regeneration steps.

APPLICATIONS

Zeolite softeners have a definite application in any process where soft water is an advantage. Laundries find a decided use for these softeners to reduce their soap consumption. Softening offers an added advantage in improving the appearance of the wash as discolorations, due to soap curds—those insoluble particles of soap formed by the reaction of soap with the hardness in the water—are eliminated. Dye houses and other textile plants where finishing is accomplished also find these softeners beneficial for the same reasons, eliminating many causes for uneven dyeing.

In certain districts where the water supplies are quite hard, many small zeolite softeners are used in the home. In some cities softeners of the zeolite type have been installed to supply the public with softened water.

In boiler feedwater conditioning, the use of zeolite softening is frequently attractive because of the simplicity of operation and control. An outstanding advantage of zeolite softening is the low hardness obtainable in the treated water. Marked reduction in the scaling properties of a water is secured by proper zeolite softening.

With the use of resinous and carbonaceous exchangers, it is possible to operate on the sodium cycle and to secure the advantages of a low hardness effluent without danger of silica pickup from the zeolite bed. Even though such exchange materials are somewhat more expensive than greensand zeolite, this increased installation cost is frequently justified by salt savings and by avoiding any silica increase while softening.

LIMITATIONS

Sodium zeolite softening should not be considered as a cure-all simply because it removes scale forming solids from the water. Sodium zeolite softeners require very little maintenance and are quite simple to operate. Plant operators can be trained to operate them properly in a very brief period because of this simplicity; however, many zeolite softeners have been installed to operate on waters entirely unsuited for their use. There are many types of waters and conditions of operation for which sodium zeolite softening is the proper solution; however, there have been numerous installations whereby the application of zeolite softening alone has increased cost of operation and added several problems which could be considered more serious than those initially present.

Turbid waters should not be passed through a zeolite softener as the accumulated deposits will coat the zeolite grains and reduce efficiency. Water for a zeolite softener should have a turbidity of less than 10 units. City supplies are generally filtered and accordingly are suitable for zeolite softening. Most well waters are relatively free from turbidity as passage through the earth usually filters out suspended matter. Surface waters generally tend to be turbid and in most cases must be filtered prior to zeolite softening. Filtration, to be properly effective, should be preceded by coagulation. With these requirements, the zeolite system becomes more complex due to the necessity of a coagulation and filtration system, increasing capital cost, space requirements and operating cost. In certain cases, filtration will be omitted, particularly in small installations, with the understanding that reduction in efficiency and life of the zeolite are to be expected.

Ferric iron is detrimental to zeolite and should be removed prior to softening. In such cases, the additional expense of an iron removal system is required.

In boiler water conditioning, zeolite has a marked advantage over lime-soda softening insofar as it more completely removes hardness. Whereas lime-soda softening may reduce the hardness to as low as 10-30 ppm, depending on the water, zeolite softening will show "zero" hardness or very close to "zero." Nevertheless, scale formation can take place in a boiler using water softened by the zeolite process. Invariably, some internal treatment is necessary in a boiler following sodium zeolite softening in order to prevent scale formation. Naturally, the quantity of internal treatment required after zeolite is less than that required after lime-soda softening. As the amount of precipitated sludge formed in the boiler by the internal treatment depends on the original feedwater hardness, it follows that the amount of suspended matter in a boiler following the use of zeolite softening will be small. Accordingly, there is less chance of the sludge baking on to the surface to form a scale than with lime-soda softening or when using internal treatment only.

One of the principal disadvantages of sodium zeolite softening is that the hardness is removed without a reduction in alkalinity or total solids. This defect can be seen from equation (1). Calcium is removed, but is replaced by two ions of sodium, weighing slightly more than the original calcium. With zeolite softened water, since the hardness has been removed and the calcium exchanged for sodium, the entire alkalinity is free to concentrate in the boiler. Unless the natural alkalinity is relatively low in comparison with total solids, zeolite softening results in high boiler water alkalinity and high carbon dioxide concentration in the steam. This condition often requires high rates of blowdown to maintain boiler water alkalinities within reasonable bounds. High alkalinities are objectionable as they tend to promote both carryover and caustic metal embrittlement (intercrystalline cracking), unless special precautions are taken with respect to chemical treatment of the boiler water.

Where silica is a problem, there is the definite possibility of silica being picked up from the zeolite by the water, thereby adding to the problem. This undesirable condition can be overcome by using a nonsiliceous zeolite material.

Sodium zeolite softened water is normally corrosive, with the severity of the corrosive characteristics dependent on the amount of dissolved gases, such as carbon dioxide and oxygen. In large cold water distribution systems, and in domestic hot water systems, serious corrosion may result following softening unless these corrosive gases are reduced to low values by adjusting pH, deaeration or applying positive corrosion inhibitors.

Many of the disadvantages outlined here for zeolite can be overcome by methods involving other types of zeolite operating on other than the sodium cycles.

Whether zeolite should or should not be used depends on many factors and any individual case can be judged only following an investigation of these factors. Zeolite softening may be coupled with other methods to provide a satisfactory solution to a problem. Zeolites fill a very important place in water conditioning, but should be used only with a full knowledge of their limitations. Entirely too many installations have been made in the mistaken belief that sodium zeolite softening offered a final solution to a problem. Especially in boiler feedwater conditioning, the proper solution to a problem is rarely achieved by the use of sodium zeolite softening alone. However, in combination with other external and internal treatment methods, zeolites perform a very useful water conditioning function.

REFERENCES

L. F. Collins, "A Study of Contemporary Zeolites", *Journal,* Am. Water Works Assoc., Vol. 29, pp. 1472-1514 (1937)

R. Kunin, "Ion Exchange Resins", 2nd Ed., John Wiley & Sons, New York, N.Y. (1958)

S. T. Powell, "Water Conditioning for Industry", pp. 146-165, McGraw-Hill Book Co., Inc., New York, N.Y. (1954)

15

Cation Exchange by Hydrogen Zeolite

YDROGEN zeolite is the name given to a group of non-siliceous organic materials, either natural or synthetic, which have the property when operated in the acid cycle, to exchange hydrogen for cations such as calcium, magnesium, sodium, etc. Upon exhaustion of the hydrogen zeolite bed, it is regenerated with acid. Non-siliceous or carbonaceous zeolite may also be operated in the sodium cycle by regenerating with sodium chloride (salt) and when used for sodium zeolite softening possesses some advantages over the siliceous zeolites.

An example of natural hydrogen zeolites are the various lignites found in the Dakotas; while sulphonated coal, coke, and synthetic resins are examples of the man-made product.

PRINCIPLES OF CATION EXCHANGE

When water containing calcium, magnesium and sodium ions is passed through a hydrogen zeolite these ions are exchanged for hydrogen, and the bicarbonate, sulfate, nitrate and chloride radicals are converted to their respective acids, viz., carbonic acid (H_2CO_3), sulfuric acid (H_2SO_4), nitric acid (HNO_3) and hydrochloric acid (HCl) as is shown by the following equations:

(1)
$$\begin{bmatrix} Ca \\ Mg \\ Na_2 \end{bmatrix}(HCO_3)_2 + H_2Z = \begin{bmatrix} Ca \\ Mg \\ Na_2 \end{bmatrix} Z + 2H_2CO_3$$

(2)
$$\begin{bmatrix} Ca \\ Mg \\ Na_2 \end{bmatrix}SO_4 + H_2Z = \begin{bmatrix} Ca \\ Mg \\ Na_2 \end{bmatrix} Z + H_2SO_4$$

(3)
$$\begin{bmatrix} Ca \\ Mg \\ Na_2 \end{bmatrix}Cl_2 + H_2Z = \begin{bmatrix} Ca \\ Mg \\ Na_2 \end{bmatrix} Z + 2HCl$$

(4)
$$\begin{bmatrix} Ca \\ Mg \\ Na_2 \end{bmatrix}(NO_3)_2 + H_2Z = \begin{bmatrix} Ca \\ Mg \\ Na_2 \end{bmatrix} Z + 2HNO_3$$

When the hydrogen zeolite becomes exhausted it is backwashed and regenerated with acid. After rinsing, the bed is again ready for use. Sulfuric acid is generally used for the regeneration process due to its low cost, although hydrochloric acid also is frequently used, particularly when high calcium water results in the precipitation of calcium sulfate in the zeolite bed.

The following equations illustrate the reactions which take place when sulfuric acid is used for regeneration:

(5)
$$\begin{bmatrix} Ca \\ Mg \\ Na_2 \end{bmatrix}Z + H_2SO_4 = H_2Z + \begin{bmatrix} Ca \\ Mg \\ Na_2 \end{bmatrix} SO_4$$

From reaction (1) it is evident that all of the bicarbonates are converted into carbonic acid (H_2CO_3). This acid is very unstable in water solution and can easily be removed by aeration or degasification.

Thus, in addition to completely removing the hardness the bicarbonate alkalinity is also removed without substituting other salts in its place and accordingly it is possible by this process to reduce the total solids. The removal of bicarbonate alkalinity without substitution of any other ion is the outstanding advantage in the use of hydrogen zeolite.

Since these materials are non-siliceous in nature no pick up of silica is experienced. Furthermore, with this type of softener it is possible to reduce to any predetermined value not only the alkalinity due to calcium and magnesium bicarbonates, but also the alkalinity due to sodium bicarbonate.

While it is possible to rid the system of carbonic acid by degasification, sulfuric, nitric and hydrochloric acids cannot be removed by this method. These acids must be neutralized, otherwise severe acidic corrosion of the metal in the system would result.

Three general methods for the neutralization of these acids are used.

HYDROGEN AND SODIUM ZEOLITE UNITS IN PARALLEL. A pre-determined percentage of raw water is passed through a sodium zeolite which is operating in parallel with the hydrogen zeolite so as to obtain the desired alkalinity in the mixed effluent. This is accomplished with simple automatic rate-of-flow controls.

The correct amount of water to pass through the hydrogen zeolite unit depends on the factors:

The alkalinity of the influent (Ar).

The free mineral acidity (FMA) of the hydrogen zeolite effluent (which depends upon the sulfate + nitrate + chloride content of the influent).

The desired alkalinity in the mixed effluent (Am).

The proper proportion can readily be calculated according to the formula:

$$\text{Percent } H_2Z \text{ treated} = 100 \times \frac{Ar - Am}{Ar + FMA}$$

The use of this formula will be clarified by an example. Consider a raw water of the following characteristics:

		ppm
Total Hardness	as $CaCO_3$ =	36
Sulfate	as SO_4 =	4
Nitrate	as NO_3 =	2
Chloride	as Cl =	6
Methyl Orange Alkalinity	as $CaCO_3$ =	34
Calcium	as $CaCO_3$ =	24
Magnesium	as $CaCO_3$ =	12
Carbon Dioxide	as CO_2 =	15

It is desired to maintain an alkalinity of 15 ppm as $CaCO_3$ in the mixed effluent.

We are given Ar = 34 ppm as $CaCO_3$
We want Am = 15 ppm as $CaCO_3$

All that is required before applying the formula is the value for FMA. Calculation of the FMA value is based upon the fact that the mineral acidity value is equal to the sum of the acids of the sulfates, nitrates, and chlorides present in the water. In addition to converting the sulfates, nitrates and chlorides to their respective acids, they must also be converted to a common denominator so that they can be added together; the common denominator $CaCO_3$ is chosen because Ar and Am are already in terms of $CaCO_3$. The constants necessary for these conversions are as follows:

SO_4 — 1.04; NO_3 — 0.81; Cl — 1.41

Therefore, the FMA value can be calculated:

4 ppm of SO_4 as SO_4 × 1.04 = 4.16 ppm of H_2SO_4 as $CaCO_3$
2 ppm of NO_3 as NO_3 × 0.81 = 1.62 ppm of HNO_3 as $CaCO_3$
6 ppm of Cl as Cl × 1.41 = 8.46 ppm of HCl as $CaCO_3$
Free mineral acidity = 14.24 ppm as $CaCO_3$

Substituting these values in the formula, we have

$$\% H_2Z \text{ treated} = 100 \times \frac{34 - 15}{34 + 14.24} = 39.5$$

$$\% Na_2Z \text{ treated} = 100 - 39.5 = 60.5$$

HYDROGEN ZEOLITE WITH ALKALI NEUTRALIZATION. Neutralization of the acidity of the hydrogen zeolite effluent is accomplished with any suitable alkali, such as caustic soda ($NaOH$), soda ash (Na_2CO_3), etc. This method is economical where the FMA in the effluent is low or where the total volume of water is small so that the cost of the chemical used is negligible.

With the water used in the example above, the quantity of caustic soda required to establish a residual alkalinity of 15 ppm, as $CaCO_3$ is determined as follows:

Add an amount of caustic soda equal to the FMA present plus enough to give the desired alkalinity in the effluent.

The amount of caustic soda required can readily be calculated according to the formula:

ppm $NaOH$ = (0.8 × FMA) + (0.8 × Am)

(The factor 0.8 in the equation is employed to convert the FMA as $CaCO_3$ and alkalinity as $CaCO_3$ to $NaOH$).

We have calculated FMA = 14.24 ppm, as $CaCO_3$
We are given Am = 15 ppm as $CaCO_3$
ppm $NaOH$ = (0.8 × 14.24) + (0.8 × 15) = 23.4

The advantage of this alkali neutralization method is that only a hydrogen zeolite unit is required. The additional investment cost of a sodium zeolite unit is avoided. Chemical treatment cost is higher than with the hydrogen-sodium zeolite units in parallel. Accordingly, the double unit process is usually employed for all systems except those where the total sulfate, nitrate and chloride content is very low or where the installation is only of small capacity.

HYDROGEN ZEOLITE—RAW WATER NEUTRA-LIZATION. Neutralization of acidity of the hydrogen zeolite effluent is accomplished by dilution with the raw unsoftened water itself. The elimination of a sodium zeolite unit is an advantage secured also by this system. However, the hardness of the mixed effluent is increased in direct proportion with the quantity of raw water used for neutralization. This method is usually feasible only on a water of low total hardness and high sodium bicarbonate alkalinity.

A non-siliceous resinous or carbonaceous zeolite, operating in the sodium cycle, is regenerated by passing a strong sodium brine solution through the bed in the same manner as in an ordinary zeolite. The sodium salt may be sodium chloride, sodium sulfate or sodium nitrate, but sodium chloride is generally used because of its lower cost. This type of zeolite softener requires the same amount of sodium chloride for regeneration as the conventional zeolite. Polystyrene type resins may be employed on the sodium or hydrogen cycle. The salt or acid requirements for the sodium or hydrogen cycle may be quite variable and will depend on the re-

generation level for the exchange capacity desired.

When the carbonaceous zeolite is operated in the acid cycle, acid requirements for regeneration will average 0.25 pound of 66° Baumé sulfuric acid per kilograin of cation exchange, or 1.75 pounds of acid per million pounds of water treated for each part per million of cation exchanged.

EQUIPMENT ARRANGEMENTS

HYDROGEN AND SODIUM ZEOLITE UNITS IN PARALLEL (Fig. 15-1). Major equipment includes:

Rubber-lined steel pressure tank to contain hydrogen zeolite, with single valve control.
Steel pressure tank to contain sodium zeolite, with single valve control.
Acid regeneration tank for hydrogen zeolite.
Salt regeneration tank for sodium zeolite.
Control for automatically maintaining desired ratio of flow to the hydrogen and sodium units.
Closed wood degasifier with trays which break up treated water into series of small streams. Air from blower then comes into intimate counter-current contact with the water and scrubs out the carbon dioxide.

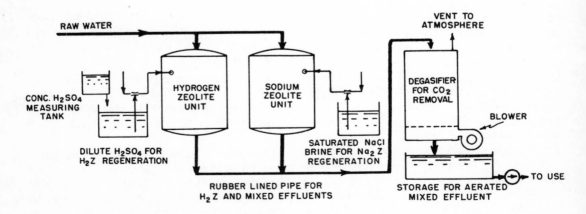

Figure 15-1 • Hydrogen and Sodium Zeolite Units in Parallel

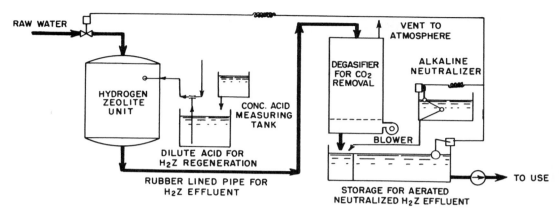

Figure 15-2 • Hydrogen Zeolite with Alkali Neutralization

HYDROGEN ZEOLITE WITH ALKALI NEUTRALI-
ZATION (Fig. 15-2). Major Equipment Includes:

Rubber-lined steel pressure tank to contain hydrogen zeolite, with single valve
control.

Acid regeneration tank for hydrogen zeolite.

Closed wood degasifier with trays which
break up treated water into series of small
streams.

Air from blower then comes into intimate

counter-current contact with the water
and scrubs out the carbon dioxide.

A neutralizing feeder.

HYDROGEN ZEOLITE WITH RAW WATER NEU-
TRALIZATION (Fig. 15-3). Major Equipment
Includes:

Rubber-lined steel pressure tank to contain hydrogen zeolite, with single control
valve.

Acid regeneration tank for hydrogen zeolite.

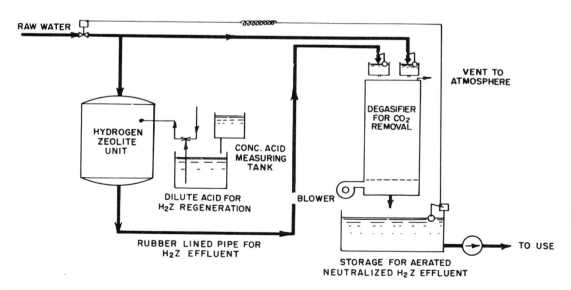

Figure 15-3 • Hydrogen Zeolite with Raw Water Neutralization

Figure 15-4 • Laboratory Testing of Ion Exchange Resins

Control for automatically maintaining desired ratio of raw water and hydrogen zeolite flow.

Closed wood degasifier with trays which break up treated water into series of small streams. Air from blower then comes into intimate counter-current contact with the water and scrubs out the carbon dioxide.

APPLICATIONS

Cation exchange by hydrogen zeolite is utilized in boiler feed water conditioning principally on a water low in hardness and high in bicarbonate alkalinity. The removal of sodium and bicarbonate ions by the hydrogen zeolite process constitutes the outstanding advantage of this process inasmuch as this removal is secured without the substitution of other ions. It is thereby possible to effect marked reduction in the solids content of a high bicarbonate water.

The hydrogen zeolite process finds extensive use in the manufacture of raw-water ice and in the carbonated beverage industry. To produce clear raw-water ice rapidly and to prevent a brittle product, the water must be low in alkalinity. In the carbonated beverage industry, low alkalinity is necessary because many soft drinks are prepared with acid extracts that require certain pH values to obtain the desired flavor.

LIMITATIONS

Before definite recommendation for this type equipment can be given it is necessary to make a thorough plant study inasmuch as operating cost is composed of several factors.

If the water is muddy, sedimentation, coagulation and/or filtration will be necessary because a clear influent must be delivered to the hydrogen zeolite unit otherwise the suspended matter will coat the grain surfaces and materially reduce efficiency. Furthermore, the influent should be free from ferric iron because iron will also be precipitated on the grain surfaces.

The cost of chemicals must be considered. In one locality, acid and salt may be expensive while in another they may be inexpensive. Installation, maintenance, depreciation, etc., all must be taken into consideration. An engineer, specializing in water treatment, should carefully evaluate the many variables and make the final recommendations for the equipment which will provide optimum results with a minimum of cost.

The properly blended and degasified hydrogen zeolite-sodium zeolite effluent is low in hardness and alkalinity, but is saturated with oxygen and is consequently of a corrosive nature. Corrosion resistant pipe or pipe specially painted or lined may be required to handle the water and deliver it to the feed water heater.

In general the hydrogen zeolite method for removing calcium and magnesium bicarbonate is more expensive than the lime-soda process, but provides an effluent of lower hardness. The operating personnel must be carefully trained inasmuch as the handling of sulfuric acid is somewhat hazardous and the control tests necessary are very important for proper operation.

This type of softening for treatment of boiler makeup water is not applicable on water of high hardness and low alkalinity or on a water high in silica. In cases where the raw water silica concentration is high, the concentration of silica becomes the controlling factor with respect to boiler concentration control. In such cases, hot process softening methods in which silica is easily removed are more suited for use in the preparation of boiler feedwater.

REFERENCES

R. F. Goudey, "Removal of Salts from Water", *Journal,* Am. Water Works Assoc., Vol. 32, pp. 435-455 (1940)

R. Kunin, "Ion Exchange Resins", 2nd Ed., John Wiley & Sons, New York, N. Y. (1958)

E. Nordell, "Water Treatment for Industrial and Other Uses", 2nd Ed., pp. 445-458, Reinhold Publishing Corp., New York, N. Y. (1961)

16

Demineralization

DEMINERALIZATION is the process of removing the mineral salts from water by ion exchange. Deionization is generally considered synonymous with demineralization. Only those substances which ionize in water can be removed by this process. With most industrial water sources, it is possible to use demineralization to remove mineral salts to the same extent or to a greater extent than would be possible with distillation. Demineralization involves two ion exchange reactions. The cations such as calcium, magnesium and sodium are removed in a hydrogen cation exchanger. The process and equipment are the same as those used for hydrogen zeolite softening. The anions, such as sulfate and chloride, are removed in an anion exchanger. Various arrangements of equipment are employed dependent upon the requirements of the installation.

Demineralization and distillation are the two most commonly used methods for producing large quantities of water with a low solids content. In comparison with the cost of producing distilled water, demineralization by ion exchange will frequently be more economical for many industries. For this reason, the process of demineralization has found wide acceptance among industries requiring process water of low solids content.

Prior to the development of the highly basic anion exchange resins, demineralization of a water by ion exchange did not lower the silica content. Without silica removal, demineralization possessed limited application for the preparation of boiler feedwater. Water of quality comparable to that of distilled water is required for high pressure boiler operation. The presence of silica in such water is most undesirable, since the silica may permit the formation of boiler tube deposits or vaporize with the steam and cause turbine blade deposits. It is therefore necessary for demineralized water to have a very low silica content in order to be useful for boiler feedwater purposes.

With the weakly basic anion exchange resins, it is possible to use fluorides to obtain silica removal with demineralization. This process did not gain wide acceptance because of the problems involved in feeding the fluoride and in disposing of the waste water from the regeneration operation. The waste water has a high fluoride content and is toxic in high concentration. With the development of the highly basic anion exchange resins, the use of fluoride is no longer necessary. The highly basic anion resins are capable of removing silica from demineralized water and the process now competes directly with distillation as a source of makeup water for high pressure boilers. In many cases, demineralization is more economical than distillation and can be operated in such a manner that the makeup water will be of superior quality to distilled water.

ION EXCHANGE RESINS

Demineralization is carried out with the use of two types of materials. The cation exchange material replaces the metallic cations with hydrogen ions. This process is identical to hydrogen zeolite softening. Sulfonated coal is sometimes used as the cation exchange material for economy in the use of acid, but it is more common to use one of the organic cation exchange resins in which the active group is a sulfonic acid group. The remainder of the resin is of such a nature that it is insoluble, chemically and physically stable, and permeable to diffusion of ions from the water.

Ion exchange is an equilibrium reaction which is reversible. In the hydrogen cation exchange resins, the active group shows a greater affinity for other cations in preference to hydrogen ion. This process is reversed when the resin is regenerated but the reverse process takes place only when the hydrogen ion is present in high concentration. The position of equilibrium depends upon the relative concentrations of cations present in the water.

During the exchange operation, the principal reaction is indicated by the following equations. In these equations, the symbol $R \cdot SO_3$ is used to represent the portion of the cation exchange material which does not go into solution.

(1)
$$R \cdot SO_3H + NaCl = R \cdot SO_3Na +$$
| hydrogen | + sodium | = sodium | + |
| exchange resin | chloride | resin | |

HCl
hydrochloric
acid

(2)
$$2R \cdot SO_3H + CaSO_4 = (R \cdot SO_3)_2Ca$$
| hydrogen | + calcium | = calcium |
| exchange resin | sulfate | resin |

+ H_2SO_4
+ sulfuric
acid

The anion exchange resins are organic resins containing active amine or quaternary amine groups. The anion exchange resins are available in two types known as weakly basic and strongly basic anion exchangers. The weakly basic type will remove sulfate, chloride and nitrate, but will not remove silica or carbon dioxide. The weakly basic resins can be used to advantage where the presence of silica in the demineralized water is not significant. The strongly basic anion exchangers will remove silica, sulfide and carbon dioxide as well as the other common anions.

The weakly basic anion exchangers can remove silica only with the feed of sufficient fluoride to convert the silicate to a fluosilicate. Silicate acts as the anion of a weak acid and is not removed by the weakly basic anion exchanger. The fluosilicate acts as an anion of a strong acid and can be removed by a weakly basic anion exchanger. This process is not applied to the preparation of boiler makeup water at the present time.

The strongly basic anion exchangers will remove the anions of both strong acids and weak acids. For this reason, direct silica removal is possible. The following equations can be used to illustrate the manner in which the anion exchange resins operate.

Weakly basic anion exchanger:

(3)
$$RNH_3 \cdot OH + HCl = RNH_3 \cdot Cl$$
| basic | + hydrochloric | = chloride |
| exchange resin | acid | resin |

+ H_2O
+ water

Strongly basic anion exchanger:
(4)
$$R_4N \cdot OH + H_2SiO_3 = R_4N \cdot HSiO_3$$
| basic | + silicic | = silicate |
| exchange resin | acid | resin |

+ H_2O
+ water

In the operation of a strongly basic anion exchanger with downward flow, it is believed that the anions of the strong acids will be removed at the top of the bed with silicate representing one of the last anions to be removed. The top of the bed is exhausted first and the portion of the bed which is effective in removing silica is gradually displaced downward. Eventually the bottom layer in the bed will no longer effectively remove silica and the effluent will show increasing concentrations of silica. When this condition is reached the bed will still remove other anions, with the result that silica break-through will take place before there is a significant rise in conductivity of the effluent.

The purity of demineralized water and distilled water is frequently expressed in terms of specific resistance or specific conductance. One micromho of specific conductance will normally indicate a dissolved solids content of 0.5-0.6 ppm. Completely pure water would have a specific conductance of approximately 0.04 micromhos due to a small quantity of hydrogen ion and hydroxide ion. These ions result from the dissociation of a small portion of the water molecules. Water of such purity

Fig. 16-1
Quality of Low Solids Water from Various Sources
(Laboratory Scale Tests)*

	Specific Conductance, micromhos
Calculated Maximum Quality	0.038
Single Distilled Water (in glass)	2.0
Triple Distilled Water (in glass)	1.0
Monobed Demineralization	0.055
28 Distillations in Quartz	0.044

* "Amberlite Monobed Deionization," Rohm and Haas Company, Philadelphia, Pa., 1950.

can not be produced by methods which are commercially available at the present time.

The purity of various types of demineralized and distilled water are outlined in Figure 16-1.

DEMINERALIZATION EQUIPMENT

The equipment employed for demineralization is similar to that employed for hydrogen zeolite softening. The piping and exchanger shells are generally lined with synthetic rubber or plastic materials. Small fittings which can not be conveniently protected by coatings are constructed of Monel, plastic, or stainless steel.

The aeration towers which are used for removal of carbon dioxide are frequently of wooden construction with any exposed metal parts of Monel, plastic, or stainless steel. Ceramic materials are also being employed.

Final effluent water lines and storage tanks should be protected with a suitable paint or lining to prevent corrosion. Such corrosion will arise from the dissolved oxygen content of the demineralized water and would contaminate the water with iron oxide.

Demineralization with silica removal may be carried out in several steps. The simplest arrangement is illustrated in Figure 16-2 in which the raw water passes through a cation exchanger directly to a highly basic anion exchanger. This arrangement is employed only when the bicarbonate alkalinity of the raw water is low. Otherwise, the cost of removing carbon dioxide in the anion exchanger becomes a sizeable factor.

An alternate arrangement is to place an aerator between the hydrogen cation exchanger and the highly basic anion exchanger, as illustrated in Figure 16-3. This arrangement is suitable for water with high bicarbonate alkalinity, since the carbon dioxide is liberated to the atmosphere in the aerator. In place of an aerator, it is possible to install a vacuum deaerator which will remove nearly all dissolved gases such as oxygen, in addition to the carbon dioxide.

Another arrangement is to pass the raw water into the hydrogen cation exchanger, then into a weakly basic anion exchanger followed by an aerator and then a highly basic anion exchanger. This system is illustrated in Figure 16-4. It is necessary to regenerate the highly basic anion exchanger with caustic soda, but the weakly basic anion exchanger may be regenerated with soda ash or with the waste regenerant from the highly basic anion unit. As a consequence, the operating cost for chemical regeneration is lower with this type of arrangement when the raw water has relatively high sulfate or chloride content.

Maximum purity of demineralized water

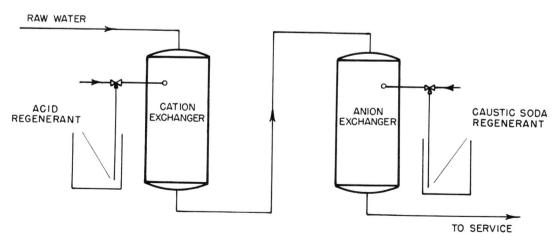

RAW WATER

ACID REGENERANT

CATION EXCHANGER

ANION EXCHANGER

CAUSTIC SODA REGENERANT

TO SERVICE

Figure 16-2 · Two-Bed System for Demineralization and Silica Removal

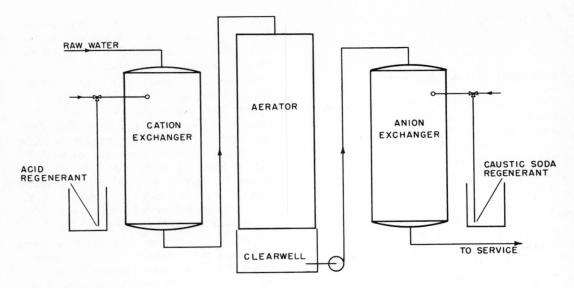

Figure 16-3 • Two-Bed System with Aerator for Demineralization and Silica Removal

can be obtained by placing a number of exchanger units in series. A similar result can be obtained by mixed bed demineralization. This arrangement uses a mixture of cation and highly basic anion resins in the same shell. Figure 16-5 illustrates the internal arrangement of the resin beds during regeneration.

During the exchange operation the two types of resins are intermixed. The resins are of different density and during backwashing will separate into two layers. Each layer is regenerated and rinsed. After rinsing the resins are remixed by air agitation and the exchange operation is resumed.

The theoretical purity of the effluent water from a mixed bed demineralizer is very high. The equipment requires a complicated ar-

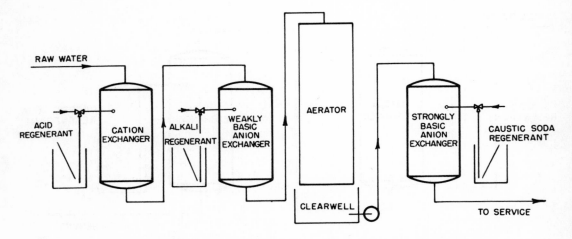

Figure 16-4 • Three-Bed System with Aerator for Demineralization and Silica Removal

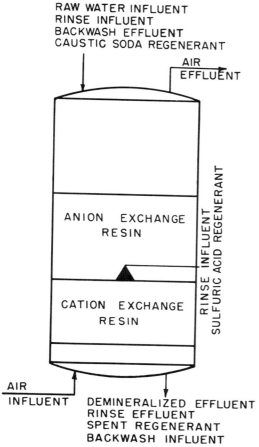

RAW WATER INFLUENT
RINSE INFLUENT
BACKWASH EFFLUENT
CAUSTIC SODA REGENERANT

AIR
EFFLUENT

ANION EXCHANGE RESIN

RINSE INFLUENT
SULFURIC ACID REGENERANT

CATION EXCHANGE RESIN

AIR
INFLUENT

DEMINERALIZED EFFLUENT
RINSE EFFLUENT
SPENT REGENERANT
BACKWASH INFLUENT

*Figure 16-5 · Arrangement for Mixed Bed
Demineralization*

rangement of valves in order to permit using caustic soda in one regeneration step and acid during the other step. There is also likely to be a variation in capacity of the unit, unless remixing of the resins after regeneration is thorough and uniform.

Regardless of the relative arrangements of the exchangers. it is essential that the influent water be free of suspended solids. Silt and organic matter are particularly objectionable, since these materials can deposit in the exchanger beds and reduce the capacity of the units by coating the beads of exchanger resin with films which either prevent or retard the movement of anions and cations through the resins. Deposits of organic matter may lead

to growth of bacteriological slime. Depending upon characteristics of the water source, the influent water to the demineralizing system may require a preliminary treatment of coagulation, filtration and possibly chlorination. However, excess chlorination will cause deterioration of the cation resin so that sometimes dechlorination is required. The usual methods of dechlorination involve the feeding of sodium sulfite or passing the water through a bed of activated carbon ahead of the cation exchanger. In some cases, cold process softening is applicable prior to the demineralizer, particularly if there are other plant water requirements for which demineralized water is not necessary.

The operation of equipment is similar to the operation of zeolite softening equipment. Operating water flow will usually be in the range of 5-8 gallons per minute per square foot of bed surface. A minimum bed depth of 30 inches is usually recommended and the bed depth will frequently be much greater in order to obtain the desired exchange capacity for the unit. Operating flow rates are· sometimes expressed in terms of gallons per minute per cubic foot of bed. In a moist condition, the exchange resins will weigh approximately 30-50 pounds per cubic foot. The cation exchange resins are heavier than the anion exchange resins.

Backwash rates of 4-8 gallons per minute per square foot are frequently employed, depending upon density of the resin and temperature of the backwash water. Higher backwash rates are required for the heavier resins and for higher water temperature, due to reduced viscosity of the water. Backwash rate is normally adjusted to provide between 50 and 100% expansion of the bed. In some plants, where the influent water is not completely free of suspended solids, it has been found advantageous to install filter bed agitators to obtain maximum cleaning of the resin during backwash.

Regenerant flow rates are usually low and close to approximately one gallon per minute per square foot. With strongly basic anion exchangers, maximum removal of silica in a given period of time will be obtained if the caustic soda solution is heated to 90-100 F, or slightly higher.

With the cation exchangers, the concentration of the regenerant solution may be in the range of 1-10% for hydrochloric acid and 1-5% for sulfuric acid. When using sulfuric acid to regenerate a resin cation exchanger it is sometimes necessary to start at a low concentration of acid, which is increased in steps if the influent water to the unit contains an appreciable calcium content in comparison to the other cations present. This procedure is necessary to avoid precipitation of calcium sulfate upon the resin. Hydrochloric acid does not require step-wise regeneration procedure. It is more difficult to handle than sulfuric acid and for this reason its use is avoided.

In the regeneration of strongly basic anion exchangers, the strength of the caustic soda solution is in the range of 2-4%. With weakly basic anion exchangers, the strength of the sodium carbonate regenerant will normally be in the range of 2-4%. Ammonia can also be used as a regenerant if silica removal is not required.

Following introduction of the regenerant solution, the unit is rinsed to remove excess regenerant. Rinsing will generally require 50 to 150 gallons of water per cubic foot of resin. About 5 to 10% of the influent water will be wasted from the system as a result of backwash and rinse operations. It should be noted that the hydrogen cation exchanger can be rinsed with raw water, but the anion exchanger must be rinsed with effluent from the hydrogen cation exchanger. Rinse water from the anion unit can be recycled to the raw water supply when the conductivity of the rinse water decreases to the conductivity of the raw water supply. A small portion of the initial rinse water from the hydrogen cation exchanger can be reclaimed and used at the beginning of the next regeneration cycle, since this water will have an appreciable acid content.

Control of demineralization plants requires determination of several factors. The hydrogen cation exchanger will have an effluent pH in the acid range and a certain value for free mineral acidity. Operation of the cation unit can be followed to some degree by means of a continuous pH recorder. Sodium will break through the hydrogen cation unit a short time before there will be a significant increase in pH. For maximum purity of the effluent water from the system, it is necessary to check the hydrogen cation exchanger effluent for sodium content when the end of the expected run approaches. If maximum purity is not essential, determination of pH and free mineral acidity are used as the control tests.

The quality of the effluent from the strongly basic anion exchanger can be checked by means of a conductivity recorder. Silica and carbon dioxide will break through the unit somewhat ahead of other anions. For minimum silica in the effluent water, silica determinations must be conducted as the end of the expected run approaches.

APPLICATIONS AND LIMITATIONS

Demineralization with silica removal has proved to be an economical method for providing makeup water for high pressure boiler operation. In many cases, it is a more economical method of makeup water preparation than distillation using single effect evaporators. Demineralization either with or without silica removal has proved to be a useful and economical process for many industries. The use of demineralized water has been applied to the manufacture of chemical and pharmaceutical products. Demineralized water is used in some textile processes, in the silvering of glass, and in some electro-plating processes. It has also been used widely in various manufacturing processes where quality of the finished product may be affected by the presence of mineral salts in water coming in contact with the product.

At the present time, hydrogen cation exchangers are available which can tolerate operating temperature as high as 250 F. Strongly basic anion exchange materials must generally be operated at a water temperature not exceeding 105 F. As a consequence, it is necessary to carry out demineralizing processes at relatively low temperatures at the present time. When the raw water source is very high in dissolved solids, evaporation will frequently prove to be the most economical method of obtaining water which will be nearly free of mineral salts. If the raw water is contaminated with substances of an organic nature, distillation may be required for purification. Coagulation, chlorination and filtration will frequently reduce organic content of water to very low values. However, not all organic materials can be completely removed by such methods. Many organic substances can not be removed by demineralization, since they do not ionize in water.

Several years ago the fluosilicic acid process for silica removal was the only one which was available for practical application to the preparation of boiler makeup water with demineralization. This process is now obsolete, having been superseded by a more efficient and economical process. Since the present methods of demineralization are comparatively new and being widely applied, it can be expected that considerable progress will be made within the next few years. Such progress will most likely result in more efficient use of regenerant chemicals and in more precise methods of operation control. These changes will permit production of demineralized water with greater purity and at lower cost.

REFERENCES

S. B. Applebaum, "Experiences With Silica Removal Demineralizer Plants", *Proceedings,* Midwest Power Conf., Vol. XIII, pp. 275-289 (1951)

H. W. Frazer, "Special Operating and Regenerating Techniques for Ion Exchange", *Proceedings,* Engineers Soc. of Western Penna., pp. 83-96 (1958)

N. W. Frisch and R. Kunin, "Long-Term Operating Characteristics of Anion Exchange Resins", *Ind. and Eng. Chem.,* Vol. 49, pp. 1365-1372 (1957)

M. E. Gilwood, C. Calmon and A. H. Greer, "Silica Removal Characteristics of Highly Basic Anion Exchangers", *Proceedings,* Engineers Soc. of Western Penna., pp. 119-130 (1951)

J. Harlow, V. J. Calise and M. Lane, "Boiler Feedwater Treatment For A High-Pressure, High-Makeup, Power And Steam Producing Plant", *Proceedings,* Midwest Power Conf., Vol. XIII, pp. 290-303 (1951)

R. Kunin, "Ion Exchange Resins", 2nd Ed., John Wiley and Sons, Inc., New York, N. Y. (1958)

F. C. Nachod and J. Schubert, "Ion Exchange Technology", Academic Press, New York, N. Y. (1956)

R. I. Smith and H. D. Reppin, "Four Years Of Operating Experience With A 3200-GPM Demineralizer", *Proceedings,* Am. Power Conf., Vol. XXIII, pp. 635-649 (1961)

17

Dealkalization by Chloride-Anion Exchange

EALKALIZATION by chloride-anion exchange is a process whereby a sodium zeolite softened water is passed through a second exchange unit which removes anions such as sulfate, nitrate, carbonate and bicarbonate. These anions are replaced by chloride. Salt is used to regenerate the chloride-anion exchanger. Since carbonate and bicarbonate ions are exchanged for chloride in this process, alkalinity reduction is achieved without the use of acid.

It is theoretically possible to employ unsoftened water as influent to the chloride-anion exchanger. However, at this stage in the development of this process, it is the consensus among equipment manufacturers that it is desirable to precede the dealkalizer with a sodium zeolite softener. With unsoftened water there is the danger of precipitating calcium carbonate and magnesium hydroxide in the dealkalizer bed. In addition, the chloride-anion exchange bed is even more critical with respect to suspended matter than the conventional sodium zeolite cation exchanger. Because the anion exchange resin is lighter than the cation exchanger, it can be backwashed only at low rates, insufficient to remove suspended matter. The use of a sodium zeolite, preceding the anion exchange, serves as an additional safeguard for the removal of suspended matter. Even for the sodium zeolite unit, turbidity of the influent water should not exceed 10 ppm.

USE FOR DEALKALIZATION

The basic usefulness of this new process lies in its ability to reduce the alkalinity of the treated water without the use of acid.

The alkalinity of a water is unchanged in passage through a sodium zeolite softener. Concentration of feedwater alkalinity in the boiler may develop high boiler water alkalinities, with possible danger of foaming and carryover of solids with the steam. In addition, decomposition of alkalinity under boiler water temperatures will produce carbon dioxide in the steam. Carbon dioxide, thus formed, is a major source of steam and condensate line corrosion.

These disadvantages to sodium zeolite softening can be minimized by acid treatment of the zeolite effluent or by employing hydrogen zeolite softening. Both of these treatment methods involve the use of acid, which is regarded with disfavor in small plants, without adequate personnel.

While not as efficient or economical as acid treatment or hydrogen zeolite softening, dealkalization by chloride-anion exchange possesses the advantage of securing similar alkalinity reduction without the necessity of handling acid.

CHEMISTRY INVOLVED

Dealkalization by chloride-anion exchange

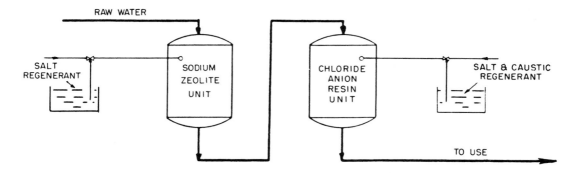

Figure 17-1 · Sodium Zeolite—Chloride Anion Exchange

makes use of highly basic anion exchange resins employed in demineralization. In demineralization, a raw water is first passed through a cation exchanger, where cations are exchanged for hydrogen ions. Calcium, magnesium and sodium are removed and the cation exchanger effluent contains sulfuric acid, hydrochloric acid, carbonic acid, etc., which are then adsorbed in passing through the second unit, the anion exchanger. The cation unit is regenerated with acid and the anion unit with alkali. This demineralization process results in the complete removal of both cations and anions, producing an effluent comparable to distilled water.

Chloride-anion exchange differs from demineralization in that cations and anions are not removed from solution, but are exchanged for an equivalent amount of other ions of less undesirable characteristics. In dealkalization, two separate units are employed. The first unit is a conventional sodium zeolite softener, regenerated with sodium chloride, which exchanges calcium or magnesium ions for sodium ions. The reactions are as follows:

$$Ca^{++} + Na_2Z = CaZ + 2Na^+$$
calcium + sodium = calcium + sodium
ion   zeolite   zeolite   ion

$$Mg^{++} + Na_2Z = MgZ$$
magnesium + sodium = magnesium
ion   zeolite   zeolite

$$+ 2Na^+$$
+ sodium
ion

Of course, as previously mentioned, anions are not affected by passage through a sodium zeolite unit. Alkalinity, sulfate, chloride, etc., pass through unchanged.

In the second unit, the exchange material is a highly basic resin anion exchange material, also regenerated with sodium chloride. In passage through this unit the sodium salts present in the influent, such as sodium bicarbonate and sodium sulfate, are converted to an equivalent amount of sodium chloride. In other words, the dealkalization unit removes the anions present in the influent by exchanging these anions with an equivalent amount

of chloride. Unlike demineralization, solids are not removed by dealkalization, but converted to the sodium chloride form. Reactions in the chloride-anion exchangers are as follows:

$$(HCO_3)^- + R \cdot Cl = R \cdot HCO_3$$
bicarbonate + chloride = bicarbonate
ion   anion   anion
            resin   resin

$$+ Cl^-$$
+ chloride
ion

$$(SO_4)^= + 2R \cdot Cl = R_2 \cdot SO_4 + 2Cl^-$$
sulfate   chloride   sulfate   chloride
ion   +   anion   = anion   + ion
           resin   resin

Of course, there is no advantage secured in exchanging sulfate for chloride. Nitrate is also exchanged for chloride in this process. Where the sulfate and nitrate content of a water is high, the cost of the dealkalization process is increased by the exchange of these ions, from which exchange no advantage is secured.

However, as indicated in the preceding reactions, bicarbonate is removed by passage of a sodium zeolite softened water through the chloride-anion exchanger and this removal of alkalinity is the chief objective of the process—namely removal of alkalinity without the use of acid.

The chemical reactions of regenerations with this process are as follows:

1st Unit—Sodium Zeolite

$$CaZ + 2NaCl = Na_2Z + CaCl_2$$
calcium + sodium = sodium + calcium
zeolite chloride zeolite chloride

2nd Unit—Chloride-Anion Exchanger

$$R \cdot HCO_3 + NaCl = R \cdot Cl$$
bicarbonate + sodium = chloride
anion   chloride   anion
resin   resin

$$+ NaHCO_3$$
+ sodium
bicarbonate

The exchange capacity of the dealkalization unit is affected by several variables. Data have been presented to the effect that capacity for the total exchangeable anions (bicarbonate, carbonate, sulfate and nitrate) will decrease with an increasing chloride content in the raw water. The total anion exchange capacity (including the raw water chloride) is not affected by variation of the percentage of the total anions which are present in the chloride form. However, since the purpose of the process is the removal of bicarbonate alkalinity, the capacity of the resin bed for bicarbonate removal will decrease with increasing chloride concentrations of the raw water.

The process is most efficient when the anions are low with the exception of bicarbonate. There is no advantage in exchanging sulfate and nitrate with chloride, and yet regenerant must be employed for this purpose. Consequently, for low cost operation, it is desirable that the sulfate, chloride and nitrate content of the raw water be low in comparison with the bicarbonate.

Exchange capacities of 5-10 kilograins exchangeable anions (expressed as $CaCO_3$) per cubic foot of resin have been reported. Improvement in exchange capacity has been noted when sodium hydroxide is used with the sodium chloride in the regenerating solution, in the ratio of approximately one pound of caustic soda for each ten pounds of sodium chloride.

At one of the first installations of the dealkalization process, it was reported that the addition of sodium hydroxide to the sodium chloride regenerant resulted in an increase in the exchange capacity of approximately 45-60%. At this plant, raw water alkalinity as calcium carbonate is 145-150 ppm and the dealkalization unit is taken off line and regenerated when the effluent alkalinity is in the range of 27-31 ppm as $CaCO_3$.

EQUIPMENT REQUIRED

The chloride-anion exchanger is similar in construction to a conventional sodium zeolite unit and equipped with the same accessories for regeneration. A resin bed depth of 30-36 inches is recommended. Operating flow rate should not exceed five gallons per square foot per minute.

Salt regeneration rates range between 3.0-4.0 pounds of salt per cubic foot of resin. It is desirable to employ softened water in preparing regenerant brine. Rinse and regenerant rates of 0.5 gallons per minute per cubic foot of resin are recommended.

APPLICATIONS

The major usefulness of dealkalization by ion exchange is in relatively small plants where the hazard of acid handling is a controlling factor in deciding the type of external treatment process to be installed. Where neutralizing amines are employed, the use of a chloride-anion exchanger may permit economy, since any reduction in the CO_2 content of the steam will be reflected in a decreased requirement for the neutralizing amine.

Only one regenerant chemical (salt) is required, although as mentioned previously, improvement in the exchange capacity may be achieved through the use of caustic soda along with the salt. There is no hazard involved in the handling of salt and it is a cheap, readily available material. Where sufficient competent personnel are not available for controlling the other methods of alkalinity reduction, the chloride-anion exchange process is definitely advantageous.

LIMITATIONS

With the installation of proper equipment and adequate personnel, there is little hazard involved in handling acid. Direct acid treatment of a sodium zeolite effluent or the use of hydrogen-sodium zeolite softening will accomplish alkalinity removal more efficiently and economically than the chloride-anion exchange process. In addition, in plants of sufficient size to justify the installation, the hot lime-hot ion exchange process will prove more economical than chloride-anion exchange.

Like other treatment methods, dealkalization by chloride-anion exchange, reduces but does not eliminate the CO_2 content of the steam. Dependent on the type of equipment in which steam is condensed and the degree of stratification of carbon dioxide in condensing equipment, severe corrosion problems can result even from relatively low CO_2 concentrations in the steam. Where filming amines are used for control of carbon dioxide corrosion, the amine feed rate is substantially independent of CO_2 concentration. The quantity of amine required is only sufficient to provide a non-wettable film on the metal surfaces. Except under unusual circumstances, it is not necessary to increase the feed rate of the filming amines because of higher carbon dioxide content of the steam. Conse-

quently, in a plant with high carbon dioxide content of the steam and satisfactory corrosion control with the filming amines, the installation of a chloride-anion exchanger to lower the carbon dioxide in the steam would not necessarily permit a reduction in the amine rate of feed.

REFERENCES

S. B. Applebaum, "Experiences with Chloride Anion Exchangers for Reducing Alkalinity Without Acid", *Proceedings*, Engineers Soc. of Western Penna., pp. 1-8 (1952)

A. E. Kittredge, "Dealkalization of Boiler Feed Water in Small Power Plants", *Proceedings*, Am. Power Conf., Vol. XV, pp. 567-572 (1953)

E. Maher, "Dealkalization System", *Industry and Power*, Vol. 63, pp. 102-103 (Sept. 1952)

18

Hot Lime-Hot Ion Exchange Softening

With the development of styrene base resins that can withstand waters of high pH and high temperature, a two-stage softening process has been developed, employing hot lime softening as the first stage followed by hot ion exchange softening as the second stage. In many cases, this method of treatment offers definite advantages over the usual two-stage hot process softeners using lime and soda ash in the first stage and phosphate in the second stage.

Although the ion exchange unit will operate satisfactorily on the effluent from hot process lime-soda softening, it is usual to use only lime treatment in the first stage softening, so as to minimize softener effluent alkalinity and thereby produce less carbon dioxide in the steam.

USE OF PROCESS

For waters containing high concentrations of hardness, alkalinity, total solids and silica, it was often found necessary to resort to hot process lime-soda softening to reduce these factors to a reasonable range for boiler feedwater purposes, even for relatively low boiler pressures. At higher boiler pressures, hot lime-soda softening alone is not completely satisfactory due to the relatively high softener effluent hardness, resulting in boiler sludge accumulations even with proper internal treatment. To overcome this difficulty, hot phosphate softening following hot lime-soda softening has often been employed to reduce the makeup water hardness to approximately 2-3 ppm.

Due to variations in composition common to many water supplies, it has often been found difficult to control chemical balances in the effluent from a hot lime-soda softener. When such variations occur, boiler water balances are upset, resulting in poor internal conditions. With two-stage hot lime soda-hot phosphate softening, any variations in the primary softener are immediately reflected in a poor effluent from the secondary softener. From the operating standpoint, either single stage hot lime-soda softening or two-stage hot lime soda-hot phosphate softening requires close attention and frequent control tests to assure proper operation at all times.

Hot lime softening alone will reduce the carbonate and magnesium hardness as well as the total solids of a raw supply. Only lime is required when the calcium exceeds the total alkalinity. On high alkalinity waters, it may be found necessary to apply calcium chloride or calcium sulfate to reduce the alkalinity to the desired range. The effluent from the lime treater, whether filtered or unfiltered, is passed through a sodium exchanger containing the styrene base resin which removes the residual calcium and magnesium salts, thereby producing a water with a total hardness in the range of 0.5 to 2 ppm.

CHEMICAL REACTIONS

Hydrated lime is employed to react with the bicarbonate alkalinity of the raw water, precipitating calcium carbonate as shown by the following reaction.

(1)
$$\underset{\substack{\text{hydrated} \\ \text{lime}}}{Ca(OH)_2} + \underset{\substack{\text{calcium} \\ \text{bicarbonate}}}{Ca(HCO_3)_2} = \underset{\substack{\text{calcium} \\ \text{carbonate}}}{2CaCO_3}$$
$$+ 2H_2O$$
$$+ \text{water}$$

To reduce silica, the natural magnesium of the raw supply can be precipitated as magnesium hydroxide which adsorbs silica from solution. Precipitation of magnesium requires a slight excess of lime and this reaction is shown by the following equation.

(2)
$$\underset{\substack{\text{hydrated} \\ \text{lime}}}{Ca(OH)_2} + \underset{\substack{\text{magnesium} \\ \text{chloride}}}{MgCl_2} = \underset{\substack{\text{magnesium} \\ \text{hydroxide}}}{Mg(OH)_2}$$
$$+ CaCl_2$$
$$+ \text{calcium} \atop \text{chloride}$$

If the quantity of natural magnesium in the raw supply is not sufficient to reduce the silica to the desired level, it will then be necessary to employ an activated magnesium oxide or dolomitic lime depending on the type water to be treated. No soda ash is employed to reduce the noncarbonate hardness since this is automatically removed by the ion exchange softener. The reactions occurring in the hot exchange softener following the hot lime softener are identical to those outlined in the chapter on sodium zeolite softening.

EQUIPMENT EMPLOYED

The equipment employed in this process is similar to that described in the chapters on hot lime-soda softening and sodium zeolite softening with only minor modifications. Figure 18-1 illustrates a typical hot lime-hot ion exchange softening process.

APPLICATIONS

This system of treatment is desirable for high pressure boilers (450 psi-1000 psi) since it produces a water of low total hardness, low silica and low alkalinity.

Low total hardness is essential for high pressure operation because of the suspended solids limitation in preventing adherent de-

posits. With the use of hot phosphate softening, difficulties with adherent boiler sludge, principally in the form of magnesium phosphate are encountered. The use of the hot ion exchange process reduces this factor to a minimum.

The normal hot lime-soda process requires maintaining an excess of carbonate alkalinity in the softener effluent to reduce calcium hardness to a minimum. The high carbonate alkalinity of the softener effluent increases the carbon dioxide content of the steam, rendering the resulting condensate more corrosive. In addition, a high blowdown rate often is necessary to restrict boiler water alkalinity within safe limits. With hot lime softening, the carbonate alkalinity of the softener effluent can be maintained at a minimum and, as a result, the carbon dioxide content of the steam will be lower than results with lime-soda softening. Blowdown for alkalinity control can be maintained at a minimum.

Following hot lime-soda softening or hot lime-soda, hot phosphate softening, calcium carbonate or calcium phosphate deposits will

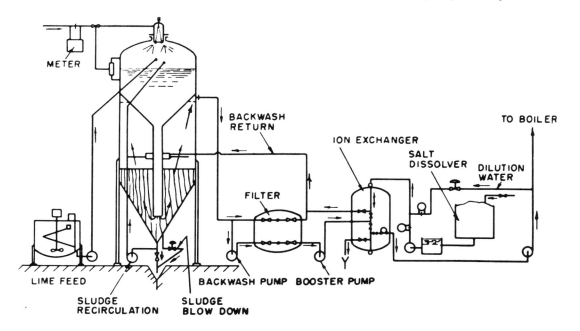

Figure 18-1 · Flow Sheet of Typical Hot Lime—Hot Ion Exchange Process

Figure 18-2—Typical Softener Effluent Analyses

| | Raw Water | Hot Lime-Soda, Hot Phosphate | | Hot Lime, Hot Ion Exchange | |
		1st Stage (Lime-Soda)	2nd Stage (Phosphate)	1st Stage (Lime)	2nd Stage (Exchange Resin)
Total Hardness ....as CaCO₃, ppm....	150	18	0-2	70	0-2
Calcium ....as CaCO₃, ppm....	120	15	0-1	67	0-1
Magnesium ....as CaCO₃, ppm....	30	3	0-1	3	0-1
"P" Alkalinity ....as CaCO₃, ppm....	0	40	30	10	10
"M" Alkalinity ....as CaCO₃, ppm....	100	60	50	20	20
Silica ....as SiO₂, ppm......	15	*	..	*	..

Treatment Requirements	Hot Lime-Soda, Hot Phosphate	Hot Lime-Ion Exchange
Lime, lbs/1000 gal.	1.0	0.9
Soda Ash, lbs/1000 gal.	0.8	..
Phosphate (D.S.P.), lbs/1000 gal.	0.18	..
Salt, lbs/1000 gal.	...	2.0

*Can be reduced to approximately 1 ppm with use of magnesium oxide or dolomitic lime.

occur in stage heaters or economizers unless the pH is reduced by the addition of an acidic material or dilution with appreciable returned condensate. Following hot lime-hot ion exchange softening, there is no danger of such deposits because the calcium and magnesium salts are practically "zero." In fact, with the use of certain types of surface active agents, the required amount of internal boiler water treatment may be fed directly to the feedline without danger of deposition. The internal chemical feed system is thus simplified since individual high pressure chemical feed pumps for each boiler are unnecessary.

Silica deposits or silica carryover with the steam are important factors to be considered with high pressure boiler operation. The silica concentration in the boiler feedwater can be accurately controlled in the first stage softener and there is no pick-up of silica as the water passes through the hot ion exchange softener. Figure 18-2 illustrates typical effluent analyses for a hot lime-soda, hot phosphate softening process and also a hot lime-hot ion exchange softening process.

LIMITATIONS

Whether an entirely new system of hot lime-hot ion exchange softening is being installed, or whether a hot ion exchange system is to be installed to supplement an existing hot process softener, the question of turbidity of the influent to the ion exchange softener is of primary importance. Excessive turbidities in the influent to the exchange softener will tend to reduce capacity and form deposits within the unit. When such plugging occurs, it becomes necessary to acid wash the ion exchanger to remove the deposits.

Even though a properly designed lime treater will normally produce a low turbidity water, there are occasions when high turbidities can occur, such as: quick load changes, overload conditions, mechanical failure of softener controls, improper chemical balances, and rapid changes in the raw supply. To prevent excessive turbidities from interfering with the hot exchange softening process, filters are normally recommended.

If the exchange units are used as filters, the flow rate in gallons per square foot per minute must be low to obtain proper filtration. Lack of filters requires a larger volume of the costly resin than for the softening alone since proper softening can be obtained at flow rates considerably higher than the acceptable filtering rate. It will also be necessary to backwash the hot exchange units at more frequent intervals than they require regeneration in order to avoid break-through of hardness, due to channeled beds. In the absence of filters, it can be generally stated that more operating attention is required. While some installations operating without filters have reported little difficulty, it is the opinion of the manufacturers that it is safer to have filters installed.

When hot exchange softening is being considered to supplement an existing hot process softener, there are many items which require detailed study. One consideration should be the turbidity in the effluent from the first stage softener and its effect on the exchange resin in the event that the installed filters were converted to hot exchange softening units.

The hot exchange resins must be backwashed during the softening phase to loosen the bed, due to the long softening runs resulting from the low influent hardness and high exchange capacity. Higher backwash rates are normally required to properly expand the bed, because of the lower density of the hot backwash water. The quantity of backwash water and rinse water per unit of time should be accurately calculated since this water must come from the hot lime softener tank and therefore may impose a serious overload condition.

In plants operating at lower boiler pressures with a reasonable quantity of return condensate, the installation of a hot lime-hot ion exchange system represents a considerable capital investment that may not be economically justified.

In many industries, the entire water supply must be lime treated to produce a water suitable for process use and consequently the installation of a hot lime softener is generally not economical. In such cases, cold ion exchange softening is generally used to complete the treatment for boiler makeup water.

From the chemical cost viewpoint, it is necessary to calculate the exact lime and salt requirements and the lime-soda requirements in each case in order to determine if any advantage exists. Also, the cost of internal treatment following the various types of external softening systems should be correlated in order to determine any economic advantage.

Like any other system of water treatment, a hot lime-hot ion exchange system has its limitations which should be thoroughly studied and evaluated in order to assure that the system is practical and economical to meet the requirements of the individual boiler system.

REFERENCES

S. B. Applebaum, "Hot Lime Treatment Followed by Sodium Zeolite", *Proceedings,* Engineers Soc. of Western Penna., pp. 127-145 (1950)

W. S. Butler, "An Inspection Report After Eighteen Months with Hot Lime Zeolite", *Proceedings,* Engineers Society of Western Penna., pp. 1-13 (1951)

V. J. Calise, "Hot Zeolite Softening", *Power Engineering,* Vol. 54, pp. 54-59 (Sept. 1950)

J. E. Harden and G. R. Hull, "Operating Experiences with a Large Hot Lime-Zeolite System for 1500 PSI Boilers", *Proceedings,* Am. Power Conf., Vol. XIX, pp. 672-684 (1957)

B. E. Varon and S. B. Applebaum, "An Application of Hot Lime Zeolite to Moderate High-Pressure Boiler Operations", *Proceedings,* Am. Power Conf., Vol. XIX, pp. 660-671 (1957)

19

Oil Removal

OIL removal is a step in the preparation of water used for process or boiler feed by which this contamination is removed by either mechanical or chemical means.

Oil which is employed for steam cylinder lubrication is usually mineral oil containing a small percentage of a compounding material or fatty oil. The use of a compounded oil provides better lubrication by emulsifying with the moisture in the steam and preventing the oil film from being washed off the lubricated surfaces. While lubrication is aided by the compounding oil, the emulsion so formed makes the removal of oil from the condensed steam more difficult.

DIFFICULTIES DUE TO OIL

The presence of oil in boiler feed water usually originates from three sources:

Exhaust or condensed steam from reciprocating engines, pumps, etc.
Steam or water used in certain process heating equipment.
Industrial wastes.

The removal of oil from boiler feedwater is desirable and necessary because of the unpredictable and objectionable effects it may have on boiler operation.

The presence of even thin films of oil on the boiler heating surfaces will seriously retard heat transfer. Oil acts as a heat insulator and prevents the rapid transmission of heat from the metal to the water. The resultant increase in metal temperature may be sufficient to cause blistering and loss of boiler tubes and plates, particularly at high boiler ratings.

The combination of oil with boiler water sludge may result in the formation of a pasty mass. Pellets of greasy sludge may form, which may be oval or spherical in appearance, or the entire mass may be deposited on the boiler surface. Circulation and heat transfer may be seriously impaired, resulting in starvation of boiler tubes or overheating due to the heat insulating effect of the oily sludge.

Where exhaust steam is used for process work involving heat exchange, it is desirable that the steam be free of oil in order that oily films may not develop on the heat exchange surfaces of radiators, calendering rolls, heater coils, etc. The presence of oil decreases efficiency by impeding the flow of heat, requiring higher back pressures on the engine exhaust in order to maintain sufficient heat flow.

Compounded oils may cause foaming of the boiler water. Animal fatty oils employed for compounding purposes are saponifiable in the presence of normal boiler water alkalinities, thus forming soap and developing a foaming condition of the boiler water. The impure steam resulting from such a boiler water may foul superheater tubes and turbine blading, destroy cylinder lubrication, clog lines and traps, etc.

Due to the difficulties that may result from the presence of oil in boiler water, the prevention of oil contamination of the boiler feedwater is recognized as highly important. The American Boiler Manufacturers Association in its standard guarantee on steam purity formerly specified that the total quantity of oil or grease, or substances which are extractable either by sulfuric ether or by chloroform, shall not exceed 7 ppm in the boiler water when the sample being tested is acidified to 1% hydrochloric acid, or 7 ppm in the feed water when the sample being tested is first concentrated at low temperature and pressure to the same ppm total solids as the boiler water.

Because of the importance of avoiding the introduction of oil into the boiler feedwater system, the decision must be made as to whether oily condensate or exhaust steam should be discharged to waste or oil removal equipment installed. Since considerable heat will be contained in the oil contaminated steam or condensate, and since this steam or condensate will usually be of a high degree of purity with respect to mineral solids and otherwise desirable for boiler feed purposes, the installation of oil removal equipment is usually justified.

OIL REMOVAL METHODS

Oil removal equipment may be divided into two types dependent upon the field of application. Baffle or centrifugal type separators can be used for the removal of oil from steam, while various adsorbents, filters and chemical coagulation can be employed for the removal of oil from liquid condensate.

OIL REMOVAL FROM EXHAUST STEAM. Baffle type separators are used to separate oil from steam. Steam containing oil impinges on a baffle and the condensed moisture and oil are thrown out on the baffle and drain down the vertical ribs into the reservoir of the separator. From this point the oil-water mixture is drained or trapped to waste. The direction of steam flow is altered horizontally and passes around the baffle. Figure 19-1 illustrates a unit of this type.

For the proper operation of such separators, it is important that the oil-water mixture be continuously removed from the separator reservoir. Frequent inspection of trap operation should be made. If the trap is not functioning properly the reservoir will fill with the oil-water mixture and overflow, in which case the oil separator ceases to function. Separator efficiency is dependent on the proper removal of the oil-water mixture from the reservoir.

Separators operating on the centrifugal principle are also employed. Receiver and purifier type separators operate on the same principle as baffle type separators but may have more than one baffle, may be filled with steel wool, and may be drained from more than one compartment.

Mechanical separators of this type are, of course, of no value for the removal of oil from liquid condensate, but are of definite usefulness in the removal of oil from exhaust steam. It is usual for such separators to be installed in the exhaust lines from engines, particularly if the exhaust steam is to be used for direct process work or in heat exchange operations. Open type feedwater heaters are customarily provided with baffle type separators on the exhaust steam inlet.

Baffle type oil separators cannot be employed with superheated steam, but must be used with saturated steam since the action of the separator depends on condensation taking place on the baffles. If oil is present in superheated steam, a de-superheater may be used to provide saturated steam or feedwater may be sprayed into the superheated steam prior to the separator.

OIL REMOVAL FROM LIQUID CONDENSATE. *Free Oil.* When oil is present as a mechanical mixture in water, direct filtration may be employed. The oil bearing water is passed through various devices, using for a filter medium some coarse material as loofa sponges, burlap, terry cloth, coke or excelsior. Equipment using the above materials as filtering media operates on the principle that the semi-porous mass, when thoroughly wet with water, will permit water to pass through but will retain the oil. Hot wells may be filled with sponges or coke designed to retain on its surface the oil present in the

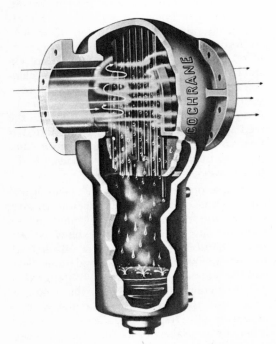

Courtesy Cochrane Division—Crane Company

Figure 19-1 • Baffle Type Oil Separator

water. Sponges are usually changed frequently and reinstalled after boiling with a caustic soda or soda ash solution for removal of the adsorbed oil. Coke beds are usually replaced with fresh coke when inspection reveals the bed to be fouled with oil.

Cloth strainers must also be removed frequently for cleaning in an alkaline solution and may be provided in the double unit type with provision for one unit out of operation at a time.

As with skimming devices, units of this type are effective only in the removal of free oil from the water. Emulsified oil is too finely dispersed to be removed by such straining action. In some cases, the labor and handling required is undesirable. Since oil contamination from reciprocating engines is usually in the emulsified form, units of this type have a restricted field of application.

Emulsified Oil. Several methods are available which will satisfactorily break the oil-water emulsion, causing the oil particles to coalesce and be readily removed by the adsorbing medium. The usual systems involve the use of aluminum and iron salts for the purpose of adsorbing the oil. While ferric sulfate has been used successfully, aluminum sulfate is the more commonly used material for this purpose. Caustic soda or soda ash is fed in addition to the coagulant in order to produce the floc of aluminum hydroxide or ferric hydroxide which coagulates and enmeshes the oil so that it can be removed by filtration. The pH of the treated water is regulated at a point that insures the most efficient coagulation.

In one type of unit, the coagulant and alkali are fed to the filter influent in proportion to the flow of condensate. Conventional pressure type filters are usually employed with the filter medium of anthracite coal. Sand or gravel as a filter is undesirable due to the pickup of silica from the filter bed by the hot condensate. Calcite filter medium is also undesirable because some of the filter bed would dissolve in the condensate, introducing calcium hardness.

In design and operation the filters employed do not differ from those used in conjunction with hot or cold process lime-soda or hot phosphate softening. The optimum filtration rate for an oil filter is two gallons per square foot of filter area per minute, this rate applying to the standard pressure type filter. As the mat of coagulated oil and adsorbing floc accumulates on the filter bed, the resistance to flow increases until a point is reached where the filter must be taken out of service and backwashed. The frequency of this operation will depend upon the load imposed upon the filter. The usual practice is to backwash when the loss in head through the filter reaches 4 to 5 psi. For backwashing purposes, hot water should be specified since the use of cold water tends to "set" the coagulated oil retained on the filter bed.

A caustic scouring tank is sometimes provided for intermittent hot scouring of the filter for the removal of oil which has not been removed by the normal backwashing operations. The hot caustic solution remains in contact with the bed for approximately one hour, dissolving and saponifying the oil. The frequency of caustic scouring is dependent upon the quantity and the type of oil contamination of the condensate.

In certain cases where the volume of condensate is large and a high degree of oil contamination exists, it is found advantageous to employ flocculating basins in the oil removal process. The chemistry and mechanics of this operation are fundamentally the same as previously described under coagulation with the flocculation and coagulation of the oil being accomplished in basins equipped for chemical feed and agitation. A retention time of one hour is usually provided. If free oil is present in the condensate together with emulsified oil, mechanical skimmers may be used to remove as much oil as possible prior to chemical treatment in the flocculating basin.

A variation of the above system involves the application of a certain amount of preformed floc to the filter bed to form an initial adsorbing mat, followed by the continuous feed of a small amount of the preformed floc

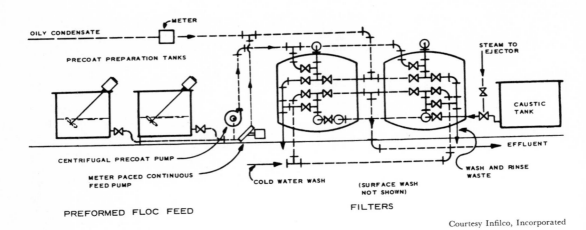

Figure 19-2 • Preformed Floc Type Oil Removal Plant

Figure 19-3 • Diatomaceous Earth Filtration System

to the condensate passing to the filters. In this instance, the coagulant and necessary quantity of alkali are added in the predetermined quantity to a chemical mixing tank where the floc is formed and aged. Figure 19-2 illustrates a system of this type.

This method of preparation and injection of the floc eliminates the need for proportioning the chemicals and results in appreciable savings in initial equipment costs. The filters used with this type system are usually the standard pressure type although some manufacturers supply units equipped with rotary surface washers or rake agitators. These special features are usually employed where the oil content of the condensate is high and difficulty in removing the oil and floc mat from the filter medium is expected.

During World War II, the need for improved oil removal methods was a primary one in the marine field. This need spurred the application of diatomaceous earth as a filter-aid and several types of filters were designed specifically for the purpose of oil removal on shipboard. Development has continued with units of this type being designed for stationary plant application. Most of the latest designs have eliminated former objections and provide easy removal and disposal of the filter cake in a backwashing operation that does not require removal of the head of the filter or the individual septa under ordinary circumstances.

The diatomite filters employ a permeable base or septum to support the filter cake. These septa include various types of filter cloths and papers, porous stone tubes, wire cloth and wire wound tubes. The usual procedure involves application of a precoat on the septa with the filter-aid recirculated through the unit for several minutes to form a porous mat. The unit is then operated to waste for several minutes to make certain the effluent is clear before cutting it into the system. The usual practice in oil removal systems is to follow the precoat with a "body" coat or continuous feed of the filter-aid into the condensate passing to the filter. Even though diatomaceous earth is abrasive,

specially designed pumps are available to handle such material. At the end of the filter run, newer designs of the filters permit the sloughing off of the filter cake by backwash or air pressure with the filter mat dropping into a hopper bottom and discharging to waste. After thorough rinsing, the unit is again ready for the precoat application.

In the event improper operation causes the septa to become fouled, they are readily removed for chemical or mechanical cleaning. The diatomite filters operate with considerably higher pressure drops than do standard pressure filters. They may operate with head losses as high as 50 psi before requiring backwashing. This operation is possible since the rigid support of the septa prevents channeling and the filtrate will remain clear even though the throughput decreases as the pressure drop increases.

In oil removal practice, it is usual to employ a precoat of filter-aid approximating one to two ounces per square foot of filter area. The body coat will vary depending upon the quantity of oil to be removed. It is necessary to employ a body coat whenever oil is present to any extent in order to maintain the porosity of the filter cake and prevent separated oil from clogging the interstices. In general, the length of run obtained on a diatomite filter depends upon the filtration rate, amount of filter-aid used and the amount of foreign matter, such as oil, present in the water.

A suitable grade of filter-aid specially processed for adsorption of oil is supplied by several manufacturers and adsorbs approximately one pound of oil for each pound of material used. An application of this type filter has produced a filtered condensate of practically "zero" oil content with an influent oil content as high as 50 ppm.

Operation of these filters requires reasonable care and adherence to operating instructions. However, their operation is no more complicated than that of standard filters.

Chemical coagulation and filtration or use of diatomite adsorption and filtration are the only certain means for the removal of emulsified oil from liquid condensate. Naturally, systems of this type are a more costly initial installation and require a greater degree of supervision than do baffle type separators or towel filters. Consequently, adsorption and filtration systems are usually installed so as to handle only the contaminated condensate. Oil free condensate such as turbine condensate is returned directly to the feedwater heater without passing through the oil removal system. By limiting the size of the equipment to the flow of contaminated condensate, the initial cost may be minimized.

The adsorption systems described have certain limitations. Those systems using a coagulant and alkali require rather rigid pH control and do not function well when the pH of the condensate is variable, requiring constant adjustment of the chemical feed. This defect is true also for the preformed floc system since introduction of the preformed floc to a condensate which does not have a satisfactory pH value will result in the solution of the floc and resulting failure of the system to coagulate and adsorb the oil.

Diatomite filters eliminate the necessity for pH control, since no coagulant is employed. Since diatomite is a siliceous material, some silica will be dissolved in the hot condensate. Usually, this silica pickup is less than 1 ppm.

ANALYSIS FOR OIL

The method to be used for the removal of oil and grease from water usually is predicated upon a chemical analysis to determine the amount and type of contamination. Oil or grease is of animal, mineral or vegetable origin and may be present in water as an emulsion, free-floating or in some cases a light petroleum fraction may be in solution.

The determination of oil or grease is based upon refluxing through a trap for volatile materials followed by solvent extraction of the remainder of the sample. Commonly used solvents are hexane, petroleum ether, benzene, chloroform or carbon tetrachloride. These solvents exert selective extraction of specific greases and oily constituents. However, nonoily materials such as phenolic compounds or colloidal sulfur may be selectively extracted to varying degrees. The method of sampling is of utmost importance. Solvent-washed glass containers should be employed using a closure with an impervious liner such as aluminum.

The definition of grease and oily matter must be based upon the procedures used, the source of contamination, the type of solvent and other factors. The interpretation of the analytical results will vary accordingly. In view of the multiplicity of the variables encountered, the Joint Committee on Uniformity of Methods of Water Examination has concluded that uniformity of methods for the determination of grease and oily matter is not practicable on the basis of present technical knowledge.

REFERENCES

G. R. Bell, "Removal of Oil from Condensate by Diatomite Filtration", *Proceedings,* Engineers Soc. of Western Penna., pp. 123-137 (1952)

V. J. Calise, "Removing Oil from Water by Flocculation and Filtration", *Power Engineering,* Vol. 58, pp. 86, 87, 110, 138 (Apr. 1954)

J. J. Maguire, "Oil Removal from Heating Surfaces", *Southern Power & Industry,* Vol. 74, pp. 52, 54, 64, 67 (Aug. 1956)

"Manual on Industrial Water and Industrial Waste Water", 2nd Ed., pp. 400-402, Am. Soc. for Testing Materials, Phila., Pa. (1959)

J. H. Richards, "Maybe It's Oil that Needs to be Removed from Boiler Feedwater", *Industry and Power,* Vol. 47, pp. 62-66 (Dec. 1944)

20

Deaeration

MECHANICAL deaeration, as applied to boiler feedwater, is the removal of dissolved gases such as oxygen, carbon dioxide and ammonia by the process of raising the water to the saturation temperature for the pressure under which the process is conducted; employing an equipment design that secures intimate mixture of the water and the scrubbing steam; and providing means for the liberal venting from the system of the gases released.

The necessity for removing these corrosive gases from boiler feedwater in order to prevent corrosion is now fully recognized. Dissolved oxygen will cause pitting and corrosion of the boiler feed lines, closed heaters, economizers, boilers, steam and return lines. If carbon dioxide is also present, the two gases acting simultaneously may be considered from 10% to 40% more corrosive than would be expected for the same quantity of the two gases acting individually.

It has been determined that oxygen is relatively 5 to 10 times more corrosive than equal quantities of carbon dioxide, and that temperature is also an important factor. For example, a condensate in which is dissolved equal molar concentrations of each gas at 194 F is 2.0 to 2.5 times as corrosive as that same condensate at 140 F. Where corrosion is caused largely by carbon dioxide, the structure and composition of the steel are factors in determining its life.

When iron or steel is brought into contact with water, iron goes into solution. A soluble compound, ferrous hydroxide is formed as follows:

$$Fe^{++} + 2H_2O = Fe(OH)_2 + 2H^+$$

ferrous ion + water = $\dfrac{\text{ferrous}}{\text{hydroxide}}$ + $\dfrac{\text{hydrogen}}{\text{ion}}$

If dissolved oxygen is present in the system, it will combine with the ferrous hydroxide to form the insoluble compound, ferric hydroxide, as shown:

$$4Fe(OH)_2 + O_2 + 2H_2O = 4Fe(OH)_3$$

$\dfrac{\text{ferrous}}{\text{hydroxide}}$ + oxygen + water = $\dfrac{\text{ferric}}{\text{hydroxide}}$

The oxygen, by removing the ferrous hydroxide from the solution, prevents equilib-rium from being established. Therefore, the reaction will proceed to completion until either the metal or the gas in the system has been entirely exhausted.

Ferrous hydroxide is an alkaline compound and its rate of solution depends upon the pH of the water with which it is in contact. The lower the pH of the water, the more rapidly ferrous hydroxide goes into solution. Condensate may contain carbon dioxide (CO_2) in solution, which, by forming carbonic acid (H_2CO_3), may lower the pH to a range such as 5.6—6.5. This low pH is more conducive to the solution of ferrous hydroxide. Hence, it is highly desirable to rid the system of carbon dioxide so as to increase the pH of the water.

Ammonia may be extremely corrosive to copper and copper bearing alloys in the presence of moisture. Corrosion of valves, fittings, turbine blading, condenser tubes, etc., may take place with sufficient ammonia contamination. In contact with copper, ammonia forms a complex copper-ammonium ion $[Cu(NH_3)_4^{++}]$ and solution of copper and copper bearing alloys may be quite rapid. A source of ammonia in the system may be from breakdown of nitrogenous matter under boiler temperatures and the evolution of ammonia with the steam.

THEORY INVOLVED

Dalton's Law states that the total pressure of a mixture of several gases is equal to the sum of the pressures which each gas would exert were it alone present in the volume occupied by the mixture.

Henry's Law states that the concentration of the dissolved gas in the solution is directly proportional to the partial pressure of that gas in the free space above the liquid, with the exception of those gases which chemically unite with the solvent. For example, carbon dioxide and ammonia unite chemically with water.

Henry's Law may be written:

$$\frac{c}{p} = K$$

where K = solubility coefficient (constant for any one temperature)

c = concentration of dissolved gas in solution

p = pressure of gas

For example, if 0.002 mol of a gas is dissolved in a certain volume of water under one atmosphere pressure, 0.004 mol will be dissolved if the pressure is doubled.

Deviations from Henry's Law may be expected when the dissolved gas undergoes a secondary reaction with the solvent, as is the case when ammonia gas is dissolved in water. Henry's Law applies only to the dissolved ammonia gas (NH_3) but the concentration in the solution is determined by analytical methods which include both the ammonia gas and the ammonium hydroxide (NH_4OH) formed.

In accordance with the basic principles contained in Dalton's and Henry's Laws, it is evident that removal of a dissolved gas from water can be effected by reducing the partial pressure of that gas in the surrounding atmosphere, regardless of the total pressure on the system. The simplest manner in which this can be accomplished is to bubble another gas through the water or to spray the water into a countercurrent flow of another gas, supplying in each case free venting of the gas from the system. In this manner, the concentration of the dissolved gas in the surrounding atmosphere is reduced by dilution with the scrubbing gas. The partial pressure of the dissolved gas in the surrounding atmosphere decreases and, in accordance with Henry's Law, to establish equilibrium the concentration of dissolved gas in the water decreases in direct proportion with its decrease in partial pressure.

Practical application of this theoretical principle is obtained in the removal of free carbon dioxide from water by blowing air countercurrent to falling streams of water as in a degasifier. Such a unit, as described under cation exchange by hydrogen zeolite, consists of slatted wooden trays to break up the falling water into thin streams and a low pressure blower to force air up through the falling streams.

Oxygen similarly can be removed from water by passing another gas counter-flow to falling streams of water. Air could not be used for this purpose because of the high percentage of oxygen (21%) in air. Nitrogen could be employed but cost would make the process impracticable.

The most desirable and practicable method of removing dissolved oxygen from boiler feedwater involves the use of the vapor of the solvent or steam as a scrubbing gas. This choice of a scrubbing gas is logical since steam is the most economical gas that could be employed, and in the process of gas removal a thermodynamic advantage is secured by heating the water with the steam.

The mechanism of gas removal from water through the use of the scrubbing action of the vapor (steam) of the solvent (water) involves two separate mechanisms as follows:

1. Mechanical separation of gas bubbles results when saturation conditions are achieved and when the vapor pressure of the liquid solvent and the solution pressure of dissolved gases appreciably exceed the pressure imposed on the system. Under these conditions, all gases become insoluble. However, saturation conditions alone do not assure complete gas removal. If only saturation conditions were necessary for gas removal, there would be no need for the complicated tray or jet design of feedwater heaters, since an open tank, filled with water at 212 F at atmospheric pressure, would accomplish complete deaeration.

2. Diffusion of gas particles to the surrounding atmosphere (without bubble formation) results when the total internal pressure of the liquid solvent and dissolved gases is less than or slightly more than the pressure imposed on the system. Ammonia removal, because of the extreme solubility of this gas, must be accomplished by diffusion rather than mechanical separation.

In the removal of dissolved oxygen from water, 90 to 95% of the initial oxygen content will leave the water immediately and without difficulty by mechanical separation when the water is heated to the saturation temperature for the pressure imposed on the system. The remaining 5 to 10% of the initial oxygen content must be removed through molecular diffusion. In ridding the system of this last 5 to 10% of the initial oxygen content, it is obvious that the rapidity of oxygen removal will be a function of the heater design and also of the rapidity with which the surrounding atmosphere is changed and gases vented from the system.

The practical considerations involved in the removal of dissolved oxygen from boiler feed water may be briefly summarized as:

Heating the water to the boiling temperature for the pressure under which the process is conducted (saturation conditions).

Providing a heater design that secures intimate mixing of steam and water.

Continuously venting from the system the mixture of gases and steam.

REMOVAL OF CARBON DIOXIDE AND AMMONIA. Unlike oxygen, carbon dioxide and ammonia do not obey Henry's Law because they unite chemically with water. At elevated temperatures their deviation from Henry's Law decreases due to decreased chemical combination with the solvent. The mecha-

nism of removal of these gases is primarily molecular diffusion rather than mechanical separation.

When carbon dioxide is dissolved in water it forms a relatively unstable compound, carbonic acid (H_2CO_3). This acid ionizes into the bicarbonate radical (HCO_3^-) and the hydrogen ion (H^+). Further ionization of the bicarbonate radical takes place to form the carbonate radical ($CO_3^=$) and the hydrogen ion (H^+) as illustrated.

$$CO_2 + H_2O \rightleftarrows H_2CO_3$$
carbon dioxide + water $\rightleftarrows$ carbonic acid

$$H_2CO_3 \rightleftarrows H^+ +$$
carbonic acid $\rightleftarrows$ hydrogen ion +

$$HCO_3^-$$
bicarbonate ion

$$HCO_3^- \rightleftarrows CO_3^= +$$
bicarbonate ion $\rightleftarrows$ carbonate ion +

$$H^+$$
hydrogen ion

The hydrogen ion concentration or pH controls the distribution of carbon dioxide among these three forms. It is only in the form of carbonic acid (H_2CO_3) that a gas solution pressure is exerted and that carbon dioxide can be removed by deaeration. Figure 20-1 illustrates the availability of carbon dioxide for removal by deaeration and indicates it is at the more acid pH values that the most efficient removal of carbon dioxide can be obtained.

When ammonia gas is dissolved in water, it forms an unstable compound, ammonium hydroxide (NH_4OH). Ammonium hydroxide ionizes to form the ammonium ion (NH_4^+) and the hydroxyl ion (OH^-) as illustrated.

$$NH_3 + H_2O \rightleftarrows NH_4OH$$
ammonia + water $\rightleftarrows$ ammonium hydroxide

$$NH_4OH \rightleftarrows NH_4^+ +$$
ammonium hydroxide $\rightleftarrows$ ammonium ion +

$$OH^-$$
hydroxyl ion

The hydroxyl ion concentration controls the distribution of ammonia between these two forms. It is only in the form of ammonium hydroxide (NH_4OH) that a gas solution pressure is exerted and that ammonia can be removed by deaeration. Figure 20-2

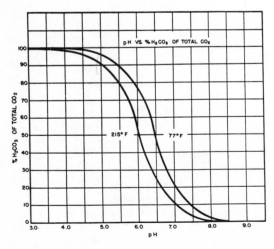

Figure 20-1 · Per Cent CO₂ Available for Removal

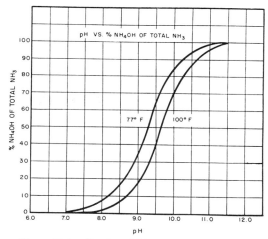

Figure 20-2 · Per Cent NH₃ Available for Removal

illustrates the availability of ammonia for removal by deaeration and indicates it is at the more alkaline pH values that the most efficient removal of ammonia can be obtained.

EQUIPMENT

In accordance with the Standards of the Heat Exchange Institute a standard deaerating unit for operation at atmospheric pressure and above includes:

Deaerating unit.
Condenser.
Integral float or floats.
Piping between deaerating heater and/or water inlet regulating valve and the vent condenser.
Water storage capacity not less than two minutes.
Weir type metering device with recording and/or integrating instrument.

Material of construction is usually cast iron for working pressures up to 20 psi with rolled steel plate for higher operating pressures.

It is standard practice to provide the storage compartment of a deaerating unit with a manhole, gauge glasses and fittings, supporting feet and openings for water connections conforming to the deaerating unit capacity.

APPLICATIONS AND LIMITATIONS

The conventional type open heater is not as efficient in the removal of oxygen and carbon dioxide as is a deaerating unit. With deaerating units, extra factors of safety are incorporated in the design and a vent condenser is employed so that a liberal amount of steam may be vented from the heater without heat waste. Ordinary open heaters are not usually designed to provide as intimate mixture of steam and water and as efficient venting as is required for more complete deaeration.

The Standards of the Heat Exchange Institute define a *deaerating heater* as an equipment for heating water by means of steam, designed so as to insure the removal from the water of the dissolved oxygen in excess of 0.03 cc per liter.

A *deaerator* is defined as an equipment for heating water by means of steam and designed so as to insure the removal from the water of the dissolved oxygen in excess of

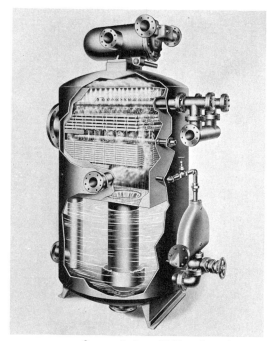

Figure 20-3 · Tray Type Deaerating Heater

Figure 20-4 · Jet Type Deaerating Heater   Courtesy Cochrane Division—Crane Company

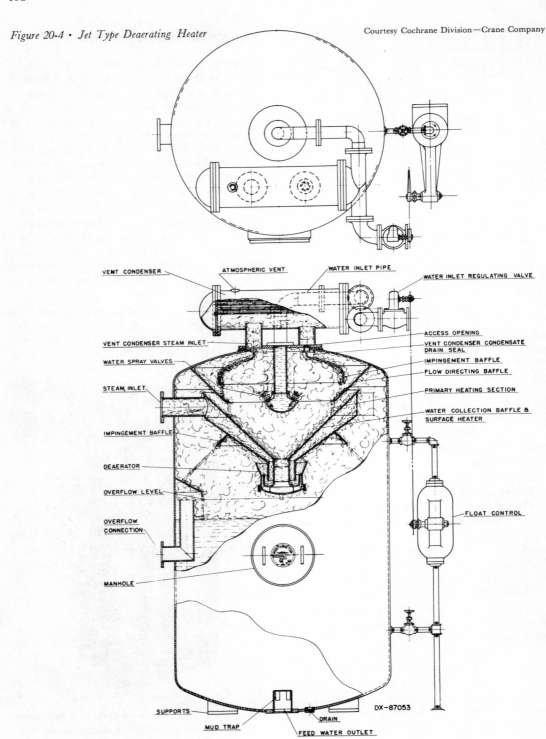

VENT CONDENSER

ATMOSPHERIC VENT

WATER INLET PIPE

WATER INLET REGULATING VALVE

VENT CONDENSER STEAM INLET

ACCESS OPENING

VENT CONDENSER CONDENSATE DRAIN SEAL

WATER SPRAY VALVES

IMPINGEMENT BAFFLE

FLOW DIRECTING BAFFLE

STEAM INLET

PRIMARY HEATING SECTION

WATER COLLECTION BAFFLE & SURFACE HEATER

IMPINGEMENT BAFFLE

DEAERATOR

OVERFLOW LEVEL

OVERFLOW CONNECTION

FLOAT CONTROL

MANHOLE

SUPPORTS

DX-87053

MUD TRAP

DRAIN

FEED WATER OUTLET

0.005 cc per liter.

There are two principal types of deaerating heaters—the tray type and the jet atomizing type. The tray type deaerating heater, as illustrated by Figure 20-3 spreads out the water in thin films by means of baffles or trays so as to insure intimate contact of the steam with the water and to provide thorough agitation. In addition, a relatively large amount of steam is vented from the unit, passing to the vent condenser where the steam is condensed and returned to the heater while the noncondensable gases are discharged to the atmosphere. The flow of steam may be counterflow to the waterflow or parallel flow may be employed. Satisfactory deaeration is obtained with each design.

In the jet atomizing deaerating heater, as illustrated in Figure 20-4, the water is sprayed into a steam atmosphere and thereby heated to within 2 to 3 F of the steam temperature. This operation removes 90 to 95% of the oxygen. The water is then delivered into a high velocity steam jet and the water is broken up, or atomized, by the action of the steam jet securing complete deaeration in this operation. Steam flow is countercurrent to waterflow. As in a tray type heater, the gases are passed through a vent condenser and the condensate returned to the heater.

The atomizing deaerator, while subject to a 0.5 psi pressure drop across the nozzle, is especially suited to handling turbid waters and those of high carbonate hardness which would tend to plug the trays in a tray type unit. The atomizing deaerator is also suited for marine use inasmuch as the deaeration will not be adversely affected by the roll of a ship which would cause uneven water distribution over the trays of a tray type unit.

In general it can be definitely stated that the production of a deaerated water of a "zero" oxygen content is not physically possible although the dissolved oxygen content may be reduced to a value below that which can be detected by chemical tests. Since an absolute "zero" oxygen in a deaerator effluent is not possible, any specification for a

"zero" oxygen feed water must be qualified as to the specific test to be employed in measuring the oxygen content.

CONDENSER DEAERATION. In central station operation, deaeration is sometimes secured by the use of surface condensers with deaerating hot wells. In such installations, a separate deaerating feedwater heater is not employed. The condensate leaving the surface condenser is guaranteed not to exceed 0.03 cc per liter oxygen content. The condenser design is such that the condensate spills into the hot well through a steam atmosphere, with liberated gases removed by the air ejector. Because of the danger of air

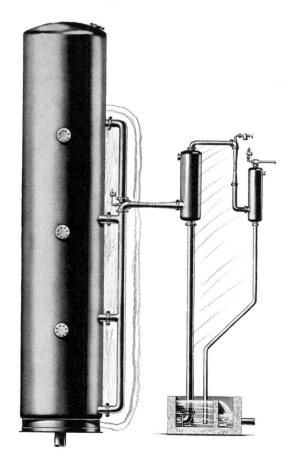

Courtesy Cochrane Division—Crane Company

Figure 20-5 · Vacuum Deaerator

leakage into the system, both on start-up and during normal operation, this system of de-aeration is not considered as good a practice as the use of a deaerating feedwater heater.

VACUUM DEAERATION. It is occasionally desirable to deaerate water at temperatures below the atmospheric boiling point of water. The object is to render non-corrosive the water in long pipe lines, for industrial process uses or in certain power plant cycles. The deaeration of cold water requires that an equipment design be employed which will divide the water into small particles to facilitate gas removal, provide venting of the gases from the unit and maintain a vacuum in the deaerator corresponding to the boiling pressure for the water temperature involved.

The incoming water is introduced usually through a spray pipe and then falls over staggered wooden trays. The object of this arrangement is to reduce the water into thin films and particles, aiding gas release. Water vapor and gases released from the water are removed through the vacuum maintained, either by steam jet eductors or by vacuum pumps.

These units are usually not designed for complete deaeration inasmuch as the size and cost of the apparatus increase sharply for the removal of the last traces of oxygen. Oxygen content has been reduced to 0.25 cc per liter with the maintenance of a 28.5 inch vacuum. Removal of small residual oxygen concentrations can be secured economically with the use of catalyzed sodium sulfite.

REFERENCES

H. A. Grabowski, H. D. Ongman, W. B. Willsey and W. Nelson, "Problems in Deaeration of Boiler Feedwater", *Combustion*, Vol. 26, pp. 43-48 (Mar. 1955)

A. L. Jones, "Deaerating Feedwater Heaters — Spray Type vs Tray Type", *Proceedings*, Engineers Soc. of Western Penna., pp. 41-55 (1949)

A. E. Kittredge, "The Removal of Dissolved Gases from Boiler Feedwater", *Proceedings*, Engineers Soc. of Western Penna., pp. 105-114 (1941)

G. T. Skaperdas and H. H. Uhlig, "Corrosion of Steel by Dissolved Carbon Dioxide and Oxygen", *Ind. and Eng. Chem.*, Vol. 34, pp. 748-754 (1942)

21

Chemical Feed Systems

THE proper introduction of chemicals is a very important phase of the treatment of water and sewage. A predetermined concentration of the chemicals must be established and maintained to secure the desired reactions. Thus, accurate and satisfactory treatment application has required the development of many types of chemical feeders.

Chemical feeding equipment can be divided into two general classifications: dry feeders and wet or solution feeders. Either type may be further classified on the basis of method of feed, that is, constant rate or proportional. Dry feeders are manufactured in two designs, volumetric and gravimetric. Solution feeders may be either of the gravity or pressure type and under some circumstances are used as a "shot feed" rather than constant rate or proportional.

Dry chemical feeders are usually applied in external treatment where large quantities of chemicals must be handled. The application of this equipment is common to sewage and trade waste treatment plants as well as water works and large industrial water conditioning plants. In these installations the demand for chemicals such as alum, lime and soda ash is frequently quite large.

The solution type of feeder provides greater convenience and accuracy when smaller quantities of chemicals are to be employed. Also, some types of chemicals can not be handled satisfactorily with a dry feeder. Solution feeders are used exclusively for the addition of secondary or internal treatment to boiler feedwater systems for the prevention of scale, corrosion and carryover. The primary or external treatment of boiler makeup water, such as softening, also usually employs the solution type of feeder since the quantity of chemicals required is relatively small.

WET OR SOLUTION TYPE FEEDERS

The type of boiler chemical feed system that should be employed in any individual instance depends primarily upon the amount and type of chemicals and for what purpose they are being used; type of boilers; whether the feed-

water passes through stage heaters or economizers, etc. For example, the feed of sodium sulfite for oxygen elimination should be continuous to the storage section of the heater or the suction side of the boiler feed pump for most effective results. A suitable chemical pump or similar device is required for the continuous feed of the sulfite solution. On the other hand, the phosphates normally used for boiler scale prevention may be shot fed through the feedlines to the boilers, provided stage heaters or economizers are not used and the number of boilers is restricted to two or three.

SHOT FEED SYSTEMS. These systems are subdivided into pot type feeders, eductor systems and automatic shot feed arrangements, in which the object of the feeding device is to rapidly introduce a unit charge of chemical treatment. Usually these systems are employed to avoid feedline deposits that might result from continuous chemical feed.

Pot Type Feeders. Probably the oldest method used for the introduction of chemicals to boilers is the pot type shot feeder which consists of a pressure tank and fittings as shown in Figure 21-1. The chemical charge is prepared by dissolving the chemicals in a bucket and then filling the pressure tank with the solution. It is necessary, of course, to drain water from the tank and open the air vent prior to pouring the chemical solution into the tank. The illustration shows the feeder connected across the boiler feed pump. Feedwater from the pressure side of the pump forces the chemical solution into the suction side of the pump. Within a few minutes, the solution will be washed out of the pressure tank and will be injected into the boiler shortly thereafter.

A system of this type is usually satisfactorily applied when the number of "shots" per day does not exceed three or four. If more frequent "shots" are required, it is possible to install a large mixing tank above the pressure tank, similar to the tank shown in Figure 21-2, thus eliminating the inconvenience of dissolving chemicals each time an addition of treatment is necessary.

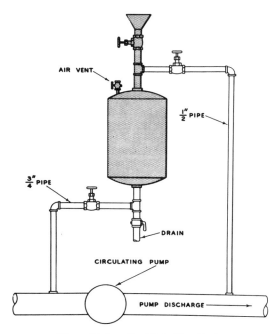

AIR VENT

1/2" PIPE

3/4" PIPE

DRAIN

CIRCULATING PUMP

PUMP DISCHARGE

Figure 21-1 • Pot Type Shot Feeder

Pot type feeders are frequently installed, in the case of small boiler plants, on the suction side of return condensate pumps or in a by-pass arrangement on the raw water line, where raw water pressure forces the chemical charge into the boiler upon by-passing the water through the feeder.

Shot feeders are convenient and economical for injecting precipitating chemicals such as phosphates, caustic soda and soda ash to boilers, thus reducing the hazard of feedline deposits caused by premature reaction of these chemicals with the incrusting salts present in the feedwater. If the chemical treatment is added frequently, the treatment will usually average itself among the boilers on line. However, the number of boilers treated in this manner generally should not exceed three, otherwise it will be extremely difficult to maintain consistent chemical balances in all boilers.

Where a large number of boilers are in use, it is relatively common practice to install a feeder for each boiler, the inlet to the feeder

being taken from the pressure side of the boiler feed pump, the outlet discharging within the boiler drum through a separate chemical feedline. With the difference in pressure between feed pump discharge and boiler drum, this type of installation is quite workable. By this means, the necessary treatment for each boiler can be injected at will. The system, while practical, is rather cumbersome in that an individual charge must be prepared for each boiler.

As is indicated by the foregoing discussion, shot feeders are not suitable for the continuous feed of chemicals such as sodium sulfite (for oxygen removal), caustic soda or soda ash (for pH adjustment) or any of the surface active organic and inorganic chemicals (for prevention of deposits in distribution lines). The shot feed of precipitating chemicals through equipment such as economizers or stage heaters is not recommended, inasmuch as the water flow through units of this nature is sufficiently slow to permit premature reaction of the treatment with the incrusting salts, forming deposits in heat transfer equipment. This condition is also accelerated by the increase in temperature associated with the operation of units of this type.

Water Jet Eductor. A second method of shot feed utilizes a water jet eductor, installed as shown in Figure 21-3. The eductor works on the same principle as an injector, using a stream of water under pressure instead of steam. Water from the pressure side of the boiler feed pump passes through a pressure nozzle within the eductor body, producing a high velocity jet. The high velocity jet creates a vacuum, drawing in the treating solution, and injecting it into the suction side of the boiler feed pump. The eductor of the size ordinarily used has a capacity of approximately 6.5 gpm.

Although the eductor is of advantage in that any amount of treatment may be injected, as compared to the restricted quantity of the "pot" type feeder, the disadvantages of shot feed are inherent in this system as well. In addition, a pressure differential of at least 4 to 1 between the pressure and suction sides

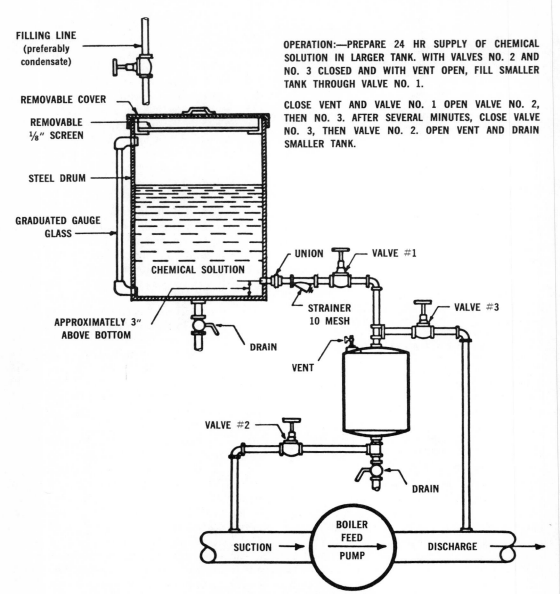

FILLING LINE
(preferably
condensate)

REMOVABLE COVER

REMOVABLE
⅛" SCREEN

STEEL DRUM

GRADUATED GAUGE
GLASS

CHEMICAL SOLUTION

APPROXIMATELY 3"
ABOVE BOTTOM

DRAIN

UNION — VALVE #1

STRAINER
10 MESH

VENT

VALVE #3

VALVE #2

DRAIN

SUCTION →

BOILER
FEED
PUMP

DISCHARGE →

OPERATION:—PREPARE 24 HR SUPPLY OF CHEMICAL
SOLUTION IN LARGER TANK. WITH VALVES NO. 2 AND
NO. 3 CLOSED AND WITH VENT OPEN, FILL SMALLER
TANK THROUGH VALVE NO. 1.

CLOSE VENT AND VALVE NO. 1 OPEN VALVE NO. 2,
THEN NO. 3. AFTER SEVERAL MINUTES, CLOSE VALVE
NO. 3, THEN VALVE NO. 2. OPEN VENT AND DRAIN
SMALLER TANK.

Figure 21-2 · Pot Type Shot Feed System Employing Treatment Storage Tank

of the pump must be available for satisfactory operation of the eductor. Also, it is not possible to introduce the eductor discharge direct to the boiler drum, in the average plant, because of insufficient pressure differential.

Steam injectors are sometimes used in the same manner as eductors. Usually, injectors do not prove suitable for continued use, since efficiency greatly depends upon proper alignment of internal parts and freedom from deposits. Chemical treatment may attack the metal used in construction of the internal parts and contact of high-temperature steam with treating solution frequently causes deposits.

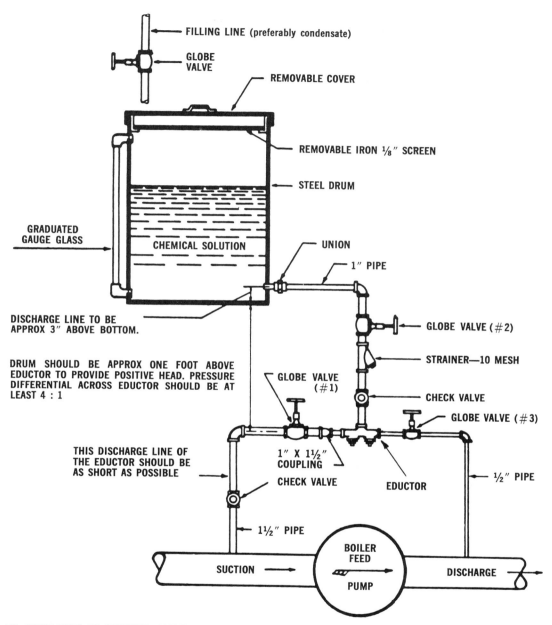

FILLING LINE (preferably condensate)

GLOBE VALVE

REMOVABLE COVER

REMOVABLE IRON 1/8" SCREEN

STEEL DRUM

GRADUATED GAUGE GLASS

CHEMICAL SOLUTION

UNION

1" PIPE

DISCHARGE LINE TO BE APPROX 3" ABOVE BOTTOM.

DRUM SHOULD BE APPROX ONE FOOT ABOVE EDUCTOR TO PROVIDE POSITIVE HEAD. PRESSURE DIFFERENTIAL ACROSS EDUCTOR SHOULD BE AT LEAST 4 : 1

GLOBE VALVE (#2)

STRAINER—10 MESH

GLOBE VALVE (#1)

CHECK VALVE

GLOBE VALVE (#3)

THIS DISCHARGE LINE OF THE EDUCTOR SHOULD BE AS SHORT AS POSSIBLE

1" X 1½" COUPLING

CHECK VALVE

EDUCTOR

½" PIPE

1½" PIPE

BOILER FEED PUMP

SUCTION

DISCHARGE

TO START FLOW OF CHEMICAL SOLUTION FROM DRUM TO BOILER FEEDWATER SUPPLY
FIRST: OPEN VALVE NO. 1
SECOND: OPEN VALVE NO. 2
LAST: OPEN VALVE NO. 3

TO STOP FLOW OF CHEMICAL SOLUTION FROM DRUM TO BOILER FEEDWATER SUPPLY
FIRST: CLOSE VALVE NO. 2
SECOND: CLOSE VALVE NO. 3
LAST: CLOSE VALVE NO. 1

Figure 21-3 • Shot Feed System Employing Eductor

Automatic Shot Feed. A small gear pump, timer controlled, is frequently employed for automatically shot feeding treatment to the suction side of the boiler feed pump. The timer is regulated to operate the pump for a variable length of time up to a maximum of ten minutes, once each hour. Water characteristics would determine whether more frequent operation would be possible and whether a "shot" of as long as ten minutes duration would be permissible.

This automatic shot feed method permits charging of the chemical tank once per day. Due to the frequent additions to the boilers, a larger number of boilers can be treated more efficiently than in the case of the pot and eductor feeders.

Gear pumps of this nature usually operate most efficiently with discharge pressures of 100 psi or less.

CONSTANT-RATE FEEDERS. A constant-rate feeder is one which will continuously add a treating solution at a fixed rate for any given control setting. The rate of feed is adjustable by manual control but is not in proportion to changing water flow. Controlled volume pumps and drip feeders are the most common units falling under this general classification.

Controlled Volume Pump. The most common example of this type of feed employs a motor-driven chemical feed pump to inject a specific quantity of chemicals into a system at a given time.

A chemical feed system of this nature is used most frequently in the continuous feed of sodium sulfite to feedwater heaters or feedlines and for discharge of precipitating chemicals such as phosphates within the boiler drum against boiler pressure. When the rate of flow is relatively constant, a system of this nature can be used to introduce treatment to once-through cooling and water distribution systems. This system is also used quite frequently to insure introduction of the proper amount of chemicals to a circulating cooling water system.

Figure 21-4 illustrates a pump of suitable type, shown as a part of a complete packaged

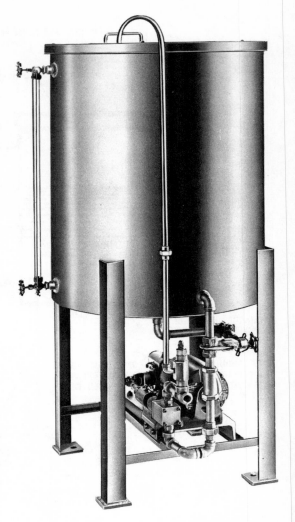

Figure 21-4 · Package Chemical Feeding System

feeding system. Figure 21-5 shows the recommended piping for any applicable positive displacement pump with separate chemical tank.

It is necessary to supply one pump or one pumping cylinder for each point of application of treatment. The capacity of the pumps used is generally in the range of 3.0–10.0 gph per cylinder. It is impossible to throttle the discharge from one cylinder satisfactorily so that several points will receive an equal amount of treatment. The discharge rate is too low to permit satisfactory division of flow,

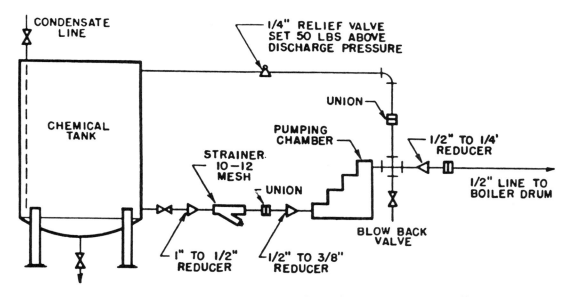

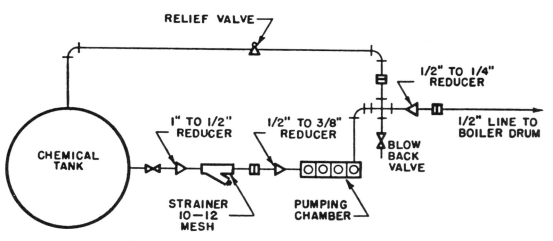

Figure 21-5 · Piping Diagram for Chemical Pump Installation

even when using various types of specially designed flow control valves.

Employment of this system of feed readily approaches proportional feed where the chemicals are injected into a large body of water, such as contained in a boiler or circulating cooling system. It is common practice to maintain certain chemical residuals in the water being treated. In the average plant con-

trol tests are conducted with sufficient frequency, so as to maintain chemical balances in the system within prescribed limits. While there will be periodic variations, this type of system will maintain chemical balances within limits, on the average. Usually, a suitable factor of safety is incorporated when prescribed limits are established by the water consultant. During the course of operation, therefore, sufficient treatment is present at all times and adjustments are readily made if the control tests so indicate. These adjustments involve changing the length of stroke on the pump or changing the strength of chemical solution being pumped.

Drip Feeder. A rather crude type of constant-rate feeder, described as a drip feeder, consists of a suitable tank with bottom take-off and control valve for governing solution discharge. By controlling the flow of treating solution by means of a needle valve, an almost constant volume of solution is added over a given period of time. As the tank empties, the solution head pressure is reduced, thus reducing the rate of feed. Dependent on total solution head pressure above the point of application, this reduction in feeding rate may or may not be of significance. This feeder is a gravity type and finds application frequently in the addition of acid and other chemicals to circulating cooling systems, air washers in air conditioning systems, and addition of sulfite and like chemicals to some point in a feed-water system permitting gravity flow.

While a feeder of this type is readily fabricated, in actual use it requires constant attention to make certain the discharge line is not plugged with some foreign material.

PROPORTIONAL FEED SYSTEMS. There are a considerable number of systems for achieving feed of chemicals proportional to the flow of water, involving a great number of mechanical and electrical principles in their operation. This discussion will be confined to the more commonly used devices and the principles upon which they are based.

Pot Type Proportional Feeds. Probably the simplest type of proportional feeder is the pot type feeder with a special opening in one end to permit charging with chemicals in briquette or lump form. A portion of the water to be treated is allowed to pass through the tank, gradually dissolving the chemicals. Feeders of this type are used for continuous and proportional feed of treating chemicals to boiler feedlines for protection of feedlines, to hot and cold water distribution systems and various types of cooling systems.

The degree of proportionality is questionable at all times, for there is little control over the solution rate of the briquettes or of the chemicals incorporated in them. This system, while it is classified as proportional, is considered only roughly so and cannot be applied where appreciable accuracy of feed is required.

A further adaptation of the pot type proportional feeder is the type commonly used to proportion alum and alkali to water systems for coagulation, or for oil removal in feed-water systems. This system also consists of a pot in which potash alum or ammonium alum, in lump form, or sal soda (crystalline sodium carbonate) are placed. An orifice is installed in the raw water line, and a line from the upstream side of the orifice leads to the under-side of the tank. From the topside of the tank, a discharge line returns to the water line just after the orifice. The resulting pressure differential causes a small stream of water to flow through the pot feeder, gradually dissolving the crystalline chemicals contained therein and introducing the treating chemicals to the water line.

This type of feeder is roughly proportional and can be used in any installation where accurate proportioning is not necessary and where the chemicals to be fed are obtainable in large crystalline or lump form. Dry or powdered materials cannot be used in a feeder of this type.

Positive Displacement Type Pump. Pumps are available that can be driven by a ratchet arm connected to a reciprocating pump or engine. These pumps can also be driven by a belt and pulley for connection to motor driven pumps which operate intermittently or under constant head conditions. By so connecting either type of pump, feed of treatment is accomplished in proportion to the flow of water through the main pump. Such a system is quite suitable for the continuous and proportional feed of chemicals to boiler feedlines, once-through cooling systems, and the like.

Electric-Motor-Driven Pumps. An electric-motor-driven positive-displacement pump can be used to provide proportional feed of chemicals to a well supply under certain conditions. The chemical pump can be controlled by the same electrical circuit that operates the well pump, so that the chemical pump operates only when the well pump is operating. Where several well pumps are used, the system may not be applicable. A system of this nature, when adaptable, provides accurate proportioning of chemicals for treatment of the well water for prevention of corrosion, scale formation and to retain iron in solution.

Meter and Timer Controlled Pumps. This system utilizes a water or steam meter equipped with an electrical contacting device that makes contact after passage of a specific amount of steam or water in the lines. Upon each contact, a stop-cycle timer is started, which operates a complete cycle. The timer is adjusted to permit the operation of the motor-driven pump a pre-set number of minutes for each contact. The time cycle is readily adjustable to provide flexibility. For the application of chemical treatment to boiler water, the control system is applied to steam, feedwater or makeup water meters. The system is usually established so that the pump will operate approximately 75 per cent of the total time, allowing ample capacity for emergencies and unusual demands on the system.

This type of system is not suitable for proportional feed of treatment to once-through systems unless the treatment is injected ahead of a large storage tank where adequate mixing can be accomplished. Also, for proportioning phosphates and other treatment chemicals direct to the boiler drums, it is necessary to supply a meter, timer, and pump for each discharge point; this makes such an installation rather expensive. If makeup water characteristics are changeable or if there is a wide variation in amounts of return condensate, boiler water balances may prove to be quite variable, even though treatment is added proportionally.

Another variation of this type of system permits the motor-driven pump to operate continuously. A meter controls the timer as before, but in this instance the timer controls the functioning of a three-way valve. Depend-

ing upon the time cycle, the three-way valve permits chemical solution or condensate to flow to the suction of the chemical pump.

It is intended that this system prevent plugging of the chemical feedlines by flushing periodically with condensate. However, considerable maintenance is usually involved with operation of three-way valves. If the chemical solution is made up originally with condensate and the solubility of the chemicals used is not exceeded, no difficulties will be experienced with plugging of chemical feedlines. In addition, the chemical feedline must be properly located within the boiler drum, in order to further prevent the possibility of plugging of the line.

Thymotrol. An electronic system employing the Thymotrol, as developed by the General Electric Co., has been adapted to the regulation of positive-displacement type pumps. Alternating current available at the plant is converted to direct current, full wave rectification being employed. A potentiometer is mounted in the water meter and governs the speed of the direct-current motor operating the pump. The setting of the potentiometer is immediately changed with any change in rate of water flow. Since the speed of a pump is constant for any potentiometer setting, regardless of load, and since the quantity of liquid pumped by any positive-displacement pump is proportional to the speed of the pump, accurate proportioning of chemical feed to the water flow is achieved with immediate compensation for changes in rate of flow.

This system has been applied in a number of instances requiring considerable accuracy, such as proportioning of lime and soda ash in the lime and soda ash softening process. The system can be applied quite readily in the treatment of large quantities of water, such as once-through cooling supplies that vary in flow, and where a suitable mixing tank or reservoir is not available. Typical examples of application of Thymotrol proportioning consist of the addition of acids or alkalies in the adjustment of the pH of a treated water, and the addition of stabilizing agents for prevention of scale in heat exchange units and similar equipment.

Pneumatic Proportioning Control. Standard meters are available which transmit controlling air signals to a stroke adjusting mechanism installed as part of a constant speed positive displacement pump. The adjustable stroke can be linked to a flow meter or other unit, such as a pH controller-recorder. When flows in the line are quite variable and it is desired to control pH, a flow meter as well as a pH controller are used to provide a signal to the pump stroke mechanism. Both variables are transmitted to a ratio controller which then sends an air signal adjusting the stroke in relation to both flow rate and pH. Figure 21-6 shows such a controlled pump, responding to two variables.

Hydraulic Type Feeders. Figure 21-7 illustrates an economical and effective feed system frequently utilized for chlorination and ammoniation of water supplies, pH adjustment, sterilization of sewage treatment plant effluent and similar applications. The system may be used for the proportional feed of chemicals to water lines for any purpose if the material used in constructing the reagent head of the pump is selected accordingly.

Most of the standard meters may be adapted as the control medium. The meter does not supply the power to operate the pump but simply controls the inflow of pressure water to the hydraulic cylinder. The design of the pump is such as to permit injection of treating solution into the pressure line. The pump is normally actuated by the pressure of the fluid present in the main line but can be separately actuated by air, steam, oil or water.

The hydraulic system is usually applicable to lines operating at pressures of 100 psi or less. The addition of the pump control mechanism does not affect the meter accuracy to any appreciable degree.

Decanting Type Feeders. This type of chemical feed system involves the use of a constant-diameter tank fabricated of material suitable for the chemicals to be handled. The tank will be flat-bottomed for handling solutions or will be equipped with a rounded bottom and motor-driven agitator for handling slurries.

The chemical solution is drawn off either at a constant rate, or proportionately, by means of a swing pipe lowered by a cable and drum arrangement, which in turn is controlled by a small fractional-horsepower motor geared to very low speed. Figure 21-8 shows a feed system of this type. This particular type is especially applicable for the feed of corrosive solutions such as acids, alum and ferric salts. By the use of rubber tubing, the contact of the draw-off system with the corrosive liquid is limited to the overflow box, which is lowered by the control device.

When operating as a constant-rate feeder, the decanting arm is lowered at a constant rate by the control mechanism. This rate is manually adjustable. If proportional feed is desired, a suitable water meter, equipped with an electrical contactor, which makes contact upon passage of a specific quantity of water, is used to control the operation of the lowering motor. A predetermined amount of solution is thereby drawn off for each contact made by the water meter.

The discharge from the decanting arm can be allowed to gravitate to the point of treatment application. Frequently, however, the discharge is introduced to a pump suction box. Several pumping arrangements exist, depending upon the service requirements. In the case of lime and soda ash proportioning, for example, a centrifugal pump is used which operates continuously, pumping the decanted solution to the point of discharge with addition of dilution water, as necessary, controlled by a float in the suction box.

A proportional-feed system of this type is sometimes used for adding phosphate and other treating chemicals to boilers, boiler feedlines or other water lines, using an intermittently-operated piston type pump, controlled by a float switch in the suction box. In some cases, a high-capacity chemical pump is employed, discharging to a common header equipped with flow control valves to permit division of flow to a number of discharge points while using only one pump.

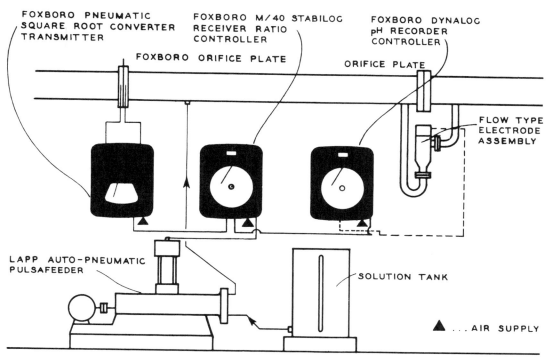

FOXBORO PNEUMATIC
SQUARE ROOT CONVERTER
TRANSMITTER

FOXBORO M/40 STABILOG
RECEIVER RATIO
CONTROLLER

FOXBORO DYNALOG
pH RECORDER
CONTROLLER

FOXBORO ORIFICE PLATE

ORIFICE PLATE

FLOW TYPE
ELECTRODE
ASSEMBLY

LAPP AUTO-PNEUMATIC
PULSAFEEDER

SOLUTION TANK

▲ ... AIR SUPPLY

Courtesy The Foxboro Company

Figure 21-6 · Automatic pH Control with Wide Flow Variations

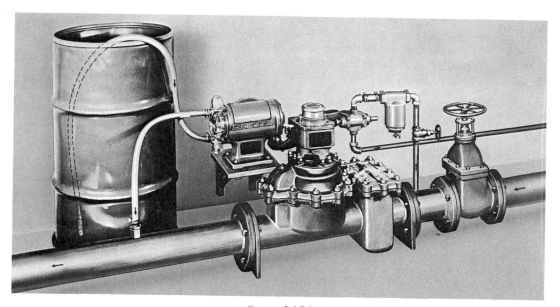

Courtesy B-I-F Industries, a Division of The New York Air Brake Company

Figure 21-7 · Meter-Controlled Hydraulic Type Proportional Feeder

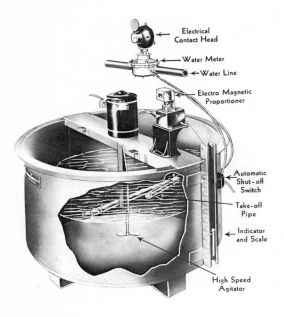

Figure 21-8 · Decanting Type Proportional Feeder

The decanting type feeder is used most frequently as a proportioning feeder for line, soda ash, coagulants, acids and other chemicals applied in the external conditioning of water. A definite advantage is the fact that only one meter and contactor is needed to control the operation of several decanting feed mechanisms. It is not generally applied for addition of phosphates and other chemicals to the boiler systems due primarily to availability of other equipment which is more convenient and less expensive. Also, discharge of phosphates to feedlines is undesirable and proportioning feed of treatment to more than one boiler with one pump and one control meter again introduces the objections outlined in the discussion of systems operating in an essentially similar manner.

Double-Orifice Type Feeders. The double-orifice type feeder is a solution feeder which normally proportions with reasonable per cent accuracy. The principle of operation involves passage of water through a primary orifice, creating a pressure differential over the orifice and a flow in the lines connected to the pressure taps. A secondary orifice in the pressure lines shunts a portion of the flowing water into the top of a pressure-tight chemical feed tank, in which the chemical solution occupies the complete volume. As flowing water enters the top of the pressure solution tank, an equal quantity of chemical solution is released from the tank at a bottom connection, entering the low pressure tap on the downstream side of the secondary orifice. The equipment is so designed that the amount of chemical solution injected is reasonably proportional to flow.

When recharging the feeder, chemicals are dissolved in an upper tank and then drained into the pressure solution tank. The density of the chemical solution is sufficient to support a special float installed in a gage glass. The float will normally sink in water. Since a definite line of demarcation exists between the water and chemical solution at all times, the float will show the amount of chemical solution present.

Final control over the chemical solution is obtained by adjusting a needle valve governing the water flow into the pressure solution tank. The feeder usually must be recharged at least once daily.

Double-orifice type feeders are frequently used for the application of various chemicals to once-through cooling water and domestic water systems to condition these waters for the prevention of scale and corrosion. This type of feeder is also employed for proportioning of alum and soda ash ahead of coagulation and oil removal systems.

Use of these feeders is generally restricted in boiler feed systems by pressure limitations. The feeder manufactured by the average supplier is usually built to operate at pressures not greater than 100 psi. Also, the pressure drop over the primary orifice is sufficient to cause steam binding of the boiler feed pumps if a sufficient static head does not exist between the feedwater heater and the suction of the feed pumps. Application of these feeders for continuous feed of phosphates and other precipitating chemicals to boiler feedlines is not desirable because of the danger of feedline deposits.

Fig. 21-9—Methods of Feeding for Common Treatment Chemicals

CHEMICAL	PROCESS USE	TYPE FEEDERS	POINTS OF APPLICATION
Alum	Coagulation Color removal	Dry Pot Type proportioning Double Orifice Decanting Pumps	Coagulation and sedimentation systems, prior to pressure filters for removal of suspended matter and oil.
Sodium Aluminate	Coagulation	Dry Decanting Pumps Shot Feeders	Usually added with soda ash to softeners. Used to some extent for internal boiler water treatment.
Coagulant Aids	Coagulation	Pumps	As primary coagulants, to chemical mixing section. As coagulant aid, to flume after primary chemical mixing or to flocculation zone of clarifier.
Ferric Salts	Coagulation Color removal Oil removal	Dry Decanting Double Orifice Pumps	Prior to coagulation and filtration systems.
Lime (Hydrated)	pH adjustment Softening	Dry Decanting Special pumps (slurry)	Prior to coagulation systems; to softeners; to treated water lines for adjustment of pH.
Soda Ash (Crystalline)	pH adjustment	Pot Type proportioning	Prior to pressure filters.
Soda Ash (Anhydrous)	pH and alkalinity adjustment Softening	All types of wet and dry feeders	To domestic systems, feedlines, softeners, coagulation and filtration systems; boilers.
Caustic Soda	pH adjustment Alkalinity adjustment Softening	All types of solution feeders	To softeners; oil removal systems; domestic water systems; boilers.
Acid Feed (H_2SO_4) (Sulfuric Acid) (H_3PO_4) (Phosphoric Acid) ($NaHSO_4$)	pH adjustment Reduction of alkalinity	Decanting Pumps	Treated water lines, prior to degassifiers or deaerating heaters; H_3PO_4 to phosphate softeners (for both softening and alkalinity reduction); tower sump or basin.
Surface Active Phosphates	Prevent calcium carbonate deposits Eliminate "red water"	All types of proportional solution feeders	Treated water lines.
Orthophosphates (Monosodium Phosphate) (Disodium Phosphate) (Trisodium Phosphate)	Prevent scale in boilers	Pumps Shot feeders	Added continuously to boiler drums; shot fed to drums or boiler feedline.
Chelating Agents	Prevent scale in boilers and economizers	Pumps	Added continuously to feedline, on pressure side of feed pumps.
Sodium Sulfite	Prevent corrosion due to oxygen in boilers, feedlines, economizers	All types continuous solution feeders	Storage section of deaerating heater; suction or pressure side of boiler feed pumps.
Sodium Nitrate	Inhibition of embrittlement	All types of solution feeders	Any point in boiler feedlines or direct to boilers.

CHEMICAL	PROCESS USE	TYPE FEEDERS	POINTS OF APPLICATION
Sodium and Potassium Chromates	Corrosion inhibitor	All types of solution feeders	To brine systems and various circulating cooling and hot water systems.
Reactive Colloids (Sodium Mannuronate) Protective Colloids (Starches) (Tannins) (Lignins)	Coagulation Particle absorption and adsorption	All types of solution feeders	To boiler feedlines; circulating cooling systems.
Amines and Related Organic Compounds	Prevention of return line corrosion	Shot Feeders Pumps	Application depends upon material used. Some materials may be added to boilers and volatilize with steam; others are added to steam line direct, requiring pumps.

DRY-TYPE FEEDERS

Dry-type feeders are generally classified as volumetric type and gravimetric type; and they are usually warranted in the larger-size plants where the quantities of chemicals that must be added to a system exceed approximately 10 lb. per hr.

VOLUMETRIC FEEDERS. In one type of volumetric feeder, the chemical is discharged from a hopper onto a circular table, which revolves at a slow and constant rate of speed. One or more multi-section feed knives extend on the table, deflecting an amount of chemical dependent upon the position of the knives. The feeder can be calibrated for use with any chemical of relatively uniform composition and density. Once calibrated, the number of pounds of chemical that will be delivered per unit of time, for the various settings of the feed knives on the rotating table, will be constant.

Chemicals removed from the rotating table are dissolved or suspended in slurry form by introduction to a dissolving pot agitated by a vortex of dissolving water or by a small motor-driven agitator.

Still another type of volumetric feeder employs an oscillating plate below the chemical hopper. The length of stroke of the plate and depth of chemical on the plate are both adjustable in order to obtain varying rates of discharge.

Accuracy of any volumetric type feeder is dependent to a large extent on the consistency of the chemical being fed. If the density or weight of the chemicals per cubic foot is subject to any great variation, then this same variation will appear in the rate of chemical feed. Certain chemicals tend to "arch" or "hang" in the feed hopper, requiring agitators or vibrators to be installed in the hoppers. Care must then be exercised to prevent packing of the chemical, for this would directly affect the accuracy of proportioning. The normal accuracy is within 5 per cent.

GRAVIMETRIC FEEDERS. Gravimetric feeders measure the chemical to be fed by weight, resulting in accuracy of proportioning within 1 to 2 per cent. A typical gravimetric feeder is shown in Figure 21-10. The chemical is fed to a traveling belt, the amount of chemical admitted being controlled by a gate, which in turn is regulated by the total weight of the belt assembly and chemical. A constant weight of chemicals is maintained on the belt and variation in rate of feed to the treater is obtained by varying the speed of the belt.

There are several variations of this principle, but essentially gravimetric feeders are scales, balanced in such a manner as to assure the delivery of the desired weight of chemicals to the system. The chemicals discharged by a gravimetric feeder are placed in solution or suspension form, in the same manner as for a volumetric feeder.

Gravimetric feeders are considerably more

expensive than volumetric types, hence are applied only to large systems where the additional accuracy is required or when chemicals are used whose variable density prevents use of volumetric feeders.

AUTOMATED FEEDING EQUIPMENT

Many installations are now equipped with some type of device which automatically controls the operation of feeding equipment.

CONTINUOUS MONITORING. The first step in providing complete and automatic control of the treatment program is the installation of continuous indicating and/or recording analyzers. These analyzers are being applied not only in monitoring plant influents and effluents, but also in the monitoring of external and internal water treating systems. Invaluable assistance can be gained by the judicious selection and installation of a continuous analyzer to monitor critical variables in a water system.

Analyzers commonly use a sampling technique whereby a discrete sample of the water is obtained, reagents are added in proportion to the sample and sufficient time is allowed for reactions. The sample-reagent solution is then discharged into a measuring cell where a photocell determines the concentration of a specific parameter. The measurement is indicated and/or recorded, and serves as the basis for manual adjustments or for remote-automatic regulation.

Continuous monitoring provides an extra measure of safety by providing around-the-clock surveillance of the system. Closer regulation of treatment parameters is gained, thereby ensuring proper system protection with minimum expenditure for treatment chemicals.

Boiler Systems. Continuous monitoring and control devices are available for the measurement of constituents, such as silica (control of demineralizer regeneration), hardness (softener regeneration), phosphate (internal treatment control) and sulfite (oxygen scavenger control). These parameters are continuously monitored, and serve as the basis for control of the specific unit or treatment

addition which the analysis represents.

Conductivity, which may be related to the dissolved solids content of a solution, is also a widely used measurement. This determination may be applied for continuous monitoring of the total dissolved solids concentration of boiler water or for automatic control of continuous blowdown. Specific conductance can serve also as the basis for monitoring condensate, and to actuate an alarm or to divert the condensate stream when impurities are present.

Recirculating Cooling Tower Systems. The class of analyzers noted in the case of boiler systems can be applied for the monitoring and control of treatment programs for cooling water systems. The differences are the range of measurement and the parameters most critical to cooling systems (e.g. chromate level, pH and conductivity).

Measuring instruments for pH and conductivity utilize electrodes which are specific for the parameters desired. In the area of chromate, an electrode has been perfected which does not require the addition of any reagent to provide the measurement. This analyzer determines the chromate level on the basis of the natural color imparted to the water by chromate treatment.

It appears that more investigation has taken place in the area of providing a completely automatic system for the control of cooling tower treating programs than in any other treatment area. Progress is evidenced by the development of a completely integrated system of critical parameter measurement and control, as shown by Figure 21-11.

CONTROL MODE. Most treatment control systems function properly using the simple on-off control mode. The method is suitable due to the large capacity of the water system when compared to the relatively small quantity of chemical addition or blowdown required by the treatment program. In fact, the sampling system used to provide a representative sample of the water being controlled is often the most distorting part of the whole analysis and control system.

Not all treatment systems can be controlled

with the on-off mode. There are occasions, such as feed of sulfite to a deaerator and treatment to a once-through cooling system, where proportional control is a requisite. However, on-off control can be applied quite successfully on most systems.

SAMPLING. The sample to the analyzer must be representative of the water in the system under control. Care and precaution must be taken in the selection of the sampling point and in sample preparation prior to introduction into the analyzer or to the electrode. This sample preparation may involve filtering of the sample, pressure and temperature reduction and, in some cases, flow control.

The manufacturer of the analyzer often provides the sampling system. Regardless of the supplier, every recommendation by the manufacturer of the control system regarding sampling should be followed to ensure accurate and reliable measurement and control.

REFERENCES

R. P. Lowe, "Chemical Feed Systems," *Proceedings*, Engineers Soc. of Western Penna., pp. 155-170 (1949)
J. H. Richards, "Chemical Feed Systems in Modern Water Treatment," *Power Generation*, Vol. 52, pp. 62, 63, 122-125 (Aug. 1948) and pp. 61-63, 118, 120, 124, 126 (Sept. 1948)
R. T. Sheen, "Liquid Chemical Feed Systems," Presented at 8th Ann. Water Conf., Engineers Soc. of Western Penna., (1947)

Figure 21-11 · Modular Automation System

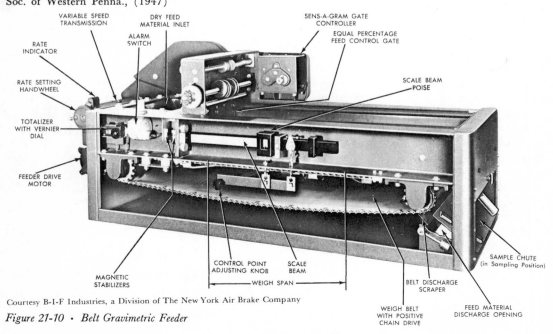

Courtesy B-I-F Industries, a Division of The New York Air Brake Company

Figure 21-10 · Belt Gravimetric Feeder

22

Boiler Scale Control

THE formation of scale and sludge deposits on boiler heating surfaces is the most serious water problem encountered in steam generation. The object of the majority of the external treatment processes is to remove from the boiler feedwater those objectionable substances which will contribute to scale or deposit formations in the boiler.

Subsidence, coagulation and filtration may be employed to remove suspended solids from the boiler feedwater and so to prevent the incorporation of mud, silt, etc., in boiler deposits. Lime-soda softening, zeolite softening and hot phosphate softening are used to remove from the boiler feedwater the incrusting salts of calcium and magnesium. Iron removal and silica removal processes have as their object the prevention of boiler scale difficulties through the removal of iron and silica, both of which may cause heat insulating deposits on the boiler surfaces.

However, no system of external softening, regardless of a high degree of efficiency, is in itself adequate protection against boiler scale without the use of supplementary internal chemical treatment of the boiler water. In all cases, there will remain some small amount of incrusting solids present in the boiler feedwater. In addition, it is also possible at time of softener regeneration, for appreciable hardness to enter the boiler feedwater system. Incomplete rinsing of a zeolite bed also will introduce to the boiler feedwater considerable quantities of scale-forming calcium and magnesium chlorides. Figure 22-1 illustrates the more common external treatment methods that are employed and the range of residual hardness that usually results.

MECHANISM OF SCALE FORMATION

The primary cause of scale formation is the fact that the solubilities of the scale-forming salts decrease with increase in temperature. Consequently, the higher the temperature (and pressure) of boiler operation, the more insoluble the incrusting salts become. No method of external chemical treatment operates at a temperature as high as that of the boiler water. Consequently, when the feedwater is elevated to boiler water temperature and concentrations, the solubility of the scale-forming salts is exceeded and they crystallize from solution as scale on the boiler heating surfaces.

The actual mechanism of scale deposition can be viewed as taking place in two distinct operations. First, the precipitation from solution of a salt such as calcium carbonate $(CaCO_3)$ and the sedimentation of this already formed precipitate on the boiler heating surfaces where it bakes in place as scale. Scale formation due to this mechanism undoubtedly does take place particularly in firetube boilers and where the boiler feedwater is high in hardness content. However, it can be stated that in general only a minor portion of scale formation develops in this manner.

The chief mechanism of scale formation is due to crystallization of scale-forming salts from a solution locally supersaturated. The thin viscous film of boiler water immediately adjacent to the heating surface tends to become more concentrated than the main body of boiler water. Consequently, the solubility of the scale-forming salts is first exceeded in this thin film on the heating surface rather than in the main body of the boiler water. Crystallization of scale results directly on the heating surface even when the solubility of the scale-forming salts has not been exceeded in the boiler water proper.

Softening Process	Residual Hardness, ppm
Cold Lime-Soda	30-50
Hot Lime-Soda	15-25
Hot Lime-Zeolite	0-2
Zeolite	0-2
Sodium-Hydrogen Zeolite	0-2
Demineralizers	0-0.5

Figure 22-1 • Common External Processes of Boiler Feedwater Preparation

EFFECT OF BOILER SCALE

Boiler scale creates a problem in boiler operation because the different types of scale formed all possess a low degree of heat conductivity. The presence of scale is therefore equivalent to spreading a thin film of insulation across the path of heat travel from the furnace gases to the boiler water. The presence of this heat insulating material will retard heat transfer and cause a loss in boiler efficiency. Stack gas temperatures may increase as the boiler absorbs less heat from the furnace gases.

There have been figures published showing large losses in boiler efficiency resulting from even thin films of scale on the boiler surfaces. Some of the early estimates of efficiency loss were erroneously high. The mechanical structure of the scale, its porosity, and thickness as well as the design and method of operation of the boiler are all factors influencing the amount of heat lost. However, it has been shown that the rate of heat transmission may be reduced as much as 10-12% by the presence of scale. While an equivalent loss in heat utilization does not result, it is possible for a scale of approximately $\frac{1}{8}''$ thickness to cause an over-all loss in boiler efficiency in the neighborhood of 2.0-3.0%. During the course of a year an increase of 2.0-3.0% in fuel consumption will amount to an appreciable monetary loss.

Even more important than the effect of scale in causing heat loss, however, is the effect of scale in causing overheating of the boiler metal and consequent tube failures. Costly repairs and boiler outage are the result of such a condition. In modern boilers with high rates of heat transfer, the presence of even extremely thin deposits of scale will cause a serious elevation in the temperature of tube metal. The scale coating retards the flow of heat from the furnace gases into the boiler water. This heat resistance results in a rapid rise in metal temperature to the point at which failure results.

The action which takes place in the blistering of a tube because of scale formation is

graphically illustrated by Figure 22-2. For simplification purposes no temperature drops through gas or water films have been shown. Section A shows a cross-section of the tube metal with a completely scale-free heating surface. There is a temperature drop across the tube metal from the outside metal temperature T_2 to the temperature of the boiler water. Section B illustrates this same tube after the development of a heat insulating scale layer. In addition to the temperature drop from T_2 to T_1, there would be an additional temperature drop through the scale layer from T_1 to T_0. This condition would, of course, result in a lower boiler water temperature T_0. However, boiler water temperature is fixed by the operating pressure and operating conditions require that the same boiler water temperature T_1 be maintained as before the development of the layer of scale.

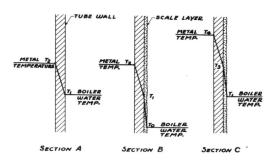

Figure 22-2 • Effect of Scale on Boiler Heating Surfaces

Section C illustrates the actual condition that develops. Starting at the base boiler water temperature of T_1, the temperature increase through the scale layer is represented by the line from T_1 to T_3. The further temperature increase through the tube wall is represented by the line from T_3 to T_4, the outside metal temperature. It can be noted that the outside metal temperature T_4 is now considerably higher than the temperature T_2 which was the outside metal temperature prior to the formation of scale on the tube surfaces.

If continued scale deposition takes place,

increasing the thickness of the heat insulating deposits, further increases will take place in the tube metal temperature until the safe maximum temperature of the tube metal is exceeded. Usually this maximum temperature is taken as 900 F.

With higher boiler pressures and attendant higher boiler water temperatures, there is less temperature difference between the boiler water temperature and the failing temperature of the metal. Consequently, tube failures can result at higher boiler water pressures with scale of considerably less thickness than would cause failures at lower pressures. This condition explains the need for the extremely close control of boiler water conditions in high pressure boiler operation.

MUD, SILT, ETC.

The use of turbid river waters as makeup to boiler systems is undesirable from several standpoints, among which is the formation of boiler scale and sludge deposits. Settling of mud at points of low flow may restrict boiler water recirculation and cause water starvation of water wall tubes. Baking of mud in place on tubes and sheets will result in their overheating and failure. Mud and silt may be incorporated in scale deposits, adding to their volume and heat insulating effect.

The removal of such suspended solids is necessary prior to the use of the water for boiler feedwater purposes. This removal is accomplished by the processes of subsidence, coagulation and filtration. No internal chemical treatment of the boiler water is designed to overcome difficulties due to suspended solids in the makeup water. The removal of these impurities by external treatment processes is required.

CALCIUM AND MAGNESIUM SALTS

The salts of calcium and magnesium are the most common source of difficulty with boiler scale. The use of external treatment processes such as lime-soda, zeolite and hot phosphate softening have as their object the re-

duction in calcium and magnesium content of the boiler feedwater. Internal chemical treatment is used to prevent deposit and scale formation from the residual hardness concentrations remaining in the feedwater, and also to maintain clean boiler heating surfaces in those cases where no external softening is employed and where all chemical treatment for scale prevention must be applied directly to the boiler itself.

Perhaps one of the most common sources of scale is the breakdown of calcium bicarbonate to form calcium carbonate under the influence of heat. This action is illustrated by the following equation:

$$Ca(HCO_3)_2 + \triangle = CaCO_3 +$$
$$\underset{\text{bicarbonate}}{\overset{\text{calcium}}{}} + \text{heat} = \underset{\text{carbonate}}{\overset{\text{calcium}}{}} +$$

$$H_2O + CO_2$$
$$\text{water} + \underset{\text{dioxide}}{\overset{\text{carbon}}{}}$$

The precipitation from solution of calcium carbonate to form boiler scale readily takes place where the boiler feedwater contains any appreciable quantity of calcium bicarbonate. The action illustrated above may also be the cause for the formation of feedline and economizer deposits and deposits on open heater trays.

Calcium sulfate is a more soluble salt than calcium carbonate and is generally found only in boilers that have not received any internal chemical treatment or have received only an inadequate quantity of internal treatment. The presence of calcium sulfate in a boiler scale can usually be taken as definite evidence that internal chemical treatment has been used only to an inadequate extent, possibly due to a flaw in the system of chemical control. All methods of internal chemical treatment rely on precipitating the calcium salts in some form other than calcium sulfate.

Figure 22-3 illustrates the solubility of calcium sulfate together with similar data for calcium carbonate. The curves illustrated show the solubility of the pure materials in distilled water solution. The presence of other salts in the solution will affect the solubilities shown and consequently it is

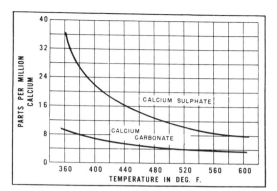

Figure 22-3 • Calcium Solubility, for Calcium Sulfate and Calcium Carbonate

necessary to employ certain factors of safety in interpreting these data. For example, the usual boiler water will contain a variety of salts in solution, tending to alter the theoretical solubilities illustrated. Specifically, in the case of calcium sulfate, an increase in the quantity of sodium sulfate present will lower the calcium sulfate solubility.

Because of the high solubility of calcium sulfate as shown in Figure 22-3 it is relatively simple to introduce chemical treatment to the boiler water and, with proper control, to avoid deposition of calcium sulfate scale.

The use of sodium carbonate (soda ash) was one of the first materials employed to prevent calcium sulfate scale formation. As can be seen from Figure 22-3 calcium carbonate is considerably more insoluble than calcium sulfate and accordingly will be preferentially precipitated. However, calcium carbonate in itself can form a hard adherent deposit and is frequently found as a constituent of boiler scale.

Calcium phosphate and calcium silicate are frequently deposited as boiler scale. Calcium silicate may be formed either from the combination of the calcium and silicate ions naturally present in the boiler feedwater or as a result of the misguided use of sodium silicate as internal chemical treatment. Calcium phosphate, on the other hand, is invariably the result of treatment of the boiler water by the use of the various phosphate salts commonly employed for this purpose.

Magnesium salts present in the boiler feedwater are usually more easily prevented from forming scale than are the calcium salts. Normally, the magnesium salts found incorporated in boiler scale are magnesium hydroxide, magnesium silicate or magnesium phosphate. The latter salt, magnesium phosphate, tends to form a very sticky deposit, not very hard in nature, but requiring turbining for its removal.

SILICA

As mentioned previously, calcium silicate deposits may prove quite troublesome in boiler operation. However, another source of concern is the tendency for silica to form scales of a complex nature, which may or may not include calcium and magnesium in their structure. Particularly in combination with aluminum, silica tends to form complex scales which have been identified by X-ray diffraction methods. Formation of such complex deposits usually occurs in boilers operating at the higher pressures and proper treatment of the boiler water requires the maintenance of both silica and aluminum concentrations at a minimum. Under such operating conditions, the prevention of complex silica scales is primarily a problem for external treatment. The maintenance of high phosphate and alkalinity concentrations in the boiler water is an aid in control of the problem, but only limited silica concentrations can be controlled. Blowdown can be used to reduce silica concentrations to tolerable levels.

The concern for silica is not always because silica concentrations are too high. In some cases, silica can be too low. This situation occurs primarily with waters that contain high magnesium concentrations and low silica values. In these special cases, magnesium will tend to precipitate as magnesium phosphate which produces a sticky sludge. Precipitation in this form is aggravated when the feedwater enters the boiler in a region of low alkalinity and poor circulation. Under these conditions, increasing the silica content of the feedwater to avoid magnesium phosphate precipitation will prove helpful. However, this practice must be applied within the normal silica tolerances established for the boiler operating pressure. Other factors that must be considered are increased boiler water alkalinity, the use of special organic sludge conditioning agents and better mixing of the feedwater within the boiler.

IRON AND COPPER OXIDES

Deposits of iron oxide, metallic copper and copper oxide are frequently found in boilers operating with very pure feedwater. In such plants, the makeup water requirements may be only 1–2% with evaporators or demineralizers supplying the makeup water needs. Deposits in drums and tubes may consist essentially of iron oxide, copper oxide and metallic copper. The usual sludge forming calcium and magnesium salts may amount to less than 5% of the boiler deposit.

The usual source of such deposits lies in corrosion external to the boiler. Corrosion of iron and steel can result in the solution of iron by the condensate or feedwater, with its subsequent precipitation under the higher temperature and alkalinity conditions of the boiler water. The usual causes of such corrosive action are dissolved oxygen and carbon dioxide. The prevention of the iron oxide deposit in the boilers requires elimination of the corrosive effect of these gases. The source of dissolved oxygen should be determined and removed through the use of mechanical and/or chemical deaeration. If evaporators are employed, carbon dioxide should be reduced to a minimum by suitable pretreatment or by changing the point to which evaporator distillate is discharged. The use of ammonia, neutralizing amines and filming amines aid in the control of this problem.

Iron dissolved in the condensate and thus introduced into the boiler can cause additional difficulties besides the deposition of iron oxide. Combination of iron with silica present in the boiler water can result in the formation of iron silicate boiler scales. The use of filming amines to control condensate

line corrosion has eliminated this problem in several instances.

Copper and copper bearing metals constitute a large proportion of the metallic surfaces exposed in a modern power station. Solution of copper from surface condensers, pump impellers, stage heaters and evaporators takes place as a result of corrosive action. Dissolved oxygen, ammonia and carbon dioxide exert the major influences in the corrosion of copper. Ammonia forms a soluble complex cupric ammonium ion which is broken down on heating and can result in deposition of copper oxide in the boiler. Where conditions are favorable to the deposition of metallic copper on the boiler metal, it is possible for localized pitting to take place beneath the deposit.

While internal corrective measures such as the use of organic sludge conditioning agents may be applied to minimize the problem of iron oxide and copper oxide deposits, the basic solution to the problem lies in correcting the corrosive condition.

In some cases, the source of iron oxide boiler deposits is not the result of corrosion external to the boiler. Corrosive attack on the boiler metal by high caustic concentrations or dissolved oxygen may be the cause of this condition.

OIL

The presence of oil in boiler feedwater is particularly undesirable. One of the most obvious difficulties resulting from oil contamination is carryover of solids with the steam. However, oil may also contribute greatly to the formation of heat insulating scale deposits and is frequently the cause of blistered tubes. Oil may be carbonized to form a hard asphaltic scale or may be absorbed by porous scale already present. Adherence of such deposits to the heat transfer surface may cause local overheating and failure of the metal.

Oil should always be externally removed from the boiler feedwater. There is no method of internal chemical treatment specifically adaptable to overcoming the hazards presented by oil contamination of the boiler water. While certain methods of internal treatment may slightly aggravate or slightly minimize the problem caused by oil, there is no method of internal treatment which can be relied upon to cope with any appreciable oil contamination. Since the extent of the difficulties caused by oil are more or less unpredictable, external removal of oil from the boiler feedwater is the only safe policy.

IDENTIFICATION OF SCALE DEPOSITS

In addition to the microscope and gravimetric chemical analyses, a useful tool in identifying boiler scale deposits is the X-ray diffraction method. Any material possessing a crystalline structure will yield a distinctive X-ray pattern which will always be the same and which can be compared with the pattern of standard materials on file. It is thus possible to identify complex chemical compounds and their individual crystalline struc-

Fig. 22-4
Crystalline Scale Constituents, Identified by X-ray Diffraction

NAME	FORMULA
Acmite	$Na_2O.Fe_2O_3.4SiO_2$
Analcite	$Na_2O.Al_2O_3.4SiO_2.2H_2O$
Anhydrite	$CaSO_4$
Aragonite	$CaCO_3$
Brucite	$Mg(OH)_2$
Calcite	$CaCO_3$
Cancrinite	$4Na_2O.CaO.4Al_2O_3.2CO_2.9SiO_2.3H_2O$
Hematite	Fe_2O_3
Hydroxyapatite	$Ca_{10}(OH)_2(PO_4)_6$
Magnetite	Fe_3O_4
Noselite	$4Na_2O.3Al_2O_3.6SiO_2.SO_4$
Pectolite	$Na_2O.4CaO.6SiO_2.H_2O$
Quartz	SiO_2
Serpentine	$3MgO.2SiO_2.2H_2O$
Thenardite	Na_2SO_4
Wollastonite	$CaSiO_3$
Xonotlite	$5CaO.5SiO_2.H_2O$

ture whereas only the hypothetical structure could be obtained from the usual chemical analysis.

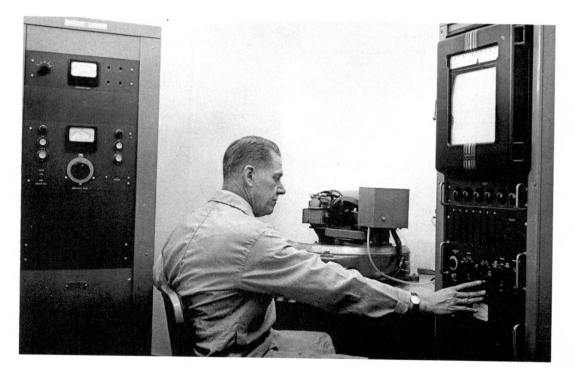

Figure 22-5 • Analysis of Boiler Deposits by X-ray Fluorescence

Figure 22-4 illustrates some of the common and uncommon constituents of boiler scale which have been identified by X-ray methods. Some of the salts could readily be determined by the conventional chemical analysis. Others, such as the complex alumino-silicates, could hardly have been identified except with the use of X-ray diffraction methods. The use of X-ray fluoresence also is developing. It is possible that X-ray fluoresence eventually will prove more useful in the identification of boiler deposits than X-ray diffraction.

INTERNAL CHEMICAL TREATMENT

For the internal chemical treatment of boiler water many strange and varied materials have been employed ranging from the earlier use of potato peelings, kerosene, molasses, etc., as "cure-alls" to the present use of specific chemicals applied to specific problems. It can be accepted as axiomatic that no one particular material is universally applicable and that a "cure-all" is a physical impossibility. Present day internal chemical treatment uses commercial chemicals with known chemical properties to accomplish certain specific objectives. Many of the chemicals commonly employed are available to all on the open market; others are proprietary in nature or their use may be subject to patent licensing. Continued research in the field of boiler water conditioning is constantly developing new materials of value and finding new uses for well known products.

The reason for the earlier use of "boiler compounds" with their usually disastrous results is that the present day highly technical science of internal boiler water treatment developed slowly and to a large extent by "trial and error" methods. Too often, the "trial and error" method was applied to industrial boiler plants without preliminary laboratory and pilot plant experimentation.

It is well to realize that the prevention of boiler scale cannot be predicted by any basic chemical principle. Where a precipitating type of treatment is employed, it is the *physical* characteristics of the precipitate formed in the boiler water that determines

whether or not the precipitate will tend to tightly adhere to the boiler heating surfaces —the *chemical* characteristics of the precipitate are relatively unimportant. Thus, from a chemical standpoint sodium silicate will precipitate the calcium and magnesium salts just as well as a phosphate or carbonate. However, it is the physical characteristics of the precipitate that are of importance, for a precipitate of calcium silicate will tightly adhere to the heating surfaces.

Today it is no longer necessary to depend on industrial application for experimentation. This work is now performed in laboratory experimental boilers and carefully studied in each stage of development before application to the industrial field. One type of laboratory experimental boiler used in this work employs ring circulation with electrical resistance heating, using specially wound coils. Electronic water level control maintains water level at ± 0.25 inches. The entire operation is automatic with automatic feedwater and treatment pump control and automatic continuous blowdown based upon boiler water conductivity. Electrical input is measured for correlation with steam production. Upon conclusion of a test run, the scaling surface is removed from the boiler, the scale dissolved in inhibited acid and analyses then conducted on the acid solution for the various scale constituents. Opportunity is provided for study of crystal structure and observation of scale adherence prior to removing scale from the heating surface. Boiler water samples secured during operation are analyzed for correlation with the scale analysis data.

As previously stated, scale is caused primarily by calcium and magnesium salts, silica and oil. Each is a separate problem and must be dealt with individually.

PHOSPHATE CONTROL. For the prevention of calcium and magnesium salts from baking on boiler evaporative surfaces, the internal treatment consists of precipitating the calcium and magnesium salts as sludge, and maintaining this sludge in a fluid form to be removed by the boiler blowdown. Calcium is considered to present a more difficult prob-

Figure 22-6 • Research Experimental Boilers

lem than magnesium. This is because the magnesium is readily precipitated by the alkalinity of the boiler water to form a sludge of magnesium hydroxide.

The most common chemicals employed for the precipitation of the soluble calcium salts are the sodium phosphates—trisodium phosphate, disodium phosphate, sodium metaphosphate and monosodium phosphate. Once any of these phosphates enter the boiler, their action is exactly the same. They are all converted into trisodium phosphate and as such react with the calcium to form tricalcium phosphate, a rather flocculent precipitate. In order for this reaction to take place, sufficient alkalinity must be present in the boiler water. At a pH value of approximately 9.5 or less the calcium is not precipitated properly. The choice of the phosphate to be used depends upon economics and upon the alkalinity of the boiler water. In some instances it is desirable to blend two phosphates to obtain the desired alkalinity. In others, it may be necessary to add alkaline materials to the boiler water such as caustic soda or soda ash.

Once the calcium and magnesium salts have been precipitated as a sludge, it is necessary to maintain this sludge in a fluid form. Generally, this is accomplished by the use of one or more forms of organic material. After a fluid sludge of calcium and magnesium precipitates has been formed, it is necessary to remove this sludge from the boilers by blowdown. The amount of blowdown required depends upon the amount of sludge formed and the nature of the sludge. Fluid sludges require less blowdown.

CARBONATE CONTROL. Another type of internal treatment for the prevention of scale is commonly known as carbonate-organic treatment. This type treatment has definite uses and limitations. Its principal application is on the so-called self-purging waters—waters in which the alkalinity is approximately equal to or greater than the hardness. This type of treatment employs relatively high concentrations of active organic materials in the boiler water together with the use of sodium carbonate (soda ash) to maintain proper alkalinity concentrations. In cases of low feedwater hardness, this type of treatment is generally not as applicable as a phosphate type of treatment. However, in a feedwater of high hardness, that is over 60 to 70 ppm, and with high alkalinity concentrations, carbonate-organic treatment can produce better results than phosphate treatment, primarily through the elimination of the heavy sludge condition which usually accompanies phosphate treatment of high-hardness feedwaters. In some instances a combination of both types of treatment has produced better results than either one singly.

ORGANIC AGENTS. The use of organic agents for the prevention of scale and sludge deposits is a necessary part of the internal boiler water conditioning for most industrial plants. Where external feedwater conditioning systems result in practically complete removal of incrusting solids and where very close chemical control is exercised, there may be no need for organic treatment. Central station operation is an example of where organics are required only for special problems. However, in a great majority of industrial plants, particularly where feedwater hardness is high, organics are a definite necessity if optimum conditions are to be maintained.

As mentioned previously, a precipitating type of internal boiler water treatment is designed to precipitate the calcium salts as tricalcium phosphate and the magnesium salts as magnesium hydroxide. Under some circumstances it has been found desirable to precipitate a portion of the calcium as calcium carbonate and some of the magnesium as magnesium silicate. These are the least adherent of the inorganic precipitates. However, even these precipitates will form scale and sludge on boiler heating surfaces, dependent on many factors such as suspended solids concentration, boiler pressure, heat transfer rate and chemical balance of the boiler water.

Organic agents are required to prevent scale and adherent sludge deposits resulting from these inorganic precipitates. It is proper internal conditioning to use inorganic agents to precipitate the incrusting solids in the most desirable inorganic form. Then the inorganic treatment may be supplemented with organic agents to complete the formation of a fluid sludge and to prevent the inorganic precipitates from adhering to the boiler heating surfaces. The organic agents commonly used in internal treatment of boiler water are tannins, lignins, starches, and seaweed derivatives.

Tannins, which are extracted from wood and bark, are organic substances of high molecular weight and complex structure. It is characteristic of these compounds that they are benzene derivatives and also are optically active. Tannins possess a glucoside structure in that sugar is produced on fermentation or hydrolysis. While synthetic compounds of tannin structure have been prepared, the tannins usually employed in boiler feedwater conditioning are of natural origin. Tannins may be conveniently grouped into catechol and pyrogallol types and mixtures of the two. Among the catechol tannins are cutch, quebracho, hemlock, larch, and gambier. Pyrogallo tannins include gallnuts, sumac, myrobalans, chestnut, valonia and dividivi. Mixed tannins include wattle bark, English oak and chestnut oak bark. These different tannins are some of the most common, but many others also exist. Commercial products in some cases contain mixtures of different tannins.

Lignin is also a complex organic substance and is the chief non-cellulose component of wood. The small portion of the total lignin present which is in a free state and which can be isolated with the use of solvents is referred to as "native lignin." Native lignin contains four methoxyl groups, four hydroxyl groups and one carbonyl group for each unit of molecular weight of 840. Commercial methods of lignin extraction cause some chemical modification in structure. One of the most useful forms in which lignin is commercially available is as the lignosulfonate, produced by the sulfite digestion process.

Starch is a high polymer carbohydrate. The structure is presumed to consist of glucose, joined by glucoside linkages. There is considerable range in the size of the molecules even in one variety of starch and the chemistry of starch is quite complex. In the natural state, starch is insoluble in water, but on boiling the individual cell walls burst and a portion is dissolved, forming a milky solution of starch paste. Commercially, starch is prepared from corn, wheat, potatoes and rice. The U. S. Navy standard boiler treatment formulation specifies the use of cornstarch for sludge conditioning and anti-foam action.

Of the seaweed derivatives, the most prominent are dispersions of sodium mannuronate, Irish Moss, sodium alginate and agar-agar. There are over 1100 kinds of seaweed from which a variety of water soluble gums can be extracted. Laminaria digitata, laminaria longicruris and laminaria saccharina are varieties of seaweed widely used for extraction purposes. The molecular weight of seaweed derivatives employed in boiler feedwater conditioning varies with the degree of polymerization and has been measured up to 250,000. Sodium mannuronate dispersions will precipitate with polyvalent positive ions such as calcium and magnesium, forming a flocculent precipitate which will adsorb suspended inorganic precipitates.

There are probably several different mechanisms by which organic substances function to hinder boiler scale formation. With the sodium mannuronate polymers, a coagulant effect is secured with adsorption of inorganic precipitates in the organic floc. With tannins and lignins it is believed that a major part of their action is in dispersion of precipitates. All of the organic agents probably exert to some extent a coating action on precipitated inorganic solids, decreasing their tendency both to cohere and adhere to boiler surfaces. Of prime importance, however, is the effect of organic agents in distorting crystal formation and thus inhibiting scale deposits directly at the point of formation. Regardless of the theory chosen to explain the action of organics, the end result with proper organic concentrations in the boiler water is the formation of a fluid boiler water sludge, readily removed by blowdown. With proper organic treatment of a boiler water there is also considerably less sludge of any sort remaining in the boiler upon opening.

Figure 22-7 shows the low and high heat transfer scaling surfaces (left—28,000 Btu/sq ft/hr and right—180,000 Btu/sq ft/hr) from an experimental boiler run without the use of an organic sludge conditioning agent. The deposit on the low heat transfer scaler was 1.20 grams/sq ft and on the high heat transfer scaler 5.80 grams/sq ft.

In contrast, Figure 22-8 shows the effect of an organic sludge conditioner under otherwise identical test conditions. The low heat transfer scaler developed a deposit of 0.03 grams/sq ft and the high heat transfer scaler a deposit of 0.12 grams/sq ft.

Figure 22-9 illustrates data typical of the results secured in experimental boiler studies by superimposing various types of organic agents on phosphate control. While different feedwaters were employed in the three series of tests covered by this figure, in each case the control run employed conventional phosphate internal boiler water treatment. By repeating the test with all conditions held constant with the exception of the additional organic treatment of the boiler water, data were secured on the scale reducing properties of the organic agents under the test conditions employed.

Figure 22-10 illustrates similar studies on the reduction of calcium carbonate type scale where no phosphate treatment was employed and the carbonate and hydroxide ions were the only inorganic precipitating agents used. Imposing organic agents under such condi-

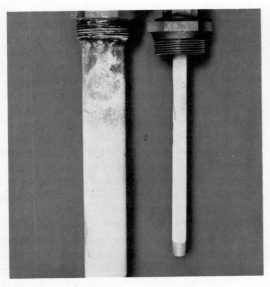

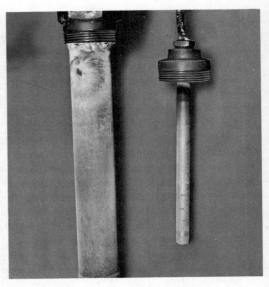

Figure 22-7 · Scalers without Organic Treatment   *Figure 22-8 · Scalers with Organic Treatment*

Fig. 22-9
Phosphate Scale Control Studies

Organic Conc. in Boiler Water ppm	Type Organic	Suspended Solids in Boiler Water ppm	Heat Transfer Rate Btu/ft²/hr	Operating Pressure psi	Scale Formed grams/ft²	% Scale Protection
0	. . . . .	400	57,000	260	1.89	. . . . .
190	Lignin	420	57,000	260	1.06	44.0%
180	Lignin	380	57,000	260	1.66	12.2%
180	Lignin	400	57,000	260	0.20	89.5%
0	. . . . .	250	24,000	320	0.684	. . . . .
150	Tannin	300	24,000	320	0.526	23.1%
150	Tannin	250	24,000	320	0.453	33.7%
150	Tannin	300	24,000	320	0.092	86.6%
0	. . . . .	900	57,000	650	3.50	. . . . .
180	Seaweed Derivative	800	57,000	650	1.98	43.5%
190	Seaweed Derivative	750	57,000	650	1.19	66.1%
180	Seaweed Derivative	800	57,000	650	0.55	84.2%

Fig. 22-10
Carbonate Scale Control Studies

Organic Conc. in Boiler Water ppm	Type Organic	Suspended Solids in Boiler Water ppm	Scale Formed grams/ft²	% Scale Protection
0	. . . . .	400	4.10	. . . . .
200	Tannin	380	2.95	28.0%
200	Tannin	400	2.13	48.0%
185	Tannin	380	1.39	66.1%

Operating Pressure: 300 psi, Heat Transfer Rate: 57,000 Btu/ft²/hr.

tions, which are similar to many types of railroad operation, can result in a marked decrease in boiler scale and sludge. While it can be demonstrated by such experimental work that a major reduction of scale and sludge deposits is obtained by superimposing the proper type of organic agent on inorganic control, the information secured on the grams of scale per square foot of heating surface is not the sole criterion for judging the applicability of a specific organic for internal boiler water treatment. Some organic agents have shown a fair degree of scale reduction, but have resulted in the development of a thin, tightly adherent scale, high in organic, and very difficult to remove from the heating surface. It is necessary to correlate with the scale formation, information on the crystal structure of the deposit, its tendencies for adherence and a complete chemical analysis of the scale itself for proper interpretation of the tests.

CHELATING AGENTS

Chelating or complexing agents have been applied for a number of years to remove deposits of calcium and magnesium salts from waterside surfaces of boilers. Developments over the past few years have shown that these agents can also prevent certain types of scale and sludge accumulations in industrial boilers.

The completely new approach to the rather common problem of preventing objectionable deposits employs the tetrasodium salt of ethylenediamine tetraacetic acid and the trisodium salt of nitrilo triacetic acid as the basic and most common chelating agents. A number of complexing and sequestering agents are used in conjunction with these basic agents in order to provide a more complete and satisfactorily controlled scale and sludge prevention program. Application is in a continuous fashion on a long-term basis.

By their chemical nature, chelating agents form complex soluble salts with calcium, magnesium, iron and copper as well as other metallic ions in exchange for sodium. Therefore, in the practical application, precipitates are avoided by the formation of soluble salts.

Proper application of qualified chelating agents involves optimum levels of suitable supplementary dispersing agents and the maintenance of favorable alkalinity as well as pH conditions. Where employed in a combination program, phosphate must be satisfactorily regulated. With these factors in balance, existing precipitated matter is removed in a controlled manner and with a controlled degree of rapidity while preventing new accumulations. Even certain complex scales, such as analcite and acmite, can be prevented or gradually removed with the application of a properly balanced chelant program.

The applicability of the chelant type of treatments is generally in the area of low feedwater hardnesses. That is, the treatment is economical for most systems where the feedwater hardness is 1.0 ppm or less. A full chelant program is seldom economical when hardness in the feedwater exceeds 2.0 ppm.

Recent developments indicate that, under certain conditions of application, chelating agents provide dispersive powers of a nature which are additive to the properties of normal organic dispersants. These characteristics can advantageously supplement standard phosphate type treatments, particularly in the cases of systems where the feedwater hardness is at a higher level. This property extends the useful range or the applicability of properly selected chelants.

Chelating agents are useful for not only problems of complex scale and sludge on waterside surfaces of industrial boilers, but also for the control of iron and copper deposits in high purity feedwater systems. However, chelating agents are not a cure-all for all types of boiler water problems. As an example, carryover problems are not corrected to any measurable degree in the average plant when a conversion to chelant treatment is made. In practically all instances, any carryover condition existing under a phosphate treatment continues unabated with a chelant approach. When mechanical or chemical characteristics quite apart from the small amount of suspended solids present cause carryover, the use of chelants does not solve the problem. Field studies, based upon the sodium tracer technique, have shown also that the application of chelating agents does not contribute to a carryover condition.

Use of a proper chelant program on a continuous basis provides certain other advantages which usually justify a higher cost. Because of the reduction in suspended solids and the elimination of precipitates, higher total solids in the boiler water and hence lower blowdown rates are possible in many instances. A further advantage of chelating treatments is the fact that temporary upsets, which may cause a scaling condition, can be mitigated with respect to aftereffects. That is, the maintenance of proper treatment balances following the upset period causes the removal of scale.

Longer and safer operation between turnarounds is possible with the advance of chelant treatments. Some states allow longer operating periods between internal inspections when waterside conditions are satisfactorily controlled, and such extension may be an incentive to apply a suitable chelant program. Also, since less work is required for cleaning waterside surfaces with an effective chelant program, less time is needed for a turnaround. Labor requirements are reduced.

Of course, close control must be maintained in order to fully gain the advantages of a properly designed chelant program. In order to aid control, the development of accurate and adequate testing methods is a continuing effort in this new field of boiler water treatment.

As indicated previously, chelants are not cure-all treatments. The application of a chelating program does not correct corrosion problems due to oxygen and/or carbon dioxide. Failure due to steam blanketing is not eliminated, and the potential for embrittlement must still be considered. As discussed in other chapters of this publication, treatments of a specific nature are required.

In some instances, the reduction of suspended solids has greatly reduced the effect of oil contamination. However, in isolated instances where contamination has been severe, superheater problems due to carbonized oil deposits have continued. It is well to note that oil contamination is an undesirable situation with respect to boiler feedwater characteristics. The best possible solution to an oil problem is to eliminate the source of contamination or to remove the oil completely from the feedwater before introduction to the boiler.

CHEMICAL TESTING

The use of internal chemical treatment, regardless of the excellence of the materials employed, is valueless unless it is closely controlled by means of daily chemical tests of the boiler water by the plant personnel. Dependent upon the nature of the treatment employed and the individual plant conditions, the control of chemical treatment and blowdown may be based on tests for hardness, alkalinity, chloride, sulfite, phosphate, chelant, silica, nitrate, specific conductance and total and dissolved solids. Not all of these tests are necessary in any one plant, but dependent upon the specific problems encountered, several of these tests may be required for proper control. In addition, special tests are occasionally necessary.

FEEDING OF INTERNAL TREATMENT CHEMICALS

A satisfactory method of feeding chemical correctives is second only in importance to the consistent control of chemical balances. However, some feedwater problems dictate the necessity of highly efficient feeding methods before adequate chemical control can be established and maintained.

Obviously for proper results and to insure maximum efficiency from any chemical treatment, continuous methods should generally be employed. Many chemicals, such as sodium sulfite and the majority of the organics, may be fed continuously to the suction of the boiler feed pump without fear of inviting feed line deposits, regulator troubles, etc.

On the other hand, phosphate treatment and in certain instances sodium carbonate and sodium hydroxide, when applied in a manner similar to the above, cause a premature reaction to take place in the boiler feed line. Precipitates such as tricalcium phosphate and calcium carbonate which result, readily interlock on water distribution and regulator surfaces to form adherent scale. These premature reactions may frequently be accelerated by high feedwater temperatures or by chemical characteristics such as high feedwater hardness, excessive feedwater alkalinity and high pH values.

Serious difficulty can be anticipated from the consistent formation of feed line deposits. Usually, erratic operation of boiler feedwater regulators is the first symptom, followed by thermal loss in economizers or the necessity for increased feedwater pressure. Eventually a point may be reached where insufficient feedwater can reach the boilers regardless of feed pump pressure. Sudden forced shut down and boiler outage results, with consequent possible equipment damage or certain loss in production schedules.

In the case of phosphates, the tendency toward premature precipitation is not confined to the orthophosphates such as trisodium, disodium and monosodium phosphate. The problem of feed line deposition is also prevalent with the use of molecularly dehydrated phosphates.

In their original or unreverted states, the molecularly dehydrated phosphates will not precipitate as readily with calcium as the ortho materials. This property is frequently utilized, in conjunction with certain surface active organics, to prevent calcium carbonate deposition. However, it should be remembered that such formulations (normally used in relatively small quantities) are designed to stabilize the natural deposition tendencies of a water. They are not expected to cope with the problem of feed line deposition resulting from the continuous feed of relatively high concentrations of chemical precipitants, such as sodium carbonate, sodium hydroxide and all phosphates.

The ideal method of adding phosphate to a boiler water for internal chemical treat-

Figure 22-11 · Section of Boiler Feedline Containing Phosphate Deposit, Resulting from Continuous Feeding of Phosphate to Cold Process Lime-Soda Softened Feedwater

ment purposes is by pumping the phosphate solution direct to a boiler drum, utilizing for this purpose a small chemical pump. This method of chemical feed is also suitable for the introduction of most other treatment materials. Sodium sulfite is usually pumped continuously to the suction side of the boiler feed pump or to the storage section of the feedwater heater. Organic sludge conditioning agents may be fed continuously to the boiler feedwater or direct to a boiler drum. Chemicals added for alkalinity adjustment, such as caustic soda and soda ash, may in some cases be fed continuously to the boiler feedwater and in other cases, dependent on feedwater characteristics, must be fed directly to the boiler drum to avoid feedline deposits.

FEEDING METHODS FOR CHELANTS

The basic chelating agents commonly used in boiler water treatment have an affinity for boiler system metals under certain conditions. Copper bearing materials, in particular, are subject to attack. Therefore, contact with copper bearing alloys in feedwater stage heaters, control valves and check valves must be avoided. Copper cooling coils for sampling should be changed to a suitable stainless steel, such as 304 or 316. Monel and similar nickel alloys are not satisfactory for this service.

Suitably diluted chelant solution is usually injected into the boiler feedwater through a properly designed stainless steel quill. This quill is best located on the pressure side of the feedwater pump, and preferably at a point where the temperature is no greater than the normal feedwater temperature.

Because of their great activity, chelating agents should be fed to a boiler system only in a continuous fashion. This method provides continuous dilution. In addition, direct feed to boiler drums should be avoided, even though a suitably designed stainless steel distribution line may be installed within the drum. The breaking of the line by chance could lead to serious and undetected corrosion problems.

REFERENCES

R. C. Corey, "What About Copper in Boilers," *Combustion,* Vol. 16, pp. 43-46 (June 1945)

J. A. Holmes, "The Development of Organics for Water Treatment," *Proceedings,* Midwest Power Conf., Vol. XIII, pp. 238-245 (1951)

J. J. Maguire, "Organic Agents in Boiler Scale and Sludge Control," *Proceedings,* Midwest Power Conf., Vol. XIII, pp. 246-256 (1951)

J. Van Brunt, "Tube Failures in Water-Tube Boilers," *Combustion,* Vol. 17, pp. 32-37 (July 1945)

J. R. Metcalf, "Chelant Treatment Programs for Boiler Water," *The Betz Indicator,* Betz Laboratories, Inc., Trevose, Pa. (June, 1967)

23

Boiler Corrosion Control

A major consideration in the design of a feedwater conditioning system is protection of boilers and accessory equipment against corrosion, both during operation and when the equipment is out of service. Except in special cases, corrosion in boilers, feed lines and economizers is due either to the influence of low pH or dissolved oxygen.

CONTROL OF pH

The solubility of iron in water increases as the pH decreases below the neutral point. The attack on steel by water with an acid pH is of a general nature over the entire surface with little tendency toward localized corrosion. The obvious method of preventing such corrosion is neutralization of the acid with an alkali. Soda ash and caustic soda are commonly employed for this purpose in the treatment of boiler feedwater. Except in special cases of corrosion in high pressure boilers, experience has shown that it is desirable to maintain a minimum boiler water pH of approximately 10.5. This pH is sufficiently high to stifle acidic attack. In the proper treatment of boiler water for control of scale and sludge deposits, the desired boiler water alkalinity and pH for prevention of acidic corrosion is automatically established. Therefore, except under unusual operating conditions, pH is not a factor in boiler water control.

Trade waste contamination of the makeup water, sugar contamination of the condensate or acidic contamination from acid pickling or plating baths are some of the most common sources of acid contamination of boiler feedwater. Acid contamination can also enter the system due to improper operation or control of hydrogen zeolite softeners.

If the makeup water or condensate is subject to periodic acidic contamination, recording or indicating instruments are desirable to maintain a check on the purity of the makeup or condensate. Such devices can be used either to operate automatic dump valves or to warn the operators to discharge the contaminated water to waste.

CONTROL OF DISSOLVED OXYGEN

Dissolved oxygen can be introduced into the system not only in the makeup water but also due to air infiltration of the condensate system. When dissolved oxygen is present in the feedwater, an attack of the feed line, closed heaters and economizer can be expected with the severity of the problem dependent on the concentration of dissolved oxygen and the temperature involved. One of the most serious aspects of oxygen corrosion is that it generally occurs as pitting so that the attack is concentrated in a small area of the total metal surface. With this type of corrosion, failures can occur even though only a relatively small portion of the metal has been lost.

The influence of temperature on the corrosivity of dissolved oxygen is particularly important in such equipment as closed heaters and economizers where the water temperature is increased very rapidly. Under such conditions, an additional driving force for the oxidation reaction is present and for this reason, even very small quantities of dissolved oxygen in feedwater can cause severe corrosion in such equipment.

When oxygen is present in the feedwater entering the boiler, a portion will be flashed and will leave the boiler with the steam. The remainder of the dissolved oxygen can attack the boiler metal. While the point of attack will vary with the boiler design and feedwater distribution, oxygen pitting is usually concentrated adjacent to the water level in the feedwater drum.

The first and most important step in eliminating the corrosive influence of dissolved oxygen is mechanical deaeration of the boiler feedwater. Efficient deaeration will reduce the dissolved oxygen content of the boiler feedwater to a very low value. It is advisable to follow mechanical deaeration by chemical deaeration in order to remove the last traces of dissolved oxygen. Where mechanical deaeration is not employed, chemical deaeration must be used for the removal of the entire oxygen content of the feedwater.

Sodium sulfite is the chemical agent most

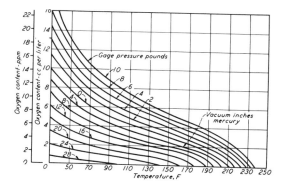

Figure 23-1 • Solubility of Dissolved Oxygen

commonly employed for chemical deaeration due to its low cost, ease of handling and its lack of scale forming properties. The oxygen scavenging characteristic of sodium sulfite is illustrated by the following reaction:

$$2Na_2SO_3 + O_2 = 2Na_2SO_4$$
sodium sulfite + oxygen = sodium sulfate

The removal of 1.0 ppm dissolved oxygen theoretically requires 7.88 ppm of chemically pure sodium sulfite. However, use of a technical grade of sodium sulfite combined with handling and blowdown losses as encountered in actual plant operation usually requires the feed of approximately 10 lbs of sodium sulfite for each pound of oxygen. Requirements will also depend on the concentration of excess sulfite maintained in the boiler water.

To assure complete oxygen removal, it is necessary to maintain a residual concentration of sulfite in the boiler water. The residual required depends on a number of factors such as the method of feed and the point of application, the dissolved oxygen concentration and the variation in the dissolved oxygen concentration of the feedwater.

Continuous feed of sodium sulfite is generally required for complete oxygen removal. In the majority of plants, the most suitable point of application is the storage compartment of the deaerating or open heater. In other plants, sufficient reaction time will be allowed with application to the suction side

of the boiler feed pump. While intermittent application is generally not recommended, it has been found in some low pressure systems that adequate protection is provided as long as the additions of sodium sulfite are made with sufficient frequency to continuously maintain the proper residual concentration in the boiler water.

Testing of the boiler water for sulfite residual and recording the quantity of sulfite required serves also as a quick check on heater deaeration efficiency in those plants where the oxygen content of the feedwater is not determined regularly. Any decrease in boiler water sulfite residual and consequent need for increased feed of sodium sulfite, is an indication that heater operation should be checked to ascertain and correct the reason for increased oxygen content of the boiler feedwater.

The speed of the sulfite-oxygen reaction is affected by a number of factors, the most important being temperature. The reaction time decreases with increased temperature. In general, the reaction speed doubles for every 10 C increase in temperature. At temperatures of 212 F and above the reaction is quite rapid. It has also been found that the presence of an excess or overfeed of sodium sulfite will increase the reaction rate. Several investigators have shown that the reaction proceeds most rapidly at pH values in the vicinity of 9.0-10.0.

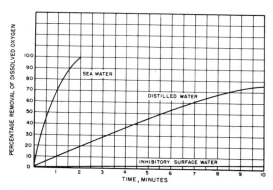

Figure 23-2 • Effect of Different Waters on Time of Oxygen-Sulfite Reaction

It has also been shown that some natural waters possess an inhibitory effect on the oxygen-sulfite reaction. Figure 23-2 shows the reaction rates at room temperature between oxygen and sodium sulfite for three different types of waters. The reaction is fairly rapid with sea water, complete oxygen removal being secured in two minutes. The reaction is much slower in distilled water, only 75% of the oxygen being removed after 10 minutes contact time. With a surface supply possessing inhibitory properties, after 10 minutes contact only approximately 3% of the oxygen has been removed.

Research directed toward increasing the speed of the oxygen-sulfite reaction has determined that certain materials act as catalysts in speeding this reaction to completion. The most suitable catalysts are the heavy metal cations of two or more valences. Iron, copper, cobalt, nickel and manganese are among the more effective catalytic aids to the oxygen-sulfite reaction. Combinations of several of these heavy metal cations have proved most effective in providing a continuously active influence on the speed of reaction.

As a result of research on catalytic aids for oxygen removal, a catalyzed sodium sulfite has been developed. Through the incoporation of suitable catalysts and sodium sulfite in one formulation, a material is available which will consistently provide practically instantaneous oxygen removal, even when the water possesses natural inhibitory properties.

Figure 23-3 illustrates test results using ordinary commercial sodium sulfite for oxygen removal at room temperature with results obtained with catalyzed sodium sulfite. As can be seen, the original oxygen content of 9.8 ppm has been reduced by sodium sulfite after 10 minutes contact to only 6.6 ppm. Little reduction has been made in the corrosive nature of the water. With treatment by catalyzed sodium sulfite, however, complete oxygen removal has been accomplished in only 20 seconds contact time. Complete elimination of the corrosivity of the water due to dissolved oxygen has been obtained in this short contact time.

Catalyzed sodium sulfite is used in low temperature systems for oxygen removal and also finds application in boiler systems where the feedwater temperature is low, where mechanical deaeration is not complete or where it is essential to obtain rapid reaction for prevention of pitting in feed lines, closed heaters and economizers.

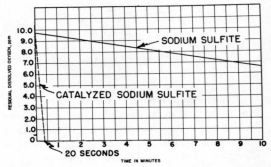

Figure 23-3 · Comparison of Sodium Sulfite vs Catalyzed Sodium Sulfite on Time of Oxygen Removal

As boiler operating pressures have increased, two disadvantages in the use of sodium sulfite as a chemical deaerant have become evident. The product of the sodium sulfite-oxygen reaction is sodium sulfate (Na_2SO_4) which increases the dissolved solids concentration of the boiler water. While the increase in dissolved solids in low or medium pressure boilers is generally of little consequence, it can be significant in high pressure boilers. Also, at high pressure, the sulfite in the boiler tends to decompose to form acidic gases, sulfur dioxide (SO_2) and hydrogen sulfide (H_2S) which can contribute to corrosion in the return system.

Hydrazine is a reducing agent which does not possess these disadvantages for high pressure operation. Hydrazine removes dissolved oxygen in accordance with the following reaction:

$$N_2H_4 + O_2 = 2H_2O + N_2$$
hydrazine + oxygen = water + nitrogen

Since the products of this reaction are water and nitrogen, no solids are added to the boiler water. The decomposition products of hydrazine are ammonia and nitrogen. The ammonia is alkaline and therefore will not attack steel. However, if present in sufficient quantity, it can attack copper bearing alloys when oxygen is present. With proper application, the concentration of ammonia in the steam can be controlled so that the danger of attack of copper bearing alloys will be minimized. At the same time, the ammonia will neutralize carbon dioxide so that return

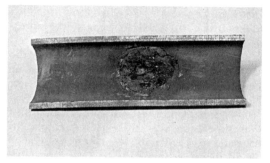

*Figure 23-4 · Oxygen Pitting in a
Two Inch Generating Tube*

line corrosion due to carbon dioxide will be reduced.

Hydrazine is a toxic liquid and therefore must be handled with the usual care observed in the handling of all toxic materials. Pure hydrazine has a low flash point so a 35% solution, which has no flash point, is usually employed. Theoretically, 1.0 ppm hydrazine is required to react with 1.0 ppm of dissolved oxygen. However, in practical application, hydrazine is usually required at approximately 1.5-2.0 parts per part of oxygen. To avoid excessive ammonia concentrations in the steam, the residual hydrazine concentration in the boiler water is usually maintained at 0.1 ppm or less.

In some instances, the feed of both sodium sulfite and hydrazine is advisable in high pressure installations. In these cases, a very low sulfite excess is carried in the boiler water so that the potential for corrosion from acidic gases is minimized but a reserve of deaerant is available to react with an oxygen surge. In conjunction with the feed of sodium sulfite, the hydrazine is fed in a quantity sufficient to maintain a very low residual

in the boiler water to remove the normal concentrations of oxygen without danger of excessive ammonia liberation.

When feedwater is employed in desuperheating, it is desirable to feed sodium sulfite after the point from which the feedwater for desuperheating is taken so as to avoid adding solids to the water. When hydrazine is used as the chemical deaerant, this precaution is not necessary since the hydrazine will not add solids to the desuperheated steam.

PROTECTION OF IDLE BOILERS

Unless proper storage procedures are followed, severe corrosion may occur in idle boilers. The method of protecting idle boilers depends primarily on the length of downtime. Dry storage is preferred when the boiler will be out of service for a month or more while wet storage may be suitable for a shorter period of downtime.

DRY STORAGE. The boiler should be drained, thoroughly cleaned and dried completely by means of hot air or a small wood fire. Close attention should be given to complete elimination of moisture from nondrainable superheater tubes. A suitable moisture absorbing material in a water tight container should be placed in the boiler drums or on top of the flues in a fire tube boiler. The most widely used moisture absorbants are quick lime and silica gel. Silica gel is more efficient in absorbing moisture and can be regenerated by heating so that it can be used over and over again. It is not a caustic substance like lime so it can be handled more easily and safely and is therefore generally preferred.

Requirements for quick lime approximate 20-30 lbs per 100 boiler horsepower or 7-10 lbs per 1000 lbs per hour boiler rating. Silica gel is recommended at the rate of 4 lbs per 100 cubic feet of internal volume.

After placing the quick lime or silica gel in the boiler, all openings should be tightly closed. The unit should be checked every two or three months, or as experience dictates, for renewal of the lime or regeneration of the silica gel.

WET METHOD. The boiler should be cleaned and inspected and then filled to the normal water level. If deaerated water is not available, dissolved gases should be expelled by boiling the water for a short time with boiler vented to atmosphere. The boiler water alkalinity should be adjusted with caustic soda to a minimum of 400 ppm. Sufficient sodium sulfite should also be added to produce a minimum sulfite residual of 100 ppm.

The quantities of caustic soda and sodium sulfite required will approximate 3.0 and 1.5 lbs respectively per 1000 gals of water in the boiler. After the boiler is cooled and before a vacuum is created, the unit should be filled completely and all connections closed.

Tests should be conducted on a weekly basis and additions of the treatment chemicals should be made as necessary to maintain the recommended minimum concentrations. When treatment additions are required, the boiler water should be circulated by means of an external pump or by lowering the water to the operating level and steaming the boiler for a short time. The boiler should then be completely flooded as outlined previously. The temperature of the boiler should be maintained as low as possible since the corrosion rate increases at higher temperatures.

When the boiler is returned to service, a high rate of blowdown should be maintained initially so that alkalinity and sulfite will be reduced to the normal operating levels rapidly.

In some small installations or where weekly testing is not practical, chromate salts can be employed to protect idle boilers against corrosion. The concentration maintained should be 2000-2500 ppm as sodium chromate. The boiler should be filled completely and closed tightly. To assure good mixing, circulation of the water with a pump is recommended. Boilers stored in this manner should be blown down heavily to dissipate the chromate color, before being returned to service. The use of chromate is not recommended if steam is to be used in cooking, sterilization or in the processing of food products since chromate salts are toxic.

Nitrogen or other inert gases may also be used for storage purposes. A slight positive pressure of the gas is maintained after the boiler has been filled to the operating level with deaerated feedwater. This method has been employed in some high pressure utility stations or similar installations where short periods of standby service are frequently required.

SUPERHEATER STORAGE. In most modern boilers it is not possible to separate the superheater section from the rest of the boiler. Accordingly, it is necessary to follow the same storage procedure for the superheater section as for the other portions of the boiler. Wet storage of drainable superheaters is relatively simple while wet storage of nondrainable superheaters is more complicated. In dry storage, care must be taken to remove all of the moisture from the nondrainable superheaters by reheating the superheaters sufficiently to evaporate all the water. This may be accomplished by means of a small fire in the boiler furnace. In some cases it may be possible to dry the nondrainable superheaters with hot air diverted from the air heaters of one of the operating boilers. Depending on the actual design, there may be a choice as to whether the dry air is directed over the external surfaces or used internally.

Since a residue will be left in nondrainable superheater tubes after boiling out, if the superheater has been flooded with water containing boiler water salts, it is desirable to employ a method of wet storage which does not involve the use of solid chemicals. Volatile chemicals or inert gas can be used in the superheater section. The volatile chemicals recommended are hydrazine and ammonia or neutralizing amine. If high purity water is not available to fill the entire boiler, the superheater tubes can be filled with condensate or demineralized water from the outlet end. The recommended treatment concentrations are approximately 100 ppm of hydrazine and sufficient ammonia ' or neutralizing amine to elevate the pH to approximately 9.0-10.0.

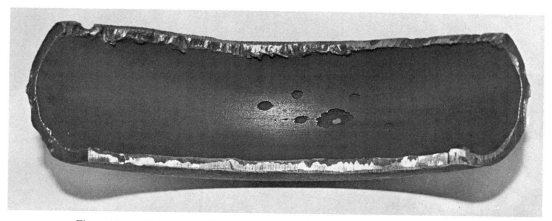

Figure 23-5 · Bottom of U-Bend in Superheater Tube Showing Pitting and Perforation

REFERENCES

H. D. Ongman, "A Study of Reducing Solutions at Steam Boiler Temperatures", *Combustion,* Vol. 24, pp. 40-44 (Feb. 1953)

R. L. Reed, "Corrosion: Its Effect in Boiler Systems", *Combustion,* Vol. 19, pp. 28-33 (May 1948) and pp. 43-49 (June 1948)

C. J. Schafer, "Protection of Idle Turbines and Superheaters," *The Betz Indicator,* Betz Laboratories, Inc., Phila., Pa. (March 1962)

"Steam: Its Generation and Use", pp. 21-18, 19, The Babcock & Wilcox Co., New York, N.Y. (1955)

"Suggested Rules for Care of Power Boilers", ASME Boiler and Pressure Vessel Code Section VII, Am. Soc. of Mech. Engineers, New York, N.Y. (1954)

24

Carryover

THE terms carryover, foaming and priming are closely associated and each term is employed in describing conditions which cause the entrainment of boiler water solids with the steam. Because priming, foaming and carryover are sometimes loosely used interchangeably, it is well to define their exact meaning.

Foaming is the condition resulting from the formation of bubbles on the surface of the boiler water. The foam produced may entirely fill the steam space of the boiler or it may be of relatively minor depth. In either case, this foaming condition causes appreciable entrainment of boiler water with the steam.

Priming is a more violent and spasmodic action, resulting in the throwing of "slugs" of boiler water over with the steam. This action is similar to the "bumping" experienced when water is boiled in an open beaker.

Carryover is the term applied to the continuous entrainment of a relatively small quantity of boiler water solids with the steam. The term carryover is also often used to cover the general conditions more exactly divided into foaming, priming and carryover.

EFFECTS OF CARRYOVER

When boiler water solids are carried over in the steam, deposits will occur in non-return and stop valves, superheaters, steam piping and engines or turbines. Such deposits can promote failure of the superheater tubes and loss in engine or turbine efficiency. Deposition on governor valves can permit overspeeding and wrecking of the machines.

Foaming or priming of the boiler water can result in a false water level reading while the thermal shock resulting from slugs of water entering the steam distribution system as a result of priming can seriously endanger all steam driven equipment. It should also be noted that when moisture is carried over with the steam a loss in thermal efficiency is experienced, as such carryover corresponds to additional blowdown through the steam line.

CAUSES OF CARRYOVER

Carryover may result from mechanical and chemical causes or from a combination of the two. Among the mechanical causes of carryover are boiler design, high water level, method of firing and load characteristics. Among the chemical causes are high total solids of the boiler water, high suspended solids, high alkalinities, oil and improper type of external or internal chemical treatment.

MECHANICAL. Boiler design will influence the solids content of the steam. Certain types of boilers are known for their ability to consistently produce clean steam while certain other types are traditionally recognized as subject to carryover.

Turbulence of the boiler water is a definite contributing factor to the mechanical carryover of boiler water solids. In older boiler designs the steam carrying or riser tubes discharged below the water level resulting in severe turbulence. To minimize this condition modern designs have the steam generating tubes discharge above water level or through steam separating devices. These devices have become quite complex and are generally very efficient. However, some pressure drop is experienced across the steam purifier and thus any leak in the equipment will result in impure steam.

High water level is another frequently encountered cause of mechanical carryover while boiler circulation is yet another factor. For example, at low load one burner may cut out and the resultant disturbance of the boiler circulation may influence the tendency to carryover.

Obviously, operation of a boiler at loads in excess of its designed rating will provide more cause for carryover than will operation within the designed rating. Sudden load changes will cause more difficulty than steady loads.

CHEMICAL. The American Boiler Manufacturer's Association stipulates in its standard guarantees on steam purity the following boiler water concentrations.

Operating Pressure, psig	Total Solids, ppm	Total Alkalinity, ppm	Suspended Solids, ppm
0 — 300	3500	700	300
301 — 450	3000	600	250
451 — 600	2500	500	150
601 — 750	2000	400	100
751 — 900	1500	300	60
901 — 1000	1250	250	40
1001 — 1500	1000	200	20
1501 — 2000	750	150	10
2001 and higher	500	100	5

The effect of dissolved solids, suspended solids and alkalinity on carryover has been a subject of considerable research. In some plants alkalinity is the determining factor while in other plants it is the total dissolved solids that limit the boiler water concentrations that can be maintained without carryover. In general, it is agreed that part for part suspended solids have a much more pronounced effect in causing carryover than dissolved solids.

The constituent having the most pronounced effect upon carryover—suspended solids—is far less frequently shown on a boiler water analysis than alkalinity, dissolved solids, sulfate, etc. Alkalinity is determined by titration with a standard acid; dissolved solids can be determined by conductivity methods or by gravimetric analysis, but suspended solids can only be determined by a tedious gravimetric procedure. If sufficient data are available, however, it is possible to calculate the suspended solids content of the boiler with reasonable accuracy.

In certain sections of the country where the raw makeup water contains a high dissolved solids content it would be impossible to operate the boilers within the limits specified in the standard steam guarantee of the American Boiler Manufacturer's Association. Boiler manufacturers are cognizant of this condition and will, in cooperation with the purchaser, supply boilers with extra large steam drums and with special baffling and steam purifying devices in order that the unusually high solids concentration of the boiler water can be maintained without detrimental carryover.

Oil present in boiler water is highly undesirable from the standpoint of carryover. Saponification of compounding agents by the alkalinity of the boiler water will produce a soap, thereby causing a foaming effect.

Internal boiler water treatment with phosphate control is standard for most types of feedwater. However, there is a tendency for the precipitated, finely divided calcium phosphate to stabilize boiler water foam, thus contributing to carryover of boiler water solids with the steam. This carryover tendency must be controlled by increased blowdown to lower suspended solids concentrations or by the use of organic agents to control this increased foam load.

The increasing amounts of various synthetic detergents and wetting agents, both for industrial and domestic use, may well lead to increased foaming tendencies for many surface supplies to which wastes are discharged. Unlike soaps, which react with the hardness present in water to form insoluble precipitates, these synthetic agents do not react with hardness and their foaming qualities are not thus eliminated, except by dilution. Contamination of surface waters by these agents in various industrial and domestic waste waters has caused difficulty with boiler foaming.

In many areas where the water supply is critical, sewage plant effluents have been used by industry for both boiler and cooling water supply. Usually, the high concentration of organic wastes present in the sewage plant effluent will lead to a foaming boiler water condition unless controlled by antifoam agents.

The conventional mineral analysis of a water does not indicate whether foaming tendencies are to be expected from organic contamination. Even a determination of the organic content of the water does not provide this information since many surface supplies from heavily wooded areas contain a relatively high organic concentration of harmless or beneficial organics of the tannin type.

While all of the factors mentioned above

possess a definite bearing on the foaming characteristics of a boiler water, because of the inter-relation of these various influences, it is not possible to generalize to the extent of specific maximum limits with respect to alkalinity, suspended solids, dissolved solids, etc. Minute traces of organic surface active contamination may materially alter the boiling characteristics of a concentrated boiler water and yet the concentration of the surface active contaminants present may be so small as to defy detection by chemical analysis.

Operating conditions also vary to such an extent and are affected by so many factors that, except in a general fashion, it is not possible to predict the maximum water solids that can be tolerated without carryover under certain operating conditions. Specific limits for any one set of operating conditions can usually be set only after a detailed individual study of operation at that particular plant.

PREVENTION OF CARRYOVER

The means that can be taken for the prevention of carryover can be divided into mechanical and chemical methods. Of course, mechanical correction is required for the minimization of carryover resulting from mechanical causes, such as change in boiler design, installation of baffles, etc. In addition various mechanical devices are employed for the separation from the steam of the droplets of boiler water carried over. Chemical methods for the treatment of the boiler water are ineffective where the cause of the carryover is mechanical. However, where carryover has a chemical origin, such as high calcium phosphate concentrations in the boiler water, proper chemical treatment methods can be highly effective in eliminating this condition.

MECHANICAL. As pressures approach critical the difference in steam and water density become progressively smaller and thus with the trend to higher steam pressures and higher steam generation, the design of steam drum internal purifying devices has become increasingly more complicated.

Primary separation of steam and boiler water is secured by means of abrupt changes in direction of flow, utilizing the difference in density of water and steam as the means of separation. Impingement of the steam and water mixture against a baffle for gravity separation may be employed or centrifugal force may be used in a separating device which causes the water to be thrown from a whirling mixture. The majority of the boiler water impurities is removed in this primary separation which also serves the purpose of removing steam from the recirculated boiler water returning to the tubes. Any appreciable amount of steam in the downcomer circuits will reduce the head available for circulation and will reduce the boiler circulation rate as a result.

Primary separation can be secured by relatively simple devices, such as "end around" baffles over the discharge of the riser tubes or curtain baffles protecting a simple dry pipe. More complicated arrangements are used to improve the efficiency of primary separation. In many industrial boilers, primary separation only is incorporated in the steam drum internals. For high pressure turbine operation, however, it is advisable to follow primary separation with a secondary separation step so as to reduce the solids content of the steam to the lowest value possible.

Secondary separation is also termed steam scrubbing and steam drying. In this process, small amounts of moisture must be separated from large amounts of steam. This separation is accomplished by providing a large amount of contact surface and frequent reversals of steam flow so that the mist of boiler water may collect and be drained from the separating unit. Steam velocity is kept low to avoid reentrainment of the separated boiler water and to insure maximum contact for deposition of the boiler water.

Steam washing is also sometimes employed to lower the solids content of the steam. Steam washing employs the incoming feedwater to mix with and dilute boiler water solids with feedwater of lower solids content, thereby securing a lowering not of the moisture content of the steam, but of its solids content. Various steam washing arrangements include bubble cap washers and feedwater sprays through which the steam must pass. A condensing type steam washer is also used in which feedwater does not directly contact the steam, but in which steam is condensed on finned tubes cooled by incoming feedwater. In this design, the steam is washed in its own condensate.

Figure 24-1 shows an installation of centrifugal primary separators in a boiler drum. Steam and water from the risers enter the separator tangentially. The water moves downward in a helical path on the inside wall of the cylinder. Centrifugal force on the mixture boiling around the cylinder separates the steam from the water. The steam then flows through the hollow space in the center and passes out of the separator into corrugated plates at the top of the cylinder, where moisture removed from the steam is arrested and returned to the cylinder. Secondary separation is secured in the steam scrubber section.

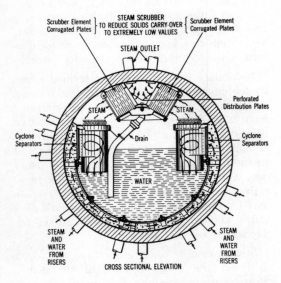

Courtesy Babcock and Wilcox Co.

Figure 24-1 • Cyclone Separators

Figure 24-2 illustrates another design of steam drum internals in which double rows of primary separators separate the entering steam-water mixture. The second stage of purification consists of so-called steam condensers which are U shaped finned tubes through which feed water flows. Because the tubes and fins are of lower temperature than the saturated steam a small portion of the steam condenses and maintains wet surfaces. Steam is thus effectively scrubbed and washed in pure condensate. The final stage of steam purification is secured in the dryer cartons.

In still another design of steam drum internals for large natural circulation boilers, the steam entering the drum (along with 20-40% water by volume) is collected in a compartment formed by internal baffles. The first stage of steam purification is in the centrifugal separator which spins the steam-water mixture, throwing water to the outside and steam to the inside. A skim-off lip above the skimmer collects the layer of water from the outer wall and returns it to the drum through the annulus surrounding the inner chamber. The steam then proceeds vertically upward to the next stage.

Secondary separation is secured in two opposed banks of closely spaced thin corrugated sheets which direct the steam in a tortuous path at low velocity. Separated moisture drains from the corrugated plates. Additional separation takes place in the drum space below the dryers and in the drying screen.

Figure 24-3 is a line drawing of another steam purifying device. In this separator the centrifugal principle is again employed for primary steam-water separation. The water is removed through the bottom of the separator through a slot discharging below minimum water level while secondary steam purification is accomplished in a unit chevron dryer as shown in Figure 24-4.

CHEMICAL. As discussed earlier the principal chemical causes of boiler water carryover are high total solids, high alkalinity levels and oil contamination. By definition the total solids

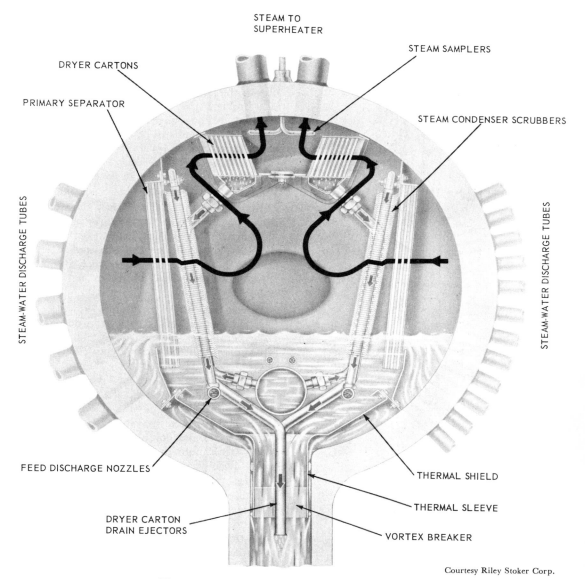

STEAM TO
SUPERHEATER

STEAM SAMPLERS

DRYER CARTONS

PRIMARY SEPARATOR

STEAM CONDENSER SCRUBBERS

STEAM-WATER DISCHARGE TUBES

STEAM-WATER DISCHARGE TUBES

FEED DISCHARGE NOZZLES

THERMAL SHIELD

THERMAL SLEEVE

DRYER CARTON
DRAIN EJECTORS

VORTEX BREAKER

Courtesy Riley Stoker Corp.

Figure 24-2 • Steam Purifier for Large Capacity Boilers

of a boiler water is the sum of the dissolved and suspended solids. Of these, the suspended solids are considered to be the more objectionable as their effect on foam stabilization is more pronounced than that of the dissolved solids. If solids are determined to be the cause of carryover, correction will normally be accomplished either by adjustment of boiler water controls, such as lowering concentrations through additional blowdown, or by change or alteration of the external feedwater treatment facilities. For example filtration following a hot process lime and soda ash softener may be inadequate permitting a

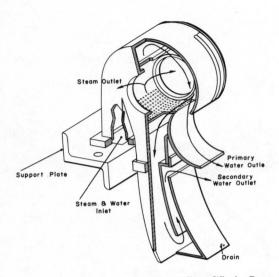

Courtesy Foster Wheeler Corp.

Figure 24-3 · Horizontal Steam Separator

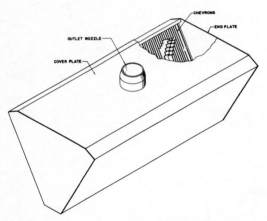

Courtesy Foster Wheeler Corp.

Figure 24-4 · Unit Chevron Dryer

higher amount of suspended solids in the boiler feedwater than can be tolerated.

Alkalinity as a contributing factor to carryover can also be corrected by adjustment or changes in internal and/or external treatment facilities. If the alkalinity is a result of the internal treatment program the use of less alkaline materials will correct the condition. Should the cause be external, additional facilities may be required such as the installation of a hydrogen zeolite unit to operate in parallel with a sodium unit thereby reducing the total alkalinity of the treated water.

The prevention of carryover difficulties due to the presence of oil in the boiler water is a problem that must be handled entirely external to the boiler itself. No method of internal treatment can be relied upon to overcome a carryover problem caused by oil contamination and the only safe policy that can be followed is the removal of the oil from the boiler feedwater.

ANTI-FOAM AGENTS. Frequently the cause of a carryover problem cannot be economically corrected through adjustment in boiler water balances or installation of additional external treatment facilities. In many such instances the use of effective anti-foam agents has provided the desired result.

During recent years highly effective organic anti-foam agents have been developed. In general the polymerized esters, alcohols and amides are the most effective agents yet developed. Various theories of foam inhibition by these compounds have been proposed and one of the most logical is to the effect that adsorption of the anti-foam agent on the metal surfaces results in hydrophobic conditions at the boiling surface. Fewer but larger steam bubbles are generated under the same heat transfer conditions and these bubbles readily coalesce in place on the heating surface, even prior to leaving that surface and rising through the boiler water. For the same amount of total steam production, tiny bubble formation is avoided and non-foaming boiler water is the result of this action.

With the use of these anti-foams it has been possible to develop boiler water concentrations in laboratory experimental boilers in excess of 150,000 ppm before carryover was experienced. While no practical use can be made of such anti-foam power it clearly demonstrates the effectiveness of the modern anti-foam. Figure 24-5 graphically illustrates the results of one such laboratory experiment.

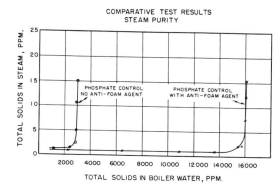

Figure 24-5 · Test Results Indicating Effect of Anti-Foam Agent

While the prime purpose of anti-foam application is the generation of high purity steam additional economic benefit is frequently experienced through reduced blowdown requirements. This has been proved on numerous occasions by actual plant studies where anti-foam was applied initially to overcome a chemical cause of carryover and, subsequent to the anti-foam feed, boiler water concentrations could be carried safely at much higher values without detrimentally affecting steam purity.

CARRYOVER STUDIES. The design of modern steam driven equipment is such that tolerance for impurities in the steam is practically non-existent. Thus there is an ever increasing demand, not only for more effective steam purifying equipment and anti-foam agents, but also for techniques to measure such impurities in fractional parts per million. This has been achieved through the development of highly sensitive conductivity equipment and the sodium tracer technique which are discussed in another chapter.

Carryover can be a serious problem in the modern steam plant and frequently the source of the carryover can only be established by exhaustive studies employing sensitive sampling and testing techniques. Science has provided the water treatment engineer with these tools and through their proper use he has been enabled to assist the plant operator in the generation of maximum purity steam consistent with minimum blowdown requirements and clean boiler internals.

REFERENCES

O. de Lorenzi, "Combustion Engineering", pp. 20-1, 2, 3, Combustion Engineering—Superheaters, Inc., New York, N. Y. (1949)

M. H. Kuhner, "How Steam Is Released in Water-Tube Boiler Drums", Power Plant Engineering, Vol. 48, pp. 92-94 (Sept. 1944)

R. A. Mumford, "A Theory of Carryover", *Combustion*, Vol. 18, pp. 39-41 (Feb. 1947)

P. B. Place, "Investigation of Carryover Problems and Identification of Types", *Proceedings*, Engineers Soc. of Western Penna., pp. 43-62 (1947)

J. H. Richards, "Solving an Unusual Case of Carryover", *Modern Power and Engineering*, Vol. 51, pp. 101, 102, 190-193 (Mar. 1957)

C. D. Shields, "Boilers: Types, Characteristics, and Functions", pp. 227-244, F. W. Dodge Corp., New York, N. Y. (1961)

25

Silica Turbine Blade Deposits

Turbine blade deposits develop from a number of causes, but the general effect is the same in all cases. That is, an adherent deposit develops in the steam passages and distorts the original shape of turbine nozzles and blades. The deposits are frequently somewhat rough or uneven at the surface, causing increased resistance to the flow of steam. Distortion of the steam passages will alter steam velocities and pressure drops, and the overall effect will be one of causing less efficient recovery of the energy which would be available from the steam. Under sufficiently severe conditions, the deposits may develop unevenly and unbalance the turbine rotor.

Corrosion or carryover are the principal causes of turbine blade deposits. Corrosion may be caused by incomplete feedwater treatment, or by incorrect lay-up procedure when the turbine is not in service. The principal cause of corrosion is oxygen in the presence of moisture, and less frequently, high carbon dioxide content of the steam together with moisture. Deposits may also originate with normal carryover, gross carryover, or selective carryover of boiler water solids with the steam.

With the deposition of solids on turbine blading, rapid loss in efficiency will occur. Records for stage pressures in the turbines will indicate progressively higher pressures. Stage pressures will increase beyond the manufacturer's recommendations, and further operation will not be considered advisable. Most important will be the increase in pounds of steam per kilowatt hour of power generated.

The term "normal carryover" refers to the carryover which occurs in any boiler operating under the best conditions. It is simply a matter of boiler design and solids content of the feedwater and the boiler water. With modern, efficient steam generators, such carryover is less than 1 ppm of total solids.

Industrial plants, at times, encounter a condition which may be described as gross carryover, but which is caused by priming or foaming of the boiler water, or by leakage of steam purifying equipment. Since such difficulties may have numerous causes such as condensate contamination or incorrect feedwater treatment, they are not considered further in this discussion. In recent years, a third and more troublesome type of carryover has been observed, and this is the specialized case of silica carryover.

Non-selective carryover of boiler water solids occurs most frequently in units operating at lower pressures, and various methods of correction are available depending on the cause. The deposits from such carryover have a large proportion of soluble salts, and washing of turbines is usually sufficient to restore full efficiency. On the other hand, when selective carryover of silica takes place, the turbine blade deposits frequently contain up to 95% silica, with the result that simple water washing is no longer adequate and specialized cleaning must be used.

OCCURRENCE OF SILICA DEPOSITS

Turbine blade deposits in which silica is a predominant constituent and which generally tend to be insoluble are very rarely encountered below 400 psi. As a result, such deposits were not recognized as an individual problem until comparatively recent years. Since that time, considerable investigation has been given to the problem and a number of groups are now cooperating to find a complete and effective solution to the problem. The problem becomes increasingly severe with increase in operating pressure. At pressures of 900 psi and above, the turbine blade deposits which contain a high percentage of insoluble silica are the rule instead of the exception.

With the development of fast steaming high pressure boilers, advancement was also made with improved ability of the units to generate steam of high purity. Limitation of total solids in the steam to a maximum value of 1.0 ppm is now a standard specification and most large high pressure units consistently operate under such conditions. When this value is compared to the solids content of the boiler water, it is seen that the process of purification is carried out to a high degree. On the other hand, even a very small solids content of the steam will amount to carry-over of several thousand pounds of boiler water solids per year from a high capacity unit. Of this quantity, only a very small percentage need remain in the turbine steam passages in order to form objectionable deposits. The problem is further complicated by the fact that there is considerable evidence to prove that silica is carried selectively from boiler water at higher pressures in such a manner that normal steam purification equipment cannot prevent contamination of the steam.

CAUSE OF SILICA CARRYOVER

A number of theories have been proposed to explain silica carryover and silica deposits in turbine steam passages. Some of the better known explanations are reviewed.

Normal carryover is due to mechanical entrainment of minute droplets of boiler water in the steam. Such droplets of water will evaporate to dryness in the superheater section of the boiler, and the solids will continue to be carried along with steam in a manner similar to that by which dust particles are carried in air. If such carryover resulted in turbine blade deposits, it is to be expected that the deposits would have a composition similar to that of the boiler water. It is apparent that other factors enter the picture, since deposits containing up to 95% silica are common.

Experimental evidence has been developed to support the theory that silica is selectively carried from the boiler as a vapor, or in solution in the steam. Other theories propose that the difficulty stems from mechanical entrainment, but assume various methods by which the deposits that result are principally silica. The proposed theories are based on melting points of various salts as they pass through the superheater tubes, adhesive properties of sodium hydroxide particles resulting from incomplete drying while passing through the superheater tubes, and the action of carbon

dioxide in the steam on deposits of sodium silicate resulting from normal carryover.

Straub has experimentally investigated the possibility of solubility of boiler water salts in steam, as well as vaporization of boiler water salts. The results of his investigations indicate that the common boiler water salts are soluble to an insignificant degree at pressures below 2400 psi. Sodium chloride appears to be the most soluble common material, and appreciable amounts may be dissolved in steam when the steam is superheated and can come in contact with solid salt. This condition is not common in normal boiler water system operation. Since solubility is based on temperature and pressure of the steam, deposition of the salt would be expected by reduction in temperature and pressure, such as occurs in a turbine.

Evidence was also obtained to support the theory that silica will actually leave the boiler as a vapor. The quantity in the steam will vary with boiler pressure and with concentration of silica in the boiler water. It was also noted that pH value of the boiler water has considerable influence on the quantity of silica in the steam. A decrease in silica carryover was noted with an increase in pH value.

Although silica is found on turbine blades as crystalline and amorphous silica (SiO_2) it has been proposed that vaporization from the boiler takes place as silicic acid (H_2SiO_3). This would account for the variation in silica carryover with pH of the boiler water. To some degree, this theory is supported by other experimental results. Other investigators have reported a definite relationship between turbine stage temperatures and the form in which silica deposits. These results throw some doubt on the theory that silica carryover is in the form of silicic acid.

REMOVAL OF DEPOSITS

Two procedures are in widespread use for removal of insoluble silica turbine blade deposits. These are caustic washing of the turbine and mechanical cleaning. Where the facilities are available, and where operating conditions permit, it is desirable to attempt caustic washing, since mechanical cleaning generally takes a longer time and proves to be more costly.

It is desirable to precede caustic washing by plain washing, in order to determine the extent to which the deposit consists of soluble salts. Shutting down and starting up a turbine after permitting the machine to cool accomplishes a certain amount of washing due to the condensation which takes place. Where temperature of the steam varies with load, a certain amount of washing can also be accomplished by operation at very light load. Where washing is desired under controlled conditions, it is preferable to use water injection in order to desuperheat the steam.

Turbine manufacturers and central power station operators have developed procedures for turbine washing which experience has shown can be safely performed without damage to the turbine. The procedures are available from a number of sources, and the operation must be carried out as recommended in order to avoid the possibility of damage to the turbine from mechanical and thermal stresses.

Caustic washing follows the same general procedure as water washing. Frequently, the washing is started by using plain water, and a solution of sodium hydroxide is gradually substituted. A 10 to 20% solution of caustic soda is generally used, although under some circumstances, a stronger or weaker solution may be desirable.

Figure 25-1 · Blading Deposit Analyzed to be 90–95% Silica

With simple washing, the progress of cleaning can be followed by measurement of specific conductance of the condensate. However, when caustic washing is being used, it is preferable to follow the progress of the cleaning by silica determinations on the condensate. Progress of the cleaning must be followed closely, in order to determine that all deposits have been removed to the greatest possible extent.

Some plants are not in a position to resort to caustic washing, since large quantities of condensate are wasted during the operation. In addition, if the deposits are sufficiently heavy, it may be desirable to use mechanical cleaning in order to insure thorough removal of all deposits.

Mechanical cleaning can be conducted by hand operations such as filing and scraping, but is generally conducted by sand blasting. Both fine sand and fly ash are widely used as the abrasive agents. During such an operation, care must be taken to prevent damage to the metal surfaces.

It is apparent that insoluble turbine blade deposits may be removed after they have developed, but it is also apparent that the procedure is costly, and in many cases highly inconvenient. Forced outage for cleaning may require overloading of other equipment, or considerable expense for purchase of power from an outside source. In the case of industrial installations, plant shutdown may even be necessary. The basic problem is therefore not one of removing deposits, but of preventing them in the first place.

PREVENTION OF SILICA DEPOSITS

The experimental work of Straub comes closest to fitting the facts of actual operating experience, and on this basis, may be applied to actual operating conditions by making suitable modifications, depending upon the circumstances of the individual problem. In units operating at 900 psi and above, it is probable that the most significant factor of corrective action is maintenance of silica content of the boiler water at least as low as 10 ppm, but preferably less than 5 ppm.

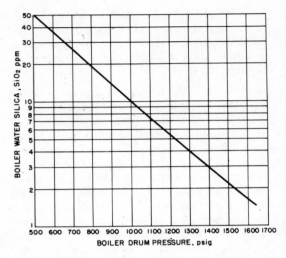

Figure 25-2 · Approximate Boiler Water Silica to Limit Silica in Steam to 0.02 ppm

Steam purification systems which wash the steam with incoming boiler feedwater which is low in silica, will slightly reduce the silica content of the steam. However, in most cases, the time of contact is too short for significant reduction.

The problem is essentially one of providing feedwater with the lowest possible silica content, and of preventing silica contamination from condenser leakage. After silica has entered the boiler water, the usual corrective action will be blowdown within the ability of the system to replace the blowdown water with suitable makeup water.

Internal treatment for removal of silica is normally not practiced, but an interesting application has been reported. Magnesium oxide is widely used in hot process softeners for silica reduction with good results. Several years ago, magnesium oxide was used internally in a 1200 psi boiler. With feed of magnesium oxide, it was necessary to discontinue feed of sodium phosphate, but particular care was taken to practically eliminate calcium contamination in the makeup water.

Condenser leakage is most readily detected by providing instruments to continuously record specific conductance of the condensate. Such equipment must be maintained in good working order and periodically checked. The chemical characteristics of the condenser cooling water must be kept in mind in interpreting conductivity results on the condensate. For example, the silica content of sea water is extremely low in comparison to the total solids content. At the other extreme, the silica content of some ground waters will be quite high in comparison to the total solids. In addition to depending upon conductivity measurements, it is also advisable to make periodic analyses for the silica content of the condensate. Determination of silica in very low concentrations can be subject to considerable error, unless the determination is conducted by an experienced analyst using the proper laboratory facilities.

The other principal source of silica contamination will originate with the makeup water. The degree to which such contamination can develop will depend upon the external system of treating the makeup water. The makeup water will usually be obtained from a source such as condensate from a system operating at lower pressure, from evaporators, or from chemically treated water.

Since it is necessary to maintain control over other factors aside from silica content, makeup water not from evaporators or condensate is usually treated to have essentially "zero" hardness. This requirement calls for final treatment such as zeolite softening, demineralization, or hot phosphate softening. However, these processes may be preceded by coagulation and filtration, hot or cold process softening using lime and other agents, and acid treatment. Choice of the exact treatment system is based upon chemical characteristics of available sources of makeup water considered in conjunction with economy of appropriate systems.

Where a high pressure system operates under conditions such that very little makeup water is required, evaporation or demineralization of the makeup water is generally the the most satisfactory system. Many industrial installations use high pressure steam for process requirements, and appreciable quantities of makeup water are required. Under these circumstances, evaporated makeup is too costly and one or more of the other systems of treatment will provide satisfactory results with favorable economy.

Evaporators may be obtained with performance guaranteed so that the distillate does not contain more than 0.5 ppm total solids with fresh water being used as evaporator feedwater. If sea water is used as feedwater the guarantee may specify that the distillate will not contain more than $\frac{1}{4}$ grain per gallon of total salts. Carryover from an evaporator corresponds to carryover from any low pressure boiler, and consists of mechanical entrainment of the shell water in the evaporator vapor. The carryover from low pressure boilers is subject to many mechanical factors, but evaporator design and operation usually tend to eliminate or reduce the factors which promote carryover. The most important factor affecting vapor purity is concentration of the shell water. Limiting concentration may be specified by the evaporator manufacturer, and if it is not, then competent advice should be secured.

Feedwater to the evaporator should be deaerated and depending upon characteristics of the feedwater, chemical treatment may also be advisable to eliminate scale formation and sludge accumulation within the evaporator shell.

The use of anti-foams to reduce carryover in high pressure boilers is well known. Similar anti-foams may be used in evaporators to improve steam purity. The need for antifoams is increasing due to expanding use of synthetic detergents which are present in increasing quantities in many surface water supplies.

The technology of demineralization has advanced to the extent that demineralization is generally the most common method of preparing makeup water for high pressure utility boilers. Present day demineralization systems will produce water with very low solids content including silica. In plants where makeup requirements are more than about 10%, demineralization may not be the most economical method. Organic contamin-

Fig. 25-3
Occurrence of Silica in Natural Waters

	Buffalo N.Y.	Elko Nevada	Laurel Miss.	Haverhill Mass.	Savannah Ga.	Warren Ohio	Phil. Is.	Sea Water
Hardness as $CaCO_3$, ppm	118	180	10	30	107	160	84	6250
Calcium as $CaCO_3$, ppm	85	135	7	25	79	105	41	1000
Magnesium as $CaCO_3$, ppm	33	45	3	5	37	55	43	5250
"M" Alkalinity as $CaCO_3$, ppm	90	436	66	17	109	24	130	115
Sulfate as SO_4, ppm	20	119	13	11	9	137	16	2650
Chloride as Cl, ppm	19	45	7	6	6	9	5	19000
Silica as SiO_2, ppm	1.6	80	50	0.8	53	0.2	90	0.02—4.0
Source	Lake	Well	Well	Lake	Well	River	Well	Ocean

ation of the available water source may make the use of ion exchange resins questionable unless thorough pretreatment is provided.

The other systems of zeolite softening, hot and cold process softening are well known and widely used. Each system has certain inherent limitations, and these are the guiding factors in selecting a suitable system. As an example, the silica removal which can be obtained with each system can be summarized in general as follows:

a. Silica reduction to approximately 1 ppm with hot process softening.

b. Forty to seventy percent silica reduction with cold process softening.

c. No silica reduction with zeolite softening, and the possibility of silica increase with a siliceous type exchange medium.

With any of the systems of treatment outlined, design and operation of the equipment as well as choice of treatment chemicals determines whether optimum results are obtained.

Some plants are fortunate in having more than one source of makeup water available. When this situation arises, a careful study should be given to each source of makeup water, in order to avoid future difficulties and provide best economy.

Figure 25-3 illustrates the wide variation in silica content of natural waters which may be encountered. Some of the waters are of course rarely encountered, but serve to illustrate the fact that where water treatment is concerned, the problem calls for individualized attention.

The means by which silica is transported from the boiler water to the turbine steam passages, and the means by which deposition takes place are problems which are still being widely investigated, and on which continuing progress can be expected. A generally applicable, clear-cut solution is not available for the problem and each plant presents an individual problem. In addition to the problem of preventing insoluble silica turbine blade deposits, a plant may be faced with the problems of preventing corrosion, scale or embrittlement. These complicating factors also influence selection of the proper system of treatment.

REFERENCES

E. E. Coulter, E. A. Pirsh and E. J. Wagner, Jr., "Selective Silica Carry-Over in Steam", *Transactions*, Am. Soc. of Mech. Engineers, Vol. 78, pp. 869-873 (1956)

F. G. Straub, "Steam Turbine Blade Deposits", Eng. Exp. Station Bul. 364, University of Illinois, Urbana, Illinois (1946)

26

Measurement of Steam Purity

Accurate measurement of steam purity is of considerable significance in the operation of a steam plant. It is particularly so for the modern higher pressure plants where tolerances for deposition can be very critical. With advancement in technique it is now possible to determine steam purity in parts per billion and it seems safe to state that present knowledge permits reliable measurement of steam contamination to a degree which should satisfy the demand of critical high pressure operation. Thus it is possible to accurately check on boiler guarantee or effectiveness of steam purifying equipment.

HISTORY OF METHODS OF DETERMINATION OF STEAM PURITY

The importance of steam purity measurement in boiler operation was investigated as early as 1865 and for some fifty years steam quality determinations were accomplished mainly by steam calorimetry. Of the many types of calorimeters developed for this purpose the most familiar was the throttling calorimeter in which a sample of saturated steam is expanded through an orifice to atmospheric pressure. The total heat in the steam sample is greater than the total heat of the saturated steam at atmospheric pressure, and the excess heat in the steam sample will superheat the expanded steam or evaporate the moisture originally present in the steam sample.

From measurements of the pressure and temperature of the inlet and outlet steam, it is possible to calculate the moisture present in the original steam sample. The accuracy of the throttling calorimeter is usually taken as $\pm 0.2\%$ moisture which can mean an appreciable error in the solids content of the steam. For example, at a boiler water concentration of 3500 ppm, an error of 0.2% moisture would correspond to an error in the calculated total solids of the steam of 7.0 ppm.

The wide use of superheated steam along with the need for more precise measurement of steam purity and our broadening knowledge of steam properties have practically eliminated calorimetric measurement.

TOTAL SOLIDS DETERMINATION

The collection of a sample of condensed steam and the evaporation of the sample to dryness and weighing of the solids residue is another method employed in the determination of steam purity. This method is cumbersome and time consuming, not lending itself to routine control. Satisfactory accuracy can be obtained only with careful handling and technique. The presence of 1 ppm of solids in the steam will yield a weighable residue of only 0.001 gram from a 1 liter sample. Naturally, therefore, a larger sample must be taken in order to avoid the error in weighing and the sample must be carefully protected from dust, etc. The large size sample must be evaporated down to dryness, under carefully controlled conditions. ASTM Tentative Methods of Test for Suspended and Dissolved Solids in Industrial Water (ASTM Designation: D-1888-61T) is intended for application to water containing 5 ppm or less of total solids, and for which samples of more than 4 liters must be evaporated. The American Boiler Manufacturer's Association stipulates that the total solids in the steam for referee analyses shall be determined by testing no less than 10 samples of condensed steam and taking the average of all results.

ROUTINE MINERAL ANALYSES

The use of the conventional mineral analyses covering such determinations as hardness, alkalinity, chloride, pH, sulfate, etc., is of little significance in the analysis of condensed steam samples except of course where the contamination of steam is excessive. The limit of accuracy of various test methods such as hardness, chloride, etc. is such that they cannot be applied where the condensed steam sample is reasonably pure.

SPECIFIC CONDUCTANCE

The specific conductance of a condensed steam sample, which is the measure of the flow of an electric current through the sample, is probably the most universally used method of determining steam purity. Pure water has a very low conductance, but as dissolved solids in a steam sample increase so does conductance. This method of determining purity is rapid and reasonably accurate.

One of the disadvantages to the use of specific conductance and which materially affects accuracy is the fact that some dissolved gases have a marked effect on the conductance of water. Such gases as carbon dioxide, ammonia and hydrogen sulfide ionize in water solution and thus interfere with the use of conductance as a measure of dissolved solids present. This interference can be appreciable when determining purity on a high quality steam sample. For example, in a sample containing less than 1 ppm dissolved solids, specific conductance may be in the range of 1.0 to 2.0 micromhos. The presence of any ammonia or carbon dioxide in this sample will materially increase the conduc-

Figure 26-1 • Specific Conductance Flow Cell and Recorder with One of the Earliest Degassers

tance reading. Ammonia will impart conductance of 8.0 to 9.0 micromhos per ppm of this gas, while carbon dioxide will increase conductance on an average of 5.0 micromhos per ppm of carbon dioxide in the lower range of concentration.

Two procedures may be employed to offset the effect of dissolved gases. One is to measure the content of the gas in the sample and apply correction to the conductance reading and the other is to degas the sample before measuring conductance. Accurate correction curves are available to establish the effect on conductance of carbon dioxide or ammonia in a sample. While constant improvements have been made in effectiveness of degassing equipment, traces of these gases can remain. A further advancement in the removal of dissolved gases has been the use of hydrogen ion exchange which can effectively reduce ammonia to a negligible value. However, should the sample being tested contain solids which are primarily in the form of sodium sulfate and sodium chloride, hydrogen ion exchange will produce acids which will result in an increase in conductance. There is no doubt that proper use of conductance and proper sample preparation have greatly increased the reliability of this method of steam purity measurement. Nevertheless the results of steam purity studies using specific conductance and recently developed tracer techniques do indicate that when measurement for solids in the order of 1.0 ppm or less is desired, the accuracy of conductance becomes questionable.

TRACER TECHNIQUES

While the steam purity guarantee for the modern high pressure steam generators states that the steam will contain not more than 1.0 ppm of total solids for given boiler water conditions, it is now generally accepted that steam purity of this order is not satisfactory for high pressure operation if deposition in superheaters or turbines is to be avoided. Tracer techniques involve testing for a component of the solids present in the boiler water, which component can reasonably be expected to be present in the steam at the same ratio to the total solids as is the case for the boiler water. For tracer technique studies published so far radioactive phosphorus (p^{32}), which was added to the boiler water and the sodium ion which is normally present as the ion in greatest concentration in the boiler water, have been employed. While the use of radio-active phosphorus resulted in

Figure 26-2 • Sodium Recording Equipment Set Up for Plant Study

extreme sensitivity, it presents a problem of handling and disposal of the boiler water and would be too costly to be practical for actual plant steam purity studies. For this reason the work on the use of tracer techniques as a means of determining steam purity has concentrated on the use of the sodium ion.

Employing a flame spectrophotometer it is possible to detect sodium content of con-densed steam with a precision of 0.0004 ppm. An average ratio of 2.5 to 3.0 ppm of solids per ppm of sodium has been established for boiler waters so the sensitivity of this tech-nique is in the range of 0.001 ppm of solids. Initially, the use of the sodium tracer tech-nique for steam purity evaluation possessed the disadvantage of the steam sample having to be tested in the laboratory. Extreme

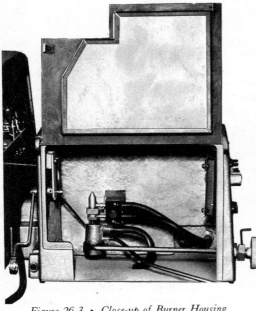

Figure 26-3 • Close-up of Burner Housing

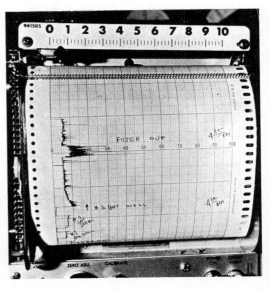

Figure 26-4 • Strip Chart Showing Effectiveness of Air Filter

care had to be taken in the sampling procedure to avoid contamination by sodium which is always present in the atmosphere to some extent. This procedure was time consuming and did necessitate frequent resampling to verify results. Steady progress, however, has been made in the technique of measuring sodium by flame spectrophotometer. It is now possible to operate the equipment in the boiler plant with continuous measurement and recording of the sodium content of a constant flowing condensed steam sample. The problem of contamination from sodium in the air was eliminated through the use of a highly effective air filter which provides a sodium free air to the burner of the spectrophotometer at a slight positive pressure. Experience gained with this equipment in many actual steam studies has shown that steam purity evaluations to the level of 0.001 ppm of solids can readily be obtained.

It is of interest to note that of the many plants which operate equipment for the continuous monitoring of steam purity by conductivity, some steam generating plants operating at extremely high pressures have found the use of conductivity to be of insufficient accuracy for their needs. As a result there are now several installations where continuous monitoring of steam purity is accomplished by constant measurement and recording of the sodium content of the steam.

STEAM SAMPLING

For our present knowledge of steam purity determination to be of practical value it is essential that the sample being tested is truly representative of the steam being generated. Detailed instructions for the installation and construction of steam sampling nozzles are available in the ASME Power Test Code and the ASTM Standards. For many years these standards have been widely accepted and it was generally assumed that with the use of either an ASTM or an ASME steam sampling nozzle, correctly installed, good steam sampling would be experienced. As methods of measuring steam purity become increasingly sensitive, it has become obvious that our analytical techniques are far ahead of our sampling techniques. A great deal of experimental work on steam sampling methods has been conducted recently in an attempt to improve knowledge of this subject. This work has been conducted under the supervision of the Steam Contamination Subcommittee of the Joint Research Committee on Boiler Feedwater Studies of the ASME.

REFERENCES

R. V. Cobb and E. E. Coulter, "The Prevention of Errors in Steam Purity Measurement Caused by Deposition of Impurities in Sampling Lines", *Proceedings,* Am. Soc. for Testing Materials, pp. 1386-1395 (1961)

W. A. Crandall and W. Nacovsky, "The Development and Operation of An Ultrasensitive Recording Flame Photometer", *Proceedings,* Am. Power Conf., Vol. XX, pp. 726-738 (1958)

J. J. Maguire, "Sodium Test Measures Steam Purity Accurately", *Power Engineering,* Vol. 62, pp. 81-82 (Sept. 1958)

S. O. Meyer, "Measurement of High Purity Steam by Continuous Sodium Recording", *The Betz Indicator,* Betz Laboratories, Inc., Phila., Pa. (Oct. 1959)

T. A. Miskimen, "Results of Steam Sampling Nozzle Tests on Evaporator Vapor", Paper Number 59-A-301, Am. Soc. of Mech. Engineers, New York, N.Y. (1959)

H. Phillips, "Closing Our Gaps in Our Knowledge of Steam Sampling", Paper Number 59-A-287, Am. Soc. of Mech. Engineers, New York, N.Y. (1959)

E. A. Pirsh and F. G. Raynor, "Instrumentation for the Determination of Steam Purity", *Proceedings,* Engineers Soc. of Western Penna., pp. 79-88 (1956)

J. H. Potter, "Steam Calorimetry", *Combustion,* Vol. 29, pp. 51-55 (July 1957)

J. K. Rice, "Steam Quality Measurements by Flame Photometer", *Proceedings,* Engineers Soc. of Western Penna., pp. 89-101 (1956)

27

Condensate Return Line Corrosion

THE problem of corrosion in return condensate systems can be brought under control in most industrial systems by one of several proven methods. This problem, once responsible for expensive maintenance costs, need no longer be of concern. In new plants, precautionary measures should be taken during design stages, rather than waiting until expensive shutdowns show the need for correction.

Figure 27-2 • Typical Grooving Attack by Carbon Dioxide

CAUSES OF RETURN LINE CORROSION

Failures most frequently occur at threaded joints because the metal thicknesses have been reduced at these points. Figure 27-1 is an example of such attack. Horizontal lines are usually more severely attacked than vertical lines due to incomplete draining of the condensate in systems that operate intermittently. The corrosive action manifests itself in the form of grooving or channeling for the most part. Figure 27-2 is a cutaway section of pipe illustrating the typical grooving attack caused by carbon dioxide. Figure 27-3 shows another pipe sample typical of carbon dioxide attack.

Figure 27-4 shows a condensate line in which the corrosive attack is primarily in the form of pitting. Such pitting attack is typical of oxygen.

The principal causes for steam and condensate corrosion are the dissolved gases carbon dioxide and oxygen. These gases must be in solution before they become aggressive. There are other influencing factors such as rate of condensation, time of contact, tem-

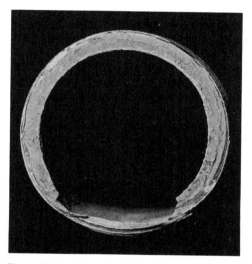

Figure 27-3 • Example of Pipe Wall Grooving by Carbon Dioxide

Figure 27-4. • Pitting Attack Typical of Oxygen

Figure 27-1 • Carbon Dioxide Attack at Threaded Joints

perature, metal heterogenity, galvanic action and others but only because they supplement the basic factors.

The corrosion reaction for dissolved oxygen may be illustrated as follows:

(1)
$$4Fe + 6H_2O + 3O_2 = 4Fe(OH)_3$$
iron + water + oxygen = ferric hydroxide

The ferric hydroxide formed may later revert to iron oxide rust as follows:

(2)
$$2Fe(OH)_3 = Fe_2O_3 + 3H_2O$$
ferric hydroxide = ferric oxide + water

When carbon dioxide dissolves in water it forms carbonic acid which is a weak acid and produces corrosion in keeping with the following equation:

(3)
$$Fe + 2H_2CO_3 = Fe(HCO_3)_2$$
iron + carbonic acid = ferrous bicarbonate
$$+ H_2$$
+ hydrogen

The above reaction proceeds rapidly at pH values below 5.9. The reaction product, ferrous bicarbonate, tends to elevate the pH and as the pH increases above 5.9, the reaction rate becomes reduced. The hydrogen formed in the reaction will also have a retarding effect particularly when the pH exceeds 5.9.

The ferrous bicarbonate formed in this reaction is soluble and can be carried along in the condensate. However, at points of pressure drop or reduced carbon dioxide content in the vapor phase it will precipitate from solution in keeping with the following reaction:

(4)
$$Fe(HCO_3)_2 = FeO +$$
ferrous bicarbonate = ferrous oxide +
$$2CO_2 + H_2O$$
carbon dioxide + water

When dissolved oxygen is also present, it will influence the reaction rate by removing the hydrogen to form water. The ferrous bicarbonate will precipitate as follows:

(5)
$$2Fe(HCO_3)_2 + \frac{1}{2}O_2 = Fe_2O_3 +$$
ferrous bicarbonate + oxygen = ferric oxide
$$+ 4CO_2 + 2H_2O$$
carbon dioxide + water

A combination of reactions (4) and (5) can be written to show the production of Fe_3O_4, the magnetic oxide of iron (magnetite) as illustrated by equation 6.

(6)
$$3Fe(HCO_3)_2 + \frac{1}{2}O_2 = Fe_3O_4 +$$
ferrous bicarbonate + oxygen = magnetite
$$+ 6CO_2 + 3H_2O$$
carbon dioxide + water

In some cases, the decomposition of ferrous bicarbonate has resulted in the production of deposits of ferrous carbonate:

(7)
$$Fe(HCO_3)_2 = FeCO_3 +$$
ferrous bicarbonate = ferrous carbonate +
$$CO_2 + H_2O$$
carbon dioxide + water

From the above reactions, it can be seen that deposits of FeO, Fe_2O_3, Fe_3O_4, $FeCO_3$ and mixtures of these can be found present in steam and condensate systems and are the type deposits usually responsible for plugging.

SOURCES OF DISSOLVED OXYGEN

Oxygen in steam and condensate systems may originate directly from the boiler feedwater or may enter at various points in the condensate system. Oxygen is present in most makeup waters and unless the makeup water is brought to saturation temperature in a properly vented open or deaerating heater, appreciable amounts will remain in the feed water entering the boilers. When the feed water is subjected to boiler temperature the oxygen will be released and a portion of it can be entrained with the steam and find its way into the condensate system. Oxygen that enters in this fashion can be coped with readily by use of mechanical or chemical deaeration of the feedwater.

In vacuum return systems or in gravity type return systems there is ample opportunity for oxygen infiltration. While condensate that is returned under pressure will usually be free of oxygen, infiltration can take place where such systems operate intermittently.

It is not uncommon for cooling water to be injected into the vacuum pumps to lower the temperature of the condensate. This practice is also followed in certain gravity type return systems where the condensate is collected in a centrally located receiving tank for pumping back to the boiler plant. The cooling water is usually laden with oxygen and its introduction into the condensate generally creates a corrosion problem that manifests itself in the form of pitting. Where cooling water must be added, it should be controlled thermostatically so that the amount introduced is held to an absolute minimum. To avoid corrosion from the introduction of cooling water, catalyzed sodium sulfite, which permits rapid reaction of the sulfite with oxygen in the cold, can be proportioned to the cooling water to react with the oxygen and eliminate it from the water.

In general, the elimination of oxygen from condensate systems can be accomplished through relatively simple means and for this reason corrosion and pitting due to dissolved oxygen is readily controlled.

SOURCES OF CARBON DIOXIDE

Carbon dioxide is the usual cause of steam and return line corrosion and the corrosion is characterized by a general thinning of the pipe wall or grooving along the bottom of the pipe.

The chief source of carbon dioxide is the bicarbonate and carbonate alkalinity of the makeup water to the boilers. The bicarbonate and carbonate alkalinity when subjected to boiler temperature undergo thermal decomposition and liberate carbon dioxide which becomes entrained with the steam. The decomposition is illustrated by the following equations:

(8)
$$2(HCO_3)^- + heat = (CO_3)^= +$$
$$bicarbonate + heat = carbonate +$$
$$CO_2 + H_2O$$
$$carbon\ dioxide + water$$

(9)
$$(CO_3)^= + H_2O + heat = 2(OH)^- +$$
$$carbonate + water + heat = hydroxide +$$
$$CO_2$$
$$carbon\ dioxide$$

Reaction (8) proceeds to 100% completion whereas reaction (9) is only partially complete with decomposition taking place to approximately 80%. Based on these reactions it can be calculated that for each 1 ppm of bicarbonate alkalinity (expressed as calcium carbonate) in the boiler feedwater, 0.79 ppm of carbon dioxide will be evolved. For each 1 ppm of carbonate alkalinity (expressed as calcium carbonate) 0.35 ppm of carbon dioxide will be evolved.

The other possible and usually minor sources of carbon dioxide are the free, gaseous carbon dioxide that is dissolved in most natural waters and the carbon dioxide which forms from decomposition of soda ash that may be used for regulation of boiler water alkalinity. Free carbon dioxide is almost completely eliminated by efficient feedwater deaeration and consequently is rarely a factor in steam and condensate corrosion. The use of soda ash is inadvisable where return line corrosion is being experienced and should be replaced by caustic soda.

CORROSIVE EFFECTS OF CARBON DIOXIDE

The curves illustrated by Figure 27-5 show that other conditions being fixed, corrosion is proportional to the carbon dioxide concentration of condensates.

The rapid increase in corrosion rate with increase in carbon dioxide concentration and with increase in flow rate is illustrated graphically.

Even at low carbon dioxide concentrations, however, corrosion can take place at isolated points in the condensate system. For example, the curve of Figure 27-5 shows that for any

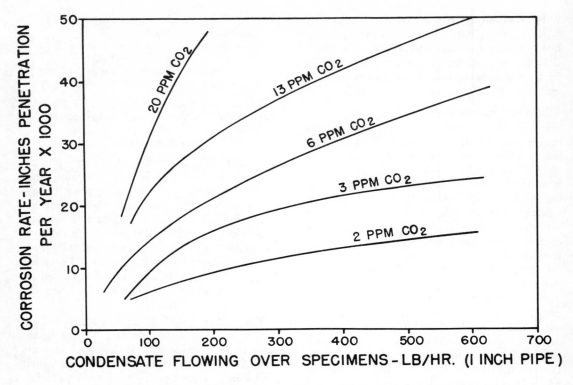

Figure 27-5 • Effect of Condensate Flow and Carbon Dioxide Content on Rate of Corrosion

concentration of carbon dioxide, the rate of corrosion increases with the quantity of condensate flowing, or in other words, corrosion is a function of the total pounds of carbon dioxide. Therefore, in a given system corrosion may only be a serious problem where the quantity of condensate handled is high, such as in the main return line.

In order for carbon dioxide to be corrosive it must be in solution. The laws of Henry and Dalton govern the solution of gases in liquids and state in simple form that the concentration of a gas dissolved in a liquid is proportional to its partial pressure (or concentration) in the contacting gaseous phase. The application of these laws serves to explain severe corrosion that occurs in units condensing steam that operate intermittently. For example, when a drier or unit heater is first supplied with steam and condensation occurs, the resulting condensate will have a

negligible amount of carbon dioxide dissolved in it, due to the fact that the partial pressure of the carbon dioxide in the vapor phase is low. Assuming that the incoming steam contains 20 ppm of carbon dioxide, the initial condensate discharged by the unit will have less than a fraction of 1 ppm. The remaining carbon dioxide will accumulate in the vapor phase above the condensate in the unit. As condensation continues the accumulated carbon dioxide will develop a partial pressure sufficiently high to permit re-solution of more and more carbon dioxide, until equilibrium is attained, under which condition the carbon dioxide content of discharged condensate will equal that of the incoming steam.

It can be calculated that the quantity of carbon dioxide that must accumulate in the gaseous phase will be in the range of several hundred to more than a thousand ppm before equilibrium conditions are attained. If such units operate intermittently, on cooling and as pressure on the unit decreases considerable quantities of carbon dioxide will go into solution. The pH of the condensate will be lowered and accelerated corrosion will take place. It is apparent, therefore, that corrosion in isolated units can take place even though the concentration of carbon dioxide in the steam is relatively low. Because of the accumulation of carbon dioxide that is possible, venting of the units continuously during operation or shortly before shut-down would prove of material benefit. It is also essential that such units be provided with proper drainage.

REDUCTION OF CARBON DIOXIDE CONTENT OF STEAM

The various softening processes in which lime is employed, such as lime softening, lime-soda, and lime-gypsum softening, secure a reduction in alkalinity by precipitation of calcium and magnesium bicarbonate by the lime. Hot lime-hot ion exchange is another example of this type of process. It should be emphasized that while these processes reduce the feed-water alkalinity, they do not completely eliminate it. With normal balances, utilizing hot process lime and soda softening and 100% makeup, the carbon dioxide content of the steam will be in the range of 17 - 21 ppm.

The various processes using acid, such as direct acid neutralization or hydrogen zeolite softening, will reduce the alkalinity of the treated water to a relatively low value. With hydrogen zeolite softening, chemical efficiency is lower, but softening is accomplished simultaneously. Where very low carbon dioxide values are required, necessary alkalinity for good boiler operation can be obtained by caustic soda addition.

Almost complete carbon dioxide removal is secured by demineralization, in which both cations and anions are removed either by aeration, vacuum deaeration, or adsorption

in the anion exchange resin. Normally, demineralization is limited to those plants where high percentage of returned condensate is expected, due to the cost of this process.

In addition to hydrogen zeolite neutralized with caustic, raw water or blending with sodium zeolite, other ion exchange processes can be used. Softeners operating on the sodium cycle do not reduce the bicarbonate alkalinity of the raw water. However, acid treatment followed by aeration can be used following the softening process. Dealkalization by chloride-anion exchange is another method, in which the makeup water is first passed through a sodium unit and then through a second anion exchange unit regenerated with salt. In this latter process, alkalinity is reduced without the use of acid, but chemical efficiency is poor compared to other systems. The use of chloride-anion exchange is generally limited to small plants where objection to handling acid is the influencing factor.

By selection of the proper external treatment processes, it is possible to produce a minimum carbon dioxide content of the steam in the range of approximately 5 ppm when using 100% makeup water. In most systems, except at points where stratification may occur, corrosion should be kept to a satisfactorily low level. Also, at this low level of carbon dioxide, neutralizing amines can be economically considered.

INTERNAL METHODS OF CORRECTION FOR CARBON DIOXIDE

Of historical interest only was the attempt to use inorganic chemicals to control carbon dioxide corrosion in condensate lines, as these methods proved to be ineffective. These methods involved the use of an alkali, such as sodium hydroxide to neutralize carbon dioxide or polyphosphates to form an iron-phosphate film. The injection of these inorganic materials to the steam was objectionable for the same reasons that carryover of boiler water solids is undesirable.

AMMONIA

Ammonia has been employed for neutralization of carbon dioxide and elevation of pH. Ammonia can be fed to the system as ammonium hydroxide (a solution of ammonia gas in water) or an inorganic salt such as ammonium sulfate can be used. At boiler temperatures, the ammonium sulfate will be decomposed with the liberation of ammonia gas with the steam.

Ammonia has been successfully employed for control of CO_2 corrosion and iron pick-up in central stations with low percentage make-up and low carbon dioxide concentration in the steam. While a reduction in corrosion of ferrous metals can be secured in this manner, copper and zinc bearing metals can be seriously corroded, particularly when oxygen is also present and there is opportunity for ammonia to concentrate. Because of the higher CO_2 concentrations usually found in industrial plants, and consequent higher ammonia requirements, the problem of copper attack limits the application of ammonia.

NEUTRALIZING AMINES

Neutralization of carbonic acid can safely be accomplished by certain volatile amines such as cyclohexylamine, $C_6H_{11}NH_2$ and morpholine C_4H_9NO. These amines when fed to a boiler volatilize with the steam and combine with the carbon dioxide in the condensate to neutralize its acidity. Unlike ammonia the amines in low concentrations are not corrosive to copper and zinc bearing metals. Control of treatment is usually based on feeding sufficient amine to raise the pH of the condensate to 7.0. Satisfactory reduction of carbon dioxide corrosion is obtained with the use of the neutralizing amines in the absence of oxygen.

Figure 27-6 shows cyclohexylamine require-

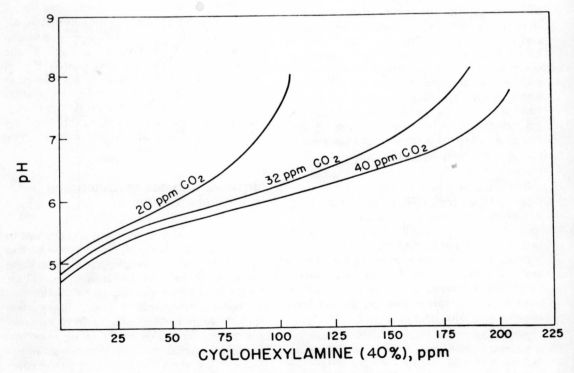

Figure 27-6 • pH Adjustment with Cyclohexylamine

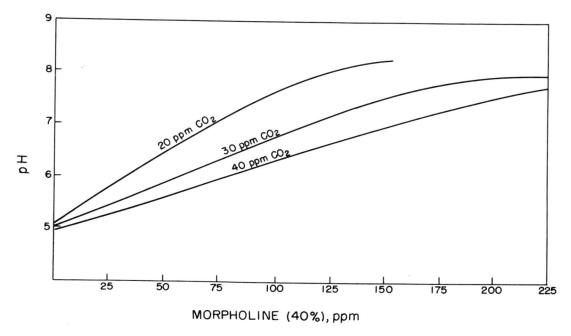

Figure 27-7 • *pH Adjustment with Morpholine*

ments for different concentrations of carbon dioxide in the condensate. Increased carbon dioxide concentrations require increased quantities of cyclohexylamine. Cyclohexylamine requirements are shown for the 40% solution since this is a common commercial strength employed to minimize fire hazard with the material. Approximately 3.0 ppm cyclohexylamine (40%) are necessary for each 1.0 ppm carbon dioxide to elevate the pH of the condensate to 7.0.

Morpholine requirements for different levels of carbon dioxide are shown in Figure 27-7. Morpholine is usually employed as a 40% solution to minimize fire hazard. Approximately 3.6 ppm morpholine (40%) are required for each 1.0 ppm carbon dioxide to elevate pH to 7.0. An interesting application of the neutralizing amines has been in the prevention of corrosion in the wet end section of high pressure central station turbines. In these sections of the turbine, condensed moisture is traveling at high velocity and tends to remove any protective oxide films. It is desirable to develop a pH of 9.0

in this section of the turbine to minimize corrosion and iron pick-up. Morpholine is particularly suited to this use, because it is less volatile than ammonia or cyclohexylamine.

The distribution ratio of ammonia and the amines can be used as one means of selecting the proper material. Distribution ratio is the ratio of the concentration in the steam compared to the concentration in the condensate. Ammonia has a distribution ratio of 10, cyclohexylamine about 3 and morpholine only 0.4. This favorable distribution ratio for morpholine makes it the more applicable amine for central stations to protect the wet steam sections in high pressure turbines, since high pH is imparted to initial condensed moisture at a minimum feed rate. Cyclohexylamine can be expected to remain with the steam. At points of initial condensation, higher rates are necessary to maintain desired pH levels. This property of cyclohexylamine, however, is of benefit in extended systems utilizing reduced pressure wet steam, especially where excess condensate is frequently trapped off.

This difference in the action of these two most commonly used neutralizing amines can be utilized to select the proper material for any given plant. Blended neutralizing amines are available, possessing the desirable characteristics of morpholine and cyclohexylamine. Such a blend may be the most applicable material in many industrial plants where protection is desired both at points of initial condensation, as in turbines, and in low pressure steam systems used for heating.

Neutralizing amines do not protect return lines against oxygen attack. However, with proper deaeration of feedwater and other steps to prevent oxygen pick-up, this disadvantage can be considered minor. Since the neutralizing amine requirement is a function of the carbon dioxide content of steam, judicious selection of external treatment methods may be necessary to achieve greatest economy.

FILMING AMINES

The filming amines function on a completely different principle from the neutralizing amines. The filming amines do not neutralize carbon dioxide. Instead, they function by forming on the metal surfaces contacted an impervious non-wettable film that acts as a barrier between the metal and the condensate, protecting against both oxygen and carbon dioxide attack. When the filming amines are adsorbed on a metal surface, water will not wet that surface. The film formed through the use of these amines is of substantially monomolecular thickness and does not increase in thickness with continued treatment. The amine will penetrate corrosion products present on a metal surface and deposit a protective film on the metal. While continuous treatment is advised, the adsorbed film on the metal surface is quite durable and is not removed during short periods of discontinued treatment.

Figure 27-8 is a photograph of two test specimens on which a few drops of water have been placed. The specimen on the left has been exposed to condensate treated with

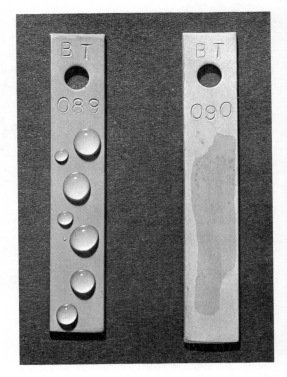

Figure 27-8 • Water Repellancy of Octadecylamine Film at Left. Untreated Specimen at Right.

a filming amine. It can be seen how the amine film causes the water to assume droplet form, on both the large and the small drops. The untreated specimen at the right does not repel water and the water spreads and wets the metal surface.

The filming amines of value in the prevention of corrosion are the high molecular weight amines and amine salts having straight carbon chains containing 10-18 carbon atoms. Octadecylamine ($C_{18}H_{37}NH_2$), hexadecylamine ($C_{16}H_{33}NH_2$) and dioctadecylamine ($C_{36}H_{74}NH$) are examples of useful materials of this type. In plant practice the most successful results have been obtained with the dispersed octadecylamine.

Octadecylamine and octadecylamine acetate are available in either dry, flaky form or in the form of a dispersion which simplifies the problem of solution and chemical feeding.

Condensate should be used in preparing the chemical soultion which is then fed with a small chemical pump to the main steam line at a point where it will be well mixed with the steam. The material is dispersed readily with the steam and is carried through the steam and condensate lines, forming a non-wettable film on the metal surfaces contacted.

Unlike the neutralizing amines which must be fed in direct proportion to the carbon dioxide concentration of the steam, filming amines are required at a rate sufficient to establish and maintain the desired corrosion resistant film on the metal surfaces.

HEAT TRANSFER

As previously stated, filming amines function as a barrier treatment forming a non-wettable film of substantially monomolecular thickness. This film does not impede heat transfer due to its very thin nature. Also, due to the non-wettable feature, dropwise condensation is promoted actually producing an increase in heat transfer. Of even greater importance from the standpoint of improved heat transfer is the ability of the filming amines to loosen and remove old corrosion films. During initial start-up, the amines are applied at a low rate to permit gradual removal of corrosion products in the system.

REFERENCES

A. A. Berk, "Treating Steam Chemically to Reduce Return Line Corrosion", *Industry and Power*, Vol. 53, pp. 79-81 (1947)

L. F. Collins and E. L. Henderson, "Corrosion in Steam Heating Systems", *Heating, Piping and Air Conditioning*, Vols. 11 and 12, Sept. 1939—May 1940 incl.

E. Elliott and P. J. Gaughan, "Plant Stops Return Line Corrosion—Saves $14,200 a Year", *Power Engineering*, Vol. 55, pp. 104-109 (Aug. 1951)

H. L. Kahler and J. K. Brown, "New Polar Film Treatment for the Control of Return Line Corrosion", *Proceedings*, Engineers Soc. of Western Penna., pp. 115-126 (1949)

G. A. Mierendorf, "Protecting Heating Units and Condensate Lines Against Corrosion by the Use of Filming Amines", *Proceedings*, Am. Power Conf., Vol. XIV, pp. 453-458 (1952)

W. A. Tanzola and J. G. Weidman, "Film Forming Corrosion Inhibitors Also Aid Heat Transfer", *The Paper Industry*, Vol. 36, pp. 48-50 (April 1954)

28

Embrittlement of Boiler Metal

INTERCRYSTALLINE cracking or caustic metal embrittlement generally occurs in boilers along riveted seams and at tube ends. Cracking of the metal may cause dangerous weakening of its structure and subsequent boiler failure.

CAUSES OF EMBRITTLEMENT

There are three factors necessary to produce intercrystalline cracking of boiler metal. These are:

1—Leakage of the boiler water must take place so as to permit escape of steam and concentration of the boiler water at the point of leakage.

2—The boiler metal must be subjected to high stress. This stress may be internal, resulting from cold working of the metal, or the stress may be external, due to expansion and contraction.

3—The concentrated boiler water must possess embrittling characteristics and chemically attack the boiler metal.

Leakage of boiler water from riveted seams or rolled-in tube ends can produce the required concentration of the boiler water. Investigations have shown that intercrystalline cracking is not produced at "normal" boiler water concentrations, but that continued evaporation may build up local concentrations of sodium hydroxide to a range such as 75,000 to 500,000 ppm which will cause intercrystalline cracking under stress and in the absence of an inhibitor.

Even in boilers with welded drums, intercrystalline cracking may manifest itself at rolled-in tube ends. In general, therefore, the power plant engineer has little control over the factors of leakage and stress.

Inasmuch as all three factors of leakage, stress and embrittling character of the boiler water are required for the production of intercrystalline cracking, if it can be definitely shown that one of these three factors is absent, it can reasonably be assumed that the danger of embrittlement is non-existent in that instance. The factor that can best be shown to be present or absent is the embrit-

Figure 28-1 • Embrittlement Cracks in a 1 Inch Plate. The Cracking in this Drum Was So Extensive that the Drum Had to be Replaced.

Figure 28-2 • Cracks in the Rolled End of a Tube. These Cracks Were Thought at First to be the Result of Excessive Rolling, but Further Investigation (and many tube failures) Showed the Cause to be Embrittlement.

Courtesy Mutual Boiler and Machinery Insurance Co.

Figure 28-3 • Mud Drum of Boiler Which Exploded as a Result of Caustic Metal Attack Weakening the Seam.

Figure 28-4 • Wreckage of the Power House Caused by the Explosion of the Boiler Shown in Figure 28-3.

tling character of the boiler water. If a boiler water is naturally non-embrittling or has been made non-embrittling by the addition of embrittlement inhibitors, the power plant engineer can neglect the other two factors of leakage and stress as affecting the embrittlement problem. However, should it be definitely shown that the boiler water *does* possess embrittling characteristics, the definite possibility exists for intercrystalline cracking should the additional factors of leakage and stress also be present.

Good engineering practice, therefore, dictates that the boiler water be investigated for embrittling characteristics. If the boiler water is found to be embrittling, naturally steps must be taken to render it non-embrittling.

EMBRITTLING CHARACTERISTICS

Naturally, it is desirable that chemical controls of some nature be established so that chemical analysis of the boiler water will indicate the ability of that boiler water to crack steel. However, the methods of studying embrittling characteristics today are more direct. They consist of placing a steel specimen in contact with a boiler water under extreme concentrations and simultaneously placing stress on the steel specimen in order to reproduce under test conditions the same circumstances which will cause cracking in

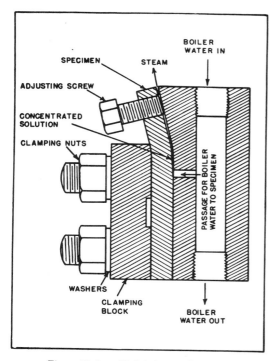

Figure 28-5 • Embrittlement Detector

the boiler itself.

This testing is conducted with the use of the Embrittlement Detector as developed by the United States Bureau of Mines. This testing unit, covered by U.S. Patents 2,283,954 and 2,283,955, is illustrated in Figure 28-5. It consists of a rectangular block 5 inches long, $2\frac{1}{4}$ inches thick and $3\frac{1}{2}$ inches wide with a $\frac{3}{4}$ inch hole bored through it, as illustrated, through which boiler water circulates. The test specimen is a steel bar 5 inches long, $\frac{3}{4}$ inch wide and $\frac{1}{2}$ inch thick which is bolted into a slot in the block by a clamping plate and four studs. The clamping of the specimen into place creates a high stress in the metal surface in contact with the block. Then, by adjustment of the clamping plate and the adjusting screw, water is allowed to ·leak out very slowly under the specimen with escape of steam leaving a concentrated solution in contact with the stressed surface. Laboratory and plant tests have

shown that cracking of the specimen will result if the boiler water is embrittling.

The Embrittlement Detector is most conveniently installed in the continuous blowdown line of a boiler. If continuous blowdown is not installed, boiler water may be taken off at any convenient point and either returned to the boiler or run to waste. The requirement is that water at substantially boiler temperature circulate rapidly through the block.

The use of the Embrittlement Detector, while requiring attention once daily, possesses the advantage of operation over a thirty, sixty or ninety day period which tends to take into account fluctuations in water characteristics during that time. In addition, the unit is operated on the actual boiler water at the plant. Occasionally, the specimen will show definite cracking on its removal from the block although in many instances the cracking is revealed only on further bending in the course of a subsequent examination of the specimen bar in the laboratory of the supervising organization.

TREATMENT METHODS

The use of sodium nitrate is practically standard for the inhibition of embrittlement. While nitrate is naturally present in many water supplies, the inhibition of embrittlement requires a definite ratio of nitrate to the caustic alkalinity present in the boiler water. The formula for calculating this sodium nitrate/sodium hydroxide ratio in the boiler water is:

$$NaNO_3/NaOH \text{ ratio} = \frac{\text{Nitrate as } NO_3, \text{ ppm} \times 2.14}{\text{M.O. alkalinity as } CaCO_3, \text{ ppm} - \text{Phosphate as } PO_4, \text{ ppm}}$$

The ratios recommended by the U. S. Bureau of Mines depend on the boiler operating pressure and are as follows:

	NaNO₃/NaOH ratio
up to 250 psi	0.20
up to 400 psi	0.25
up to 700 psi	0.40

Figure 28-6 illustrates the 'before and after' appearance of two test specimens exposed in

*Figure 28-6 • Detector Specimen Bars
from a 300 psi Boiler*

a plant operating at 300 psi. The first bar cracked badly. Sodium nitrate was then employed for correction of the embrittling characteristics of the boiler water. The second bar, which exhibits no cracking, was obtained after the use of sodium nitrate.

Coordinated pH-phosphate control prevents the boiler water from developing embrittling characteristics by eliminating 'free' sodium hydroxide from the boiler water. Since it is desirable to avoid low pH in the boiler water, the proper pH is provided through the use of an agent such as trisodium phosphate. Figure 28-7 illustrates the approximate pH of solutions of trisodium phosphate of various PO_4 content. To insure the absence of 'free' sodium hydroxide and the absence of any alkalinity other than that of trisodium phosphate, it is necessary to maintain the pH of a boiler water below the curve. This coordinated pH-phosphate method of preventing embrittlement is primarily applicable to plants employing evaporated or deionized makeup water. Although the curve in Figure 28-7 can be used as a guide in the

control of this method of preventing embrittlement, it is advisable to check on the hydroxyl ion content of the boiler water.

STATUS OF PROBLEM

A large portion of our present knowledge of intercrystalline cracking and of the means that can be taken to combat this condition is due to the study of this subject at the U. S. Bureau of Mines under the sponsorship of the Joint Research Committee on Boiler Feed Water Studies. Development of the Embrittlement Detector by W. C. Schroeder and A. A. Berk of the U. S. Bureau of Mines was a great step forward in this work. Industry as a whole is indebted to these research investigators for the continuous logical development of the basic principles involved and for the continuous follow-up on methods of preventing embrittlement.

From the viewpoint of the power plant engineer, therefore, the status of the embrittlement problem may be briefly summarized. Embrittlement may strike unexpectedly, when we least anticipate it. It may occasion costly repairs as well as serious interruption in production. Each engineer should know whether his boiler water can cause intercrystalline cracking of the boiler metal if the required leakage and stress conditions are also present. The embrittling characteristics

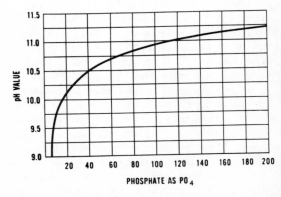

*Figure 28-7 • Approximate pH Values of Trisodium
Phosphate Solutions*

of the boiler water can readily be checked in the plant itself through the use of the Embrittlement Detector under the direction of a supervising laboratory. If embrittling characteristics of the boiler water are found, there are definite established methods available for overcoming such undesirable conditions. Application of specific chemicals or methods of treatment can be tested by further embrittlement test runs until specimens no longer crack in the Detector. It is then possible to establish controls over the embrittlement inhibitor and to so control the boiler water as to maintain it in a nonembrittling condition.

REFERENCES

A. A. Berk and W. C. Schroeder, "A Practical Way to Prevent Embrittlement Cracking", *Transactions,* Am. Soc. of Mech. Engineers, Vol. 65, pp. 701-711 (1943)

A. A. Berk, "The Prevention of Embrittlement Cracking", *Transactions,* Am. Soc. of Mech. Engineers, Vol. 73, pp. 859-864 (1951)

J. D. Betz, "Preventing Boiler Metal Embrittlement", *Petroleum Refiner,* Vol. 24, pp. 98-102 (July, 1945)

O. H. Preis, "Embrittlement A Modern Menace", *Power Engineering,* Vol. 64, pp. 68-69 (Apr. 1960)

S. F. Whirl and T. E. Purcell, "Protection Against Caustic Embrittlement by Coordinated Phosphate pH Control", *Proceedings,* Engineers Soc. of Western Penna., pp. 45-53 (1942)

29

Boiler Blowdown Control

The term blowdown means to eject or drain a portion of the water from a system. Boiler water blowdown is the removal from a boiler of some of the concentrated water to be replaced with feedwater, thus effecting a general lowering of concentrations in the boiler.

Boiler blowdown is usually expressed in percentage and is defined as follows:

$$\frac{\text{Quantity blowdown water}}{\text{Quantity feedwater}}(100) = \% \text{ Blowdown}$$

Thus a 5% blowdown means that 5% of the water fed to the boiler is removed by blowdown. The percent blowdown normally is determined by means of the chloride test. The formula and its algebraic derivation is shown in Figure 29-1.

PURPOSE FOR BLOWDOWN

Under normal operating conditions the only reasons for boiler blowdown are to lower the suspended solids and dissolved solids content of the boiler water. These solids are brought in by the feedwater and since the steam leaving the boiler is relatively pure, concentration of solids will develop in the boiler water. Excessive amounts of suspended solids will cause deposition of sludge and may alter the surface tension of the boiler water This effect, in turn, may be severe enough to cause carryover in the absence of suitable anti-foam agents. Excessive amounts of dissolved solids have the same deleterious effects as suspended solids and, in addition, when the solubility of the salts present in the boiler water is exceeded, scale will be deposited.

Fig. 29-1
Algebraic Proof of Blowdown Formula

Let x = quantity feedwater
    y = quantity blowdown water
    a = chloride concentration in feedwater
    b = chloride concentration in boiler water
    k = percent blowdown

Therefore: by definition of percent blowdown

$$k = \frac{100\ y}{x}$$

Since the total chlorides entering boiler must equal total chlorides leaving boiler

$$xa = yb$$

Multiplying both sides of equation by $\dfrac{100}{xb}$ equals

$$\frac{100\ a}{b} = \frac{100\ y}{x}$$

Since by definition $\dfrac{100\ y}{x} = k$, then

$$k = \frac{100\ a}{b} \quad \text{or}$$

$$\frac{\text{Cl in feedwater}}{\text{Cl in boiler water}} \times 100 = \% \text{ blowdown}$$

The American Boiler Manufacturer's Association in its standard guarantee of steam purity stipulates the following limits for solids content of a boiler water:

Operating Pressure, psig	Total Solids, ppm	Suspended Solids, ppm
0- 300	3500	300
301- 450	3000	250
451- 600	2500	150
601- 750	2000	100
751- 900	1500	60
901-1000	1250	40
1001-1500	1000	20
1501-2000	750	10
2001 and higher	500	5

These recommended limits for solids are not entirely applicable to each individual case. Rather, they are limits of a general nature, providing a suitable basis from which to vary solids in accordance with the specific needs of a particular plant.

In the past few years, highly effective anti-foam agents have been developed and in many instances, where they have been properly applied, excellent steam purity has been produced even though the total solids content of the boiler water was maintained considerably in excess of the range stipulated by the A.B.M.A. In fact, in many cases the effect of boiler water solids on steam purity need no longer be considered in controlling boiler water balances and therefore the sole controlling factor in boiler blowdown is the need to control sludge concentrations in the boiler for the prevention of deposits on the boiler heating surfaces.

The total solids content of the boiler water, however, is only one factor controlling boiler blowdown. In many cases, especially boilers operating above 600 psig, blowdown is based upon limiting the silica content of the boiler water below certain values so as to limit the amount of silica vaporized with the steam. Vaporization of silica with the steam is not usually a problem where boiler pressures are maintained below 400 psig. Unless silica values are properly restricted, a siliceous type of scale may be deposited on the boiler heating surfaces. Therefore, it is quite possible to find a plant operating with an apparently high blowdown rate even though A.B.M.A. limits might permit higher solids and the use of an anti-foam might permit a very high total solids content before carryover occurred.

In addition to silica, other chemical factors which frequently limit or control the final percentage of blowdown are alkalinity and suspended solids. The two objectives governing the boiler water limits which are established are the production of pure steam and the obtaining of clean boiler heat transfer surfaces.

In addition to the chemical balances maintained in the boiler water, there are many mechanical factors which influence the total solids concentrations which can be carried safely. These include boiler design, rating, water level and load characteristics and whether water level and load variations are relatively constant or subject to extremely rapid variation.

MANUAL BLOWDOWN. There are two principal types of boiler water blowdown—intermittent manual blowdown and continuous blowdown. Manual blowdown, or sludge blowdown, is necessary for the operation of a boiler regardless as to whether or not continuous blowdown is also installed. The blowdown take-off is usually located at the lowest part of the boiler so that in addition to

lowering the dissolved solids concentration of the boiler water, it will also remove a portion of the sludge which is generally more concentrated in the lower part of the boiler.

When continuous blowdown is also installed, the primary purpose of manual blowdown is to remove the suspended solids or sludge which may have accumulated in the area. In most cases, it is necessary to employ two or more short sludge blowdowns per day in order to procure proper sludge removal. However, in cases where the boiler feedwater is exceptionally pure, such as resulting from an evaporator or with a high percentage of returned condensate, blowdown can be employed less frequently as very little sludge is formed in the boiler.

When continuous blowdown is not installed, it is necessary to use the manual blowdown to control concentrations in the boiler water. Whenever the dissolved solids or suspended solids approach or exceed predetermined limits it is necessary to use manual blowdown to lower these concentrations. In practice, the valve of the bottom blowdown is opened periodically in accordance with an operating schedule and/or chemical control tests. From the standpoint of control, economy and results, frequent short blows are preferred to infrequent lengthy blows. This is particularly true when the suspended solids content of the water is appreciable. Figure

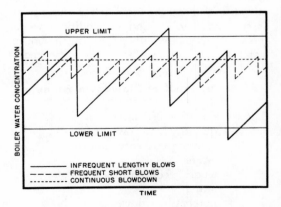

Figure 29-2 • Effect of Different Types of Blowdown on Boiler Water Concentrations

29-2 illustrates a hypothetical case. With the use of frequent short blows, a more uniform concentration of the boiler water is maintained and in general a smaller quantity of water is blown down because of the better control.

Bottom blowdown, properly controlled, accomplishes the lowering of the dissolved solids and suspended solids, providing for satisfactory boiler operation. It is frequently undesirable, however, from an operating standpoint, to blow down a boiler manually with sufficient frequency to properly control concentrations. This condition is especially true if the boiler feedwater is high in solids content.

CONTINUOUS BLOWDOWN. Continuous blowdown as the name implies is the continuous removal of concentrated water from the boiler. It offers many advantages not provided by the use of bottom blowdown alone. Continuous blowdown may be viewed as an extension of the practice of frequent short blows. In actual plant practice, periodic adjustments are made in the setting of the control valve in order to increase or decrease the amount of water blown out of the boiler in accordance with controlled test results, thus making it possible to maintain close control of boiler water concentrations at all times.

Another important advantage of continuous blowdown is that heat recovery is possible. With the use of an efficient heat exchange unit the only heat loss is the terminal difference between the incoming cooling water and the blowdown water to the sewer. This terminal difference usually amounts to approximately 20 F.

The use of the flash steam principle prior to a heat exchange unit further increases the possible savings which can be realized by continuous blowdown. By flashing a portion of the boiler water into steam at a lower pressure, the resulting low pressure steam can be used quite readily for process heating or, as is the usual case, for feedwater heating by direct introduction to the feedwater heater. With the use of a flash tank in conjunction with a heat exchanger, a smaller

heat exchanger can be used, providing a definite savings in initial cost of equipment since a considerable portion of the heat recoverable from the boiler blowdown is contained in the amount of flash steam obtained.

Figure 29-3 illustrates typical calculations for determining the savings involved in a heat recovery system utilizing a low pressure flash tank and heat exchanger. Installation of heat recovery equipment is of value only when the low pressure steam or heat recovered from the blowdown water can be utilized for increasing the feedwater temperature. If an excess supply of exhaust or low pressure steam is already available, naturally, there would be no savings and installation of heat recovery equipment would not be justified.

Other applications of continuous blowdown water and methods of recovering the heat from this water are practiced. Under certain conditions, an advantage is obtained in the recirculation of boiler water blowdown to hot process softeners. In other instances, a small portion of the blowdown water is returned to the feedwater heater for the purpose of elevating the feedwater pH value and thus decreasing the possibility of corrosion in the feed lines.

EQUIPMENT EMPLOYED

MANUAL BLOWDOWN. The equipment employed for manual blowdown of the boiler is considered a part of the boiler and is installed along with the unit. This equipment generally consists of a take-off line, a quick opening valve and a shut-off valve. The take-off line is always located in the lowest part of the boiler proper where it is anticipated the greatest concentration of sludge will form and also to permit proper draining of the unit.

Water tube boilers of various types generally have more than one blow-off connection, one or more being installed so as to blow down from the mud drum and additional connections may be made to various headers. Blowdown connections are installed on the

Figure 29-3—Typical Calculations on Savings Possible through Use of Heat Recovery on Continuous Blowdown. Basis—1 Day

Evaporation = 5,000,000 lbs steam

Boiler pressure = 200 psig

Feedwater temperature = 200 F (live steam used)

Makeup water temperature = 60 F

Rate of blowdown = 5.0%

Boiler efficiency = 75%

Fuel = Oil at 150,000 Btu/gal, 7.0¢/gal delivered and fired

Feedwater = Steam plus blowdown

$$\text{Feedwater} = \frac{5,000,000 \text{ lbs}}{0.95} = 5,263,000 \text{ lbs}$$

Blowdown = 263,000 lbs

Employing a flash tank at 5 psig, the quantity of 5 psig steam available may be calculated from the formula:

$$\% \text{ flashed steam} = \frac{H_b - H_f}{V_f} \times 100$$

Where H_b = heat of liquid at boiler pressure, Btu/lb
     H_f = heat of liquid at flash pressure, Btu/lb
     V_f = latent head of vaporization at flash pressure, Btu/lb

$$\% \text{ flashed steam} = \frac{362 - 196}{960} \times 100 = 17.3$$

Flashed steam available at 5 psig = 263,000 lbs X 0.173 = 45,500 lbs

Total heat of flashed steam at 5 psig = 1,156 Btu/lb

Heat savings in flashed steam = 1,156 Btu/lb – 28 Btu/ lb X 45,500 lbs = 51,324,000 Btu

The drain water from the flash tank is passed through the heat exchanger and thence to the sewer. It is assumed that the temperature of the water leaving the exchanger is 20 F above the incoming makeup water or 80 F.
    Heat of liquid at 80 F = 48 Btu/lb
    Heat of liquid at 5 psig = 196 Btu/lb
    Heat recovery = 148 Btu/lb

Heat savings from heat exchanger = 263,000 lbs X 0.827 X 148 Btu/lb = 32,190,000 Btu

Total heat savings = 51,324,000 Btu plus 32,190,000 Btu = 83,514,000 Btu

At a boiler efficiency of 75% there is actually utilized 150,000 Btu/gal X 0.75 = 120,000 Btu/gal oil.

$$\text{Fuel savings} = \frac{83,514,000 \text{ Btu}}{120,000 \text{ Btu/gal oil}} = 696 \text{ gal}$$

Daily savings = 696 gal X 7¢/gal oil = $48.72

headers for the chief purpose of blowing down these sections of the boiler in order to remove suspended solids which may accumulate at such points and cause a restriction of circulation. Usually, the boiler manufacturer will stipulate certain restrictions in the blowdown of these water wall headers and, in all instances, the recommendations of the manufacturer should be followed.

DECONCENTRATORS. A deconcentrator is a cylindrical tank so connected to the boiler as to receive concentrated boiler water. By means of special baffling, a settling of the suspended solids takes place and a clarified water is returned to the boiler. Periodic blowdown of the deconcentrator results in the blowdown of water containing a higher percentage of suspended solids as compared to the normal boiler water. A deconcentrator in no way affects the dissolved solids or alkalinity content of the boiler water. Theoretically, deconcentrators should be of value in cases where excessive suspended solids or sludge develops. In actual plant practice, however, they can be recommended only on rare occasions since installation of softening equipment can be more readily justified in most such instances.

SURFACE BLOWDOWN. Connections are installed occasionally with the take-off line located slightly below the working water level for the purpose of skimming sediment and oil from the surface of the water and the name, surface blowdown, is generally applied to such an installation. The end of the take-off line may be equipped with a funnel or similar device in an attempt to make the installation more effective. A further refinement of this idea involves the application of a floating trough which is designed to remove water at a point close to the boiling surface regardless of any variations in water level in the boiler. Skimming devices, in general, have been more commonly applied in marine practice and have not found wide application in stationary plants.

CONTINUOUS BLOWDOWN. Continuous blowdown equipment is usually considered auxiliary boiler equipment although many manufacturers now install the internal collection pipe or at least will make provision for such an installation during the course of manufacture. The exact location for the continuous blowdown take-off line within the boiler depends primarily upon the water circulation circuits which are involved. The take-off line is installed in such a manner as to assure the removal of the most concentrated water from the boiler. It is essential also that possible short-circuiting of boiler feedwater or chemical feed solution into the take-off line be avoided. The size of the lines and control valve depends upon the feedwater characteristics, quantity of blowdown required and the boiler rating. Figures 29-4 and 29-5 illustrate the method of installation in typical boilers. In most boilers, the take-off line is located approximately two inches below low water level although in certain boiler designs, the take-off line is located close to the bottom of the drum at a point where the most concentrated water is found.

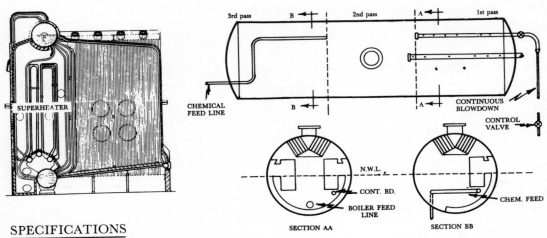

SPECIFICATIONS

CONTINUOUS BLOWDOWN:—Take-off pipe should be ____" extra heavy iron pipe located under cyclone separators in 1st gas pass and at least 2" below low water level. End of pipe should be capped and ____" hole drilled therein. On top side of pipe, ____ equally spaced ____" holes should be drilled. External to drum, install globe valve and reduce line to ____" pipe. Install forged steel ____" ____ -V port flow control valve similar to the Hancock Flocontrol at convenient location.

CHEMICAL FEED:—Distribution line should be ____" extra heavy iron pipe installed beneath cyclone separators in 3rd gas pass and at least 2" below low water level. Line should remain open ended, discharging at point between 2nd and 3rd gas passes, as indicated.

NOTE:—Use iron or steel valves and piping on all continuous blowdown and chemical feed piping.

Figure 29-4 • Continuous Blowdown and Chemical Feed for B & W Type F and FH Boilers

---

BLOWDOWN CONTROL

It is important that blowdown be such that boiler water concentrations do not exceed certain limits. Likewise, it is equally important that excessive blowdown be avoided because of the heat units that are wasted as well as the additional chemical treatment required to react with the additional incoming feedwater. Therefore, it is essential that a system of control be established so as to maintain blowdown within determined limits. In order to illustrate the savings which may be obtained by proper blowdown control, Figure 29-6 shows the amount of heat saved when assuming a reduction in blowdown from 6% to 2%. In order to maintain an economical

blowdown rate, it is essential that suitable boiler water tests be conducted in order to obtain a constant check on concentrations developing in the boiler water. Regardless of the factor limiting the boiler water concentrations, the control of boiler blowdown is usually based on the determination of total solids content of the boiler water, determined gravimetrically, the dissolved solids as measured by specific conductance, the chloride, sulfate, silica or alkalinity content of the boiler water or any combination of these tests.

TOTAL SOLIDS. Determination of the total solids content of the boiler water provides an excellent control over blowdown. While usually applicable from a technical standpoint,

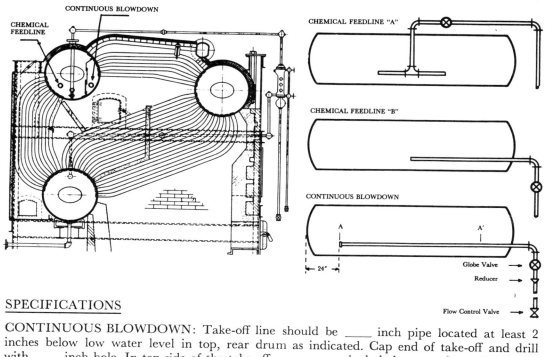

SPECIFICATIONS

CONTINUOUS BLOWDOWN: Take-off line should be _____ inch pipe located at least 2 inches below low water level in top, rear drum as indicated. Cap end of take-off and drill with _____ inch hole. In top side of the take-off, _____ . _____ inch holes spaced equally should be drilled within length A – A'. Immediately external to the drum, install globe valve and reduce line to _____ inch. Insert _____ inch, forged steel, _____–V port flow control valve at an easily accessible location.

CHEMICAL FEED: Distribution line should be _____ inch pipe discharging open ended approximately 2 inches below low water level and external to trough if provided. With tee arrangement as in illustration "A", the open ends should discharge at third points of drum.

NOTE: Use extra heavy iron or steel piping and fittings for all continuous blowdown and chemical feed lines.

Figure 29-5 • Continuous Blowdown and Chemical Feed for Three-drum, Bent-tube Boiler

---

it is rarely employed as the analysis requires much time and is too difficult for a routine control. There are objections to the use of the total solids test for calculation of the rate of blowdown. A comparison of the total solids content of the boiler water with the total solids content of the boiler feedwater will not necessarily provide an accurate measure of the concentration that has taken place within the boiler due to the boiler water samples not showing a representative suspended solids content, effect of internal treatment, breakdown of bicarbonates and

carbonates liberating carbon dioxide gas, etc. DISSOLVED SOLIDS. Determination of the specific conductance of a boiler water will provide an accurate measure of the dissolved solids content and usually can be applied to blowdown control with considerable advantage. However, calculation of the rate of blowdown on the basis of the relative specific conductance of the feedwater and boiler water is not technically correct. Not only will specific conductance be affected by loss of carbon dioxide with the steam and the solids introduced by internal chemical treatment,

Figure 29-6—Typical Calculations on Savings Possible Through Reduction in Blowdown. Basis—1 Day

Evaporation ..... $= 2,000,000$ lbs. steam

Boiler Pressure ... $= 200$ psig gage

Feedwater Temperature .... $= 215$ F

Makeup Water Temperature ... $= 60$ F

Present Blowdown Rate .... $= 6\%$

Reduced Blowdown Rate .... $= 2\%$

Boiler Efficiency .. $= 80\%$

Fuel $=$ Oil at 150,-000 Btu/gal., 7.0¢/gal. delivered and fired

Feedwater .... $=$ Steam plus blowdown

Feedwater at 6.0% Blowdown ..... $= 2,128,000$ lbs.

Feedwater at 2.0% Blowdown ..... $= 2,041,000$ lbs.

Saving in Feedwater .... $= 87,000$ lbs.

Heat of Liquid at Boiler Pressure, Btu/lb. .... $= 362$

Heat of Liquid at 60 F, Btu/lb. .... $= 28$

Heat Saving, Btu/lb. .... $= 334$

Total Heat Saving $= 87,000$ lbs. x 334 Btu/lb. .... $= 29,058,000$ Btu

At Boiler Efficiency of 80% There is Actually Utilized 150,000 Btu/gal. x 0.80 .... $= 120,000$ Btu/gal.

Fuel Savings $= \dfrac{29,058,000 \text{ Btu}}{120,000 \text{ Btu/gal.}} = 242$ gal.

Daily Savings $= 242$ gal. oil x \$0.07/gal.
$= \$16.94$

but the specific conductance of a dilute solution such as feedwater and a concentrated solution such as boiler water cannot be compared directly. The specific conductance of a sample is caused by ionization of the various salts present in the sample. In dilute solutions, ionization increases and greater specific conductance results. In more concentrated solutions, ionization is repressed and specific conductance decreases per part of salt present. This effect is illustrated by the fact that the solids content of very dilute solutions such as condensate may be calculated by using a factor of 0.5 to 0.6 ppm of dissolved solids per micromho of specific conductance. In more concentrated solutions, such as boiler water, the factor will vary between the limits of 0.55 and 0.9 ppm of dissolved solids per micromho of specific conductance. If gallic

———————————————————

$\longrightarrow$

This chart is used to calculate the percent of boiler water discharged by a continuous blowdown system that can be flashed into steam at a reduced pressure and recoverable as low pressure steam for heating or process.

EXAMPLE: A boiler operates at a pressure of 450 psig. Continuous blowdown amounts to 10,000 pounds per hour. What percentage of blowdown water can be recovered as flashed steam at 5 psig?

SOLUTION: Locate 450 psig on lefthand axis. Follow horizontally toward the right to the intersection with 5 psig "flash" curve (point A). Drop vertically downward to the bottom axis and read 25.5%. (25.5% of 10,000 pounds per hour blowdown $=$ 2550 pounds per hour of flash steam at 5 psig pressure.)

These curves have been prepared from the formula:

Percent flashed steam $= \dfrac{H_B - H_F}{V_F} \times 100$ **where**

$H_B =$ heat of liquid at boiler pressure in Btu/lb

$H_F =$ heat of liquid at flash pressure in Btu/lb

$V_F =$ latent heat of vaporization at flash pressure in Btu/lb

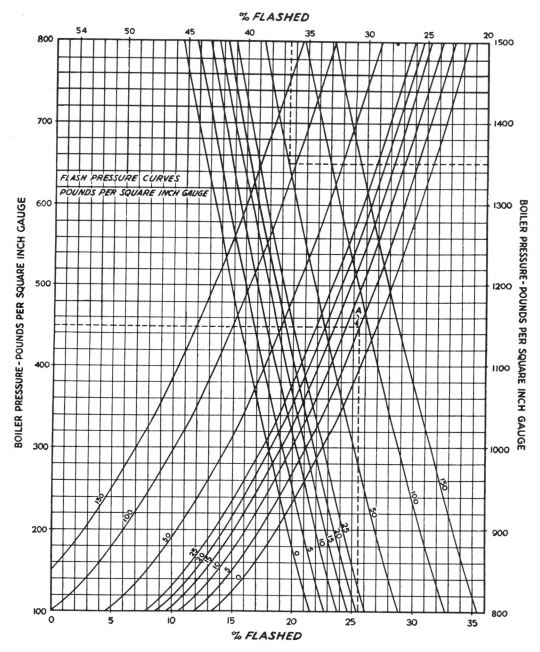

Figure 29-7

Flashed Steam Recoverable from Continuous Blowdown Systems

NOTE: For boiler pressures between 100 and 800 psig, use "flash" pressure curves slanting from lower lefthand to upper righthand corner and the bottom axis. For boiler pressures above 800 psig, use "flash" pressure curves slanting from lower righthand to upper lefthand corner and top axis.

acid is employed to neutralize the phenol-phthalein alkalinity, the specific conductance multiplied by the factor 0.9 will give a very close approximation of the actual dissolved solids content of the boiler water.

SULFATE, SILICA AND ALKALINITY. Under certain circumstances, the sulfate, silica and alkalinity content of the boiler water can be used for blowdown control where they are factors which, in that particular case, limit the boiler water concentrations that may be safely tolerated. Usually, these determinations are not suitable for calculation of the rate of blowdown since both sulfate and silica may be removed from solution as scale. The use of sodium sulfite will increase the sulfate content of the boiler water and alkalinity is usually affected by either variable softener balances or by the internal treatment employed. All these conditions prevent accurate determination of the relative feedwater and boiler water concentrations which is the basis for calculation of the rate of blowdown.

CHLORIDE. The chloride determination can be used not only for blowdown control, but it is also suitable for the accurate calculation of the rate of blowdown provided the chloride concentration of the feedwater is sufficient to permit accurate measurement. Since chloride is not subject to precipitation in the boiler water, the determination of the relative chloride concentrations of the feedwater and boiler water provides the most accurate basis for calculation of the rate of blowdown. Therefore, the percent blowdown can be calculated substituting the determined chloride values in the formula as shown in Figure 29-1.

The chloride test is unsuitable for this calculation only in those cases where the feedwater chloride is quite low, as in the range of 0.5-1.0 ppm. In this range a slight analytical error in determining feedwater chloride

content will cause an appreciable error in the calculated rate of blowdown.

SPECIFIC GRAVITY. The specific gravity of a boiler water is proportional to the dissolved solids. However, the accuracy in determining dissolved solids by means of a hydrometer measuring the specific gravity of a boiler water is so poor that it cannot be recommended for proper blowdown control.

CONCLUSION

It is to the benefit of any plant to maintain boiler water concentrations consistently at the optimum value. This control is necessary to assure the production of pure steam and maintain heat transfer surfaces free of scale and other objectionable deposits. The economics of blowdown requires careful study in order to make certain that blowdown is established upon a proper basis, taking into account all chemical and mechanical factors affecting the problem. Material savings in fuel and water consumption may be made either by the application of proper chemical treatment methods or by the installation of heat recovery equipment. The entire subject of blowdown is of sufficient importance to justify in every case a suitable study of all factors pertaining to it.

REFERENCES

O. de Lorenzi, "Combustion Engineering", pp. 21-17 & 18, Combustion Engineering—Superheaters, Inc., New York, N. Y. (1949)

W. L. Nieland, "Control and Economics of Boiler Blowdown", Combustion, Vol. 16, pp. 34-38 (Oct. 1944)

W. L. Nieland and J. H. Richards, "Boiler Blowdown Control", Industry and Power, Vol. 57, pp. 64-68 (Mar. 1954)

R. T. Sheen, "Continuous Blowdown on Boilers", Power Plant Engineering, Vol. 49, pp. 90-93 (Jan. 1945)

C. D. Shields, "Boilers: Types, Characteristics, and Functions", pp. 227-244, F. W. Dodge Corp., New York, N. Y. (1961)

30

Chemical Cleaning of Boilers

ONE of the most serious problems encountered in steam generation is the formation of scale and sludge deposits on boiler heating surfaces. The presence of oil on boiler heating surfaces may also give rise to serious difficulties. In high pressure generating stations boiler deposits containing metallic copper and copper oxide have been experienced. This condition may result in boiler tube failures. In addition to mill scale, new boilers also contain deposits of oil, grease and protective coatings. It is important that the proper steps be taken to remove deposits from the boiler heating surfaces. Removal of deposits may be effected by one or a combination of chemical methods, depending on the particular nature of the deposit.

ALKALINE BOIL-OUT

The presence of oil in the boiler feedwater originates from the exhaust steam or conden-

sate from steam engines or pumps. It may also originate from steam or water used in certain processes. Even thin films of oil on boiler heating surfaces may seriously interfere with normal heat transfer and the resultant increase in metal temperature may be sufficient to cause blistering and loss of boiler tubes and plates.

For the removal of oil and grease from boiler heating surfaces an alkaline boil-out is used. With new boilers the alkaline boil-out removes the protective coatings applied during erection together with oil, grease and any dirt that may have accumulated during erection. The boil-out should be so formulated to provide the greatest detergent, emulsifying and dispersive action on the greases and oils normally found in new boilers. With boilers that have been in operation, the boil-out should exert the same effect on oil present as a result of feedwater contamination.

While it is not possible to obtain maximum

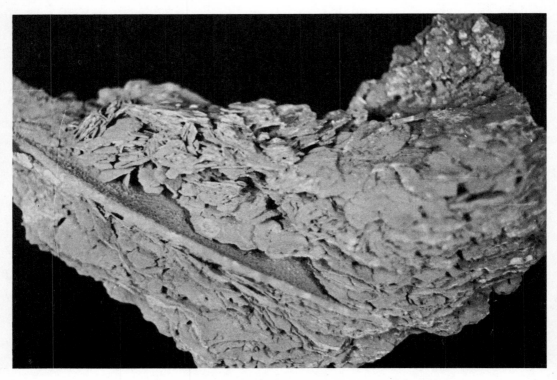

Figure 30-1 • Thin Scale Particles Cemented into a Dangerous Mass

emulsifying and dispersive action by the use of inorganic chemicals alone, readily available inorganic chemicals may be used when a specially prepared boil-out mixture cannot be obtained. One of the most satisfactory combinations of inorganic chemicals includes 3 pounds of caustic soda, 3 pounds of disodium phosphate and 1 pound of sodium nitrate for each 1000 pounds of water required to fill the boiler to operating level. Because of the high alkalinity developed during the boil-out, the sodium nitrate is included in the combination as a precaution against caustic metal embrittlement.

Prior to boiling-out a boiler, it is advisable to replace the normal high pressure gauge glasses with temporary glasses to prevent attack on the glass. After addition of the required quantity of boil-out material, all manholes should be closed and the boiler filled to the top of the gauge glass with the vents open. The boiler should be fired at a low

rate in accordance with recommendations of the manufacturer. When steam is flowing freely from the vents, all vents should be closed except those specified by the manufacturer on boilers containing superheaters, where superheater protection is required.

The pressure is then raised to a maximum of 25 psi and maintained for approximately 48 hours. For high pressure boilers it is usual to boil-out at one-half the operating pressure to obtain circulation. In all cases the recommendations of the manufacturer should be followed regarding boil-out pressure. The boiler should be blown down one-half gauge glass approximately every eight hours through the bottom blow-off valve. Where there is more than one blow-off connection, alternate valves should be used. After each blowdown the boiler should be refilled to the top of the glass.

After completion of the boil-out the unit is cooled slowly, drained and flushed thoroughly

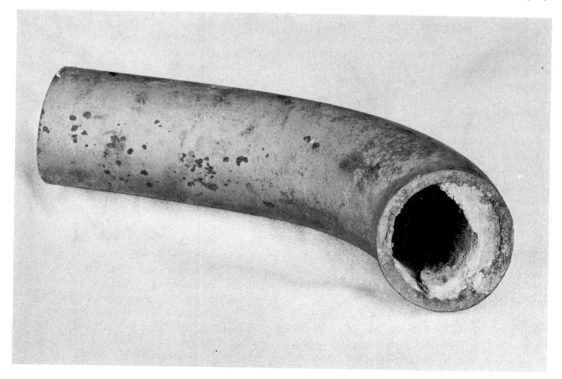

Figure 30-2 • This Superheater Tube Showing Carryover Deposits is an Application for Chemical Cleaning

with a high pressure hose. If inspection should indicate that any scum or oil remains, the boil-out procedure should be repeated. Some loose mill scale may be removed from a new boiler during the boil-out process. However, removal of mill scale is not the primary objective of the boil-out since acid cleaning is required for effective removal of mill scale.

INHIBITED ACID CLEANING

The principal cause of scale formation on boiler heating surfaces is the fact that the solubility of scale forming salts decreases with an increase in temperature. When the feed water temperature is elevated to boiler operating temperature, the solubility of scale forming salts is exceeded and crystallization takes place on the boiler heating surfaces. The use of inhibited acid for the removal of scale from boiler and metal surfaces has been practiced for many years. Within the past few years, however, there has been a considerable development in the technique and a number of new inhibitors are now available. Acid cleaning requires no great dismantling operation and labor cost is held to a minimum. Scale is removed from all surfaces reached by the acid solution and the cleaning, in most cases, is more complete than could be obtained by mechanical means.

By acid cleaning the internal metal surfaces of a boiler are left metal clean and as such the true condition of the metal is revealed. Opportunity is provided for more complete inspection of questionable areas within the boiler tubes, headers and drums. In many cases pits and pitted areas may go unnoticed until inspected after acid cleaning. Cleaning down to the metal surface will help reveal any stress areas and cracks which may be due to fatigue, embrittlement or corrosion.

Acid cleaning of new boilers is considered desirable by some for the removal of mill scale. Mill scale is the term generally applied to the oxide film produced when iron and steel surfaces are heated and cooled during manufacture and fabrication. Mill scale consists of black magnetic iron oxide. The presence in the boiler water of the black iron oxide suspension may cause a new boiler to run "black water" for several weeks under some conditions. These iron oxide deposits also may accumulate to a point where they impede circulation and interfere with heat transfer. They may also cause obstructions in steam separators and dryers, possibly affecting the flow of steam in the drums. A carryover condition may be aggravated, causing iron oxide to deposit in superheaters, strainers and turbine blading. In the presence of the alkaline boiler water, concentrated corrosion can occur at breaks in the mill scale layer and tube failures may result due to these pits. Before acid cleaning, a new boiler should be given an alkaline boil-out so as to remove oil, grease, protective coatings and any dirt that may have accumulated on these surfaces during erection.

Prior to acid cleaning the usual protective measures should be taken such as replacement of any brass or bronze parts temporarily with steel or steel alloy equipment. Steps should be taken to provide for proper venting of acid vapors and any valves connecting the boiler with the main steam header should be closed.

HYDROCHLORIC ACID. Inhibited hydrochloric acid is most widely used in acid cleaning because of its relatively low cost and the number of satisfactory inhibitors presently available. Two general methods used in acid cleaning of boilers are the "circulation" method and the "fill and soak" method. In the first method, the cleaning solution is circulated continuously through the unit until the cleaning action is completed, as shown by tests on the effluent. This method is suitable for units with positive liquid flow paths and offers the advantage of regular checking during the cleaning operation. In the second method the cleaning solution is permitted to soak in the unit for a prescribed length of time. This method is used where positive circulation of the cleaning solution cannot be readily obtained.

In the "circulation" method the unit is filled to overflow with clean warm water at the maximum temperature permitted for the particular inhibitor used. This water is circulated until a constant temperature is obtained on the effluent which is returned from the highest point of the unit to a tank equipped with a clean water line, steam line and drain. For circulation, a corrosion resistant pump should be employed. Inhibited acid is added in sufficient quantity to provide an acid solution of proper strength entering the unit and this feed is continued until tests on the effluent solvent indicate a maximum acid content has been reached. The concentration of acid used will generally vary from 3 to 6%, depending upon the particular conditions. Should continued testing of the effluent solvent reveal a 1% drop in acid content, sufficient inhibited acid should be added to maintain the desired acid content of the solvent influent. Circulation of the solvent through the unit continues until the acid content of the effluent is constant, thus indicating the end of the reaction between the solvent and the boiler deposit.

Following acid cleaning, the boiler is drained and flushed with clean warm water until tests on the returned flushing water show it to free of acid and soluble iron salts. Flushing is followed by a neutralizing or metal conditioning boil-out. Soda ash is generally used for this purpose although trisodium phosphate, sodium tripolyphosphate, sodium chromate, caustic soda or other chemicals may be used. The alkaline boil-out serves to neutralize any residual acid, releases from the metal surface the hydrogen generated during the cleaning procedure, and provides a slightly protective film on the metal surface. To aid in neutralization the unit can be fired at 50 psi or somewhat higher after circulation of the neutralizing solution has been stopped and the water level dropped to normal. During this period the unit should be vented on occasion to permit escape of the liberated gases.

At the conclusion of this boil-out the unit is drained and flushed with clean warm water. If the boiler is to stand idle for more than a few days before being returned to service, steps should be taken to protect the metal surfaces from corrosion. This protection can be accomplished by employing either the wet or dry lay-up procedures.

In the "fill and soak" method inhibited acid is added in the proper ratio with warm water or condensate (at the maximum temperature permitted for the inhibitor) to give a cleaning solution of the desired acid strength and the unit is filled to overflow. The vent is opened and soaking is carried out for a predetermined length of time, depending upon the type and estimated quantity of deposit and on the rate of reaction between the deposit and solvent, as indicated by laboratory tests.

At frequent intervals samples can be drawn from available points and tested for acid strength. However, these samples will not be indicative of conditions throughout the unit although they will give an indication as to the amount of deposit removed. Vent gases may contain hydrogen and therefore open flame is not permitted in the venting area. With new boilers the soaking period, using this method, may be approximately six hours although treatment may be discontinued after a shorter period, depending upon control tests.

At the end of the acid cleaning period the unit is flushed with clean warm water as described previously. The neutralizing solution is added and the unit is permitted to stand for a short period of time. The level can then be lowered to normal and the unit fired as described under the "circulation" method. Following this neutralizing boil-out the unit should be drained and flushed, as previously described. Also, if the boiler is to stand idle for more than a few days, proper steps should be taken to protect the metal surfaces.

In addition to the properly inhibited acid it may be desirable under some conditions to include certain inorganic chemicals which will aid in the removal of one particular constituent of the scale. The use of the proper wetting agent along with the inhibited acid serves to reduce the rate of corrosive attack on the metal during cleaning. The lower the degree of wetting of the metal by the inhibited acid, the greater is the effect of the wetting agent in reducing the amount of corrosion.

Sulfuric acid and nitric acid may also be used in chemical cleaning. Sulfuric acid is economical and may be easily inhibited. However, it does form insoluble salts, such as calcium sulfate, during the cleaning process. Although nitric acid is relatively inexpensive, there are only a few suitable inhibitors available. Both sulfuric acid and nitric acid are dangerous to handle and therefore extreme care must be taken when these acids are used.

PHOSPHORIC ACID. Inhibited phosphoric acid has been used successfully for removal of mill scale from new boilers. This agent possesses certain advantages over inhibited hydrochloric acid when used for chemical cleaning. Inhibited phosphoric acid can be boiled in the unit by direct firing of the boiler with neglible attack on the boiler metal and it does not create a problem of noxious or corrosive fumes. Natural circulation resulting from this direct firing promotes good distribution of the cleaning solution. Boiler surfaces cleaned with phosphoric acid are resistant to corrosion whereas metal surfaces freshly cleaned with inhibited hydrochloric acid react with the atmosphere to form rust if not properly protected during draining, and especially if left in a moist condition, such as before neutralization.

Prior to cleaning with inhibited phosphoric acid, a new boiler should be given an alkaline boil-out, as previously described. A 5% inhibited phosphoric acid solution boiling at atmospheric pressure has been successfully used in the removal of mill scale from new boilers. Following the cleaning, some authorities recommend that an acid rinse be employed for removal from the boiler surfaces any iron that may have deposited upon draining the acid cleaning solution. A 0.1% solution of phosphoric acid may be used as a rinse. The final step in the cleaning procedure consists of an alkaline treatment for purpose of neutralizing the remaining acid and for conditioning of the metal surfaces.

REMOVAL OF COPPER DEPOSITS

The increased use of copper and copper alloy equipment in the feedwater cycle has given rise to a new problem of boiler deposits in high pressure generating stations that have low makeup water requirements. Deposits have been composed principally of iron oxide, metallic copper and copper oxide. While acid cleaning is the answer to the problem of removing iron oxides, difficulties may arise due to acid cleaning when copper or copper oxides are present in the sludge. Although metallic copper is relatively insoluble in hydrochloric acid, it tends to go into solution during acid cleaning due to the presence of ferric ion in the acid solution. Copper can then replate on the boiler surfaces and it may adhere to these surfaces.

When the boiler is returned to service, the copper may be loosened from the boiler surfaces and deposit in areas where circulation is less rapid. Under these conditions normal circulation may be affected and over-heating may occur, resulting in tube failures. While copper deposits may be removed mechanically, this is a long, expensive process and as such would nullify any benefits gained in acid cleaning. As in any mechanical process there are locations that cannot be cleaned mechanically and thus deposits not removed would be potential sources of difficulty during later operation.

Various chemicals have been used for removal of copper deposits from boilers. In some cleaning operations, the solvents were ammonia base oxidizing agents and the effectiveness of these solvents is based on the reaction of the oxidizing agent with metallic copper to form cupric oxide. This oxide is dissolved in ammoniacal solution to form the familar cupric-ammonium complex ion. This series of reactions is reversible and it is necessary that certain fundamental conditions be maintained. During the treatment period excess oxidizing agent must be available in the solvent and the ammonia present must be maintained at a uniformly high level of concentration. The cupric-ammonium ion concentration must be uniform throughout the solvent.

The first solvents used for removal of copper from boilers were those containing chlorate as the major oxidizing component. One of this type of solvent, made up of sodium chlorate, ammonia and ammonium sulfate, must be used at temperatures in excess of 175 F in order to rapidly oxidize and dissolve copper. Another type solvent, containing sodium chlorate, slight amounts of potassium bromate, ammonia and ammonium nitrate, must be used at temperatures between 140 F and 190 F. With this solvent the bromate reacts first and limited amounts of chlorate react depending on the temperature maintained.

With the use of these solvents the boiler is generally fired intermittently to obtain required temperature and to induce circulation. Certain disadvantages are connected with the use of these solvents. Where over-heating occurs at localized areas of the boiler, increased attack on the boiler metal by the oxidizing agent will occur. In over-head areas, the ammonia content may be depleted causing copper already taken into solution to replate on the boiler metal. In the cleaning process, any ammonia driven off into the air space in the boiler drums decreases the concentration of the solvent, rendering it less effective.

Another type of solvent contains ammonium persulfate, ammonia and sodium hydroxide. This solvent is highly reactive with metallic copper even at room temperatures. The solvent is recirculated in the boiler for a short period, then the unit is drained and flushed with clear water. While the solvent may be used at room temperature there are some disadvantages inasmuch as it reacts rapidly with iron as well as copper. As such, accurate chemical control of both oxidant consumption and quantity of copper dissolved is difficult.

Another type of solvent that has been used successfully contains potassium bromate, slight amounts of sodium chlorate, ammonia and ammonium carbonate. The bromate is the principal oxidizing agent. The solvent is circulated continuously through the boiler at a temperature of 140 F to 160 F. While this type of solvent dissolves copper at a less rapid rate than solvents containing persulfate, it is faster acting than the chlorate type solvents. During the cleaning action analytical control can be set up to measure rate of oxidant consumption and quantity of dissolved copper in the solvent.

More recently, ammoniated citric acid has been employed for removal of water side deposits containing high percentages of copper oxide. Also, complexing agents specific for copper have been used in an acid medium for single stage cleaning of metal surfaces containing significant quantities of copper oxide in a multi-component deposit.

OTHER ACIDS

In the past few years, sulfamic acid (NH_2SO_3H) has come into use for chemical cleaning of equipment. This material, blended with an inhibitor, is available in powder form and becomes active as an acid cleaner when placed in solution. In the cleaning operation the solution of inhibited sulfamic acid is handled in a manner similar to that described previously. Inhibited sulfamic acid has an advantage over hydrochloric acid inasmuch as it is easier to handle, does not produce noxious fumes on dissolving and is less corrosive than inhibited hydrochloric acid, particularly at higher concentrations and temperatures. Sulfamic acid, while more expensive than either hydrochloric or sulfuric, is effective in removing calcium carbonate scale as well as iron oxide and organic deposits. However, its rate of reaction is slow against calcium sulfate. In chemical cleaning, sulfamic acid has been used primarily for small boilers and other plant equipment such as condensers and compressors.

Citric acid $(C_6H_8O_7)$ may also be used in chemical cleaning of power plant equipment. Recirculation of a 3% solution of inhibited citric acid at elevated temperature has been successful in removal of deposits from boilers and other power plant equipment. The ease of removal depends on the composition and quantity of deposit. The addition of a wetting agent to the cleaning solution may hasten removal of deposits. Where a boiler deposit is found to be particularly resistant, the addition of ammonia to the citric acid solution in sufficient quantity to elevate the pH, tends to speed removal. In recent years, citric acid has been used successfully in cleaning of stainless steel superheater tubes of utility boilers.

Citric acid may be used for removal of mill scale from new boilers. Prior to use of the acid the boiler should be given an alkaline boil-out to remove oil, grease, protective coatings and any dirt accumulated during erection. Following draining and flushing of the boiler a 3% inhibited citric acid solution at elevated temperature is added and circulated throughout, until all mill scale is removed. Periodically the iron content of the cleaning solution is checked to determine efficiency of the cleaning action.

CONCLUSION

Deposits of oil and grease as well as boiler scale, iron oxide and copper deposits may be removed from the boiler metal surfaces by chemical cleaning. When employing any of the chemical cleaning methods the proper technique must be followed and the necessary precautions taken. With regard to boiler scale, it should be recognized that acid cleaning is not a substitute for proper feedwater conditioning practices.

Although the technique of acid cleaning has progressed to a point where there is little danger from corrosion during the cleaning process, it is advisable that the procedure be performed under the supervision of experienced personnel. During acid cleaning every safety precaution must be exercised. The ever present danger of hydrogen explosion exists because hydrogen is evolved in the reaction of acid with iron. In pockets where hydrogen mixes with air, any spark or open flame will ignite the mixture. Other gases may also be generated during the cleaning process, such as hydrogen sulfide. Therefore, adequate venting is essential.

Personnel handling any acid as well as most inhibitors, should be fitted with proper safety clothing, including protective goggles and rubber gloves. Protective masks are also necessary for some vapors produce a suffocating effect and irritate the mucous membranes.

REFERENCES

S. Alfano, "Cleaning The Iron System Using Ammoniated Citric Acid", *Combustion*, Vol. 33, pp. 17-24 (May 1962)

P. H. Cardwell and L. H. Eilers, "Use of Wetting Agents in Conjunction with Acid Inhibitors", *Ind. and Eng. Chem.*, Vol. 40, pp. 1951-1956 (1948)

"Chemical Cleaning of Internal Heating Surfaces", Bulletin G-39A, The Babcock & Wilcox Company, New York, N. Y. (1946)

C. M. Loucks, "Chemistry Tackles Plant Maintenance", *Chemical Engineering*, Vol. 69, pp. 103-120 (Mar. 5, 1962)

31

Cooling Water Treatment: Once-Through Scale Control

THE term "cooling water" is applied wherever water is circulated through equipment to absorb and carry away heat. This definition includes air conditioning systems, engine jacket systems, refrigeration systems as well as the multitude of industrial heat exchange operations, such as found in oil refineries, chemical plants, steel mills, etc.

The once-through system, as the name implies, is one in which the water is passed through the heat exchange equipment and the cooling water is then discharged to waste. Usually, a once-through system is employed only where water at suitably low temperature is readily available in large volume and at low cost. The usual source of once-through cooling water is from wells, rivers and lakes where the cost involved is that of pumping only. In a once-through system, no evaporation takes place and consequently the water does not concentrate. Circulating water characteristics are the same as the makeup water.

SCALE FORMATION

Deposits in lines, heat exchange equipment, etc., may originate from several causes. For example, the precipitation of calcium carbonate will form scale, but products of corrosion also result in a deposit of iron oxide. In speaking of deposits which form in cooling water systems, it is important to bear in mind the mechanism causing the deposit, otherwise confusion may result. In general, the term

"scale" applies to deposits which result from crystallization or precipitation of salts from solution. Wasting away of a metal is the result of corrosion. While a deposit results in both cases, the mechanism of formation is different and different corrective methods are required to prevent the deposit.

Calcium carbonate is usually the chief ingredient of scale formed in once-through cooling water systems. Calcium carbonate is more insoluble than calcium silicate and calcium sulfate and this fact accounts for its more frequent appearance in the form of scale. Figure 31-1 illustrates analyses of several typical scales formed in once-through cooling water systems. It can be noted that the combination of calcium and carbonate accounts for the major portion of each deposit.

The factors which affect scale formation are temperature, rate of heat transfer, the calcium, sulfate, magnesium, silica, alkalinity, dissolved solids and pH of the water. In a once-through system, the magnesium, silica and sulfate concentrations are normally sufficiently low that these factors do not enter into the problem.

In 1936, the work of Prof. Langelier was published dealing with the conditions at which a given water is in equilibrium with calcium carbonate. The use of the equation developed by Langelier made it possible to predict the tendency of natural or conditioned water to either deposit calcium car-

Figure 31-1—Analysis of Typical Scales from Once-Through Cooling Water System

	%	%	%	%
Calcium as CaO	47.2	34.4	43.5	52.3
Magnesium as MgO	2.1	1.7	0.6	4.1
Iron as R_2O_3	3.1	22.7	10.72	3.00
Aluminum as Al_2O_3	1.5	4.2	0.88	0.20
Carbonate as CO_2	34.2	22.9	34.0	35.2
Sulfate as SO_3	0.9	0.1	1.4	0.3
Silica as SiO_2	4.9	9.8	2.1	1.1
Loss on Ignition	5.9	4.1	6.4	2.1

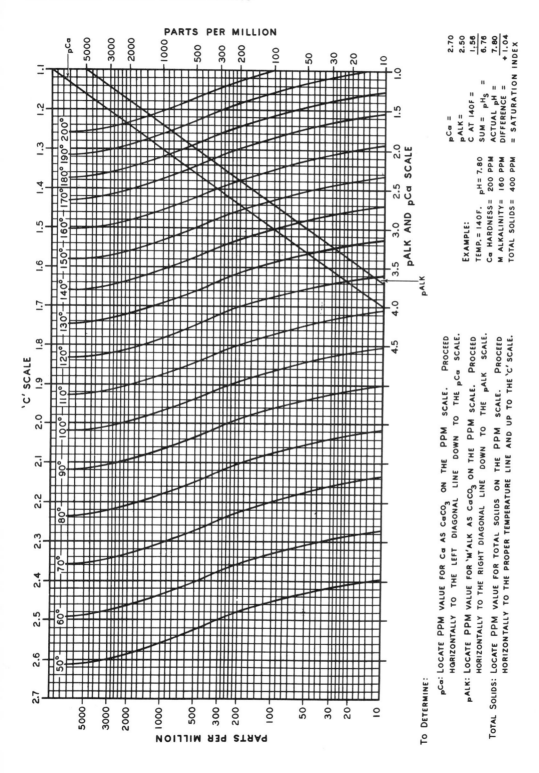

Figure 31-2 • Langelier Saturation Index Chart

To Determine:

pCa: LOCATE PPM VALUE FOR Ca AS CaCO₃ ON THE PPM SCALE. PROCEED HORIZONTALLY TO THE LEFT DIAGONAL LINE DOWN TO THE pCa SCALE.

pALK: LOCATE PPM VALUE FOR 'M'ALK AS CaCO₃ ON THE PPM SCALE. PROCEED HORIZONTALLY TO THE RIGHT DIAGONAL LINE DOWN TO THE pALK SCALE.

TOTAL SOLIDS: LOCATE PPM VALUE FOR TOTAL SOLIDS ON THE PPM SCALE. PROCEED HORIZONTALLY TO THE PROPER TEMPERATURE LINE AND UP TO THE 'C' SCALE.

EXAMPLE:

TEMP.= 140F.   pH= 7.80
Ca HARDNESS= 200 PPM
M ALKALINITY= 160 PPM
TOTAL SOLIDS= 400 PPM

pCa =	2.70
pALK =	2.50
C AT 140F =	1.56
SUM = pHs =	6.76
ACTUAL pH =	7.80
DIFFERENCE =	+1.04
= SATURATION INDEX	

bonate from solution or to dissolve calcium carbonate with which the water is brought in contact. The equation takes into consideration readily obtained analytical values such as pH, calcium, total alkalinity, dissolved solids and temperature.

In simplified form, and for waters in the pH range of 6.5-9.5, Langelier's equation for the pH at which the water is in equilibrium with calcium carbonate (pHs) may be written as follows:

$$pHs = (pK_2{}^1 - pKs^1) + pCa + pAlk$$

The two latter terms of the above equation are negative logarithms of the molal and equivalent concentrations of calcium and titratable base respectively. The terms $pK_2{}^1$ and pKs^1 are respectively the negative logarithms of the second dissociation constant for carbonic acid and the activity product of calcium carbonate. The difference ($pK_2{}^1 - pKs^1$) varies with ionic strength and temperature. The term pHs represents the pH at equilibrium assuming no change has taken place in the water bringing it to equilibrium.

The Saturation Index is defined as the algebraic difference between the actual measured pH of the water and the calculated pHs at saturation with calcium carbonate.

$$Saturation\ Index = pH - pHs$$

This index shows qualitatively the tendency for deposition or solution of calcium carbonate. A positive Saturation Index will indicate a tendency to deposit calcium carbonate. A negative Saturation Index will indicate an undersaturation condition with respect to calcium carbonate and hence a tendency to dissolve any existing calcium carbonate. A "zero" Saturation Index denotes that the water is exactly at equilibrium with respect to calcium carbonate.

Langelier's Equation has been slightly modified by other investigators. Various nomographs have been prepared to simplify the calculation of the pHs. A nomograph suitable for this purpose is shown in Figure 31-2. It should be emphasized that the Saturation Index is only a measure of the directional tendency or driving force of a water. It is in no way intended to be a measure of capacity.

While a high hardness water, with a positive Saturation Index will definitely lead to calcium carbonate scale formation, a low hardness water, with the same positive Saturation Index, may not form any appreciable calcium carbonate scale.

In an attempt to secure a quantitative index, Ryznar has proposed the Stability Index. This index is empirical, based on a study of actual operating results with waters of various saturation indexes.

$$Stability\ Index = 2(pHs) - pH$$

With waters having a Stability Index of 6.0 or less, scaling increases and the tendency to corrosion decreases. When the Stability Index is above 7.0, a protective coating of calcium carbonate scale may not be developed. Corrosion would become an increasingly greater problem as the Stability Index increases above 7.5 or 8.0. In some cases, the use of the Stability Index along with the Saturation Index will help in predicting more accurately the scaling or corrosive tendencies of a water.

PREVENTION OF CALCIUM CARBONATE SCALE

Because of the large volumes of water used in once-through systems, external softening of the raw water is not usually economically feasible as a means of scale prevention. However, a softening plant may be installed to supply softened water for a variety of plant purposes which may also include some once-through cooling uses. In such cases, the treated water balances are controlled so as to provide a Saturation Index that will prevent calcium carbonate deposition at the temperatures involved.

However, once-through cooling water is generally not softened by external treatment processes even though such softening facilities may be installed for other plant uses. The chemical treatment cost in softening the large volumes of once-through cooling water is usually prohibitive. The investment cost in the treatment plant for handling such large volumes of water is also another factor discouraging such softening.

The most common method employed to inhibit calcium carbonate scale formation in once-through cooling water systems is the use of various anti-nucleating agents. Except under unusual conditions, these materials provide very satisfactory inhibition of scale formation, at a low chemical treatment cost.

An anti-nucleating agent employed for this purpose is one which possesses the property of preventing crystal growth and thereby scale formation. In effect, these agents broaden or increase the solubility of the scale forming salts and permit an oversaturated condition to exist without precipitation from solution. The materials most commonly used include the polyphosphates, tannins, lignins, starches, polyacrylates and combinations of these materials. By blending several of the various agents it is possible to secure the additive benefits of each for application to that particular problem.

In addition, chelants can be used in certain types of once-through cooling water systems for the purpose of chelating metal ions, such as calcium and magnesium. Chelants react stoichiometrically, and the reaction products are usually very stable. Typical agents of this type are ethylenediamine tetraacetic acid, citric acid and gluconic acid.

Crystal distortion has been advanced as one of the main forces in reducing carbonate scale by the use of anti-nucleating agents. Figure 31-4 illustrates crystals of pure calcium carbonate at 450 magnifications. Figure 31-5 is a photomicrograph of crystals of calcium carbonate formed in the experimental laboratory system shown in Figure 31-6. The crystal distortion shown by Figures 31-7, 31-8 and 31-9 illustrates the effect of various treatments. Laboratory correlation of crystal distortion with the amount of scale actually formed on the heat transfer surface indicates that those which do not produce crystal distortion also do not reduce the amount of scale formation.

Study of the inhibitory effects of various agents for the prevention of calcium carbonate deposition can be made with relatively simple once-through laboratory systems. In systems of this type, the feed water of definite composition is pumped at a constant rate through a scaling chamber, and scale formation develops on a cartridge heater. Temperature, rate of flow and electrical input are automatically controlled.

Consistent results are obtained with the use of the same type of heating surface. Figure 31-6 illustrates a system of this type.

Figure 31-3 is illustrative of the data secured under such controlled conditions in the prevention of calcium carbonate scale formation. While most of the starches tested exhibit relatively low power in preventing calcium carbonate scale under test conditions, appreciable power is shown by some of the tannins and lignins. The most effective results have been secured with blends of several different agents. For example, some agents exhibit very high scale prevention powers per ppm in the low treatment range of 1-5 ppm. Increasing amounts of treatment above this range does not result in any appreciable increase in scale prevention powers. Other materials show practically a straight

Fig. 31-3

Effect of Surface Active Treatments in Reducing Calcium Carbonate Scale

Treatment Conc., ppm	Type Organic	Heat Transfer Rate Btu/ft^2/hr	CaCO$_3$ Scale Grams/ft^2	% Scale Reduction
0	—	16,000	26.8	..
50	Starch A	16,000	23.3	13
50	Starch B	16,000	26.8	0
50	Starch C	16,000	18.2	32
0	—	24,000	18.7	..
50	Tannin A	24,000	16.4	12
50	Tannin B	24,000	6.6	65
50	Tannin C	24,000	12.3	34
0	—	17,000	34.6	..
50	Lignin A	17,000	25.6	26
50	Lignin B	17,000	38.1	—10
50	Lignin C	17,000	10.7	69
0	—	17,000	37.7	..
2	Blend A	17,000	18.1	52
25	Blend B	17,000	5.6	85
25	Blend C	17,000	2.7	93
50	Blend D	17,000	0.4	99

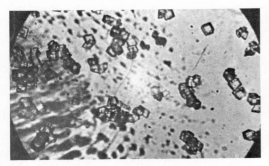

Figure 31-4 · Pure CaCO₃ (Merck), 450 Magnifications

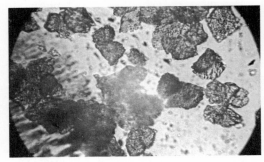

Figure 31-7 · Distorted CaCO₃ Crystals with Tannin Treatment

Figure 31-5 · CaCO₃ Crystals (17,000 Btu/Ft²/hr), 450 Mag. No Treatment

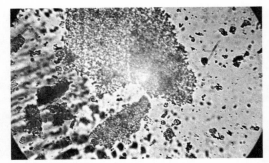

Figure 31-8 · Distorted CaCO₃ Crystals with Polyphosphate Treatment

Figure 31-6 · Once-Through Cooling Water Experimental Unit

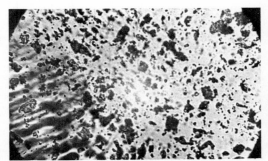

Figure 31-9 · Distorted CaCO₃ Crystals with Polyphosphate—Tannin Treatment Blend

line relationship with scale properties increasing in direct proportion to the concentration of treatment employed. By combining two or more such agents into a blended treatment, it is possible to secure their additive benefits over a wide range of treatment concentrations. The results in Figure 31-3 for such a combination treatment indicate the high degree of scale preventive power that can be incorporated into a single blended treatment.

With the use of anti-nucleating agents, it is possible to secure complete prevention of calcium carbonate precipitation unless the water is highly supersaturated with respect to calcium carbonate at the temperature of use. In such cases, it is necessary to decrease the positive Saturation Index, usually through the use of acid treatment. Complete elimination of the positive Saturation Index is not required under such circumstances, but only enough adjustment in this index to bring the water thus treated within the effective range of surface active agents.

IRON DEPOSITS

A special case of scale formation from ferrous bicarbonate may be encountered on once-through cooling water systems employing iron bearing well waters. This precipitation of iron can be prevented by the use of sequestrants or dispersants, which are very specific in their activity on ferrous or ferric ions. Dispersants are adsorbed on the iron particles while the iron is still in the ionic form. Residual charges on the adsorbed particles are similar, and hence cause a stable, dispersed condition. Polyphosphates, lignin derivatives and organic phosphates are examples of treatments employed for this purpose.

Iron deposits also result from corrosion products. In this case, the basic problem is prevention of the corrosion, although polyphosphates may be employed to minimize the "red water" problem, as discussed more fully in the next chapter.

REFERENCES

H. L. Kahler, "Once-Through and Recirculating Cooling Water Studies," *Proceedings,* Engineers Soc. of Western Penna., pp. 39-62 (1944)

W. F. Langelier, "The Analytical Control of Anti-Corrosion Water Treatment," *Journal,* Am. Water Works Assoc., Vol. 28, pp. 1500-1521 (1936)

J. W. Ryznar, "A New Index for Determining Amount of Calcium Carbonate Scale Formed by a Water," *Journal,* Am. Water Works Assoc., Vol. 36, pp. 472-486 (1944)

J. M. Donohue, "Organic Topping Agents," *Southern Engineering,* Vol. 85, pp. 52-54 (Jan. 1967)

32

Cooling Water Treatment: Once-Through Corrosion Control

CORROSION of ferrous metals in distribution systems, once-through cooling water systems, plant piping, etc. is a serious problem from several standpoints. Not only is the line replacement costly in itself, but the labor cost of removing and replacing buried lines, or those imbedded in walls, is very high. Corrosion products also reduce the carrying capacity of lines, increase frictional resistance and pumping costs. The iron oxide formed as a result of corrosive action occupies a volume many times greater than the original metal and eventually may result in complete blockage. "Red water," due to corrosion products, gives an unsightly appearance to the water and may interfere with processes sensitive to iron.

CAUSES OF CORROSION

Corrosion is defined as the destruction of a metal by chemical or electrochemical reaction with its environment. In the corrosion of ferrous metals in contact with moisture, reversion of the metal to the oxide form takes place. The driving force or the tendency to corrode is electrochemical. However, the rate at which corrosion proceeds is dependent on the resistance to continued attack caused by the products of the corrosion reactions.

In water systems, the principal factors influencing the corrosion of ferrous metals are the water characteristics, temperature, rate of water flow and contact with dissimilar metals. The chief variables controlling the corrosive characteristics of a water are its dissolved oxygen concentration, carbon dioxide content, pH and dissolved solids. Other factors are involved, of course, such as the possible presence of free mineral acid, hydrogen sulfide, sulfur dioxide, etc. In general, however, dissolved oxygen and carbon dioxide are the chief problems, with pH directly affected by the carbon dioxide concentration. Increased dissolved solids, particularly chloride and sulfate, enhance the corrosive effect of oxygen and carbon dioxide.

WATER CHARACTERISTICS. *Dissolved Oxygen.* Oxygen attacks ferrous metals, causing corrosion and pitting. Oxygen reacts with hydro-

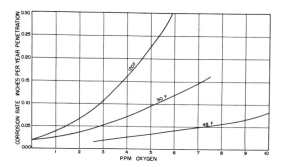

Figure 32-1 • Effect of Oxygen Concentration on Corrosion at Different Temperatures

gen at the cathodic surface, forming water and depolarizing the surface, thus permitting additional iron to dissolve. Figure 32-1 shows the effect of oxygen concentration on the corrosion of low carbon steel specimens at different temperatures. Philadelphia (Delaware supply) tap water was used in these tests, with a pH of 6.7. Linear rate of flow past the test specimens was 2.5 feet per second.

The chief source of dissolved oxygen in water is contact with the atmosphere. Deep well waters are usually devoid of oxygen, while most surface supplies are saturated with oxygen. The solubility of oxygen in water is dependent on the temperature and atmospheric pressure. Increased pressure increases oxygen solubility, while increase in temperature lowers the solubility of oxygen.

Generally, oxygen produces an easily identified corrosion in the form of small pits or depressions. As corrosive attack continues, the pit usually increases, not only in area but also in depth, and the nodule of corrosion products becomes enlarged. The detrimental effects of corrosive attack are more severe when this corrosion is localized in the form of pits than would be the case if general metal wastage occurred at the same rate over a large area. The centralization of corrosion at the points of pitting permits deeper penetration of the metal and more rapid failure at these points.

pH. At pH values below approximately 4.3 (the region of free mineral acidity), the chief controlling factor in promoting corrosion is pH. Acid waters, such as those contaminated with acid mine drainage, are quite corrosive. Neutralization of such acidic characteristics is a necessity for practically every water use. However, in the range of most natural waters, between pH 6.0-8.0, the pH of the water is not the controlling corrosive factor, in the presence of oxygen.

Carbon dioxide concentration, pH and alkalinity of a water are directly related. For a given alkalinity, the higher the carbon dioxide, the lower the pH. In the absence of oxygen, as encountered with the use of deep well water, pH is a controlling influence on the corrosion rate. At lower pH values, corrosion increases. Carbon dioxide is a factor in such corrosion since it influences pH. In the presence of oxygen, however, carbon dioxide like pH is not the major influence on the rate of corrosion.

Dissolved Solids. In general, increase in the dissolved solids content of a water increases the corrosivity. Higher solids content increases the conductivity of the water, thus favoring increased corrosion. The chloride ion, in particular, accelerates corrosive action although at very high concentrations (brine) a decrease in corrosivity is observed. Various explanations have been advanced for the corrosive effect of higher dissolved solids and one logical theory involves the effect of ions in destroying the coating of corrosion products on the metal. High chloride concentrations, for example, also hinder the formation of protective coatings by inhibitors, such as the chromates.

EFFECT OF TEMPERATURE. The chemical reactions of corrosion increase in rate with increase in temperature. Reference to Figure 32-1 shows the accelerated corrosion at 90 F and 120 F, in comparison with 48 F for various oxygen concentrations. Increased temperature decreases water viscosity and thus increases the diffusion rate of oxygen. Electrical conductivity is increased at higher temperatures, thus producing an effect similar to increase in dissolved solids content. Pitting may be enhanced where adjacent metal areas vary in temperature, with the hotter sections

anodic to the colder areas.

EFFECT OF FLOW RATE. Increase in the rate of flow tends to increase the rate of corrosion. Figure 32-2 illustrates data secured through the exposure of $\frac{1}{4}''$ tubular low carbon steel specimens to Philadelphia (Delaware supply) tap water at a temperature of 120 F. The corrosion rate increases rapidly with increases in the rate of flow although at higher flow rates this influence is less marked. Similar effects have been noted on tests with Pittsburgh, Pa. tap water and with sea water. The influence of flow rate on corrosion is probably primarily the depolarization effect secured by bringing larger quantities of oxygen into contact with the cathodic surface, together with the effect of greater amounts of ions (such as chloride and sulfate) on the anodic surface.

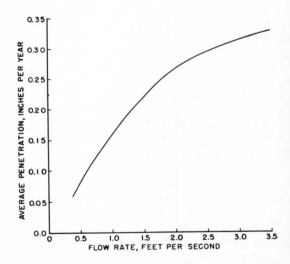

Figure 32-2 • Influence of Flow Rate on Corrosion

DISSIMILAR METALS. The corrosion that occurs from the contact of dissimilar metals is known as galvanic action. The tendency of a metal to dissolve and enter solution as an ion is measured by the electrode potential between the metal and its ions. The listing of the electrode potentials of the various metals constitutes the familiar Electromotive Series. The electrode potential of hydrogen is defined as zero. The metals higher in the table are considered able to displace those metals lower in the table.

The Electromotive Series cannot be interpreted as a precise indication of galvanic action. The potentials of the various metals can be altered by ion concentration, temperature, and the corrosive environment. Consequently, in practical service conditions, it is possible to reverse the order in which some adjacent metals are listed in the Electromotive Series.

Figure 32-3 lists a galvanic series of metals and alloys, based on corrosion testing experience. While closely allied to the Electromotive Series, it is based on practical experience rather than theoretical consideration alone. It will be noted that some of the metals are grouped together. Metals so grouped possess little tendency to produce galvanic corrosion of each other and from a practical standpoint are relatively safe to use in contact with each other. However, coupling of two metals from different groups and distant from each other in the list will result in galvanic, or accelerated, corrosion of the one higher in the list. The tendency for galvanic corrosion is increased when the metals coupled together are far apart in the list. While such a galvanic series is a useful guide, it should not be interpreted as an absolute rule under all corrosive service conditions.

Corrosion of ferrous metals in the presence of moisture is a truly vast subject and it is possible to only touch upon the various influencing factors in this discussion. Many other variables will affect the corrosion rate, such as the homogeneity of the metal, condition of the metal surfaces, ratio of surface areas exposed by two dissimilar metals, static and cycling stresses, oxygen concentration cells, etc. Water characteristics also are influenced by factors such as hydrogen sulfide, chlorine, and biological influences which can markedly influence the corrosion rate. The technical literature on corrosion is quite voluminous. In addition, several excellent books on this specific subject are included among the chapter references and should be consulted by those wishing to delve more deeply into this complex subject.

Fig. 32-3

Galvanic Series of Metals and Alloys*

CORRODED END

(anodic, or least noble)

Magnesium
Magnesium alloys

Zinc

Aluminum 2S

Cadmium

Aluminum 17ST

Steel or Iron
Cast Iron

Chromium-iron (active)

Ni-Resist
18-8-Cr-Ni-Fe (active)
18-8-3-Cr-Ni-Mo-Fe (active)

Hastelloy C
Lead-tin solders
Lead
Tin

Nickel (active)

Inconel (active)

Hastelloy A
Hastelloy B

Brasses
Copper
Bronzes
Copper-nickel alloys
Titanium
Monel

Silver solder

Nickel (passive)
Inconel (passive)
Chromium-iron (passive)
18-8 Cr-Ni-Fe (passive)
18-8-3 Cr-Ni-Mo-Fe (passive)

Silver

Graphite

PROTECTED END

(cathodic, or most noble)

* "Corrosion Testing Bulletin," International Nickel Company, 1944.

PREVENTION OF CORROSION

The prevention of corrosion in once-through systems is accomplished either by forming a calcium carbonate scale on the metal surface to act as a protective coating against corrosion, by elimination of the corrosive oxygen itself from the water, or by the use of relatively small quantities of organic and inorganic corrosion inhibitors.

CALCIUM CARBONATE PROTECTIVE SCALE. The Langelier Saturation Index is useful in predicting the tendency of a water to deposit or dissolve calcium carbonate. The Saturation Index can be used as a guide in the controlled deposition of calcium carbonate scale. If such a scale can be deposited uniformly over the metal surfaces throughout the system, it will act as a physical barrier, preventing contact of the water with the metal surface. The corrosive oxygen content of the water cannot contact the metal and corrosion is prevented. In effect, a protective coating similar to cement lining of the pipe has been formed.

In order to develop the positive Saturation Index required for deposition of calcium carbonate, it is necessary to adjust the pH, alkalinity or calcium content of the water so as to raise the pH slightly above the calculated pH of saturation. The materials employed for this purpose may be soda ash, caustic soda and lime (calcium hydroxide). Lime is usually the most economical alkali to employ since it raises the calcium content as well as the alkalinity and pH. A lesser amount is thus required to develop the pH of saturation.

• Theoretically, it is possible to control the deposition of calcium carbonate scale to such a point that protection against corrosion is provided, and the scale film is sufficiently thin to be non-objectionable. However, such a treatment method is more theoretical than practical inasmuch as a definite positive Saturation Index of a certain value pertains only for the temperature for which it has been calculated. With different temperatures throughout a cooling water system, the maintenance of a protective film on the metal surface at the point of lowest temperature produces an oversaturated condition at the point of higher temperature. If the calcium carbonate balance is so set that only a small amount of deposit will form at the higher temperature, none will form at the lower temperature and no protection against corrosion will be provided at that point. In addition, within the limits of plant control, it is exceedingly difficult to control scale formation to such an exact point as to provide protection against corrosion and yet not interfere with heat transfer.

The controlled formation of calcium carbonate scale as a means of corrosion prevention is successfully employed in some water works distribution systems where increase in temperature is not encountered. For industrial cooling water systems, however, where heat transfer is involved, this method of corrosion prevention is impractical, except under ideal control conditions.

MECHANICAL DEAERATION. The corrosive qualities of a water can usually be practically eliminated by oxygen removal by deaeration. Vacuum deaeration for once-through cooling water systems has been applied successfully to a number of installations. Where oxygen removal is not complete, the remaining traces of oxygen can be removed chemically with catalyzed sodium sulfite.

Of course, there is considerable investment cost, as well as continued operating cost, involved with vacuum deaeration. These factors have hindered the more widespread use of this method. Under certain circumstances, however, vacuum deaeration is unquestionably the most effective means of corrosion control and gradual extension of its use is to be expected in the future.

CHEMICAL DEAERATION. Sodium sulfite is commonly used in the treatment of boiler feedwater as a chemical deaerant and reacts with dissolved oxygen as follows:

$$Na_2SO_3 \quad + \quad O \quad = \quad Na_2SO_4$$
sodium sulfite + oxygen = sodium sulfate

This reaction proceeds rapidly at temperatures of 212 F and above. However, at cold water temperatures, the reaction between sodium sulfite and dissolved oxygen is quite slow. The slowness of this reaction has prevented the use of sodium sulfite in the chemical deaeration of cold water. In a once-through system, for example, with both oxygen and sulfite existing unreacted, the treated water may pass completely through the system before any appreciable oxygen removal has taken place. Of course, under these circumstances, no reduction will take place in the corrosive qualities of the water.

The development of catalyzed sodium sulfite has overcome the slowness of the oxygen-sulfite reaction at cold water temperatures and makes technically practical the removal of oxygen in once-through cooling water systems. In general, oxygen removal is complete within 20 seconds contact time, as discussed under the subject of boiler corrosion control. Naturally it is necessary to feed the catalyzed sodium sulfite in direct proportion to water flow in order to continuously achieve complete oxygen removal.

Because of the relatively large amount of catalyzed sodium sulfite required for oxygen removal (10 parts catalyzed sodium sulfite for each 1 part of dissolved oxygen), the use of chemical deaeration is restricted by economic factors. In once-through systems using large volumes of water, vacuum deaeration may prove more economical. In smaller systems, the investment cost in vacuum deaeration may not be warranted and the use of catalyzed sodium sulfite may be justified. Usually, catalyzed sodium sulfite is well justified following vacuum deaeration to remove the last traces of oxygen at a nominal cost.

CORROSION INHIBITORS. The corrosion inhibitors most widely employed in industrial once-through cooling water systems are the polyphosphates, silicates, the Dianodic combination of phosphates and chromates, and the Zinc Dianodic combination of zinc, phosphate and chromate. Other agents are used on occasion. In fact, from a technical standpoint only, any of the methods of corrosion inhibition employed in recirculating systems can be used satisfactorily in once-through systems. For example, the use of 300-500 ppm chromate would provide as satisfactory results in a once-through system as it does in a recirculating system. However, the cost of the chemical treatment would be so high as to be impractical. The chief problem in corrosion prevention in once-through systems is not lack of satisfactory corrosion inhibitors, but rather the difficulty of securing corrosion protection at the low treatment concentration economically permissible in treating such large water flows. For this reason, the corrosion inhibitors used are fed usually only in sufficient quantity to minimize or control severe corrosion. Only rarely, is sufficient treatment applied to stifle corrosive attack. The reasons for this practice are not technical, but economic.

Polyphosphates. Polyphosphates are a special class of phosphates, corresponding to molecularly dehydrated orthophosphate. Unlike orthophosphates, the polyphosphates possess marked surface active properties, useful in the control of scale formation and in minimizing tuberculation. Examples of polyphosphates are sodium tripolyphosphate, sodium hexametaphosphate and sodium decaphosphate.

Polyphosphates are widely used in the treatment of once-through systems, particularly city distribution systems. Remarkable results can be secured from the use of as little as 2 ppm polyphosphate, a concentration usually employed in these systems. The polyphosphates are quite effective in reducing tuberculation in distribution lines and in minimizing "red water" troubles. However, these results are secured without appreciable reduction in corrosion rate.

In once-through systems, and with the use of such low treatment concentrations, flow rate is quite important since this is the factor that determines the supply of treatment to the metal surface. Dependent upon the flow rate selected for test purposes, wide variations are secured in the corrosion inhibition properties of the polyphosphates.

Figure 32-4 shows results secured in an experimental laboratory once-through system employing Philadelphia (Delaware supply) tap water at 160F and 3.8 feet per second

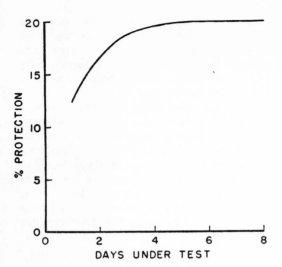

Figure 32-4 • Inhibition of Corrosion with 2 ppm Polyphosphate

flow rate. Polyphosphate was employed at 2 ppm. Comparison of weight loss data with the untreated water shows the treated run levelling off at a corrosion rate approximately 20% below that of the untreated water. Reduction in metal loss by this low concentration of polyphosphate is not outstanding, but the benefits secured in reducing tuberculation and "red water" are greatly in excess of what would be expected from this reduction in corrosion rate.

The ability of the polyphosphates to form complexes with iron naturally present in the water, or that resulting from corrosion, results in retention of the iron in solution and the prevention of "red water" difficulties.

Corrosion of ferrous metal piping results in the formation of iron oxide corrosion products many times more voluminous than the metal lost from the pipe wall. At the usual pH values in distribution systems, tubercules of corrosion products are considerably greater than at low pH values, where there is a greater solution effect from the more acidic condition. Increase in pH value of the water, short of pH 10.0-11.0, is not effective in reducing tuberculation.

Tuberculation is responsible for reducing

the carrying capacity of the lines and making necessary periodic mechanical or chemical cleaning. The loss in head caused by tuberculation requires increased pump pressures and causes higher pumping costs.

Figure 32-5 illustrates results obtained over several months operation with untreated water and water treated with 2 ppm polyphosphate. Results were obtained at a flow rate of 3.2 feet per second. The loss in head with the untreated water is an indication of the effect of tuberculation in increasing the resistance to flow. The use of 2 ppm polyphosphate resulted in only minor head loss, equivalent after eight months operation to only 10% of the head loss encountered without polyphosphate treatment. In these tests, tuberculation was effectively minimized by the use of this minute amount of polyphosphate.

Silicates. Sodium silicate has been employed for many years to reduce corrosion in once-through systems. Considering the long period of time this material has been employed, there is surprisingly little quantitative data

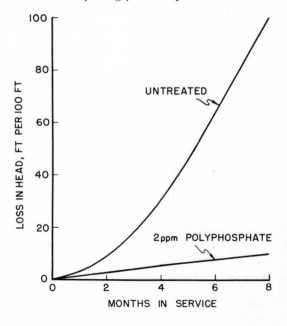

Figure 32-5 • Reduction in Tuberculation by Polyphosphate

in the technical literature concerning its corrosion inhibition properties in water systems.

Sodium silicate has been recommended as a corrosion inhibitor primarily for the treatment of relatively soft waters and based on increasing the silica content of the water by 8 ppm as SiO_2. Sodium silicate is available in different grades with varying ratios of Na_2O to SiO_2 and consequently varying alkalinity. The alkalinity supplied by sodium silicate is undoubtedly useful in neutralizing carbon dioxide and increasing pH.

Figure 32-6 shows results in a laboratory once-through system under the same conditions used in securing the data for Figure 32-4. Flow rate was 3.8 feet per second, temperature was 160 F and Philadelphia tap water was used. Liquid sodium silicate (28% SiO_2) was fed at the rate of 100 ppm and it will be noted that weight loss was decreased approximately 17%, as compared with an untreated condition. Sodium silicate at 100 ppm thus provided lesser corrosion protection than polyphosphate at 2 ppm, under these test conditions.

Similar data has been secured under different test conditions, all indicating only

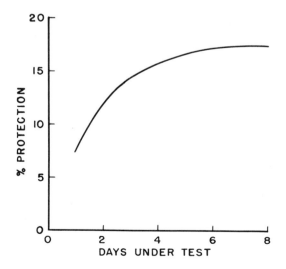

Figure 32-6 • *Inhibition of Corrosion with 100 ppm Sodium Silicate (28% SiO₂)*

minor corrosion inhibitory properties for sodium silicate, as measured by metal loss. Without question, however, "red water" difficulties are reduced with the use of sodium silicate, although the manner in which the silicate functions is not entirely clear.

Dianodic-Zinc Dianodic. The Dianodic system of treatment, utilizing the two anodic inhibitors, phosphate and chromate, was used to improve results obtained with polyphosphates and silicates. Laboratory and plant results showed 50%-60% reduction in overall corrosion and tuberculation. However, treatment residuals of 12-16 ppm were just outside of an economical treatment level for once-through systems. It was therefore necessary to search even further for an acceptable treatment.

Addition of zinc to the two anodic inhibitors resulted in a cathodic-anodic system of protection. The new three component treatment was used in the range of 8-12 ppm and the data indicated 75%-90% reduction in corrosive attack. By applying the principles of pretreatment for rapid film formation even greater protection can be secured. Many plants have adopted the use of phosphate-chromate-zinc for maximum protection of once-through cooling water systems at this acceptable cost level.

Figure 32-7 shows three groups of uncleaned and cleaned steel test specimens. The two specimens on the left were exposed to a test water with no inhibitor present. In each of the three groups of specimens the one on the left is uncleaned while the one on the right has been cleaned. With the untreated water the uncleaned surface was coated with a bright red oxide.

The middle group of specimens was exposed to the test water with 6 ppm polyphosphate present as an inhibitor. Less corrosion was shown although tuberculation developed as shown by the uncleaned specimen on the left.

The third group of specimens, on the right, were exposed to the test water treated with 8 ppm of the zinc-phosphate-chromate combination. The uncleaned specimen had

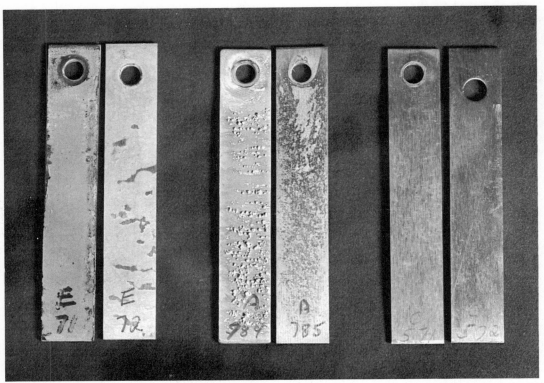

Figure 32-7 • Three Groups of Uncleaned and Cleaned Test Specimens Exposed to the Same Test Water with—No Inhibitor Treatment—Polyphosphate—Zinc-Phosphate-Chromate

Figure 32-8 • Enlargement of Cleaned Specimen with No Inhibitor Treatment

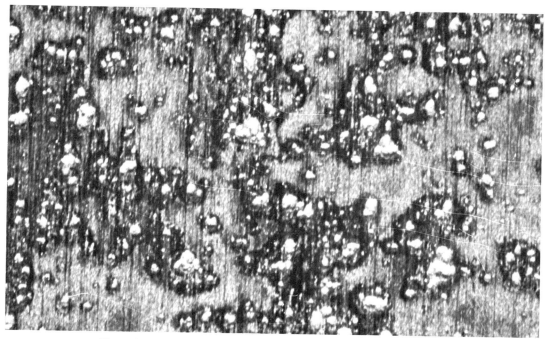

Figure 32-9 • Enlargement of Cleaned Specimen with Polyphosphate Treatment

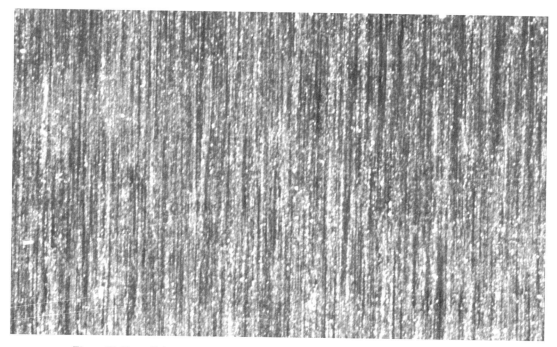

Figure 32-10 • Enlargement of Cleaned Specimen with Zinc-Phosphate-Chromate Treatment

a characteristic greenish cast, sometimes identified as interference colors.

Figure 32-8 shows an enlargement of the cleaned specimen with no inhibitor treatment. Nearly complete attack of the specimen is shown with only a small area in the center and lower left exhibiting the original streaked appearance of a new specimen.

Figure 32-9 is an enlargement of a section of the specimen exposed to the polyphosphate treated test water. The pits beneath the tubercles are clearly apparent.

Figure 32-10, inhibited by the zinc-phosphate-chromate combination, shows nearly complete reduction of the pitting function and little evidence of general corrosive attack.

These laboratory results have been transferred directly to once-through cooling systems that have experienced severe corrosion in the past. The use of Zinc Dianodic has made it possible to bridge the gap between 'fair' protection and the 'uneconomical' treatments for once-through cooling water corrosion problems. It is also possible to use a bare minimum of chromate salts in this balanced three component system, thus reducing the objection in overall plant waste water. Ultimate dilution to negligible quantities is the usual end result in nearly all cases. This treatment is not acceptable for potable waters. Work still continues in the organic line to find an acceptable, as well as economical, treatment for corrosion control of water used for human consumption.

REFERENCES

U. R. Evans, "The Corrosion and Oxidation of Metals: Scientific Principles and Practical Applications", St. Martin's Press, Inc., New York, N. Y. (1960)

R. J. McKay and R. Worthington, "Corrosion Resistance of Metals and Alloys", Reinhold Publishing Corp., New York, N. Y. (1936)

P. E. Pallo, "A Study of Corrosion Control With Sodium Hexametaphosphate", *Journal,* Am. Water Works Assoc., Vol. 38, pp. 499-510 (1946)

F. N. Speller, "Corrosion Causes and Prevention", McGraw-Hill Book Co., Inc., New York, N. Y. (1951)

H. H. Uhlig, "The Corrosion Handbook," John Wiley & Sons, Inc., New York, N.Y. (1961)

33

Cooling Water Treatment: Open Recirculating Scale Control

THE use of a recirculating system, in which a cooling tower, spray pond, evaporative condenser and the like serve to dissipate heat, permits great economy in makeup water requirements. With dwindling supplies of fresh cold water available for industry's cooling requirements, increased use must be made of recirculating systems in which the cooling water is used over and over again. A typical flow sheet of an open recirculating system is shown in Figure 33-1.

After passage of the circulating water through the heat exchange equipment, the water is cooled in passing over the cooling tower. This cooling effect is produced by evaporation of a portion of the circulating water in passing over the tower. By virtue of the evaporation which takes place in cooling, the dissolved solids in the water become concentrated. The evaporation must be replaced by makeup water. The quantity of water lost by evaporation can be calculated from the conditions of the inlet and outlet air. The evaporation loss will amount to approximately 0.85%-1.25% of the rate of circulation of water over the tower per 10 F drop of water temperature through the tower. For practical purposes, this figure may be taken

as 1% per 10 F temperature drop through the tower.

The circulating water becomes more concentrated than the makeup water due to this evaporation loss. Cycles of concentration is the term employed to indicate the degree of concentration of the circulating water as compared with the makeup. For example, 2.0 cycles of concentration indicates the circulating water is twice the concentration of the makeup water.

While the evaporation loss tends to cause the water to concentrate, the windage or drift loss, which is the loss of fine droplets of water entrained by the circulating air, tends to limit the degree of concentration. The amount of windage loss varies with the type cooling tower used, but the following may be taken as typical windage losses based on the rate of circulation.

Spray Ponds = 1.0%-5.0%
Atmospheric Towers = 0.3%-1.0%
Mechanical Draft Towers = 0.1%-0.3%

The windage also represents a loss of water from the system and this likewise must be replaced by makeup. Therefore, the evaporation loss plus the windage loss is equal to the

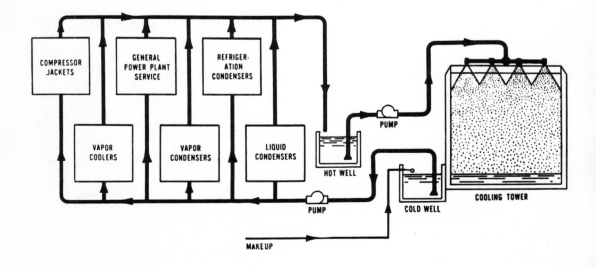

Figure 33-1 • Typical Flow Diagram of Open Recirculating Cooling Water System

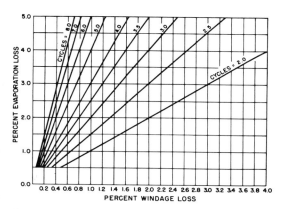

Figure 33-2 • Relationship between Evaporation Loss, Windage Loss and Cycles of Concentration

makeup required.

Both evaporation loss and windage loss are expressed as percentage of the rate of circulation. As an example, if the temperature drop across the tower were 20 F, an evaporation loss of 2.0% would result. If the tower were the atmospheric type, with a windage loss of 1.0%, the total makeup would be 3.0% of the rate of circulation. A circulation rate of 10,000 gallons per minute would require a makeup of 300 gallons per minute, or approximately 430,000 gallons per day.

The relationship between evaporation loss, windage loss and the cycles of concentration the water will undergo is illustrated by Figure 33-2. To illustrate the use of the curves, assume a 20 F temperature drop through the tower. This figure corresponds to an evaporation loss of 2.0%. From the typical windage losses illustrated for a spray pond, assume a windage loss of 2.0%. From the curves it will be noted that 2.0 cycles of concentration will develop. If the tower were of the atmospheric type and a 1.0% windage loss were assumed, with the same temperature drop through the tower, 3.0 cycles of concentration would result. In the case of a mechanical draft tower with a windage loss of 0.3% and the same temperature drop, approximately 7.5 cycles of concentration would develop. It therefore can be seen that the type tower limits the maximum cycles that can develop in a cooling water system.

SCALE FORMATION

In open recirculating systems, where the water is concentrated by evaporation, the problem of scale formation is increasingly troublesome. A water that possesses scale forming tendencies under once-through conditions becomes much more scale forming when concentrated. Even a water which is not scale forming on a once-through basis usually will become scale forming when concentrated two, four or six times.

In addition, while calcium carbonate scale formation is the primary problem in recirculating systems as well as in once-through systems, it is also necessary to take steps to prevent the deposition of calcium and magnesium silicate and calcium sulfate scales in recirculating systems. Scales of this nature usually are not a problem under once-through conditions.

The curves in Figure 33-3 will serve to give some idea of the relative solubility of calcium carbonate compared with calcium sulfate. While the various forms of calcium sulfate are illustrated, the one normally encountered in cooling water systems is gypsum. Due to the fact that calcium carbonate is considerably less soluble than calcium sulfate, the type scale formed in open recirculating systems is principally calcium carbonate in the great majority of cases. Typical analyses of scale samples are shown in Figure 33-4.

The main factor controlling the increased tendency for scale formation in open recirculating systems is the increased concentration, due to cycles of concentration. Langelier's Saturation Index can be used as a guide to predict the tendency toward scale formation.

Figure 33-5 shows makeup and circulating water analyses from a plant with a maximum circulating water temperature of 140 F. Calculation of the pHs at 140 F on the makeup water yields a value of 7.8 resulting in a negative or non scale-forming Saturation Index of —0.8. The Stability Index of 8.6 also indicates a non scaling condition. These conclusions would pertain if there were no concentration of solids, as in a once-through system.

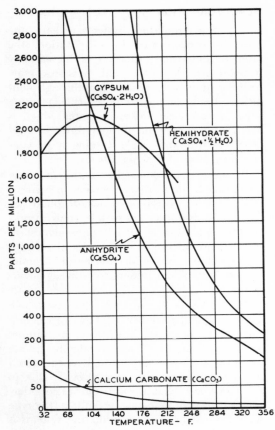

Figure 33-3 • Solubility of Calcium Carbonate Compared to Calcium Sulfate

Figure 33-4—Typical Analysis of Scales From Open Recirculating Systems

Source	Condenser, %	Pipe Cooler, %
Calcium as CaO	49.79	39.85
Magnesium as MgO	2.42	2.20
Iron as Fe_2O_3	0.61	6.98
Aluminum as Al_2O_3	0.21	0.52
Carbonate as CO_2	39.00	30.20
Sulfate as SO_3	1.29	0.50
Silica as SiO_2	0.15	3.85
Loss on Ignition	6.05	15.00

At 2.0 cycles of concentration, the pHs is 7.3, equivalent to the circulating water pH. Stability Index of 7.3 also indicates a non scaling condition. At two cycles of concentration, calcium carbonate scale would not be expected.

At 3.0 cycles of concentration, a positive Saturation Index of 1.5 is obtained and a Stability Index of 5.3. These values indicate an appreciable tendency toward calcium carbonate scale formation. It would not be safe to exceed 2.0 cycles of concentration with this water, without employing some form of treatment. With organic and inorganic surface active agents, it would be possible to maintain 3.0 cycles of concentration without calcium carbonate scale formation, but this concentration could not be tolerated without such treatment.

Fig. 33-5—Circulating Water Analyses

	Makeup	Circulating Water at 2.0 Cycles	Circulating Water at 3.0 Cycles
Total Hardness as $CaCO_3$	60	120	180
Calcium as $CaCO_3$	50	100	150
Magnesium as $CaCO_3$	10	20	30
P Alkalinity as $CaCO_3$	0	0	10
M Alkalinity as $CaCO_3$	50	100	150
Sulfate as SO_4	40	80	120
Chloride as Cl	10	20	30
Silica as SiO_2	5	10	15
		Above values expressed in ppm	
pH	7.0	7.3	8.3
pHs (140F)	7.8	7.3	6.8
Saturation Index	—0.8	0.0	+1.5
Stability Index	8.6	7.3	5.3
Interpretation	Non scale forming	Non scale forming	Scale forming

SCALE PREVENTION

The problem of scale prevention in open re-circulating systems is similar to the problem in once-through systems. However, the problem is more severe in recirculating systems and, while essentially the same types of treatment are used, higher treatment concentrations in the circulating water are necessary, because of the increased scaling potential.

Figure 33-6 shows a laboratory experimental cooling tower system used in the study of scale formation in open recirculating systems. In a system of this type it is possible to automatically control temperature, heat input to the scaling chamber, cycles of concentration, blowdown and makeup. The effect of different treatment concentrations can be determined at different scaling loads.

As is to be expected the principles established in the control of calcium carbonate scale formation in once-through systems also hold true under recirculating conditions. Those anti-nucleating agents which cause crystal distortion are the most effective in decreasing scaling tendencies. Figure 33-7 illustrates at 450 magnifications typical crystals of calcium carbonate scale formed under recirculating conditions. Figure 33-8 shows the crystal distortion secured under the same conditions with a blended phosphate-tannin treatment.

In general, blended treatments of organic and inorganic agents have shown the greatest effectiveness in scaling inhibition. The concentrations required range between approximately 30-100 ppm in the circulating water. Of course, these concentrations must be divided by cycles of concentration in order to express treatment concentration on a make-up water basis. For example, at a circulating water concentration of 60 ppm treatment, if the system were operated at 5.0 cycles of concentration, the treatment required would be 12 ppm or 0.1 pounds per 1,000 gallons makeup water.

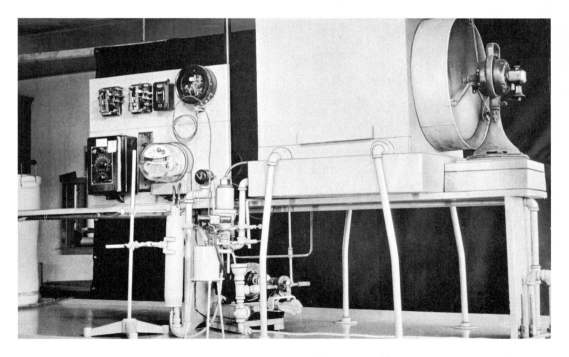

Figure 33-6 • Laboratory Experimental Recirculating Cooling Water System Used to Evaluate Scaling Tendencies

The solubility of calcium sulfate has been extended in cooling systems through the use of dispersants, sequestrants or chelants. Dispersants prevent buildup of particle size through adsorption, which involves electrostatic forces. Sequestrants and chelants function through electron transfer, forming a water soluble complex with calcium.

As an example of the power of dispersants, in one tower system a study was conducted using a combination organic-phosphate dispersant. This study indicated that the cooling system could be operated at 145% over the saturation level of calcium sulfate without deposition occurring in the system.

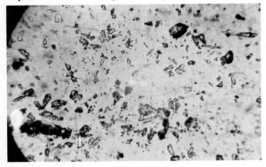

Figure 33-7 • CaCO₃ Scale Formation without Treatment in Recirculating System at 27,000 Btu/Ft²/Hr Heat Transfer. 450 Mag.

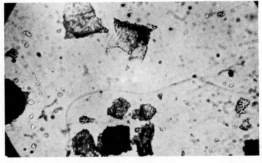

Figure 33-8 • CaCO₃ Scale Formation with Polyphosphate-Tannin Treatment in Recirculating System at 27,000 Btu/Ft²/Hr Heat Transfer. 450 Mag.

CONTROL OF CYCLES

The concentration of scale forming solids that takes place in a cooling tower system introduces a problem not encountered in once-through scale prevention. Except in an extraordinary case, calcium carbonate scale formation can be prevented in once-through systems by the simple device of using increased treatment concentrations for increased scaling loads. However, in open recirculating systems it is possible to reach such a degree of oversaturation of calcium carbonate that even increased treatment concentrations can not control the scale problem. No increase in treatment, within economic limits, will control the oversaturated condition that can develop under some circumstances at high cycles of concentration.

To avoid such an oversaturation with respect to calcium carbonate, and also to control formation of calcium sulfate, calcium silicate and magnesium silicate, it is necessary to limit cycles of concentration. By thus limiting the concentration of the circulating water, the degree of oversaturation can be restricted to within the effective range of the treatment employed. Where the natural windage loss is insufficient to limit cycles of concentration, it is necessary to supplement the windage loss by means of blowdown.

Blowdown consists in removing a portion of the concentrated circulating water and replacing it with fresh makeup water, thus securing a lowering of the concentration in the system. Blowdown can be either intermittent or continuous. Continuous blowdown is preferred, controlled by a flow control valve on a separate line to waste. The blowdown valve control setting is varied to maintain cycles of concentration within safe limits to prevent scale formation.

The amount of blowdown required to limit cycles to any predetermined value can be calculated through the use of the basic formula:

$$\text{Cycles of Concentration} = \frac{\% \, E + \% \, B}{\% \, B}$$

where % E = Evaporation loss, expressed as percent of circulation rate.

% B = Combined windage and blowdown loss, expressed as percent of circulation rate.

Derivation of this formula is as outlined

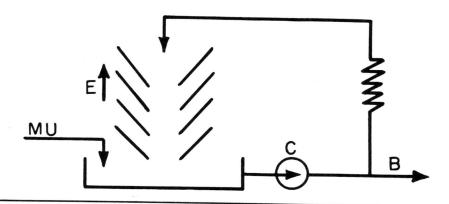

TERMS:

E = Lbs of water evaporated.

B = Lbs of water lost by windage and blowdown.

Mu = Lbs of makeup water.

C = Lbs of water circulated.

Cl_{MU} = Chloride of makeup water.

Cl_E = Chloride of water evaporated.

Cl_C = Chloride of circulating water.

Cl_B = Chloride of water lost by windage and blowdown.

PROOF:

By definition, cycles of concentration is the term employed to indicate the degree of concentration of the circulating water as compared with the makeup water. Since chlorides remain soluble on concentration, the term cycles of concentration is best expressed as the ratio of the chloride content of the circulating and makeup waters.

(1) Cycles of concentration $= \dfrac{Cl_C}{Cl_{MU}}$

Since makeup water is added to the system in an amount equivalent to the water lost from the system:

(2) Mu = E + B

At equilibrium conditions, the chloride entering the system must equal the chloride leaving the system.

Therefore:

(3) $Mu \times Cl_{MU} = (E \times Cl_E) + (B \times Cl_B)$

However, chlorides are not lost by evaporation, and therefore $Cl_E = O$. Equation (3) then becomes:

(4) $Mu \times Cl_{MU} = B \times Cl_B$

At equilibrium conditions the chloride concentration of the blowdown water is the same as the circulating water. Substituting in equation (4):

(5) $Mu \times Cl_{MU} = B \times Cl_C$

Rearranging the terms:

(6) $\dfrac{Cl_C}{Cl_{MU}} = \dfrac{Mu}{B}$

Substituting from equation (1)

(7) Cycles of concentration $= \dfrac{Mu}{B}$

Substituting from equation (2)

(8) Cycles of concentration $= \dfrac{E + B}{B}$

Multiplying through by percentage (%)

(9) Cycles of concentration $= \dfrac{\% E + \% B}{\% B}$

Fig. 33-9—Derivation of Formula for Calculation of Cycles of Concentration

in Figure 33-9. While this formula has been expressed in percentages, other units can be used provided all quantities are expressed in the same units. The formula may also be rearranged to solve directly for blowdown as follows:

$$\% \ B = \frac{\% \ E}{(cycles-1)}$$

As an example, if we were to attempt to use the makeup water in Figure 33-5 in a cooling tower system without treatment, it is obviously necessary to limit cycles of concentration to 2.0.

With the following basic data, calculations can be made:

Rate of circulation = 10,000 gpm

Temperature drop through tower = 20 F

Type tower = Induced draft

If we take as windage loss, the fairly high figure of 0.3%, we can calculate the cycles of concentration that will develop.

$$Cycles = \frac{\% \ E + \% \ B}{\% \ B} = \frac{2.0 + 0.3}{0.3} = 7.7$$

Obviously, additional deconcentration by blowdown is necessary in order to restrict cycles to 2.0. This blowdown can be calculated as follows:

$$\% \ B = \frac{\% \ E}{(Cycles-1)} = \frac{2.0}{2.0-1.0} = 2.0$$

Combined windage and blowdown losses are 2.0% and if the windage loss is 0.3%, the blowdown loss must be 1.7% of the rate of circulation, equivalent to 170 gpm. The flow control valve on the continuous blowdown can be sized accordingly. Since evaporation loss is also 2.0%, makeup is 4.0% or 400 gpm.

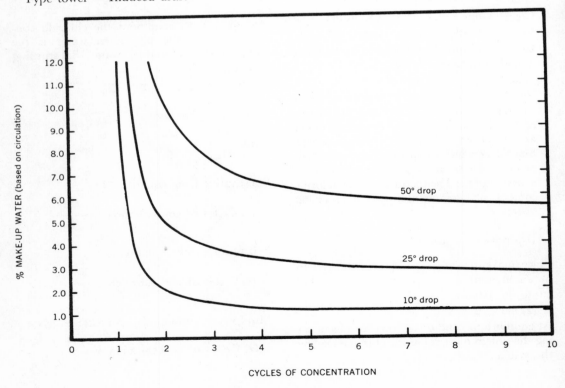

Figure 33-10 • Makeup Water Requirements vs. Cycles of Concentration

ACID TREATMENT

While blowdown is an effective method for limiting cycles of concentration and hence the scaling potential of the circulating water, it is not always possible to use excessive rates of blowdown to accomplish this objective. In many localities, the supply of fresh water is either limited or costly. It may be desirable to resort to treatment measures which will permit higher cycles of concentration in the circulating water, with consequent lower rates of blowdown.

Figure 33-10 shows the relationship between makeup water requirements and cycles of concentration at different temperature drops across a tower. Curves are based on an average value of 1% evaporation loss per 10 F drop across a tower. It can be noted how sharply makeup requirements decrease as cycles are increased up to approximately 5 cycles. There is not usually much advantage to be secured in reducing makeup water requirements by increasing cycles of concentration above 5.0. In some cases, however, it may be desirable to carry very high cycles of concentration, where permitted by water characteristics, in order to conserve on chemical treatment.

In those cases where lowered blowdown rates are desirable, either for technical or economic reasons, it is necessary to resort either to softening of the makeup water to lower the scale forming solids or to use acid treatment of the circulating water.

External softening of the makeup water can be accomplished through the use of cold process lime, lime-soda or lime-gypsum processes and by zeolite softening. The operation of the softening processes is as described in the chapters on these subjects. In general, these external softening processes can not be justified economically in comparison with acid treatment. While exceptions exist, acid treatment is usually more economical in continuous chemical cost. In addition, the large investment cost in softening equipment is avoided.

Where acid treatment of the circulating water is employed, sulfuric acid is generally used because of its low cost. The objective of acid treatment is to reduce the scaling tendency, but not to develop an acid condition in the circulating water. In fact, acidity is to be avoided. Sufficient acid is employed to reduce, but not eliminate the alkalinity of the circulating water.

By the use of acid treatment, the calcium bicarbonate is converted to the more stable and more soluble calcium sulfate, as illustrated by the following reaction:

$$Ca(HCO_3)_2 + H_2SO_4 = CaSO_4 + 2CO_2$$

calcium + sulfuric = calcium + carbon
bicarbonate acid sulfate dioxide
$$+ 2H_2O$$
$$+ water$$

It can be seen from this equation that acid treatment decreases the alkalinity and, by virtue of this reaction, minimizes the degree of oversaturation with respect to calcium carbonate. The calcium sulfate formed in this reaction, as shown by the curves in Figure 33-3, is considerably more soluble than calcium carbonate and therefore a greater concentration of this salt can safely be tolerated.

An example of the advantages of acid treatment is shown in Figure 33-11. In this plant, heavy scale formation occurred even with low cycles of concentration, when no chemical treatment was used. After a survey of plant conditions, the use of scale inhibiting treatment, together with alkalinity adjustment with acid, was recommended. Increased cycles of concentration, and a lower blowdown rate, were easily tolerable under these conditions, with complete freedom from scale formation.

The first column of Figure 33-11 shows the characteristics of the plant makeup water. The second column illustrates the circulating water analysis, without treatment. It can be seen that the system was under 3.2 cycles of concentration. With 50 ppm of calcium hardness in the makeup water, at 3.2 cycles of concentration, the circulating water should contain 160 ppm calcium hardness if none precipitated in the form of scale or sludge. The presence of only 70 ppm calcium in the circulating water represents only 44% of the expected amount. The analysis of the circulating water confirmed the heavy scale formation experienced in the plant operation.

In the third column is shown the characteristics of the circulating water with acid treatment and a scale inhibiting treatment. It can be seen that by virtue of the acid treatment, the methyl orange alkalinity has been limited to 125 ppm and the sulfate content of the water has sharply increased. The addition of the acid, however, has permitted the maintenance of 8 cycles of concentration, compared with 3.2 cycles of concentration on the untreated water. At 8 cycles of concentration, with 50 ppm of calcium in the makeup water, 400 ppm of calcium would be expected in the circulating water. It can be seen that 385 ppm of calcium are present, which represents 96% maintained in the soluble form.

It would have been possible to decrease alkalinity below 125 ppm and to maintain still higher cycles of concentration. In this particular case, there was no appreciable gain to be secured by such a procedure.

Operating data shown indicate that by this treatment procedure, blowdown was reduced from 152 gpm to 40 gpm, decreasing makeup water requirements from 524 gpm to 412 gpm.

It is advisable where acid treatment is employed to make the acid feeding equipment as automatic as possible so that frequent adjustment is not required by operating personnel. In many cases, the investment in automatic pH control for governing acid feed is advantageous.

In cases where the sulfate content of the makeup water is already quite high, the supplementary feed of sulfuric acid may not be permissible, if calculations show that the solubility of calcium sulfate will be exceeded in the circulating water. Under these circumstances, hydrochloric acid may be used instead of sulfuric acid for alkalinity adjustment. It is also in such cases that external softening of the makeup water for reduction in calcium hardness becomes advantageous.

Occasionally, a proposal is made to control the pH of the circulating water by means of recarbonation. The use of carbon dioxide will reduce pH, but it will not reduce alkalinity. On each pass of the circulating water

Fig. 33-11—Effectiveness of Acid Treatment in Eliminating Scale and Reducing Blowdown

	Makeup Water	Untreated Circulating Water	Treated Circulating Water
Total Hardness as $CaCO_3$	85	160	655
Calcium as $CaCO_3$	50	70	385
Magnesium as $CaCO_3$	35	90	270
P Alkalinity as $CaCO_3$	0	25	0
M Alkalinity as $CaCO_3$	180	470	125
Sulfate as SO_4	25	80	1520
Chloride as Cl	40	128	320
Silica as SiO_2	8	20	60
		Above values expressed in ppm	
pH	7.1	8.9	7.9
Cycles of Concentration		3.2	8.0
Operating Data			
Circulation, gpm		12,000	12,000
Evaporation, gpm (3.0%)		360	360
Windage, gpm (0.1%)		12	12
Blowdown, gpm		152	40
Makeup, gpm		524	412

over the tower, the carbon dioxide added for pH control will be aerated from the circulating water, down to its equilibrium value for those particular conditions. Consequently, to secure any pH reduction from the use of carbon dioxide, it would be necessary to add an amount equal to that required if all the water circulated were on a once-through basis. The carbon dioxide will not recycle. Consequently, for all but the most unusual circumstances, recarbonation is not practical as a means of pH control in open recirculating systems.

Sulfur dioxide is occasionally used as a means of alkalinity adjustment. Sulfur burners generate sulfur dioxide which combines with water and oxygen, simply as an alternate method of supplying sulfuric acid.

While the discussion in this chapter has been confined to the problems and control of scale in open recirculating systems, it is only rare that such systems are treated for scale control alone. Corrosion is an ever-present problem. It is not sufficient to adequately control scale formation and to permit corrosion to progress. Corrosion control measures must be combined with scale prevention treatment, as discussed in the next chapter, in order to provide a satisfactory balanced treatment program.

REFERENCES

L. D. Betz and J. J. Maguire, "Problems in the Treatment of Cooling Water in Industrial Plants", *Proceedings,* Midwest Power Conf., Vol. XI, pp. 318-328 (1949)

R. P. Gulley, "Modern Cooling Tower Water Treatments", *Petroleum Refiner,* Vol. 39, pp. 165-168 (Apr. 1960)

W. A. Tanzola, "Cooling-Water Systems and Their Chemical Treatment," *Petroleum Refiner,* Vol. 23, pp. 375-382 (Oct. 1944)

J. M. Donohue and G. A. Woods, "On Stream Desludging Restores Heat Transfer," 23rd Annual NACE Conference (1967)

34

Cooling Water Treatment: Open Recirculating Corrosion Control

THE prevention of corrosion in open re-circulating cooling water systems is a problem on which much research effort has been expended in recent years. As a result, effective anti-corrosion measures have been developed which can be applied in most instances at reasonable cost. In earlier years, many recirculating systems were not treated for corrosion prevention because the corrosion inhibitors then known were required at high concentrations with consequent high treatment cost. Today, it has been demonstrated repeatedly that the cost of corrosion prevention treatment is minor compared with the savings to be obtained in equipment replacement, down time and production loss. Corrosion control in open recirculating systems is, in reality, more important than scale control. Scale can be removed by acid cleaning or mechanical cleaning. The damages wrought by corrosion may require the complete replacement of heat exchangers, pumps, lines, etc.

CAUSES OF CORROSION

The causes of corrosion discussed in once-through systems also apply to open recirculating systems. However, the problem in recirculating systems tends to be intensified as compared with once-through systems.

The intimate contact of the cooling water with air in passing over the tower renders the circulating water continuously saturated with dissolved oxygen. This corrosive gas is, therefore, continually present in maximum amount and is the major source of corrosion difficulties. Where towers are located in industrial areas, the air also may be contaminated with gases such as sulfur dioxide, ammonia and hydrogen sulfide.

The concentration of dissolved solids, particularly chloride and sulfate, on cycling in an open recirculating system also adds to the corrosion load and makes more difficult the prevention of corrosion by inhibitors.

Most recirculating systems contain dissimilar metals. For example, the use of steel tube sheets with admiralty heat exchanger tubes is common practice. Such galvanic influences increase the problem of corrosion control.

Open recirculating systems, to a greater extent than once-through systems, are subject to outside contaminating influences. Sand and dust may be blown into the circulating water. Fibres may break loose from the tower wood. Sludge and slime accumulations collect in the tower sump. Where such deposits lodge on metallic surfaces, there is the opportunity for development of an oxygen concentration cell, and severe localized pitting.

Because of the effect of all of these corrosive factors, corrosion control in open recirculating systems represents an aggravated problem as compared with once-through systems.

PREVENTION OF CORROSION

The methods employed for corrosion control of open recirculating systems primarily involve the use of corrosion inhibitors. However, controlled calcium carbonate scale deposition, as well as deaeration, have been employed.

CALCIUM CARBONATE PROTECTIVE SCALE. The use of this treatment method was discussed under corrosion control in once-through systems. The same comments apply to its use in recirculating systems. Basically, since proper treatment of recirculating systems requires that heat exchange surfaces be scale free, this method of control is impractical except under unusual circumstances.

MECHANICAL DEAERATION. While vacuum deaeration has been applied to small cooling tower systems, this method of corrosion control is not practical for large installations. The deaerating unit must be sized to remove oxygen from the full flow of oxygen saturated circulating water, since the oxygen content is replenished in passing over the tower. Installation and operating costs make this method impractical for all but the smallest installations although the method is highly effective from a technical standpoint.

CORROSION INHIBITORS. In cooling water

systems, the corrosion inhibitors most frequently employed are the chromates and polyphosphates. Other corrosion inhibitors such as nitrites, silicates, amines and various other organic agents also are employed to a lesser extent.

An anodic inhibitor is one that restrains the anodic corrosion reaction:

$$Fe = Fe^{++} + 2e$$

Examples of anodic inhibitors are sodium and potassium chromate, nitrite, phosphate and hydroxide.

Cathodic inhibitors are those that restrain the cathodic corrosion reaction:

$$O_2 + 2 H_2O + 4e = 4 (OH)^-$$

Salts of metals which form sparingly soluble hydroxides, oxides and carbonates, such as zinc and nickel, act as cathodic inhibitors. Calcium carbonate is also a cathodic inhibitor. In general, any treatment which forms an adherent coating on the metal surface functions as a cathodic inhibitor. An ideal inhibitor would be one which would develop a dense protective coating of minimum thickness and which would deposit evenly at both hot and cold sections of the system.

It is characteristic of anodic inhibitors that they are efficient corrosion inhibitors if used in sufficient quantity to completely stifle corrosive action. However, if used in insufficient amount to completely stop attack, corrosion is severely localized in the form of pitting. Failure of the metal by perforation may occur more quickly than if no inhibitor had been added.

Chromates. From the standpoint of saving metal, by providing a high percentage corrosion protection, the various chromate salts are the most effective corrosion inhibitors in use. With adequate chromate concentrations, corrosion rates can be reduced 95% or more in comparison with an untreated condition. Such corrosion prevention is substantially higher than can be secured by any other chemical inhibitor. A disadvantage of low chromate concentrations, however, is that isolated pitting of the metal is not completely stifled. The small amount of corrosive attack which does occur is localized in the form of

pitting and the small amount of metal loss that does take place is concentrated in a small area.

This pitting effect, and the resultant tuberculation from the corrosion products, represents the major disadvantage in the use of chromate salts for corrosion inhibition. It is possible to minimize this tendency for pitting by using higher chromate concentrations, particularly under severely corrosive conditions. However, economic factors usually limit the treatment concentration that may be employed so that the isolated pitting encountered with lower chromate concentrations has been accepted as inevitable and the primary disadvantage of an otherwise fine corrosion inhibitor.

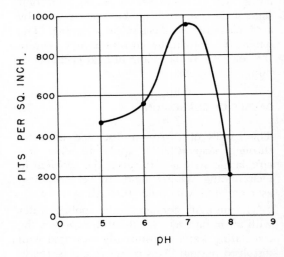

*Figure 34-1 • Variation in Number of Pits with pH—
Low Chromate Concentrations*

Figure 34-1 illustrates the influence of pH on the frequency of pitting at low chromate concentrations. The number of pits per square inch of test specimen surface, at a chromate concentration of 60 ppm, rises to a maximum at pH 7.0 and then drops off sharply at pH 8.0. At all pH values shown, however, pitting is excessive.

Usually, satisfactory corrosion control can be secured with the maintenance of 300-500 ppm chromate in the circulating water. However, in many cases, concentrations of 500-

1000 ppm, and even higher, have been found necessary to control the tendency toward pitting. Naturally, the use of such high chromate concentrations has made the use of this material too costly in many instances.

Polyphosphates. Phosphates, particularly the polyphosphates, are also widely used in cooling water treatment. The ability of phosphate to prevent metal loss is far inferior to chromate and, in addition, pitting with phosphate treatment is encountered to an even greater extent than with chromate. Unlike chromate, higher phosphate concentrations usually are not practical because of the precipitation of calcium phosphate. Phosphate, however, does possess the advantage of reducing tuberculation, thereby minimizing head losses due to corrosion products. Although pitting will occur, the dispersing or cleaning action of the phosphate prevents the buildup of iron oxide tuberculation products, maintaining the surface in a relatively clean condition and reducing friction losses.

Because of this solubilizing action, exposed metal surfaces with phosphate treatment usually present a clean appearance, relatively free of corrosion products. Instead of forming iron oxide tuberculation products over a pit, these corrosion products are continuously removed from the surface by the phosphate concentration present in the circulating water.

On the other hand, surfaces exposed to cooling water containing low chromate concentrations may show tuberculation in the form of corrosion products from scattered pitting. The steel savings of the chromate treatment may be 50-100 times as great as the phosphate treatment and the number and depth of pits only a small fraction of that experienced with phosphate treatment. However, a casual observation of the metal surfaces may erroneously indicate the phosphate treatment to be superior to the chromate. Evaluation of the merits of the respective treatments, unless extended over a long period of time, can best be made from weight loss data on test specimens exposed in the system and from microscopic examination and measurement of pit depth.

Figure 34-2 shows the metal loss from steel test specimens exposed in a continuous flow system at a flow rate of 0.36 feet per second at 120 F. Polyphosphate was fed at the rate of 90 ppm, as $Na_{12}P_{10}O_{31}$. The initial attack decreased on longer exposure as shown by the slope of the curve, but steel loss continued at an excessive rate.

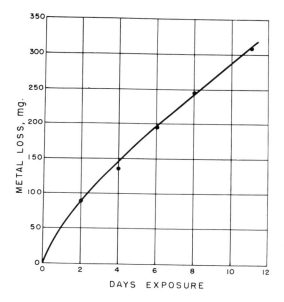

Figure 34-2 • Metal Loss with High Phosphate Concentrations

A factor limiting the use of phosphates in the treatment of recirculating cooling water systems is the reversion of polyphosphate to orthophosphate. The orthophosphate form provides less corrosion inhibition than the polyphosphate form. In addition, orthophosphate reacts with the calcium content of the circulating water to precipitate calcium phosphate, which can form a troublesome deposit on heat exchange surfaces. Reversion of polyphosphate to orthophosphate is increased by long retention time of the system and by higher water temperatures. Blowdown from the system must be adjusted so as to avoid exceeding the solubility of calcium phosphate.

DIANODIC METHOD. As previously stated, if
anodic inhibitors are present in insufficient
quantity, corrosion will be localized in the
form of pitting. Both chromate and polyphosphate are anodic inhibitors, but the different
action of these two materials as corrosion inhibitors led to an investigation of the possibility of combining the desirable effects of
both. The Dianodic method resulting from
this research, was introduced approximately a
decade ago, and employs a dual treatment of
molecularly dehydrated phosphates and chromates over a selective pH range. This method
produces effective control over pitting and
tuberculation even with the relatively low
treatment levels of 40-60 ppm. The superior
corrosion protection secured and the low cost
of treatment has encouraged wide use of the
Dianodic method. Corrosion rates of 1 mil per
year or less for steel are common with the
pitting function completely prevented or definitely stifled. Corrosion rates with copper and
its alloys are even lower—often less than 0.3
mils per year. Figure 34-3 illustrates the
results secured from an actual operating
system.

Figure 34-4 illustrates the reduction in pitting secured with Dianodic at 60 ppm, compared with the results for sodium chromate
at 60 ppm over the pH range of 5.0-8.0.
Figure 34-5 shows this same comparison with
60 ppm of polyphosphate.

Continued research has permitted the de-

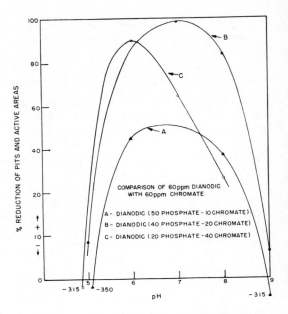

Figure 34-4 • Reduction in Pitting by Dianodic Method
vs. Chromate

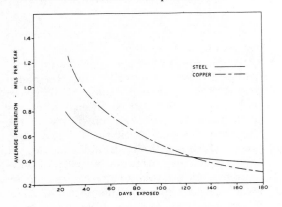

Figure 34-3 • Corrosion Control of Steel and Copper
Specimens with Phosphate-Chromate Control

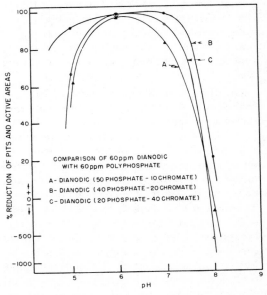

Figure 34-5 • Reduction in Pitting by Dianodic Method
vs. Phosphate

Figure 34-6 • Chromate Pits at 18 Magnifications

Figure 34-7 • Phosphate Pits at 18 Magnifications

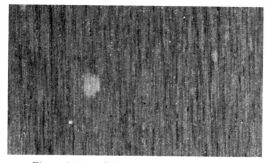

Figure 34-8 • Dianodic Method Specimen at 18 Magnifications

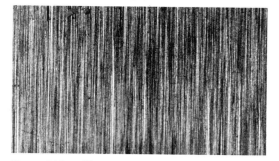

Figure 34-9 • Unexposed Specimen at 18 Magnifications

velopment of many variations of the original Dianodic method to meet specific requirements for the individual cooling water system and to cope with the many variables that enter into the corrosion problem. The Dianodic methods include: Phosphate Dianodic; Zinc Dianodic; Fluoride Dianodic; Chromium Dianodic; as well as combinations of these methods.

Phosphate Dianodic. The Phosphate Dianodic method, which makes use of polyphosphate in combination with chromate over a controlled pH range, eliminates the pitting function that is produced by the individual components when used separately. Figures 34-6 through 34-9 illustrate the control of pitting by the Dianodic method compared to phosphate and chromate when used separately. The shallow anodic areas that may develop with the use of this combination treatment have no appreciable depth and are rapidly rendered inactive. In many cases, even these shallow anodic areas do not develop.

The use of the Dianodic method to reduce pitting and tuberculation does not involve any sacrifice in the control of general corrosion. Figure 34-10 shows the average and maximum penetration values obtained from weight loss data for 3 treatment methods. Phosphate concentration was 4-8 ppm, chromate approximately 200 ppm and the Dianodic concentration was 60 ppm. These results show that the Dianodic method is equal

Figure 34-10—Plant Comparison of Three Treatment Methods

Treatment	Average Penetration, mpy*	Maximum Penetration, mpy*
Low Phosphate	21.0	660
Chromate	3.3	150
Phosphate Dianodic	2.0	20

*mpy = mils per year = 0.001 inch per year

to chromate in prevention of general corrosion and far superior to phosphate from this standpoint. While the major advantage of the Dianodic method is reduction of pitting, general metal loss is controlled as effectively as with high chromate.

Severe tuberculation can result from chromate treatment due to the formation of iron oxide over the isolated pits. With phosphate treatment, there is very little tuberculation because of the dispersing action of the phosphate. While pitting with phosphate treatment takes place to an even greater extent than with chromate, the corrosion products are dispersed by the phosphate and the metal surface maintained relatively free from tuberculation.

Results in the prevention of tuberculation with the Dianodic method are superior even to phosphate treatment, as shown by Figure 34-11. The Dianodic combination acts to dis-

Figure 34-11 • Tuberculation of Nipple Threads at 0.5 ft per sec flow rate. Left Specimen—Phosphate. Center—Chromate. Right—Dianodic

perse any corrosion products and since pitting is reduced to a minor quantity, there is little corrosion product to be removed.

Plant results with Phosphate Dianodic have been excellent. Treatment concentrations will vary with the individual operating conditions and may range between 30 and 100 ppm depending on water characteristics, temperature, cycles of concentration, retention time and other factors. Well established rules have been developed through years of experience over a wide range of conditions to permit the selection of the proper treatment levels, proper treatment ratios and pH range to assure maximum protection and the most economical cost for the individual system.

Zinc Dianodic. In spite of the wide coverage permitted by the Phosphate Dianodic method some limitations are encountered where calcium of the makeup water is high or the reversion of polyphosphate to the orthophosphate form is abnormal. Under these conditions it may not be possible to establish or maintain the most effective ratio of phosphate to chromate without encountering deposition of calcium phosphate. In these cases, Zinc Dianodic can be used effectively. The superimposing of zinc on the phosphate-chromate combinations permits a greater latitude on phosphate levels or, at the same phosphate levels, improves corrosion protection. For example, when normal phosphate levels cannot be maintained due to some limiting factor, such as high calcium or a high reversion rate of the phosphate, phosphate level may be decreased and zinc superimposed. In this case, the zinc takes up the slack and acts as a cathodic inhibitor to stifle the corrosion reaction. With the introduction of Zinc Dianodic, even broader coverage is possible and this combination of zinc, phosphate and chromate minimizes, if not eliminates, most limitations to use of the Dianodic method.

The Zinc Dianodic method is quite versatile and can be operated in the 'soluble range' or the 'coating range'. In the 'soluble range' or film forming range, pH and zinc values are set below the point where zinc phosphate will precipitate. Under these conditions no visible coating is formed except at points where the pH is elevated by local cell action. For example, if local cell action takes place, the area undergoing attack is the anode and the area surrounding the point of attack is the cathode. The cathodic reaction is:

$$O_2 + 2H_2 + 4e = 4(OH)^-$$

The hydroxide thus formed is sufficient to elevate the pH and cause deposition of zinc phosphate which stifles the cathode reaction.

In the coating range, the zinc and pH are set above the pH of saturation of zinc phosphate which results in a coating formation over the entire system. After the desired coating is formed, the zinc and pH levels are adjusted downward so as to just maintain the coating intact and to repair the coating at any point where cell action may start. In both cases, it can be seen that the function of zinc is one of a cathodic inhibitor or barrier type treatment. Generally, however, the use of the 'coating range' is restricted to the treatment of once-through systems.

In the control of corrosion, it is important that rapid film formation be accomplished to stifle the corrosion reactions. The use of Zinc Dianodic permits rapid film formation and is an excellent pretreatment for steel heat exchangers.

Fluoride Dianodic. Fluoride Dianodic was developed to handle waters contaminated with aluminum. Surface supplies that are turbid must be clarified to remove suspended solids that would otherwise settle on heat transfer surfaces. It is common practice to coagulate and settle surface supplies without the benefit of filtration when the water is used as makeup to open recirculating systems. The low turbidity from the modern type clarifier usually permits this practice. However, where aluminum is used as a coagulant and floc carryover takes place, fouling of the heat exchangers with aluminum deposits can result.

The fouling materials are most commonly aluminum hydroxide and aluminum phosphate. The presence of aluminum interferes with the Phosphate Dianodic method by forming a soluble aluminum polyphosphate complex. The Fluoride Dianodic method makes use of the fluoride ion to preferentially complex the aluminum ion. The soluble complex thus formed acts dianodically with chromate and aids in avoiding fouling and stifling of corrosion.

Chromium Dianodic. The original applications of Phosphate Dianodic to many refinery cooling water systems uncovered many instances where leakage from the process side was taking place. Where sour crudes are being processed, the leakage contaminates the cooling water with hydrogen sulfide, mercaptans and organic matter. Formerly, such leakage went undetected for appreciable periods of time and usually was discovered only after

extensive damage was done to the system. With the application of Dianodic, the chromate component of the treatment is reduced by these contaminants to trivalent chromium and leakage is readily detected. Where possible the leakage should be corrected immediately to minimize the heavy corrosion load imparted by hydrogen sulfide. In many cases, immediate correction of the leakage is not possible and a suitable method of treatment in the presence of process leakage becomes necessary. This requirement led to the development of Chromium Dianodic which makes use of chromium phosphate as a barrier type treatment during periods of leakage.

ORGANIC BASE TREATMENTS. Recent developments in research have made available organic base inhibitors that can effectively replace chromate treatments in certain systems. Although not as dependable as chromate base treatments in systems with high corrosion loads, the organics can often produce satisfactory results while eliminating the need for chromate removal.

The most effective treatments of this type include zinc and polyphosphate with organic. Some of the newer processed lignin derivatives have demonstrated their abilities as cooling water inhibitors, particularly when supplemented by zinc. Another successful inhibitor system is a combination of a polar organic sulfur, zinc and polyphosphate. This treatment provides a barrier of a thin, but adherent, nature that protects metal surfaces from corrosive attack. Results comparable to the Dianodic method are possible under many conditions, but treating costs will normally run somewhat higher.

Polar organic sulfur compounds, zinc and polyphosphate are not compatible in a single feeding system. Two feeding tanks are normally required.

Lignin derivatives and organic sulfur inhibitors are not compatible with chlorination, so non-oxidizing biocides must be used. However, non-oxidizing biocides provide effective slime and algae control at costs approaching those of chlorination.

MISCELLANEOUS INHIBITORS. Sodium nitrite can be used as a corrosion inhibitor in open circulating cooling water systems. While nitrites are sometimes regarded as reducing agents, they do possess oxidizing properties and probably for this reason tend to render metal surfaces passive to corrosive attack in weakly alkaline solutions. In acid solutions, however, nitrites do not render iron passive.

In order to establish a protective iron oxide film it is usually necessary to feed sodium nitrite at a much greater concentration initially than normally required. The rate of feed can be reduced to normal once the protective film has been established. For most effective results, sodium nitrite should be fed continuously to the system. Decomposition difficulties frequently make it difficult to maintain effective nitrite concentrations in the circulating water without excessive feed rates.

Both oxidizing and reducing agents tend to destroy nitrite and certain bacteria also cause its decomposition. Where nitrite concentrations can be continuously maintained at an effective level, satisfactory protection of ferrous metals is secured. Nitrite is not very effective in the prevention of attack on copper or copper alloys.

The polyphosphates are versatile materials and many other agents have been employed in conjunction with the polyphosphates in an attempt to improve their corrosion inhibitory properties. Complex cyanide synergists alter to some degree the typical pitting attack. Various organic materials of the sulfur and nitrogen bearing type have also been used. Mercaptobenzothiazole is an example of this group which has been found to minimize the typical phosphate pitting function of ferrous metals as well as improve the protection afforded copper and its alloys. Mercaptobenzothiazole possesses the disadvantage of not being compatible with chlorination.

Various chromate base inhibitors also have been used in which organic materials are either combined with the chromate or blended into the formulation. With both the polyphosphate-organics and the chromate-organics, zinc salts have been used to add corrosion inhibitory properties.

CHROMATE REMOVAL

Regulations regarding the quality of plant effluent may restrict the concentration and/or form of chromate in water discharged to sewers, streams or other bodies of water. However, in many cases it is better to apply the Dianodic method of treatment and remove chromate from the discharge water than it is to use an inferior non-chromate treatment.

Chromate removal can be accomplished with various commercially available chemicals. The procedure used is reduction of hexavalent chromate to the trivalent chromium form, followed by elevation of pH for precipitation of the reduced chromium. Reducing agents employed most commonly for this purpose include sulfur dioxide, ferrous sulfate, sodium bisulfate, sodium metabisulfate, sodium sulfite and hydrogen sulfide. The reaction generally proceeds more rapidly at lower pH levels, such as 3.0. Depending on the pH of the reaction, the reducing agents can also react with oxygen in the cooling water blowdown.

A typical removal system is designed for the addition of sulfuric acid to reduce the pH of the discharge water to 3.0, followed by the injection of sulfur dioxide at approximately one part per part of chromate. A mixing facility is provided, and then lime is fed to increase the pH to 8.5. A retention and sedimentation basin or lagoon allows settling of chromium hydroxide.

The design of a removal system and chemical requirements for a given installation must be based on individual plant conditions.

FACTORS INFLUENCING CORROSION LOAD

It has been pointed out previously that, in plant operation, numerous factors contribute to the corrosion load.

The effect of increased temperature is shown by Figure 34-12. Test specimens exposed on the pump discharge, at a temperature of 80-90 F showed considerably less weight loss than specimens exposed at the

Fig. 34-12—Simultaneous Plant Tests at Different Temperatures in the Same System

PUMP DISCHARGE (80—90 F)		
Days Exposed	Loss, mgs	Penetration, mpy
28	66	2.2
42	64	1.4
56	78	1.3

RETURN LINE (110—120 F)		
Days Exposed	Loss, mgs	Penetration, mpy
28	92	3.1
42	143	3.2
56	163	2.8

(Recirculating water analysis: Calcium as $CaCO_3$ 256 ppm, Magnesium as $CaCO_3$ 144 ppm, Methyl Orange Alkalinity as $CaCO_3$ 16 ppm, Sulfate as SO_4 1400 ppm, Chloride as Cl 1700 ppm, pH 5.9 to 6.3.)

higher (110-120 F) temperature. A Dianodic concentration of 60 ppm was maintained in the circulating water and it can be noted that the attack decreased with time, showing stifling of the corrosion reaction.

In the application of treatment to a system that has already suffered serious corrosion, invariably old corrosion products will slough off during the initial treatment period. These corrosion products will migrate to other sections of the system and some will settle at points of slow circulation. The new areas exposed at points of sloughing off will become anodic to the adjacent corroded areas. At the same time, when the migratory corrosion

Fig. 34-13—Effect of Deposits on Corrosion Load and Treatment Level

TREATMENT LEVEL = 70 ppm (DIANODIC)		
Days Exposed	Pump Dicharge Loss, mgs	Penetration, mpy
30	576	18.2
60	1451	23.0
90	1310	13.8
112	1459	12.4

Days Exposed	Return Line Loss, mgs	Penetration, mpy
30	738	23.2
60	1777	28.0
90	1488	15.7
112	2151	18.2

TREATMENT LEVEL = 200 ppm (DIANODIC)		
Days Exposed	Return Line Loss, mgs	Penetration, mpy
14	163	11.0
28	73	2.5
42	116	2.6
56	131	2.2

products settle on uncorroded surfaces, such as the test specimens, cell action takes place and serious corrosion results. The corrosion load during the sloughing off period is quite high and temporarily imparts an added corrosion load that must be dealt with during this period.

Figure 34-13 shows data collected at one plant at which Dianodic treatment had been applied to a system that had undergone very serious corrosion. It will be noted that the corrosion rates at both the hot and cold test rack were quite high and the losses in the hot were higher, as would be expected. It should further be noted that the losses were not consistent. For example, both 90-day specimens show lower losses than the 60-day specimens. This condition was due to the incidence of migratory corrosion products accumulating on the specimens, setting up cell action and accelerating attack. The corrosion load imparted by this condition was more than could be handled by the 70 ppm treatment level and it was necessary to temporarily increase treatment to 200 ppm to bring the attack under control.

Suspended matter aside from corrosion products produce a similar increased corrosion load. Dust blown into a tower basin in quantities and fiber thrown from tower wood also are detrimental. Figure 34-14 will also serve to illustrate the marked corrosion load imparted by corrosion products and foreign matter. These data were secured by installing

Fig. 34-14 Effect of Suspended Solids on Corrosion Load

Days	Pump Discharge (Unfiltered) Loss, mgs	Penetration, mpy
14	51	3.5
28	221	7.5
42	205	4.6
56	509	8.6

Days	Return Line (Filtered) Loss, mgs	Penetration, mpy
14	78	5.3
28	137	4.6
42	58	1.3
56	76	1.3

(Recirculating water analysis: Calcium as $CaCO_3$ 12 ppm, Magnesium as $CaCO_3$ 6 ppm, Methyl Orange Alkalinity as $CaCO_3$ 60 ppm, Sulfate as SO_4 1800 ppm, Chlorides as Cl 1600 ppm, pH range 6.5 to 6.7)

a small homemade filter ahead of the test rack in the hot return line. It will be noted that the losses for the cold, unfiltered water are substantially higher than losses for hot filtered water. Normally, the hot specimens would show a much higher loss than the cold specimens. Specimens in the hot were only subjected to the corrosion load imparted by the water characteristics. Specimens in the cold line were subjected to the corrosion load imparted by the water characteristics and the suspended matter. In spite of the fact that the water was saturated with oxygen, and the chlorides as Cl and the sulfates as SO_4 were each on the order of 1500 to 1800 ppm, it will be noted that this corrosion load was minor compared to the corrosion load imparted by the suspended matter.

Fig. 34-15—Weight Loss Data on Steel Specimens Coupled to Admiralty Specimens

Metal	Loss, mgs	Penetration, mpy
Uncoupled		
Steel	22	0.50
Admiralty	13	0.27
Coupled		
Steel	148	3.34
Admiralty	7	0.15

(All strips were 1 by 3 in. size exposed for 21 days in the cracked oil tower overhead cooling box. Average water temperature, approximately 95 F)

In many systems the foreign matter may be due to sand or silt carried in with the makeup water. Where such contamination has an adverse influence on the corrosion rate and requires high treatment concentrations to stifle attack, filtering of the makeup water will prove advisable. In some cases, the foreign matter originates from other sources such as dust, lint or fibers blown into the tower, and filtering of the makeup water will not accomplish a solution to the problem. In these cases, the installation of a side stream filter should be given consideration. The cost of side stream filtration may be justified economically where excessive quantities of treatment are required to stifle attack due to suspended or foreign matter.

Bimetallic contact and the resultant cor-

rosion of the less noble metal presents one of the most difficult problems in plant operation. Figure 34-15 shows the weight loss data for coupled and uncoupled steel and admiralty specimens, properly insulated and exposed simultaneously in the same cooling box.

The losses for steel and admiralty, uncoupled, were negligible. The coupled specimens showed a marked increase in attack on the steel specimens. While the average penetration was not high, most of the attack was concentrated. This bimetallic attack can be reduced by increasing the Dianodic treatment concentration over the 60 ppm level employed in this system. However, only 15% of the heat exchange equipment in this system was vulnerable to bimetallic attack. Increase in chemical treatment to control a problem in a minor part of the system may not be justified.

Other means of controlling bimetallic corrosion frequently are justified. Cathodic protection by magnesium anodes, the use of insulating gaskets and use of protective paints are all measures that properly should be applied to this problem. The cost of the high level of chemical treatment required for control of bimetallic corrosion usually is not justified in comparison to these other measures.

CORROSION OF NON-FERROUS METALS

Copper and more particularly its alloys represent the non-ferrous metals most frequently encountered in cooling water heat exchangers. While these alloys are considered relatively resistant to corrosion, they are subject to attack by many factors both chemical and mechanical.

Among the more common types of attack encountered are dezincification, impingement, erosion corrosion, stress cracking and fatigue cracking. Because of the many copper alloys available it is possible to select an alloy that best meets the requirements for the particular service condition. For example, in refinery heat exchangers the inhibited admiralty alloys are most widely used because of their good resistance to corrosion, particularly dezincification.

The chemical factors that cause corrosion of the copper alloys are low pH values, ammonia, cyanides, hydrogen sulfide and sulfur compounds, as well as excessive chlorine residuals. When attack takes place, the copper content of the circulating water will increase. The increased copper content produces an added corrosion load that adversely affects the steel parts of the system. The copper can plate out or deposit on the steel parts and create cell action that will cause serious pitting of the steel.

Fig. 34-16—Typical Inhibition of Admiralty by Various Treatments

Treatment	Average Penetration, mpy
Chromate	0.1
Dianodic	0.1
Polyphosphate	2.0
Polyphosphate-Mercaptobenzothiazole	0.3
Polyphosphate—Ferrocyanide	1.0
Untreated	2.0

(Philadelphia (Delaware) supply, 500 ppm added chloride, oxygen saturated, 120 F, velocity 2.5 feet per second. Treatment level 50 ppm.)

Chromates and chromate base materials such as the Dianodic and Zinc Dianodic treatments offer maximum protection to copper and copper alloys. Excellent protection is afforded even at pH values as low as 5.7 and the tolerance for ammonia, cyanides, chlorine residuals and elevated temperatures is improved. Figure 34-16 compares the results of the various treatments in protecting admiralty. It will be noted that the chromate and chromate base materials offer maximum protection. These tests were run at velocities of 2.5 feet per second. At lower velocities and elevated temperatures the superiority of the chromate base materials is even more pronounced.

SUMMARY

The problem of corrosion in open recirculating systems is intensified as compared with once-through systems. Aggravating influences are the continuous saturation of the circulating water with oxygen, the concentration of dissolved solids due to cycling and contamination of the circulating water by suspended matter.

Maximum heat transfer efficiency demands freedom from scale formation and tuberculation. Corrosion control is a necessity. While high chromate concentrations of 300-500 ppm will control most corrosion problems, in many cases this treatment cost cannot be justified.

The Dianodic approach to corrosion control has proven to be highly versatile, with excellent corrosion and scaling protection provided even under unusual or extreme conditions. The presence of reducing agents such as hydrogen sulfide or mercaptans need no longer be considered an excuse for inferior corrosion control. Periodic process leaks, except for economic reasons for product saving, do not necessarily require immediate emergency shutdown. From the standpoint of corrosion control, these leaks usually can be tolerated with some sacrifice in corrosion protection, by use of properly designed Dianodic treatment or revision in the treating program during these emergencies. Other unusual corroding or scaling conditions, such as aluminum and copper contamination, have also been well contained.

REFERENCES

H. L. Kahler and C. George, "A New Method for the Protection of Metals Against Pitting, Tuberculation and General Corrosion", *Corrosion*, Vol 6, pp. 331-340 (1950)

H. L. Kahler and P. J. Gaughan, "Protection of Metals Against Pitting, Tuberculation, and General Corrosion", *Ind. and Eng. Chem.*, Vol. 44, pp. 1770-1774 (1952)

H. L. Kahler and C. George, "Decreasing Cooling Water Corrosion", *Petroleum Refiner*, Vol. 34, pp. 144-148 (July 1955)

H. L. Kahler (to Betz Laboratories, Inc.), U. S. Patent 2,711,391 (June 21, 1955)

H. L. Kahler, C. A. Bishof and W. A. Tanzola (to Betz Laboratories, Inc.), U. S. Patent 2,848,299 (Aug. 19, 1958)

H. L. Kahler and C. B. George (to Betz Laboratories, Inc.), U. S. Patent 2,872,281 (Feb. 3, 1959)

H. L. Kahler and W. A. Tanzola (to Betz Laboratories, Inc.), U. S. Patent 2,900,222 (Aug. 18, 1959)

W. A. Tanzola, "Corrosion Control in Cooling Water Systems", *The Petroleum Engineer*, Vol. 25, pp. C57-60 (April 1953)

35

Cooling Water Treatment: Closed Recirculating Systems

THROUGHOUT the years the problems connected with the removal of heat from engines and compressors have received considerable attention from engine manufacturers, plant operating personnel, and water treatment consultants.

Engines and compressors first were designed for use with low temperature water at low velocity. These designs resulted in a large temperature rise through the system which set up unequal stresses in the metal, causing serious failures. To overcome this problem and to increase the efficiency of the equipment, manufacturers' designs have been changed so that the modern engines now operate with a rapid flow of water at a relatively high temperature, and with a temperature rise of only 10 to 15 F throughout the system.

At one time, little if any attention was given to the cooling water. It was not uncommon to use water on a once-through basis, taken from a stream that was subject to marked variations in dissolved solids and more particularly in suspended solids. Well waters high in hardness often were used so that heavy scale formation was common. Soon it was learned that scale formation and deposit accumulation from suspended solids could not be tolerated.

In other cases, cooling of the engines was accomplished with an open recirculating system using a cooling tower or a spray pond for dissipation of the heat. This method of cooling was a step in the right direction and permitted better control of the problems of scale formation, corrosion and slime. However, water-side problems could not always be solved economically, even with this type system.

ADVANTAGES OF CLOSED SYSTEMS

The closed recirculating system then became popular, and this type of system has been widely accepted as one of the most desirable ways of dissipating heat from the modern engine. This type of system is ideally suited to modern engine and compressor operation because a large quantity of water, at carefully controlled temperatures, can be circulated through the equipment. From the standpoint of water caused problems, the small makeup water requirements of the closed recirculating system greatly simplify the situation. The only makeup required is to replace losses from leakage at the pump packing or from drainage of the system for repairs. Little, if any, evaporation loss takes place.

Because the closed recirculating system greatly simplified the water caused problems, it was frequently assumed that no water treatment was necessary. This assumption proved erroneous. Corrosion in closed cooling water systems serving the modern engine can lead to serious problems. As a result of metal loss, leaks often develop which cause loss of cooling water and seriously increase makeup requirements and once again intensify the water problem. The corrosion products that develop often cause plugging of the narrow cooling passages, restrict flow, decrease heat transfer and result in rapid deterioration of the engine.

An increase in water temperature will increase corrosion by dissolved oxygen. In a vented system this tendency is opposed by the decreased solubility of oxygen at higher temperatures. This fact, of course, is the basis of mechanical deaeration.

Figure 35-1 illustrates data on the increase in corrosion at higher water temperatures for two different conditions. Curve A represents results obtained in a completely closed system without venting of the oxygen to the atmosphere. The increase in the corrosion rates with temperature is practically a straight line. Curve B shows data secured in a vented system. Note the curves are practically parallel up to approximately 170 F. Curve B then drops off since the lower solubility of oxygen at increasing temperatures in a freely vented system is decreasing the corrosion rate faster than it is increased by the temperature rise. However, in many closed systems it is not possible to freely vent the dissolved oxygen which is added in the makeup water. Release of the oxygen at points of high heat transfer (and high temperature) can result in severe corrosion.

The metals of construction in the modern engines, compressors, and cooling systems are many and include cast iron, steel, copper, various copper alloys and aluminum as well as solders. Nonmetallic components such as natural or synthetic rubber, asbestos and carbon also are involved. Wide temperature variations are encountered up to 180 F or higher and down to ambient (when the engine is off line) with a corresponding variation in oxygen content. The waters used in the cooling system vary in composition with geographical location. Because of these many variables, there is ample opportunity for oxygen pitting, galvanic action and crevice attack. Untreated systems will suffer serious deterioration from these forms of corrosion.

The use of a closed recirculating system does minimize makeup water requirements and therefore the use of softened water, condensate, or even demineralized makeup water becomes economically feasible thus eliminating the problem of scale formation. The low makeup requirements also make it possible to economically treat the system with adequate concentrations of effective corrosion inhibitors.

CORROSION CONTROL

The three most common types of corrosion inhibitors used for closed cooling water systems are the chromate base materials, the nitrite base materials and the soluble oil inhibitors. Of these three basic types, the chromate base materials are most commonly used. Buffered chromates in the range of 500-1000 ppm are satisfactory for waters low in chlorides and where bi-metallic influences are not encountered. Where chlorides of 100 ppm or more are present, increased concentrations of buffered chromate types of treatment may be necessary. When bi-metallic couples such as steel and copper are also present even greater treatment levels are required on the order of 2000 ppm or more. When aluminum or its alloys are also present the problem of preventing corrosion is even more difficult. The bi-metallic couple most difficult to cope

with is that of copper and aluminum. Buffered chromate concentrations of 5000 ppm or more usually are not adequate. It becomes necessary to use other additives such as nitrates or silicates to supplement the chromate base materials.

In systems that utilize mechanical seals on pumps, the chromate content of the circulating water is best limited to a maximum concentration of 250 ppm. This limitation usually eliminates leakage of chromate bearing water through the seal. Such leakage could result in damage to the mechanical seal by the attrition effect of chromate crystals.

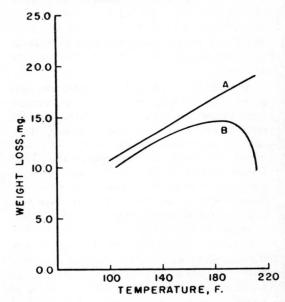

Figure 35-1 · Effect of Temperature on Corrosion Rate in Open vs. Closed Systems

In closed systems that must be protected against freezing during winter operation alcohols or glycols are often used. While buffered chromates may be used with methyl alcohol anti-freeze solutions, it is essential that the pH be maintained consistently at a high level; otherwise reduction of the chromate will take place. Glycol anti-freezes and chromate base treatments are not compatible. The non-chromate type treatments are better suited for handling closed systems containing anti-freezes.

The problem of toxicity of high chromate concentrations on occasion may restrict the use of these materials, particularly when frequent draining of the system is necessary. However, usually provisions can be made to handle situations of this type.

Another problem sometimes is encountered where the use of chromate base materials may not be applicable. Compressor stations that handle gas high in hydrogen sulfide content sometimes are plagued with leakage of the gas from the power cylinder into the water circuit. In these cases reduction of chromate will take place leading to ineffective corrosion control and deposit formation.

The nitrite base materials find frequent use in the treatment of closed recirculating systems, particularly in those situations where the chromate base materials are not applicable. Nitrite is a suitable corrosion inhibitor for iron and steel when the pH value is maintained in the alkaline range. Nitrite is not an effective inhibitor for copper and its alloys and can not cope adequately with couples of these metals with steel. Accordingly, other inhibitors that are specific corrosion inhibitors for copper must be used with the nitrite. When aluminum is also present in the system, the corrosion problem is intensified and nitrates and silicates must be used to supplement the nitrite. The nitrite base treatments are poly-component, and are required usually at considerably higher treatment levels than the chromate base materials. These treatments have the advantage of being compatible with anti-freeze solutions and are less objectionable from the standpoint of

toxicity. Their primary use is to handle these situations.

Soluble oils are good corrosion inhibitors and afford excellent protection to ferrous metals, copper and steel couples, and are effective even when aluminum is present. Cavitation erosion attack also is controlled effectively by these inhibitors. For the most part soluble oils owe their effectiveness to their polar properties which permit adsorption of a film that acts as a barrier to corrosion. These agents must be used at relatively high treatment concentrations, on the order of 1 to 2 percent or higher in some cases.

It is essential that these inhibitors be efficiently buffered and emulsified, otherwise heavy fouling of the cooling system can take place. Serious interference with heat transfer and overheating have resulted under these conditions. It is essential also that natural rubber hoses and gaskets be replaced with synthetic rubber to avoid difficulties with swelling and softening of these components.

REFERENCES

F. E. Clarke, "Cooling Water Treatment For Naval Diesel Engines", *Proceedings,* Engineers Soc. of Western Penna., pp. 1-15 (1956)

M. Darrin, "Chromate Corrosion Control For Engine-Jacket Water", *Corrosion and Material Protection,* Vol. 4, pp. 6, 8-11 (May-June 1947)

F. L. LaQue, "The Water Side Deterioration of Engine Cylinders", *Power Engineering,* Vol. 58, pp. 76-77 (Jan. 1954)

F. N. Speller and F. L. LaQue, "Water Side Deterioration of Diesel Engine Cylinder Liners", *Corrosion,* Vol. 6, pp. 209-215 (1950)

B. C. Thiel, "Controlled Water Jacket Cooling Reduces Maintenance Costs", *Petroleum Refiner,* Vol. 23, pp. 85-91 (June 1944)

36

Pretreatment and On-Stream Cleaning

THE advances made in the control of corrosion in open recirculating cooling water systems over the past decade have been phenomenal. The Dianodic methods for corrosion control are capable of decreasing the corrosion rate of steel to 1 mil per year or less with the pitting function totally prevented or definitely stifled. Excellent protection is secured with treatment concentrations generally in the range of 30 to 100 ppm, depending on operating conditions and water characteristics. Because steel can be protected economically many of the newly designed plants include all-steel heat exchangers in place of the more costly and more commonly used admiralty tubed heat exchangers. The cost of all-steel heat exchangers is approximately 60% of the cost of heat exchangers constructed with admiralty tubes. Under these conditions the capital investment for a new plant is considerably less when steel is used.

However, the design engineer should be cognizant of all factors that have a bearing on the service life of steel tubed heat exchangers. The experiences of one plant designed with all-steel heat exchangers will illustrate several of the precautions that are necessary if the expected service life is to be secured. Shortly after this new plant went into operation, it was found that pressure drops across many of the heat exchangers were greater than anticipated. Examinations of the heat exchangers revealed that heavy tuberculation was present in the steel tubes and in the water boxes. Some of the tubes were blocked with tubercules that had broken free from other locations. It was evident that the handling of the bundles during construction of the plant permitted corrosion to start. The pressure of other work attendant with start-up did not allow sufficient time for initial cleaning of the heat exchangers for removal of debris, grease, and corrosion products that had accumulated during construction. No pretreatment of the heat exchangers was employed and the intermittent operation of the system permitted frequent periods of inadequate inhibitor concentrations so that corrosion progressed at a rapid rate.

A marked difference in the care of handling steel tubed heat exchangers compared to handling admiralty tubed heat exchangers is evident from this and similar experiences. The corrosion rate of steel under these adverse conditions is many times greater than the corrosion of admiralty and the quantity of corrosion products produced is proportionally greater. When steel tubed heat exchangers are employed, it is essential that care be exercised in the initial handling of the bundles to avoid corrosion during construction and initial start-up. It is mandatory to clean steel bundles and to pretreat them to render the metal surfaces passive.

PRETREATMENT

Most methods of corrosion control are based on forming a film that acts as a barrier to stifle corrosion. The rate at which the film or barrier forms will largely determine the effectiveness of the treatment. Materials that do not form films rapidly will permit corrosion to take place and the result will be incomplete film formation and continued corrosion. The rate at which the film forms is related to the inhibitor concentration.

The function of pretreatment is primarily to permit rapid film formation to stifle the corrosion reaction immediately by formation of a uniform impervious film. Under these conditions the low treatment levels will maintain the film intact and avoid the accumulation of corrosion products.

Reference to Figure 36-1, Curve A, shows the high initial corrosion rate of steel when exposed to Philadelphia tap water, fortified with 500 ppm of chloride, and at a temperature of 120 F. The application of 30 ppm of Zinc Dianodic markedly decreases the rate of corrosion (to less than 1.5 mils per year at the end of 3 days). However, if the steel is first pretreated for rapid film formation with a treatment concentration of 500 ppm of Zinc Dianodic for only 4 hours and thereafter treated with 30 ppm Zinc Dianodic an even greater reduction in the initial corrosion rate as well as the over-all corrosion rate results, as shown by Curve C.

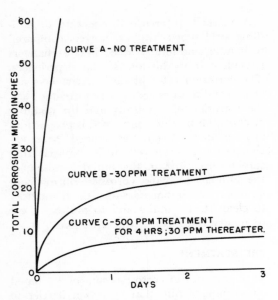

Figure 36-1 • *Effectiveness of Pretreatment in Decreasing Initial Corrosion Rates*

The data contained in Figure 36-2 demonstrate the superior qualities of the film formed by 500 ppm of Zinc Dianodic compared to 5000 ppm of chromate. Pretreatment with 5000 ppm of chromate for 2 hours permitted a 50% reduction in weight loss and a corresponding reduction in the amount of corrosion products that accumulate. However, pretreatment with 500 ppm of Zinc Dianodic for 2 hours permitted more than an 80%

Figure 36-2 • *Left - No Pretreatment. Center - 5000 ppm Chromate. Right - 500 ppm Zinc Dianodic*

reduction in weight loss and a negligible accumulation of corrosion products.

The low treatment levels normally used for corrosion control in open recirculating systems should be viewed as the quantities required to maintain the film intact and to heal the slight breaks that may occur from minor variations in environment. Whenever any serious changes in environment occur that cause destruction of the film, corrosion products can accumulate before the film is re-established by the low treatment levels. Under these conditions, in order to secure maximum corrosion protection and to minimize accumulation of corrosion products, treatment levels should be increased to re-establish the protective film as rapidly as possible.

Pretreatment of steel heat exchangers is required . . .

. . . for all new bundles
. . . whenever the exchangers are acid cleaned
. . . whenever low pH is encountered
. . . whenever serious process leakage occurs
. . . immediately following start-up after inspections.

CARE OF STEEL EXCHANGERS

INITIAL TREATMENT. The care of new steel heat exchangers should start with the writing of the specifications. The design engineer should include as part of the specifications, a requirement that the units be delivered free of debris, grease and other foreign matter that may initiate corrosion, and that the units be protected from the weather during transit and prior to installation. As soon as possible after installation, and prior to placing the system in full operation, pretreatment should be applied to the circulating water to permit rapid film formation. A procedure of this type will avoid excessive pressure drops and assure maximum protection of the units as well as materially aid in achieving the anticipated service life of an all-steel system.

OTHER FACTORS. Once the film is properly formed, the normal treatment levels will serve to maintain the film and prevent corrosion under normal operating conditions. However, there are a number of factors that can destroy the film to such a degree that higher than normal treatment levels will be required to re-establish the film rapidly. For example, when an individual heat exchanger is acid cleaned, the film will be completely destroyed. Acid cleaning will leave the steel surfaces in a very active state and the initial corrosion rate will be very high. The normal treatment levels usually will not permit sufficiently rapid re-establishment of the film. Therefore, following acid cleaning and flushing, the unit should be pretreated.

The modern day corrosion inhibitors function best in a pH range of 6.0-7.0. This same pH range permits maximum protection to tower wood and is usually the pH range required to avoid calcium deposits. Therefore, acid treatment of the circulating water to control pH is a common practice. In the great majority of these systems excellent control of pH is maintained. On occasion, however, low pH values may develop. If low pH is permitted for any extended period of time, partial or complete destruction of the protective film may occur. When this occurs, treatment levels should be increased to re-establish the film as soon as possible.

In other systems, process leakage may introduce hydrogen sulfide and mercaptans. This type contamination will have an adverse effect on most films. Also, leakage of this type usually produces a drop in pH as well. Until such time that the leakage can be corrected the system should be blown down heavily. If it is established that a particular heat exchanger is a chronic offender, it should be equipped with blowdown facilities so that as much of the blowdown as possible is taken from the offending heat exchanger. Following correction of the leak, treatment levels should be increased to rapidly re-establish the film.

The periodic inspections required for most systems will produce conditions during start-up that may increase the initial corrosion rate. For example, brushing or manual cleaning of the water boxes or other parts of the heat exchanger may partially or totally remove the protective film. Debris and migratory corrosion products may settle at various points in the system. These and many other factors will create conditions conducive to corrosion. Pretreatment by the use of higher than normal treatment levels during start-up will assure rapid repair of the protective film and minimize the accumulation of corrosion products.

The precautions outlined above will be instrumental in achieving maximum service life from all-steel heat exchanger systems.

GENERAL APPLICATION

While much attention has been focused on the use of pretreatment for all-steel systems because of the higher corrosion rates that can occur, the principles of pretreatment have application to and will prove beneficial for cooling water systems in general. It is true that the initial corrosion rates for admiralty tubes or tubes of copper alloys in general are materially lower than for steel, and therefore the effects of these less voluminous corrosion products are not as pronounced. However, where admiralty tubed heat exchangers are employed the systems are bimetallic since the shells and water boxes are constructed of steel. While the admiralty heat exchanger tubes are not adversely affected, the steel components of these units do undergo an initially high corrosion rate and produce voluminous corrosion products that interfere with proper and complete film formation. The application of the principles of pretreatment for rapid film formation, followed by the use of normal treatment levels for film maintenance will prove of benefit in minimizing corrosion of the steel parts of the system. In general, improved heat transfer, longer service life and less plant maintenance are the benefits that will be secured.

ON-STREAM CLEANING

A type of fouling that is not truly scale or biological slime is often encountered in cooling tower systems. This fouling is that caused by a combination of mud, silt and metal oxides held together by organic matter. Generally, the inorganic portion is an accumulation of airborne particles or suspended matter from the makeup supply. The organic matter can be caused by process contamination of the cooling system, or by organic naturally present in the makeup water.

Unless removed or controlled, fouling seriously interferes with operation of a cooling water system. Outage is frequently forced by decreasing flow rates or by insufficient heat exchange through accumulated masses.

In the past, generally this type of fouling has been removed from heat exchange equipment by mechanical means or by acidizing with the system out-of-service. During the last few years, many successful on-stream cleaning programs have been performed with the aid of newly developed dispersants or coagulants.

An on-stream cleaning program is usually modified to suit the individual chemical and mechanical requirements of a particular system. A typical desludging program is conducted for 72 consecutive hours with the dispersant concentration at the recommended level. The pH is decreased 1.0–2.0 units during this time, and blowdown is increased to lower cycles of concentration. After completion of the cleaning program, the system is passivated by a high concentration of the corrosion inhibitor.

In tower systems suffering continuous or heavy fouling, quite often it is more effective to apply a continual maintenance dose of an antifoulant than to resort to periodic cleaning. Deposition can be minimized or prevented by application of the proper antifoulant for the conditions involved at low treatment levels.

The new chemical antifoulants function to prevent agglomeration of particles, and are most effective against foulants when still in the ionic or colloidial forms. Chelants, such as ethylenediamine tetraacetic acid, sequestrants, such as polyphosphates, dispersants, such as sodium lignosulfonate, and coagulants, such as polyacrylamide, are employed for this cleaning function. Treatment levels vary from 1.0 ppm to 300 ppm, depending on the nature of the fouling matter and the type of antifoulant. Products have been developed specifically for iron problems, for bentonitic silt and for aluminum as well as for general fouling conditions.

REFERENCES

L. F. Probst, "Pretreatment for Effective Corrosion Control," *The Betz Indicator*, Betz Laboratories, Inc., Phila., Pa. (Nov. 1960)

37

Acid Feeding to Cooling Water Systems

A NUMBER of different systems are employed for the addition of acid, involving an even greater number of variations in feed equipment. Typical systems and typical equipment are discussed here but these are by no means the only acceptable systems or equipment.

The application of acid, usually sulfuric acid, in the treatment of cooling tower circulating waters is a generally accepted practice. Acid is a necessary adjunct in the treatment of many waters used in cooling tower systems and is used for the purpose of reducing the total alkalinity concentrations which would otherwise develop.

By acid treatment the formation of calcium carbonate scale is prevented, deposition of calcium phosphate is controlled and delignification of tower wood is also controlled. The advent of treating systems which function most effectively in the pH range of 6.0-6.5 has increased interest in acid feed and brought the need for better equipment and closer control.

The types of systems or equipment for acid addition can be divided into several categories such as proportional feed and constant rate, gravity or pressure systems, and concentrated acid feed or dilute acid feed. The drip feeder and decanting feeders are typical of the gravity units while eductors,

air pressure systems and pumps are typical of the pressure type. While most of these units are operated in a constant rate manner with manual adjustment, many methods can be made proportional to makeup water flow or pH by the addition of suitable metering and control equipment.

The primary purpose of this discussion is to offer suggestions and information concerning practical acid handling and feeding systems and to outline some of the precautions which are necessary in any well designed system. Because of the many factors influencing the selection of suitable acid feed equipment, such as the type and quantity of acid to be fed, labor requirements, and purchase and installation costs, each system requires designing on an individual basis.

HANDLING AND STORAGE OF CONCENTRATED ACID

Concentrated sulfuric acid is usually shipped in glass carboys or in tank trucks or cars. Figure 37-1 shows a typical acid storage system and, when sized properly, will be able to receive full tank car or tank truck shipments while maintaining an adequate reserve. Where acid is delivered in carboys, a number of foot and hand operated air pumps are available, from different manufacturers, for the purpose of emptying these carboys. A

Figure 37-1 • Acid Delivery, Storage and Transfer System

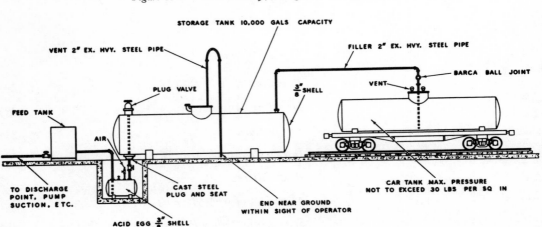

small electrically driven air pump is also available and suitable for emptying of carboys. The pump uses a self-sealing rubber connection in the throat of the carboy and, when operated, develops approximately 2.5 psi, forcing acid through the discharge tube. The corrosive liquid contacts only the tubing through which it flows.

When storage tanks are employed for the handling of large scale deliveries, the tank is usually located so as to provide gravity flow of acid to the day tank or point of use. In emptying shipping containers, it is essential that excessive air pressure is not used. When transfer pumps are needed for introducing acid to the storage tank, it is well to maintain a pressure of approximately 5 psi on the tank car or truck in order to supply a steady flow of acid to the suction side of the transfer pump.

Complete precautions to be followed when handling sulfuric acid with particular reference to unloading of tank cars and trucks are covered in Manual Sheet TC-1 issued by the Manufacturing Chemists Association of the U. S. This bulletin may be purchased at nominal cost from the association at 1825 Connecticut Avenue, N. W., Washington 9, D. C. Those responsible for handling tank car and tank truck equipment and fittings should be completely familiar with the entire contents of this bulletin.

CONSTANT RATE ACID FEED (Small Quantities)

Simplified drip and syphon feed systems involve the least expenditure of time and equipment in setting up an acid feed system. However, syphon feed is generally unsatisfactory. Gravity feed control is improved by employing a sludge pot or strainer. A large area filter using glass wool provides the best removal of suspended matter from the acid before the acid reaches the needle control valve. These systems are suitable only for the addition of small quantities of acid and where continuous attention is possible.

The above described methods of feed are usually adequate for feeding concentrated acid quantities up to 2 or 3 gallons daily.

Larger quantities are better handled by equipment described in the next section.

CONSTANT RATE ACID FEED (Large Quantities)

Controlled air pressure, with flow measured by a rotameter on the air line, can be used to provide close control over the feed of acid from a day tank to the point of discharge. This arrangement is illustrated in Figure 37-2.

Suitable decanting feeders similar to that illustrated in Figure 37-3 are available. The larger and more expensive types are usually lead lined and offer the least difficulty in feeding acid when the acid used has considerable sediment. These units can be supplied either as adjustable constant rate feeders or the feeder may be controlled to provide acid feed in proportion to makeup water addition or pH control. The smaller rotary-dip types have shown satisfactory service when properly installed and maintained. These units are usually made of polyvinyl chloride (PVC) plastic for those parts in contact with the acid, with acid resistant metals used wherever possible in other parts of the equipment.

A type of pump commonly employed in the metering of acid to a cooling system is illustrated in Figure 37-4. The unit is a diaphragm type pump and acid does not come in contact with working parts of the pump other than the check valves. All materials in direct contact with the acid are made of acid resistant or non-corroding metals and plastics.

Acid pumps, when used in metering service, require the removal of all suspended matter from the acid. Sediment present in commercial acid will cause the check valves to clog and the pump will cease to function in such instances. Therefore, a sludge pot is desirable and a glass wool filter is mandatory on the pump suction line if attention-free service is to be expected from the pump. Several suitable diaphragm type pumps are available on the market covering all sizes and capacities which may be required.

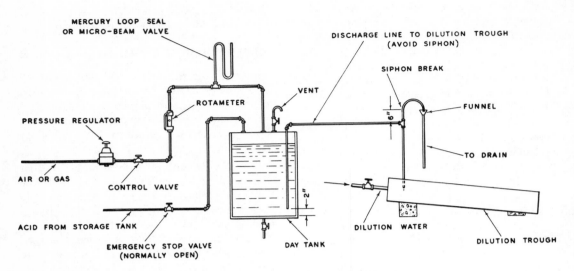

Figure 37-2 · Air Pressurized Feed System

PROPORTIONAL ACID FEED

A pH controller, equipped for starting or
stopping electrical equipment, can be used to
control the flow of acid into a system by
regulating a solenoid operated shut-off valve
or motor driven pump. A variation of this
system involves the use of a diaphragm valve
governed by the pH controller, usually
through an air operated motor. This method
of feed of acid is continuous and proportional,
the diaphragm valve opening wider to permit
more acid to flow into the system whenever

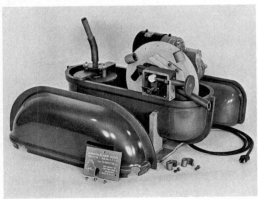

Courtesy Clarkson Co.

*Figure 37-3 · Rotary Dip Decanting Feeder of PVC
Construction*

Courtesy Lapp Insulator Co., Inc.

*Figure 37-4 · Diaphragm Pump Equipped with Auto-
matic Stroke Adjustment*

Figure 37-5 • *Automatic pH Control Using Positioning Control Valve*

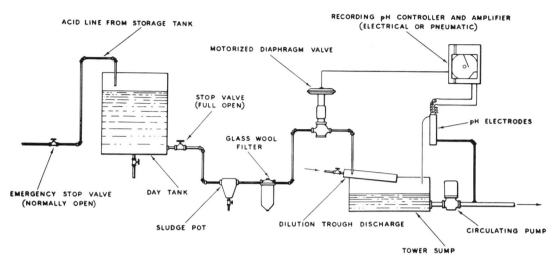

required. Likewise, as acid requirements decrease due to decreased flow of water or lower pH, the diaphragm valve will close down and decrease the feed of acid. The control valves are constructed of acid resistant alloys and plastics also. A typical system of this type is shown in Figure 37-5.

A rather deluxe system of acid control can be employed when desired, by utilizing a variable speed motor driven pump together with a variable stroke mechanism. Usually, in such instances, the driving motor speed is controlled by a flow meter with the stroke variations controlled by a pH controller. An electronic control system is used to supply the power to operate the variable speed motors.

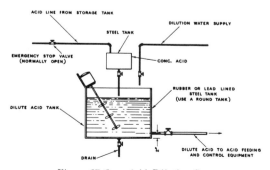

Figure 37-6 • *Acid Dilution System*

HANDLING DILUTE ACID

When the quantity of concentrated acid to be fed is small and does not permit easy addition to a system, a dilute acid feed system may be set up. Certain precautions must be followed in order to obtain proper service life from the equipment. Figure 37-6 illustrates a suitable method for handling the dilution problem.

In preparing dilute acid, not less than 18 gallons of water should be used for each gallon of concentrated acid (66° Baumé sulfuric acid). The dilute acid tank should be filled with the proper amount of water and the mixer started. The concentrated acid must be added to the water, as indicated in the diagram. The dilution should proceed slowly in order to avoid excessive heating, which may buckle the tank lining. When draining the concentrated acid into the water, a draining time of at least two minutes per gallon should be allowed. Dilution should proceed more slowly, if necessary. The concentrated acid tank should be used for measuring only, not storage.

In some instances, porcelain crocks can be used in place of lined tanks. In any case, the crock *must* be placed inside a steel tank for safety reasons. Crocks have not proven to be

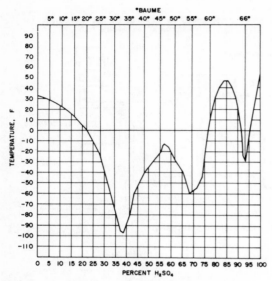

Figure 37-7 • Freezing Points of H₂SO₄ Solutions

particularly long-lived in such applications and complete rupture of the crock with a full load of acid could be disastrous. Also, under no circumstances, should an ordinary unlined steel tank be used for the dilution tank.

The freezing point for various strengths of sulfuric acid is given in Figure 37-7. It will be noted that 93% acid (66° Baumé), the strength most generally used, has a freezing point of −29 F. As such, insulating precautions are needed only in the coldest areas.

USING SULFUR BURNERS

Interest develops periodically in the application of sulfur burners for acid treatment of various water supplies. In certain instances, sulfur burners are ideally suited as in the case of some applications in the paper industry. On the other hand, for cooling water treatment, the sulfur burner has not proved sufficiently reliable and trouble-free. The disadvantages, in most cases, far outweigh the saving in cost of acid. In most instances, combustion difficulties create excessive maintenance demands. In addition, the use of sulfur dioxide gas, resulting from the burning

sulfur, will cause some reduction of chromate in those systems which are treated with chromate base corrosion inhibitors, causing an increase in treating costs.

PROPER POINTS FOR ACID DISCHARGE

A typical mixing trough as recommended for the introduction of acid to a typical cooling tower system is shown in Figure 37-8. Makeup flows up to 500 gpm are satisfactorily acid treated and passed through such a trough although, in many instances, a small portion of the makeup water, between 20 and 50 gpm, is by-passed through a suitably sized trough and provides sufficient dilution water for the average system. The discharge from a properly constructed trough of this type may be introduced to the flume leading to the cold well or into the sump close to the pump suction in large systems. The discharge point should be in the range of 25 feet away from the pump suction, as a minimum.

Installations should be avoided which provide for the introduction of acid, concentrated or diluted, into the makeup water line or into the circulating water line where reaction will take place and carbon dioxide will be released. Even though the acid may be intermixed with the water in special alloy spools or other mixing devices, severe corrosion will develop in those portions of the lines composed of ordinary steel and very short service life can be expected. Likewise, if such lines should discharge close to concrete surfaces, attack of the concrete may take place as well.

Dependence upon check valves should be avoided completely where they are expected to prevent the backing up of water from a makeup line, for example, into the acid line. When check valves fail in such service, very rapid corrosion of the acid line develops, particularly since the temperature is elevated by the contact of water and concentrated acid—the resulting situation can become quite dangerous.

It is just as important to design proper methods of introducing acid to a system as

CONSTRUCT TROUGH AND BAFFLES OF REDWOOD OR CYPRESS

WIDTH AND HEIGHT OF TROUGH TO BE BASED UPON AMOUNT OF WATER USED. FIGURE HEIGHT OF SIDE AS TWICE EXPECTED WATER DEPTH.

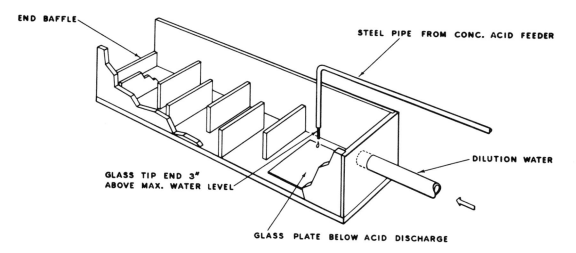

END BAFFLE

STEEL PIPE FROM CONC. ACID FEEDER

DILUTION WATER

GLASS TIP END 3" ABOVE MAX. WATER LEVEL

GLASS PLATE BELOW ACID DISCHARGE

Figure 37-8 · Acid Dispersal and Dilution Trough

it is to select dependable feeding equipment. In general, the acid should be so introduced that no other material may enter the acid line under any circumstances. The final discharge of acid treated water should be into a section, where low pH water cannot attack pumps or piping materials or concrete. Any released carbon dioxide may be readily aerated from the treated water.

ACID FILTERS

Of all the pieces of equipment available, probably the most important to the continuous trouble-free functioning of feeding systems employing pumps and control valves is the glass wool filter. All commercial acid has varying quantities of sediment and it is quite possible for these small particles to gradually clog any feeding system since the actual flow of acid in most plants is a small amount. Glass wool filters and sludge pots eliminate practically all feeding interruptions due to sediment. Figure 37-9 shows a typical glass wool filter for application in concentrated acid feeding systems.

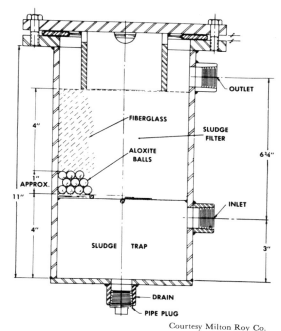

OUTLET

FIBERGLASS

SLUDGE FILTER

4"

ALOXITE BALLS

6¾"

1" APPROX.

11"

INLET

4"

SLUDGE TRAP

3"

DRAIN

PIPE PLUG

Courtesy Milton Roy Co.

Figure 37-9 · Combination Sludge Trap and Glass Wool Filter for Pump Suction Line

MATERIALS OF CONSTRUCTION

While sulfuric acid is considered a strong acid, the properties of the concentrated acid allow certain materials to be used in contact with it and give satisfactory service life. For example, steel is normally used for storage tanks and provides satisfactory service when moisture is removed from air drawn into the tank by means of suitable water absorption materials. Steel may be used for pipe lines carrying concentrated acid where the lines are kept full of concentrated acid at all times. In some instances, it is desirable to consider the installation of PVC or some chrome-nickel alloys for piping in order to provide further dependability.

Steel day tanks which are refilled daily or oftener should be lead lined in order to provide satisfactory life because of the corrosion which develops with a thin film of acid on the tank surfaces remaining in contact with the surrounding air as the acid level is drawn down. Discharge piping, as previously noted, should not be connected into any other line where back pressure may force water into the acid piping or system. In addition, where acid is dripped into contact with the water, precautions such as the glass tip on the end of the line and the glass drip plate in the mixing trough add considerably to the freedom from maintenance problems.

Pump bodies and valves may be made of cast iron, but usually better service life is obtained when suitable alloys or plastics are employed and the increased life compensates for the increased cost several times over.

SOME MAJOR SAFETY RULES WHEN HANDLING ACID

In unloading tank cars, use clean, dry air at no more than 30 psi. Contents of tanks should be thawed only in strict accord with recognized practice and never by using torches or building a fire under the car or around the tank.

When unloading carboys, use approved pumps or low air pressure not exceeding 3 psi. If this is not sufficient, use small self priming transfer pumps.

Avoid excessive pressure in acid lines.

No section of an acid line should be valved shut without suitable vents—action of the acid upon piping may cause sufficient pressure to develop to burst the line.

Proper drainage and reservoir facilities should be provided for any tank which may overflow or leak. Reservoir pits may be filled with limestone.

A plug type valve should be used in storage tanks for safety shut-off in case of line breakage. Use only one valve between the storage tank and day tank. Lubricate valves with acid-resistant grease and test operate twice weekly. Ordinary grease is not acid-proof.

Air vents should be piped to a point close to the ground in order to avoid dangerous splashing in case the tank overflows.

All measuring or day tanks should be of lead or lead lined steel or other acid resistant materials. All lined tanks should be circular.

Proper clothing should be worn by all persons working with acid. Rubber gloves, rubber aprons and close fitting goggles should be worn. Water in ample quantity must be immediately available.

Proper care in handling of fittings is necessary. Proper installation of fittings and lines will prevent splashing, leakage or spraying. Fittings should never be struck with tools or other hard objects for any purpose and especially where fittings are under pressure or acid tanks are full.

Open flames of any kind and smoking should be prohibited in acid areas due to the danger of hydrogen explosions. For illumination, use approved safety flashlights or suitable electric lighting, designed for hazardous areas.

Proper mixing of acid with water to be treated is essential. Mixing troughs should provide an intimate mixture of makeup water and acid, discharging at a point in the tower as far removed from the intake to the circulating pumps as practicable. This procedure will prevent stratification of the acid which may cause considerable damage to pumps and concrete. Makeup quantities up to 500 gpm may be treated in this manner.

The ends of discharge lines from acid feeding equipment should be equipped with glass tips in order to prevent corrosion of the tip in the corrosive atmosphere. A glass plate should be placed on the bottom of the mixing trough at the point of acid introduction in order to prevent attack at this point.

Suction for acid feeders should be drawn at least 2 inches above the bottom of the day tank and the day tank periodically should be drained completely in order to remove accumulating sediment. The acid purchased should be sampled frequently to make certain that a high quality acid is being obtained with a minimum of sediment. Excessive sediment seriously interferes with the operation of pumping or gravity feed operations.

Solenoid valves and check valves should not be relied upon where large quantities of acid are involved.

Water should *never* be introduced into sulfuric acid. Feeding systems should be designed to prevent the possible introduction of water to concentrated acid in the event of mechanical failure or human error.

REFERENCES

W. J. Gossom and J. O. Johnson, "Cooling-Tower Water Treatment", *The Oil and Gas Journal,* Vol. 55, pp. 91-95 (Dec. 9, 1957)

J. H. Richards, "Chemical Feed Systems in Modern Water Treatment", *Power Generation,* Vol. 52, pp. 62, 63, 122-125 (Aug. 1948) and pp. 61-63, 118, 120, 122, 124, 126 (Sept. 1948)

J. T. Russell, "Chemical Costs Drop Sharply in This Installation for Automatic Treating of Cooling Water", *The Oil and Gas Journal,* Vol. 53, pp. 109-111 (July 12, 1954)

38

Slime and Algae Control

INDUSTRIAL users of cooling water systems have long recognized the need for control of biological fouling in order to avoid loss in heat transfer and to minimize the added corrosion load imposed by slime and algae growths. While difficulties due to biological fouling are encountered in both once-through and recirculating cooling water systems, the problem is more severe in open recirculating systems. Exposure of the circulating water to sunlight in cooling towers and spray ponds favors the growth of algae. Increases in temperature, concentration of bacteria food and the greater incidence of air-borne contamination increase the slime-forming potential in open recirculating systems.

Because slime and algae problems are encountered to a greater extent in open recirculating systems, this discussion has been directed to the control of biological fouling in such systems. However, the difficulties described and the principles of their control are applicable in most cases to once-through systems as well.

DIFFICULTIES DUE TO BIOLOGICAL FOULING

Biological fouling in open recirculating cooling systems is the result of excessive growth and development of different members of the lower forms of plants, namely: algae, fungi and bacteria. In general, the principal difference between algae and fungi is that algae are capable of manufacturing their own food whereas fungi cannot. Except for autotropic types, such as iron consuming and sulfate reducing types, bacteria do not manufacture their own food.

Because sunlight is necessary for growth and development of algae, abundant algae growths occur in spray ponds and in exposed parts of cooling towers. The principal types of biological growths that occur in the non-exposed portions of a cooling system are referred to as slime. Slime is an accumulation of microorganisms and their excretions together with whatever inorganic and/or organic debris may become embedded in the mass. The microorganisms usually found in

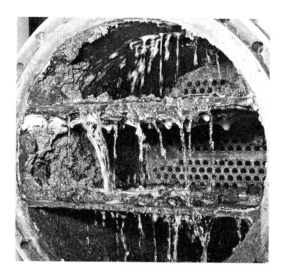

Figure 38-1 • *Serious Fouling with Slime Growths*

these deposits are various bacteria, filamentous fungi, yeast and occasionally protozoa. Slime growths may also contain dead algae which have migrated from other areas and have become entrapped in the mass. Slime growths may occur in illuminated areas or in dark areas. In general, dark areas favor the growth of slime since the microorganisms involved do not utilize light in the manufacture of their food but are totally dependent upon the food available in the cooling water.

Slime deposits on process equipment will so retard heat transfer as to create a serious loss in efficiency. Biological fouling on metal surfaces will create differential oxygen concentration cells and result in serious pitting of the metal surfaces. Figure 38-1 illustrates a heat exchanger that is seriously fouled with slime growths.

CONTROL OF BIOLOGICAL FOULING

Many different types of chemical agents are employed for microorganism control in recirculating cooling water systems. The primary purpose of the chemical agent is to kill and/or inhibit the growth and accretion of

Figure 38-2 • *Common Microorganisms Found in Cooling Water Systems*

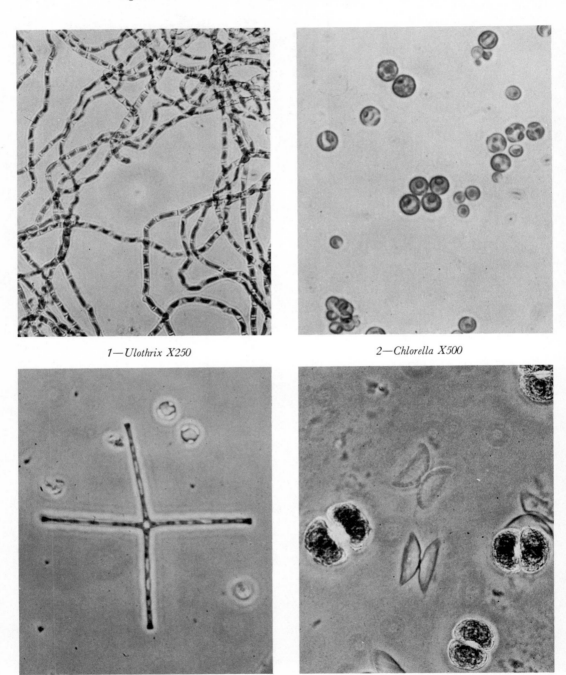

1—*Ulothrix X250*   2—*Chlorella X500*

3—*Asterionella X250*   4—*Cosmarium X250*

organisms. If a given toxicant is present in a sufficient quantity or is highly toxic, the bacteria will be killed. However, at levels below its killing concentration, the chemical used will only inhibit the growth of the organism. At extremely dilute concentrations it is not uncommon for the chemical agent to actually stimulate the growth of microorganisms. Many substances will kill microorganisms only at high concentrations, but they inhibit growth and development at significantly lower concentrations. Such substances are known as bacteriostatic agents whereas those chemical agents that kill bacteria are known as bactericides. Dilute solutions of a bactericide may act as a bacteriostatic agent when its concentration is too low to kill bacteria.

CHLORINE. Chlorine is probably the agent most widely employed for control of microbiological deposits in recirculating systems. In the absence of substances which cause a high

Fig. 38-3—General Comparison of Chlorination Programs

Program	Remarks
Continuous Chlorination —Free Residual	Most effective
	Most costly
	Not always technically or economically feasible due to high chlorine demand.
Continuous Chlorination —Combined Residual	Less effective
	Less costly
	Inadequate for severe problems.
Intermittent Chlorination —Free Residual	Usually effective
	Less costly than continuous chlorination
Intermittent Chlorination —Combined Residual	Least effective
	Least costly

chlorine demand, chlorine is usually the most economical method of treatment. A survey of 16 Gulf Coast refineries and chemical plants shows that continuous chlorination is employed in 24 towers and intermittent chlorination in 10 towers. Commercial biocides are used in 26 towers either alone or in conjunction with chlorine. One tower is treated with sodium hypochlorite and in only one tower are no slime control measures employed.

Chlorine is highly toxic and acts quickly to kill bacteria. A chlorine residual of 0.3-1.0 ppm will usually destroy most microorganisms. However, since chlorine acts on all oxidizable material, the chlorine demand of a water is greatly increased by the presence of organic matter, hydrogen sulfide and ferrous iron. Thus, sufficient chlorine must be added to the water to develop the residual necessary for toxicity and to satisfy the demand of other materials present in the water which are readily oxidized or possess the ability to absorb chlorine.

Chlorine is stable in neutral, acid and alkaline waters although its germicidal efficiency is reduced somewhat under alkaline conditions. When large amounts of chlorine are required, it is generally obtained in liquid form for economy and convenience, and fed to the system by means of a chlorinator. Because of its corrosivity, the use of chlorine involves some hazards in handling. However, satisfactory chlorination equipment is available for this purpose.

The amount of chlorine required for the control of biological fouling in any individual system is governed by numerous factors. There may be wide variations in chlorine requirements between different tower systems in the same plant. Chlorine requirements are affected by the quality of the makeup water to the system, water temperatures in the system, air to water ratio of the system, the amount of contamination by reducing agents and the type and amount of bacterial and fungal contamination.

The manner of chlorine feed, whether continuous or intermittent, and the residual chlorine for control of the problem are also individual to a specific system and will vary between towers in the same plant. For control of the slime and algae problem in any system, it is necessary:

1. That sufficient chlorine be fed to secure the necessary residual chlorine content of the treated water.

2. That this necessary chlorine residual be maintained in the system for the time interval for microorganism control.

CHLORINE RESIDUAL. While a chlorine residual of 0.3-1.0 ppm normally is adequate to kill most microorganisms contaminating cooling water systems, it is necessary in many cases that a free chlorine residual be present rather than a combined residual. The free available chlorine residual is defined as that portion of the total residual chlorine which will react chemically and biologically as hypochlorous acid or hypochlorite ion. It is in this form that chlorine exerts the most potent bactericidal effect. The combined available chlorine residual is defined as that portion of the total residual chlorine which will react chemically and biologically as chloramine or organic chloramines. In this form, chlorine is a relatively mild bactericide and oxidizing agent. Investigations have shown that for a 100% bacterial kill with the same contact time, approximately 25 times as much combined residual chlorine is required as is necessary with a free residual. To obtain a 100% kill, using the same amount of free and combined available residual chlorine requires approximately 100 times as long a contact period for a combined residual as is necessary for a free residual chlorine.

CHLORINATION PROGRAMS. Chlorination programs used in recirculating cooling systems fall within the categories listed in Figure 38-3.

While continuous chlorination is obviously advantageous from the standpoint of effectiveness, it also is the most expensive method. In addition, continuous chlorination of a recirculating cooling water system is not always practical and may not be economical. Because of its volatility, chlorine is aerated from the water in passing over a tower or spray pond. The presence of any organic agents in the cooling water treatment will increase the chlorine demand as will the presence of reducing agents due to process leaks. If contaminants such as hydrocarbons, mercaptans and sulfides are present in excessive quantities, it may be impossible to feed sufficient chlorine for control of slime.

Complete sterility of the circulating water is not possible because of continuous contamination by air-borne organisms. However, sterility is not necessary for control of organic growths. It is necessary only to reduce the bacterial population to the point where troublesome accumulations are avoided.

Intermittent chlorination is a common practice because of the economy that can be secured. It is usually possible to adequately control biological fouling by means of a program of intermittent chlorination. Of course, the schedule of chlorine feed and the residual maintained must be tailored to the particular

Fig. 38-4—Relative Toxicity of Different Phenolic Compounds

Compound	Test Organism			
	Aerobacter aerogenes	Bacillus mycoides	Aspergillus niger	Penicillium expansum
	Inhibiting Concentration in ppm			
Chloro-o-phenylphenol	40	25	35	35
2-tert-butyl-4-chloro-5-methylphenol	35	6	95	75
4, 6-dichlorophenol	30	0.7	2000	40
o-benzyl-p-chlorophenol	55	5	80	80
Sodium salt of:				
o-phenylphenol	200	200	150	150
2, 4, 5-trichlorophenol	20	15	15	7
chloro-2-phenylphenol	60	30	55	30
2-chloro-4-phenylphenol	45	20	65	50
2-bromo-4-phenylphenol	60	15	150	80
2, 3, 4, 6-tetrachlorophenol	400	7	20	30
pentachlorophenol	200	4	25	30

problem. However, a program that is generally successful is to chlorinate daily until a free residual of 1 ppm chlorine has been maintained for a four hour period on the cooling water returned to the tower. The period of chlorination may exceed four hours because of the time required to raise the residual to 1 ppm at which level the residual should be maintained for four hours' time. Adjustment in this basic schedule can be made in accordance with the severity of the problem and the plant conditions observed. There are many different chlorination program variations between continuous chlorination to a free residual as the most effective and most expensive program, and intermittent chlorination to a combined residual as the least effective and least expensive.

EFFECT OF CHLORINE ON TOWER WOOD. While chlorination usually will prove to be an over-all satisfactory method for control of biological fouling in recirculating cooling water systems it must be used judiciously since excessive concentrations of chlorine have an adverse effect on cooling tower wood. The subject of cooling tower wood deterioration is covered in a separate chapter. In recirculating cooling water systems that employ cooling towers, there has been an increased trend toward the use of non-oxidizing biocides to replace or to supplement the use of chlorine. The expanded use of non-oxidizing biocides has resulted from the realization that chlorine alone does not handle the complete microbiological problem of a cooling tower system. Chlorine does not minimize biological attack of the tower wood and moreover can have an adverse effect on tower life. An effective slime control program should handle the complete microbiological problem. It should have as its objectives, prevention of loss in heat transfer, minimizing corrosion and should protect the tower wood. Accordingly, where chlorine is used for slime control it is advisable to periodically feed a non-oxidizing biocide so that biological surface attack of cooling tower wood can be minimized.

BROMINE. Bromine is quite similar to chlorine in its chemical properties and it is natural that

some investigations would be conducted on the usefulness of bromine in microorganism control. Some applications of bromine have been made to recirculating cooling water systems, particularly on the West Coast. The conclusions reported from several installations are conflicting. Some plants apparently have obtained satisfactory slime control through the use of bromine alone. In other applications, it has been concluded that bromine is most effective when used as an intermittent "shock" treatment in conjunction with continuous chlorination.

The use of bromine is not widespread. Probably the most important single factor retarding interest in bromine is the hazard involved in its handling. Bromine is a very active oxidizing agent, both as a liquid and a vapor. Serious hazard exists by contact with the liquid or inhalation of the vapor. The maximum allowable concentration in air is less than one half that of chlorine. The liquid rapidly attacks the skin and other tissues to produce irritation and burns which heal very slowly. The vapor concentration considered safe for eight-hour exposure is less than 1 ppm while a concentration of 10 ppm can hardly be tolerated. Because of its hazardous nature and because of its relatively high cost, it seems unlikely that bromine will find wide use for microorganism control in cooling water systems.

ACROLEIN. Acrolein, a highly reactive liquid agent, provides exceptionally good control against microbiological growths in once-through and recirculating water systems. The material is particularly useful where chlorine and/or non-oxidizing biocides are ineffective for problems of high organic demand water, process contamination and marine infestation.

The specially stabilized biocide exhibits a broad spectrum of biological activity at extremely low concentrations. Normally, a residual in the order of 0.2–1.0 ppm is adequate to kill most microorganisms that contaminate cooling water systems. This level is particularly toxic to sedentary marine growths.

Another important advantage of acrolein is its ability to function as a herbicide in controlling submerged and floating weeds as well as algae in irrigation canals, ditches, ponds and other bodies of water. This biocide exhibits a remarkable and unique specificity for aquatic plants as compared to terrestrial plant life. Although considerable data in different environments have been accumulated, the aquatic toxicity of acrolein has not been definitely established for all species of fish. The material is extremely toxic in some cases, whereas the tolerance is reasonably high under other conditions and for certain species of fish.

Precautions must be taken when handling acrolein. However, a specially designed pressure feed system available for this biocide embodies several safety features so that the agent can be applied without hazard.

Acrolein is completely noncorrosive to all metals, which is another advantage over chlorine. Also, the biocide may be deactivated whenever desired by injecting sodium sulfite into the water stream. Approximately 3.0 ppm of sulfite per 1.0 ppm of acrolein is required for this purpose. The reaction is rapid, and occurs over a broad pH range (5.0–7.0 optimum).

Acrolein residuals can be determined by means of a specific analytical test. The method is accurate to the range of 50 parts per billion.

From a cost standpoint, acrolein will not replace chlorine for all industrial cooling systems in the near future. However, this liquid material has an important economical position as a biocide where high organic demand waters are used, process contamination occurs, marine and sedentary organisms plug equipment and corrosive attack is a problem.

CHLORINATED PHENOLS. Phenolic materials have been used extensively for germicidal purposes in medicine. Many phenolic materials and particularly the chlorinated phenols have found use in industrial microbiological control. The toxicity of these materials varies widely between different species of bacteria and fungi. Figure 38-4 shows data taken from the work of Shema and Conkey and illustrates the inhibiting concentration of various phe-

nolic and chlorinated phenolic compounds to standard test organisms. The bacteria used in these tests were Aerobacter aerogenes, a capsulated non-sporeforming organism and Bacillus mycoides, a sporeforming bacterium. The fungi employed were Aspergillus niger and Penicillium expansum. It can be noted that a material may be inhibitory to the growth of bacteria at relatively low concentrations as in the case of 4, 6-dichlorophenol, but requires high concentrations of 2000 ppm to exhibit inhibitory power against the fungus Aspergillus niger. The sodium salts of tetrachlorophenol and pentachlorophenol are inhibitory at low concentrations against the fungi and Bacillus mycoides, but concentrations of 400 ppm and 200 ppm are necessary to inhibit the growth of Aerobacter aerogenes.

It should be realized that the results obtained by a given laboratory procedure do not necessarily indicate the dosage required to give satisfactory microorganism control in the field nor do the data indicate the relative effectiveness of each material under the different field conditions encountered. Rather, such laboratory data indicate that there are wide variations in the effectiveness of a toxicant against different organisms and that effective control of a microbiological complex sometimes can be achieved only through a combination of several treatments.

The chlorinated phenols which have been most widely used in recirculating cooling water systems are the sodium salts of trichlorophenol and pentachlorophenol. Sodium pentachlorophenate is probably in most widespread use either alone or combined in commercial formulations with sodium trichlorophenate. Sodium pentachlorophenate is a soluble and stable material. It does not react with most inorganic or organic chemicals which may contaminate a cooling water system. A broader spectrum of biological activity can be achieved by combining the use of more than one chlorinated phenolic compound such as, for example, the simultaneous use of a trichlorophenate with a pentachlorophenate. Additional benefits may be gained by the combined use of metallic ions such as copper and zinc. Where a concentration of 200 ppm of a single phenolic compound may be required for satisfactory control of organic growths, combinations of this type have been successful in the range of 60-100 ppm.

Because of the toxicity of the chlorinated phenols to fish and animals, some precautions may be necessary to control the concentrations in the blowdown water from the cooling system. Care also must be exercised in handling these materials since the dust is irritating to the mucous membranes of the eyes, nose and throat. If the concentrated material is permitted to remain in contact with the skin, a rash may develop. With ordinary precautions in handling, however, no difficulties are to be expected.

CONTINUOUS VS. SHOCK TREATMENT. With the chlorinated phenols, as in chlorination, there are many different feeding programs that can be employed, ranging on the one hand from the continuous maintenance of a high concentration in the circulating water to the other extreme of intermittent addition of the material in low concentration at infrequent intervals. As with chlorination, the slime control program must be fitted to the individual system conditions.

In any program for the continuous maintenance of a given toxicant concentration in the circulating water, it is necessary that the concentration maintained be at an adequate level. One program originally suggested for sodium pentachlorophenate involved continuous feeding of the material so as to maintain a concentration of approximately 20 ppm in the system. This method has been unsuccessful because 20 ppm is inadequate for inhibition of the microbiological complexes existing in most recirculating systems. On the other hand, programs of continuous feeding are necessary in particularly difficult cases which cannot be controlled by a program of "shock" treatment. In one plant using a makeup water with a high degree of sewage contamination, all shock treatment programs were ineffective and satisfactory control of the problem was secured finally by the continuous maintenance in the system of a 200 ppm concentration of the toxicant. Intermittent shock treatment at this 200 ppm level was ineffective. Whether the feeding program is continuous or intermittent, it is important that the concentration of slime control agent

Fig. 38-5—Relative Toxicity of Quaternary Ammonium Compounds

	Aerobacter aerogenes	Inhibiting Concentration, ppm		
		Bacillus mycoides	Aspergillus niger	Penicillium expansum
Dilauryldimethylammonium chloride	1500	35	> 3000	> 3000
Dilauryldimethylammonium oleate	> 3000	40	> 3000	> 3000
Dodecyltrimethylammonium chloride	80	65	> 3000	> 3000
Trimethylammonium chloride	1500	35	> 3000	> 3000
Octadecyltrimethylammonium chloride	> 3000	55	> 3000	> 3000
N-alkylbenzyl-N, N, N-trimethylammonium chloride	500	4	> 3000	2500
Mixture of alkyl-9-methyl-benzyl ammonium chlorides	150	15	> 3000	> 3000
Lactoxymercuriphenylammonium lactate	40	15	> 3000	800
Alkyldimethylbenzylammonium chlorides	65	6	> 3000	> 3000
3, 4-dichlorobenzylammonium chlorides	700	3	> 3000	> 3000
Phenylmercuric trihydroxyethylammonium lactate	15	1	35	45
Phenylmercuric triethanolammonium lactate	20	4	65	70
Mixture of alkyldimethylbenzylammonium chlorides	200	7	> 3000	> 3000
*Benzyltriethylammonium chloride	> 3000	> 3000	> 3000	> 3000
*Benzyltrimethylammonium chloride	> 3000	> 3000	> 3000	> 3000
*Cetyldimethylammonium chloride	1600	5	> 3000	> 3000
*Lauryldimethyl-benzyldiethylammonium chloride (75%)	350	5	> 3000	> 3000

*Values obtained in Laboratories of Betz Laboratories, Inc.

developed in the system exceed the minimum inhibitory concentration. Otherwise, either continuous maintenance of a non-inhibitory concentration, or shock treatment to such a level will not bring control of the problem.

Since it is necessary to develop an effective concentration of the slime control agent in the system, whether continuously or intermittently, it is obviously desirable from an economic standpoint to employ intermittent feeding if the problem can be controlled by these measures. Unless the system has an unusually low retention time, there will be no marked difference in the inhibitory concentration required with continuous versus intermittent feed.

In setting a schedule for intermittent feeding of the slime control agent, it is necessary to determine the concentration to be developed in the system and the frequency with which the shot will be repeated. The theoretical depletion of the slime control agent from the system can be determined by the formula:

$$\log C_f = \log C_i - \frac{BD \times T}{2.303\ V}$$

where:

C_f = final concentration, ppm
C_i = initial concentration, ppm
BD = blowdown and windage loss, gpm
V = system capacity, gallons
T = time, minutes

A program that has been found practical in a shock treatment program is to repeat the slug of treatment when the concentration has been depleted to 25% of the original concentration. On this basis, the formula above can be simplified as follows:

$$T = 1.385\ \frac{V}{BD}$$

where:

T = retention time, days
V = system capacity, gallons
BD = blowdown and windage loss, gallons per day

Solving this equation for T (retention time) will indicate the frequency with which

the slug of treatment should be repeated. The formula is independenent of the initial concentration developed by the slug of treatment and holds so long as the final concentration for repetition of the slug is taken as 25% of the original value.

This formula is useful in setting a feeding schedule and is valid for slime control agents which do not volatilize in passage over the tower and which are not consumed by reaction with other substances in the system. It is desirable to check the schedule in any water for the slime control agent. However, once the schedule has been checked by such analyses a regular program of shot feeding can be established, feeding the slime control agent every three, five, etc. days as necessary.

COPPER SALTS. Algae are sensitive to very small amounts of copper ion and copper sulfate was one of the earliest materials used as an algicide. The copper ion in distilled water solutions is also toxic to bacteria, but this effect is nullified by the presence of other ions and organic matter.

Although algae in general are sensitive to quite low concentrations of copper, there is considerable variation in the killing dose for different species.

While copper salts are toxic to fish, various fish exhibit different degrees of sensitivity toward the copper ion. Investigations have shown that fish mortality is not due entirely to the toxic effect of the copper ion in the treated water. The mortality has been shown to be due partially to clogging of the gills with dead organisms that have previously existed in the water.

The effectiveness of copper salts in the control of algae is nullified at the higher pH values since the copper ion is precipitated as insoluble copper hydroxide. However, by employing copper salts in conjunction with stabilizing agents, toxicity is greatly increased and the precipitation of the copper ion is prevented. Further improvements include the use of wetting agents which permit the copper ion to penetrate the various slime and algae growths.

Figure 38-6 · Culturing of Algae under Laboratory Conditions

Copper sulfate alone is rarely used for control of biological fouling in recirculating cooling systems. The copper ion is corrosive to iron, steel, aluminum and other metals. Moreover, recirculating systems rarely are afflicted only with the problem of algae and other agents are required for bacterial control. Even specially prepared copper base algicides, that have been stabilized to avoid precipitation of the copper ion, and blended with other toxicants to control bacteria, must be used judiciously.

QUATERNARY AMMONIUM COMPOUNDS. There are a great number of quaternary ammonium compounds available to industry and these compounds are effective germicides in many applications. Figure 38-5, taken partially from the work of Shema and Conkey, shows data on the relative toxicity of several quaternaries. It can be noted that there is

considerable difference in the effectiveness of various quaternaries against the test organisms. All quaternaries listed were relatively ineffective against the fungi, with the exception of those containing mercury in the molecule.

It is characteristic of the quaternaries that their bacterial properties are reduced in the presence of soap, protein and high ionic concentrations. It has been found that certain of the quaternaries react with or are absorbed by organic matter found in industrial recirculating cooling water systems and a loss of effectiveness results. Some volatilization also occurs over a cooling tower, thereby increasing losses from the system.

Despite these disadvantages from the standpoint of practical application to recirculating cooling water systems, some success has been achieved with the use of quaternaries, particularly when combined with metallic ions, such as copper. The quaternaries are effective wetting agents and aid penetration of organic growths because of this property. In general, like the chlorinated phenols, their most efficient method of use has been in shot fashion. The periodic addition of high concentrations to the circulating water, repeated at regular intervals, has been found more effective in controlling organic growths than attempts to continuously maintain a lower concentration in the circulating water.

MISCELLANEOUS TOXICANTS. The inorganic mercurials such as mercuric chloride are considered too toxic to humans for use in recirculating cooling water systems. Organic mercurials have been developed in an effort to retain the bactericidal properties of mercury, while reducing the toxicity of these materials. Some of the organic mercurial compounds may be aerated readily from a cooling tower system thus allowing only a short contact time with the slime-forming organisms. Such materials should not be used in any cooling tower system where the spray might contact humans or where, because of volatility, the compound will be present in the air breathed. In general, both the inorganic and organic mercurials are considered too toxic for use in cooling water systems. In addition, the mercury ion, even in low concentrations, will add appreciably to the corrosive qualities of a water.

Potassium permanganate, similar to chlorine, is a powerful oxidizing agent and effective in the control of slime-forming organisms. However, potassium permanganate acts on all oxidizable material present and manganese dioxide precipitates as a result of the reduction of the permanganate. The resulting sludge is the chief factor limiting the use of permanganate.

Iodine and silver have been used to a limited extent in the sterilization of drinking water and in swimming pool control, but have not been found adapted to use of cooling water systems.

Biological and medical literature refer to hundreds of chemical agents which are useful in controlling microbiological activity. Only a small fraction of this number have been applied to the control of biological fouling in recirculating cooling water systems. Many of these chemical agents are ruled from consideration immediately because of cost. Many of these materials are effective only in high concentrations such as 5%, 10% or more. Others are ineffective under the conditions of use in a cooling water system, due to volatility, reaction with organic matter, reaction with inorganic ions naturally present or the chemical treatments in use for control of scale or corrosion. Of the great number of bactericidal and bacteriostatic agents known, few can qualify for use in recirculating cooling systems, principally because of the factors of cost, effective concentrations and compatibility in this environment.

GENERAL CONSIDERATIONS IN SELECTING SLIME CONTROL AGENTS

As mentioned previously, chlorine is probably the most widely used agent for microorganism control in cooling water systems. The decision whether to use chlorine or another slime control agent is usually made by balancing continuous chemical operating cost against equipment installation and maintenance costs.

Where liquid chlorine can be used, chemical cost will usually be lower than with other toxicants if chlorine is purchased in the larger one ton containers or tank cars, at their lower price. However, the installation cost of chlorinators and facilities for handling bulk chlorine shipments is quite appreciable. Maintenance of this equipment is an added cost.

On the other hand, other slime control agents are usually furnished in readily handled containers in liquid, powder or briquette form. No feeding facilities are required where the toxicant is shot fed and the material is added only once every several days. No continuous attention to feeding equipment is necessary and there is no installation cost to be written off.

Where the system is sufficiently large and the problem sufficiently acute, the installation and maintenance expense of chlorination facilities will be justified. Where the cooling water system is relatively small or where there is only infrequent necessity for slime control agents, it will be more economical to employ agents other than chlorine. The simplicity of feeding and handling liquid or briquetted materials is particularly attractive in the small installations and where there is only periodic need for slime control measures. Even where the control of biological growths is handled normally by the use of chlorine, there will frequently exist the need of additional slime control agents. For example, during periods of contamination of the cooling water by reducing agents, chlorination facilities may be inadequate for the quantity of chlorine required under these circumstances. Addition of agents such as the chlorinated phenols or the various commercial combinations, may be necessary to control organic growths during such periods. Even where the increased chlorine dosage can be handled by the feeding equipment installed, it may be more economical to use another slime control agent at such times rather than to employ the greatly increased amounts of chlorine required during periods of contamination.

At the present time, there is no single toxic agent which is completely effective for the control of biological fouling in all types of industrial cooling water systems. There are faults inherent in all of the toxicants in common use. Chlorine is highly effective and rapid in bactericidal action, but chlorine consumption is greatly increased by the presence of reducing agents. Chlorine does not afford protection to biological attack of cooling tower wood. Moreover, chlorine must be used judiciously to avoid chemical attack of cooling tower wood. The chlorinated phenols

and other materials may present a problem of fish toxicity in the blowdown discharge. Copper salts are more specific to algae than to bacteria and are rendered ineffective by precipitation at higher pH values. Quaternaries are affected by ions and organic matter.

All of these chemical agents are not equally economical and efficient. Selection of toxicants must be based on the microbiological associations encountered. Frequently, more than one toxicant is desirable to control, for example, both a bacteriological slime and/or algae problem. Methods and frequency of chemical feeding must be varied to suit the individual problem. Slime control agents vary in the rapidity of their action and must be selected with a knowledge of the retention period in the system. Compatibility of the toxicant must be studied in relation to other treatments used for scale and corrosion control. Local conditions governing discharge of blowdown water from the cooling system must be considered. Selection of the proper method of control of microorganisms in recirculating cooling water systems, therefore, requires evaluation of numerous factors.

REFERENCES

F. E. Hale, "The Use of Copper Sulphate in Control of Microscopic Organisms," Phelps Dodge Refining Corp., New York, N. Y. (1954)

B. F. Shema and J. H. Conkey, "Relative Toxicity of Disinfectants Available for Use in the Pulp and Paper Industry," Tappi, Tech. Assoc. of the Pulp and Paper Ind., Vol. 36, pp. 20A, 22A, 24A, 26A, 28A, 30A, (Nov. 1953)

B. F. Shema and J. H. Conkey, "Relative Toxicity of Disinfectants Available For Use in the Pulp and Paper Industry—1954 Supplement," Biological Control Committee, Am. Paper and Pulp Assoc., New York, N. Y. (1954)

J. M. Donohue, A. J. Piluso and J. R. Schieber, "New Type Biocide Produces Cost Savings in Slime Control," 22nd Annual NACE Conference (1966)

39

Cooling Tower Wood
Deterioration

OVER the past decade considerable attention has been focused on the problem of cooling tower wood deterioration—and for good reason. Complete collapse of some cooling towers has occurred. In other cases, supports have deteriorated and fans have fallen through the tower. Accidents have occurred due to collapse of ladders, decking and other parts of the tower. Wood deterioration has shortened the life of cooling towers from the anticipated 20-25 years to 10 years or less in many cases. Repair and replacement costs have been excessive, and cooling tower operation has been inefficient.

Redwood is the most commonly used material for cooling tower construction. It has been used for this purpose almost since the advent of cooling towers themselves. Originally, this material was selected because of high strength to weight ratio, ready availability, ease of fabrication, cost, and natural resistance to decay. Other species are used for this purpose, particularly Douglas Fir and less frequently cypress and pine.

Wood is composed of three main components: cellulose, lignin and natural extractives. The cellulose exists as long fibers, almost identical to cotton fibers, and gives wood its strength. Lignin acts as a cementing agent for the cellulose. The extractives contain most of the natural compounds which contribute to the resistance to decay. In general, the more highly colored woods are the more durable. A typical analysis of redwood, based on dry weight, will show approximately 50% cellulose and hemi-cellulose, 30% lignin and 20% extractives. The extractives in redwood make this material one of the most resistant to decay. Unfortunately, the extractives present in all woods are largely water soluble and will be leached from the wood by the circulating water. The strength of the wood does not appear to be affected by leaching. However, the wood does become more susceptible to decay.

Exceptionally good service was obtained from redwood during its initial use and it is reasonable to expect that this good service would be obtained today if redwood were still subjected to the same conditions. The large, open natural draft tower was the first type used to cool water. The flow of air through this tower is dependent upon wind velocity and upon the draft produced by the chimney design of the tower. In general, the conditions in these towers from the biological point of view were not nearly so critical. The few natural draft towers which have been in service for the past 20 years or more, are still in a remarkable state of preservation. Because natural draft towers do not exhibit rapid loss of wood structure or strength as a result of attack by decay organisms, does not mean that decay is non-existent but rather it indicates that biological deterioration is not the limiting factor affecting the life of these towers.

The development of the mechanical draft tower has resulted in greater cooling efficiency. A smaller tower is required to supply the process with cooled water, and in addition these towers also give more reliable and uniform performance because they are not dependent upon wind velocity for their operation. Even though mechanical draft towers are more efficient than atmospheric towers, they impose a completely different set of conditions upon the wood. The general design of a mechanical draft tower is more conducive to biological and chemical attack than the natural draft tower. The drift eliminators, cell partitions, doorways, and the compact design of the mechanical draft towers create a greater number of areas where environmental conditions are ideal for the growth and development of objectionable microorganisms. In addition, the amount of water and air handled per unit area is higher and inoculation of the system with air borne organisms is at a greater rate.

TYPES OF WOOD DETERIORATION

Cooling tower wood is subject to three main types of deterioration: chemical, biological, and physical. It is rare when one of these types of deterioration is present without the other. In most cases, these different types of

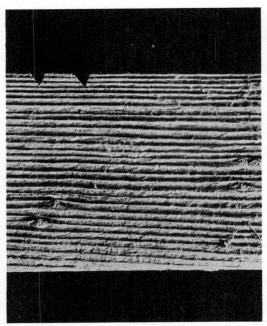

Figure 39-1 • Delignified Wood—Caused by Chemical Attack

Figure 39-2 • Checked, Brash Wood—Caused by Biological Surface Attack

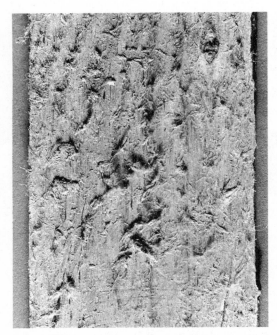

Figure 39-3 • Fibrillated Wood—Caused by Chemical Attack

Figure 39-4 • Internal Decay of Redwood Structural Member Showing White Fungus Mycelium

deterioration occur simultaneously. When deterioration occurs it is sometimes difficult to determine which type of attack is predominately responsible. However, it is evident that physical and chemical deterioration will render the wood more susceptible to biological attack.

CHEMICAL ATTACK. Chemical deterioration of cooling tower wood commonly is manifested in the form of delignification. Since the lignin component of the wood is affected and removed by this type attack, the resultant residue is rich in cellulose. The chemicals most commonly responsible are oxidizing agents such as chlorine, and alkaline materials such as sodium bicarbonate and sodium carbonate. The attack is particularly severe when the combination of high chlorine residuals and high alkalinity concentrations are maintained simultaneously.

Typically, the wood takes on a white or bleached appearance and the surface becomes fibrillated. This attack is restricted to the surface of the wood and the strength of the unaffected area is not impaired. However, severe thinning of the wood will occur wherever cascading water has an opportunity to wash away the surface fibers. In serious cases, the loosened fibers have caused plugging of screens and tubes, and have served as focal points for corrosion at areas where the fibers accumulate in heat exchange equipment.

Chemical attack most frequently occurs in the fill section and flooded portions of the tower where water contact is continuous. However, it will occur also in those areas where alternately wet and dry conditions develop—such as on the air intake louvers and other exterior surfaces. Chemical attack occurs also in the warm, moist areas of the plenum chamber of the tower as a result of chlorine vapors and the entrainment of droplets of tower water.

BIOLOGICAL ATTACK. Biological attack of cooling tower wood can be divided into two basic types—soft or surface rot and internal decay.

The organisms that are responsible for attack of cooling tower wood are those that can utilize cellulose as their source of carbon in their growth and development. Degradation of the cellulose is accomplished by the secretion of enzymes which convert the cellulose into compounds that can be absorbed by the organisms. The attack tends to deplete the cellulose content of the wood and leaves a residue rich in lignin. Characteristically the wood becomes dark in color and loses much of its strength. The wood may also become brash, soft, punky, cross-checked or fibrillated. The principal cellulolytic organisms isolated from cooling tower wood are primarily fungi, which include the classical wood destroyers (Basidromycetes), and members of Fungi Imperfecti. However, bacterial organisms that exhibit cellulolytic properties also have been isolated but their exact role in cooling tower wood deterioration is yet to be determined. The wood destroying organisms are common air and water borne contaminants, and are widely distributed in nature.

The classical *internal decay* is restricted generally to the plenum areas of the tower, such as cell partitions, doors, drift eliminators, decks, fan housing and supports. It is

Figure 39-5 • Structural Member Showing Sound Outer Surface and Typical Internal Decay

the more insidious of the two types of biological attack. It is characterized externally by an apparently sound piece of wood, which upon breaking shows severe internal decay. Because the decay is internal, it is difficult to detect in its early stages. Rarely is internal decay found in the flooded portions of the tower such as the fill section. In these sections, the wood is saturated completely with water which excludes oxygen from the interior of the wood. The lack of oxygen limits the growth and development of these organisms.

Soft or *surface rot* is found predominantly in the flooded sections of the tower but also occurs in the plenum areas. The water flowing over the wood surfaces in the flooded portions contains enough oxygen to support growth. Surface rot is detected more readily, and its effect is less severe than internal decay.

In addition to oxygen, moisture and temperature have a marked bearing. Locations where the moisture content of the wood range between 20 and 27% and temperatures range between 88 and 105 F, usually permit optimum growth and development of the organisms.

PHYSICAL AND OTHER FACTORS. One of the major physical factors is the effect of temperature on wood. Wood technologists have long recognized that high temperatures have an adverse effect on wood. It is known that continuous exposure to high temperatures will produce gross changes in anatomical structure and will accelerate loss in wood substance. These resultant effects will weaken the wood and predispose it to biological attack, particularly in the plenum areas of the tower.

There are other factors which also have a bearing on the deterioration of tower wood. For example, areas adjacent to iron nails and other iron hardware usually deteriorate at an accelerated rate. These areas invariably lose much of their strength and the wood will crumble easily in the fingers. Slime and algae growths and deposition of dust and oil can all aid the growth and development of

the soft rot organisms.

Preferential erosion of the summer wood is relatively common in tower fill. In severe cases of erosion significant losses of wood can result in very short periods of time. Extremely high concentrations of dissolved solids are to be avoided where there is opportunity presented for alternately wetting and drying of certain wood areas. While natural salts have been shown to possess little tendency to attack wood, crystallization of these salts in dry areas may rupture the wood cells.

CONTROL OF WOOD DETERIORATION

The only effective method of protecting operating cooling towers is to adopt a preventive maintenance program. The preventive measures for the flooded sections of the tower where attack of the chemical and biological types is limited to the surfaces of the wood are relatively easy to accomplish. The preventive measures for the non-flooded portions of the tower where internal decay is the primary concern are more difficult and the success of the program is largely dependent on adopting the necessary measures before infection reaches serious proportions.

FLOODED SECTION. The control of chemical and biological surface attack of cooling tower wood in the flooded portions of the tower is a water treatment problem that requires:

1. Control of pH of the circulating water below 8.0 and preferably in the range of 6.0 to 7.0.

2. The use of non-oxidizing biocides alone for control of slime and prevention of biological surface attack.

3. Where chlorine must be used—chlorine should be restricted to 1.0 ppm or less and preferably in the range of 0.3 to 0.5 ppm. In addition, the supplemental use of a non-oxidizing biocide should be employed to control biological surface attack.

In order to minimize delignification, pH of the circulating water should definitely be maintained below 8.0 and preferably lower. Fortunately, most modern treatments for control of corrosion function best when pH is maintained around 6.0-7.0. This pH range corresponds to the range best suited for minimizing attack of wood.

Surveys have shown that in tower systems where non-oxidizing biocides alone are used for control of slime, surface attack is at a minimum. Accordingly, when it is economically feasible non-oxidizing biocides should be used in preference to chlorine.

Where chlorine must be used for control of slime it is necessary that chlorine be used judiciously. Undoubtedly, many of the systems that have shown rapid or excessive attack from the use of chlorine have lacked adequate control of chlorination. In many of these cases, the chlorine residual has been improperly determined, determined at the wrong point for proper control, not checked frequently enough or neglected entirely. In the majority of the systems using chlorine for slime control, the chlorine residual is checked (as it should be) in the water returning to the tower, not after the water cascades through the tower. The water in passing through the tower will have its chlorine residual decreased to very low values or depleted entirely. The reduction in chlorine residual occurs partially due to aeration but mainly through reaction with the wood. Where attempts have been made to control chlorine residuals after the water has passed through the tower, excessive chlorine residuals have been permitted to contact the wood and accelerated chemical attack has been the result.

In instances where intermittent chlorination has been practiced, initially the duration of the chlorination period and the rate of chlorination may have been established properly by testing for the chlorine residual. However, all too often, after initially establishing the rate and duration, infrequent or no further testing for chlorine residual is made. Since the chlorine demand of most circulating waters will vary, this practice has led to low residuals and poor slime control or to high residuals and excessive attack of the wood.

The prevalence of biological attack of cooling tower wood in systems using chlorination has led to the conclusion that chemical attack predisposes the wood to biological attack. In cases where carefully controlled chlorination has been practiced and chemical attack of the wood surfaces is low, studies have been conducted to check the incidence of fungi on the surfaces of the wood and in the subsurface sections. Microtome sections of the wood, such as that shown in Figure 39-8, reveal a high incidence of fungi in the wood from the fill and plenum areas of the tower. These studies indicate that chlorination alone is not effective in controlling the organisms responsible for attack of wood. The judicious use of chlorine requires low residuals be maintained. As the water cascades through the tower the residuals are depleted. The air-borne organisms can and do accumulate readily on the surfaces of the wood and grow and develop in the subsurface sections. Similar studies conducted for systems that use non-oxidizing biocides alone for slime control show that the incidence of fungi on the wood surfaces is negligible. Since these biocides do not react with the wood, they are able to penetrate the wood and effectively control the causal organisms. Accordingly where chlorination must be practiced the supplemental use of a non-oxidizing biocide is recommended to assure maximum tower life.

One standard procedure currently utilized to aid in minimizing biological attack in the flooded portions of the cooling tower requires adding a non-oxidizing biocide to the system approximately once every three months. The concentration of biocide used is in the range of 60 to 120 ppm. The purpose of this treatment is to kill the organisms that have accumulated on the surface and subsurface portion of the wood in the fill or flooded portions of the tower. Supplemental benefits are also secured in that the non-oxidizing biocide will carry down into the lower depths of the cooling tower sump where it is difficult to maintain a chlorine residual. Muck and debris accumulate in these areas and provide ample food for growth and development of microorganisms.

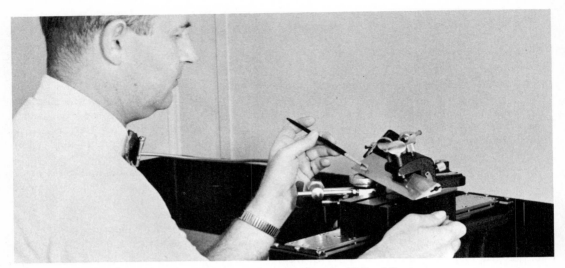

Figure 39-6 • Sectioning of Wood by Use of a Sliding Microtome

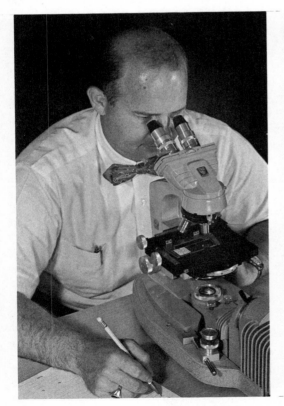

Figure 39-7 • Microscopic Examination of
Cooling Tower Wood

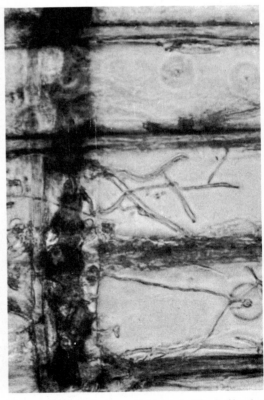

Figure 39-8 • Microtome Section of Wood Showing
Fungus Hyphae Growing through Wood Cells

These areas serve as a point of inoculation, particularly for sulfate reducing bacteria. The supplemental use of non-oxidizing biocides serves to eliminate this point of infection.

In many cases, it is possible to use a variety of treatment programs which combine the use of chlorine and a non-oxidizing biocide. Where a combination program is possible, chemical attack can be held to a minimum and biological attack can be controlled effectively.

It should be evident that if the makeup water is taken from a stream, river or other surface supply that is not pretreated or clarified, high bacteria counts can enter with the makeup water. In addition, these sources of makeup water usually contain organic matter and other contaminants that serve as food for bacteria as well as increase the chlorine demand of the water. Where water of this type is used, the slime potential is usually heavy and continuous chlorination to a free residual is generally necessary. To minimize the amount of chlorine that contacts the wood many plants have adopted the practice of chlorinating the makeup to secure a total bacteria kill and to minimize bacteria food entering with the makeup. Under these conditions, the slime potential will be substantially reduced and an intermittent chlorination program can be adopted for the circulating water alternating weekly or biweekly with the use of a non-oxidizing biocide.

The adoption of these measures will effectively minimize attack of wood in the flooded portions of the tower and will also aid in minimizing surface attack in the plenum areas of the tower.

NON-FLOODED SECTION. The preventive maintenance program for the non-flooded or plenum areas of the tower requires:

1. Thorough periodic inspections
2. Replacement of damaged wood with pressure treated wood
3. Periodic spraying of the plenum areas with fungicides.

A thorough inspection of the cooling tower should be conducted at least once per year and certainly more frequently if a preventive maintenance program is not in use.

Although soft rot or surface attack occurs in the non-flooded portions of a tower, the effect on loss on wood structure is not as severe as in the flooded areas. This is due primarily to the fact that the wood is not subject to erosion by cascading water. The principal and most serious problem in the non-flooded area is internal decay. When internal decay is restricted to white pocket rot, the affected areas can be very small and easily missed. As a general rule internal decay is detected usually only after extensive damage has occurred. It is very important to look for signs of internal decay in structural members. This is sometimes revealed by abnormal sagging or settling of the wood. When obvious decay is not evident, it is advisable to secure samples of the wood for microscopic examination to determine whether the internal areas of the wood are infected with fungi.

Replacement of infected wood is necessary to retard spread of infection to adjacent sound members. A weakened section will cause additional weight load to be shifted to sound sections of the structure. These in turn may crack under the increased load and become more susceptible to spread of internal decay. The infected wood should be replaced with pressure treated wood. Several different wood preservatives are available as well as a choice of wood species. Willa discusses a seven year study of eight different pressure treatments. On the basis of incidence of internal decay the treatments can be listed in the following order of effectiveness:

1. Creosote
2. Ammonical Copper Arsenite
3. Acid Copper Chromate and Copper Naphthenate
4. Chromated Copper Arsenate
5. Pentachlorophenol
6. Fluoride Chromate Arsenate Phenol
7. Chlorinated Paraffin

Periodic spraying with an effective fungicide is the third essential step in an effective preventive maintenance program. The purpose of spraying the plenum areas with a fungicide is to render the wood resistant to spread and growth of wood destroying fungi. Diffusion of fungicide into the wood at best permits penetration of the wood to a depth of 1/16″ to 1/4″. The degree of penetration is dependent on the preparation given the wood and to some degree on the concentration of fungicide sprayed. The objective is to spray a sufficient concentration of fungicide so that the wood remains fungistatic until the next semi-annual or annual inspection and spraying.

WOOD EXAMINATION

Since several types of wood deterioration are possible in cooling towers, physical inspections along with periodic laboratory examinations of wood samples should be scheduled regularly. In this connection, service laboratories are equipped with specialized equipment to determine all of the important data needed to comprehensively evaluate the condition of tower wood.

Microscopic examination of the wood reveals the degree of grooving, erosion, surface structure and depth of surface attack. Specimens are broken to determine whether the wood is brash, and the degree of brashness as well as apparent loss in structural strength are recorded. Macroscopic study reveals the physical aspects of the wood, whether or not chemical and/or biological factors are present and, if so, to what extent. Figures 39-1 to 39-3 inclusive demonstrate some of these physical characteristics that are helpful to fully evaluate the condition of cooling tower wood.

Microtome studies of wood cells, as shown in Figures 39-6 to 39-8, are of assistance in determining the extent of microbiological deterioration. These microtome sections are usually 25 microns in thickness, and permit viewing of the internal structure of the wood. This examination indicates to the analyst the extent of infection, and whether the infection is due to bacterial or fungal activity. From this study of the wood cells, the microscopist

determines whether any fungi present are cellulolytic (wood destroying) or simply fungus organisms.

The most beneficial test when evaluating cooling tower wood is commonly known as the zone of inhibition test. This test determines the relative penetration of any fungicidal agent employed and the degree to which this material is present. Also determined is the susceptibility of the wood to support fungal growth and to become decayed if inoculated with wood destroying organisms.

Briefly described, the zone of inhibition test consists of placing two ½ inch squares of the wood specimen on nutrient agar previously seeded with a wood rotting organism, such as Aspergillus niger or Chaetomium globosum. The plates are then incubated for seven days at 28 C. After the elapsed incubation period, the plates are evaluated for their degree of protection or susceptibility.

A complete zone of inhibition exists when no fungal spores of the test organism are present in a clear zone around the test block. This preventative barrier against fungal infection develops when the effects of a fungicidal application are still present in the wood and inhibit the growth of wood rotting organisms.

A partial zone of inhibition is one which shows some growth of the test organism around the block, but the growth of fungal spores of the test organism is retarded. This partial zone indicates that some residual fungicide or natural inhibitory properties are still present in the wood.

No zone of inhibition is exhibited by a specimen of low resistance, so the growth of the test organism or other organisms inherent in the wood occurs around the block. This growth indicates that the wood is susceptible to fungal attack. Corrective measures must be taken in order to control the spread of fungus in the sound members of the tower.

Figure 39-9 shows two of the conditions that aid the analyst in determining whether or not inhibitory power from a preservative treatment or from the natural property of the wood is at an effective level. This zone of inhibition test may be used to evaluate the residual effect of fungicidal treatment or the degree of resistance restored by an application of fungicide.

METHODS OF SPRAYING

The most effective method of spraying is the direct or manual method. This method is very similar to painting in that the concentrated fungicide is applied directly to the wood by the use of spraying equipment handled by an operator or team of operators. This method of application proves most effective since small areas can be covered thoroughly by the fungicide, and special attention can be given to spraying the joints, holes and other access points into the wood.

Direct spraying can be hazardous unless proper precautions are taken to protect the operator. Figure 39-10 shows an operator properly equipped. He is clothed in air-fed coveralls with the legs secured with tape at the ankles. The outer clothing consists of a rain suit. The rubber gloves are vulcanized to the sleeves of the suit and the legs are secured to the arctics with tape at the ankles. The sandblaster's hood is in place and its air feed can be seen from the rear. The air-fed coveralls and sandblaster's hood permit the operator to stay cool and comfortable while spraying.

OTHER METHODS

In order to decrease labor costs and to further minimize the hazards of direct spraying other methods have been considered. Steam spraying through a permanent piping arrangement has been used. In this procedure the fungicide is forced into the steam and is transported into the cell by the steam. It is essential that the distribution piping be designed properly in order to secure complete coverage. The use of steam causes dilution of the fungicide and compared to direct spraying a relatively dilute solution contacts the wood. As a result the quantity of toxicant that penetrates the wood is smaller and more frequent spraying is necessary to maintain the wood fungistatic.

Recently a revised method of spraying the plenum areas of cooling towers has been introduced. This new method is designed to minimize the hazards and high cost of direct spraying while maintaining its major advantage, namely: spraying of a concentrated solution of fungicide so that the frequency of spraying will be required only once or twice per year. Pneumatic spraying with a portable rig equipped with an atomizing nozzle similar to that shown in Figure 39-11 is used. The rig is inserted through holes in the deck of the tower so that spraying can be accomplished from outside the tower.

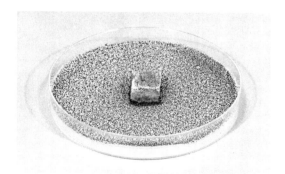 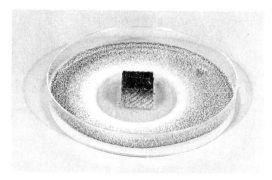

Figure 39-9 • Test Blocks of Wood on the Surface of Inoculated Nutrient Agar. The Block on the Left Shows No Resistance to the Test Organism. The Block on the Right, which has had Fungicide Spray Treatment, Shows a Clear Zone of Inhibition

Diffusion and spray methods are limited for the most part to penetration of the outer surfaces of redwood. Therefore it is essential

Figure 39-10 · Direct Fungicide Spraying by Properly Equipped Operator

that preventive maintenance be started before infection takes place and preferably before the interior parts of the wood lose much of their natural resistance. Under these conditions new infection can be prevented and the life of the tower extended. Where the tower has undergone a serious degree of infection and it is likely that infection cannot be contained by following the normal preventive maintenance program, then consideration can be given to sterilization of the wood by elevating the temperature of the internal portions of the wood to 150 F and maintaining this temperature for two hours.

REFERENCES

W. A. Dost, "Certification of Redwood and Effect of Oxidizing Agents on Redwood in Cooling Tower Service", *Proceedings,* Engineers Soc. of Western Penna., pp. 77-83 (1959)

B. F. Shema, "Clarification of Cooling Tower Wood Deterioration", *Proceedings,* Engineers Soc. of Western Penna., pp. 69-74 (1959)

Unpublished data, Betz Laboratories, Inc., Phila., Pa.

J. L. Willa, "Report On Field Wood Preservation Studies", *Proceedings,* Engineers Soc. of Western Penna., pp. 83-96 (1959)

Figure 39-11 · Portable Rig for Pneumatic Spraying

40

Air Conditioning Systems

AIR conditioning is considered a modern luxury but it has been used for many years in industry for drying, humidity control and for dust and smoke abatement. Air conditioning is used for health purposes and has proven beneficial in increasing the efficiency of working personnel.

Air conditioning has been defined as the process of treating air so as to control simultaneously its temperature, humidity, cleanliness and distribution to meet the requirements of the conditioned space. The temperature of air is controlled by passing the air over chilled or heated coils or by exposing the air to a spray of water of controlled temperature. Removal of moisture from the air is accomplished by cooling the air by chilled coils or by direct water spray. Dehumidification is also accomplished by sorbent materials such as silica gel. Washing of the air with water sprays may also serve to moisten the air and commonly has an important function in dirt and odor removal.

The basic components of an air conditioning system are the refrigeration machine, a system of heat rejection and a cooling distribution system. The two types of refrigeration commonly used with air conditioning are the refrigerant (Freon) compression system and the absorption system. Absorption systems used in air conditioning have a lithium salt solution as the refrigerant and steam as the energy source.

In industrial or commercial size air conditioning systems, heat rejection almost invariably is accomplished by water. Once-through cooling is sometimes used. However, municipal restrictions on water consumption, and the water costs, usually result in evaporative cooling for all but very small installations. Evaporative condensers or economizers, as well as cooling towers, are used for evaporative cooling. Occasionally a spray pond may be used. By recirculating water in an evaporative cooling system, the water makeup requirement is reduced to less than 3% of the water used for once-through cooling.

Air conditioning capacity is measured in tons of refrigeration. A ton of refrigeration

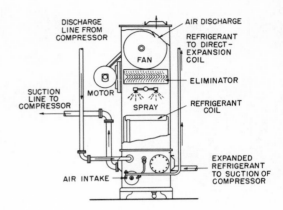

Figure 40-1 • Evaporative Condenser

is defined as the capacity to remove heat at the rate of 12,000 Btu per hour. Freon systems require for heat rejection the evaporation of approximately 1.5 gallons of water per hour per ton of refrigeration. An absorption system, because of the additional steam heat input, requires the evaporation of approximately 3 gallons of water per hour per ton. These water evaporation requirements are based on air conditioning operation at rated capacity. The average operating load on an air conditioning system during the operating season will be less than rated capacity. Usually the average operating tonnage will be in the range of 30-60% of rated tonnage.

Cooling distribution throughout the building is accomplished by a variety of methods. Air can be passed over coils chilled by direct expansion of refrigerant and then circulated. In larger systems, water is chilled and this water is circulated in a closed system to fan units where the air is blown over coils chilled by the water. Sometimes these closed water systems are used for the dual purpose of winter heat. The chilled water may also be recirculated through one or more air washers, either in closed coils, or as the spray water. Where the chilled water is in a closed system the air washers will have individual spray water systems.

In considering water treatment, the water systems associated with air conditioning can be classified into the three general categories of open recirculating cooling water systems, closed water systems, and air washers or open chilled water systems.

OPEN RECIRCULATING COOLING WATER SYSTEMS

The water in open evaporative cooling systems is subject to the problems of scale, corrosion and slime and algae.

As water is evaporated in the cooling tower or evaporative condenser, pure vapor is lost and dissolved salts will concentrate in the system. When cycles of concentration develop sufficiently the solubility limit of a salt, usually calcium carbonate, will be exceeded and precipitation will occur. The result is scale deposits on hotter surfaces such as in the tubes of the condenser. Deposits result in high head pressure and reduced efficiency.

Control of scale in open cooling systems is discussed in detail in Chapter 33. In air conditioning systems provision for continuous blowdown, or bleed, is usually adequate for scale control. The importance of continuous bleed, as opposed to periodic draining, cannot be overemphasized for the water content of most air conditioning cooling systems is quite small compared to the amount of water evaporated. Excessive solids can develop in less than a day of operation. Continuous blowdown is usually provided by running a valved line from the discharge of the recirculating water pump to the sewer.

When the water is extremely hard and high in alkalinity, feed of sulfuric acid or an acid salt, in addition to blowdown, may be necessary for scale prevention. Feed of an acidic material requires care in handling and good control and is not used unless the blowdown rate otherwise necessary would be excessive. Zeolite softening of the makeup water is another method of scale control. However, zeolite softening does not decrease the alkalinity of the makeup water. When alkalinity as well as hardness is high in the makeup water, a higher blowdown rate still will be necessary to prevent high alkalinity and pH of the recirculating water and consequent attack of cooling tower wood, copper alloys and

galvanizing in the system. Polyphosphates are of some value for scale control, but again care must be taken in their application. Excessive feed can result in calcium phosphate deposits.

The water in open recirculating cooling systems will be saturated with oxygen and consequently quite corrosive. In addition, those air conditioning systems located in urban areas are often subject to the absorption of acidic gases from the air. Acidic pickup can be beneficial in reducing scaling tendencies, but excessive absorption of acid gases can result in severely corrosive conditions.

The corrosion inhibitors used in open systems are generally the same as those described in Chapter 34. Chromate base treatments are commonly used, provided there is no objection to the color of the water. The drift loss from a cooling tower with high chromate treatment will cause staining. Chromates may also be limited in application from the standpoint of disposal of the blowdown water.

Nitrite base treatments have been used where chromates cannot be applied. Nitrite is colorless, but it has several disadvantages. A treatment level approximately twice that of chromate must be used for equivalent protection. In addition, nitrites are subject to biological degradation requiring the greater use of biocides to maintain concentration of the corrosion inhibitor and to control development of biological slime and algae. Proprietary formulations have been developed combining the biocide with nitrite.

The use of certain organic base treatments in place of nitrite is a more desirable approach to the problem of providing an adequate non-chromate inhibitor. Treatment levels are essentially the same as with nitrites, but the problem of biological degradation is no longer encountered. Some organic base treatments impart a light brown color to the treated water, while others still produce a colorless solution.

Since the heat load on air conditioning systems is generally quite variable, depending upon weather conditions, water balances tend to be irregular. Consequently, in order to provide a protective margin, inhibitor treatment levels are usually maintained higher than in industrial cooling tower systems.

Algae and biological slime in open cooling water systems are usually controlled by chlorinated phenols, fed in a shot fashion. Application of chlorine gas can be effective, but this requires chlorination equipment and specific controls, which are not practical for most air conditioning systems. Chlorine also can be applied as a hypochlorite. However, hypochlorites must be used frequently and with care so that corrosion will not be increased and tower wood affected by excessive chlorine.

AIR WASHERS

Air washers can function to moisten the air in the winter and dehumidify the air in the summer, in addition to controlling air temperature. In winter operation, spray water evaporates so that the washer then operates like a cooling tower or evaporative condenser. Cycles of concentration develop and scale can occur. Scale is not common, however, since operating water temperatures are usually ambient or lower. Dehumidification is achieved by maintaining the temperature of the spray water below the dew point of the entering air. In such summer operation the condensation of water from the air results in dilution of mineral salts in the recirculating water and overflow of water from the sump or pan of the washer.

Chromate base treatments provide optimum corrosion protection. However, because of the possibility of airborne contamination from chromate dust collected in air ducts, under certain circumstances use of materials approved by the United States Food and Drug Administration is desirable. These materials include the polyphosphates and silicates.

When washers are operating as dehumidifiers the corrosion potential will be less than when humidifying. Since the water condensed from the air contains no dissolved salts, the water will be low in electrical conductivity

and therefore less corrosive. This condition is generally true except for the important fact that the air being washed quite frequently has sufficient acidic contamination to lower the pH of the spray water to a point where severe acidic corrosion can occur. This condition requires the feed of an alkaline material, such as soda ash. It is also good practice to use a corrosion inhibitor in air washers both winter and summer.

One of the functions of air washers is to remove dust, smoke and odor from the air. Usually the air being washed will contain numerous microorganisms together with materials which act as food for the bacteria. Consequently, the development of biological slime is a usual problem in air washers. Unfortunately, the more effective slimicides such

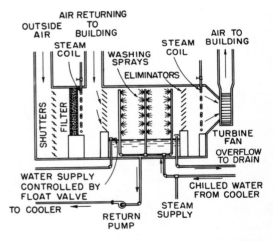

Figure 40-2 • Air Washer with Open Chilled Water System

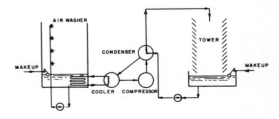

Figure 40-3 • Air Conditioning System: Cooling Tower and Freon Refrigeration with Closed Chilled Water System and Air Washer

as chlorine, trichlorophenates and organic sulfur compounds impart an odor to the air so that they cannot be used in air washers. Sodium pentachlorophenate can be used judiciously although it is not particularly effective unless applied in combination with other toxicants. The quaternary ammonium compounds have little odor, but again they are more effective when used in conjunction with other biocides. Periodically, air washers should be sterilized by stopping air flow and recirculating a solution of hypochlorite or a non-oxidizing biocide. The washer should then be thoroughly hosed, washing off deposits of slime and miscellaneous dirt, all of which should be cleaned from the pan of the washer.

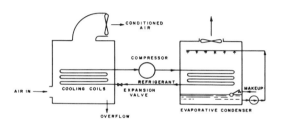

Figure 40–4 • Air Conditioning System: Evaporative Condenser with Freon Refrigeration by Direct Expansion

CLOSED WATER SYSTEMS

Closed systems are not subject to scale except in the case of abnormal water makeup to a hot water system when the water has a scaling tendency. Under these circumstances zeolite softening of the makeup water is necessary.

The corrosion potential in closed water systems is not great but the systems are often very sensitive to corrosion because of fouling of automatic valves and vents by corrosion products. Theoretically, closed recirculating water systems should not require corrosion inhibitors. The oxygen introduced with the initial fill of water should be soon depleted

by attacking system metals and corrosion no longer occur. However, the systems in fact commonly have sufficient water loss and air leakage to justify the cost of protective treatment.

The inhibitors used are chromate or nitrite based. The amount of inhibitor used will depend upon the temperature of operation of the system with higher temperatures requiring higher levels of treatment. Since these systems use no additional chemical treatment after the initial charge, it has been common to use relatively high treatment concentrations for a margin of safety.

There have been indications that high chromate concentrations shorten the life of mechanical seals on pumps. Where pumps are equipped with mechanical seals, lower chromate concentrations in the range of 200-300 ppm are sometimes used. This chromate level reportedly is low enough so that the seal life is not effected. However, there is a possibility that this concentration of chromate will not be sufficient to stifle corrosion in the system, particularly if there are areas of stagnant conditions or bimetallic couples. The development of corrosion products resulting from continuing corrosion may possibly shorten the life of mechanical seals. The data available at this time regarding this matter are highly contradictory and inconclusive.

CONTROL OF WATER BALANCES

Weather changes cause water concentrations in open cooling water systems to be erratic, particularly in air washers. Air conditioning systems are designed for considerations other than water treatment. To reduce weight cooling towers located on roofs may have no water sump. The lower water capacity of the system then causes more rapid change of water concentrations because of shorter retention time. Also, evaporative condensers and air washers have pans of small water capacity to minimize space and weight requirements. Cooling towers may be located near smokestacks where pickup of dirt and acidic gases is excessive. Air conditioning units are sometimes installed and operated in a manner such that considerable overflow of water from the system occurs on shutdown and there are instances where additional makeup water has been used during hot weather to reduce water temperature. These are some of the factors which can complicate a water treatment program.

In open systems, continuous blowdown, continuous feed of the corrosion inhibitor and daily testing of the water are definitely necessary for best protection. Some systems are treated and controlled on the basis of weekly tests, but this requires good proportioning of chemical treatment at higher cost for feeding equipment and will require more chemical treatment to assure adequate protection at all times.

CHEMICAL FEED METHODS

Unless an open cooling water system has a large water content, shot feed of the corrosion inhibitor is not satisfactory. The effectiveness of treatment will be in direct relation to the amount of inhibitor in the water so that it is necessary to maintain a certain minimum concentration of chemical treatment. Continuous blowdown is necessary to prevent scaling and, correspondingly, continuous chemical feed is necessary to maintain adequate treatment levels. If treatment is shot fed once per day, it must be fed far in in excess of its required treatment level if the minimum treatment concentration is to be maintained until the next shot feed.

Figure 40-5 illustrates the rate of decrease in treatment concentration under average conditions with continuous blowdown. It will be seen that a shot feed of 3,000 ppm must be made in order that there will still be a minimum concentration of 200 ppm at the end of 24 hours. If treatment were to be maintained within the normal limits of 200-400 ppm at all times, shot feed every six hours would be necessary. More than three times as much treatment is required when shot feeding once a day as when treating continuously in order to maintain the same protection.

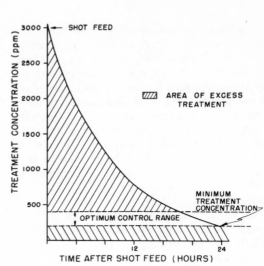

Figure 40-5 • *Waste of Chemical Treatment with Shot Feeding*

Chemical treatment can be fed continuously by direct exposure of the dry chemical treatment to water in the basin of the air conditioning unit. Rate of feed is adjusted by controlling the amount of chemical exposed to water. Sometimes the treatment can be formulated to dissolve slowly with the rate of addition being controlled by using more or less of the formulation submerged in the basin. Regulation requires trial and error since several factors, such as water turbulence, affect the rate of solution. Serious overfeed can occur if the air conditioning unit is shut down without removing the chemical treatment.

One of the simplest continuous chemical feed devices is the drip feeder, a chemical solution tank with a valved discharge line at the bottom. The treatment is dripped into the sump or pan of the air conditioning unit by adjustment of the valve. This feeding device is seldom entirely satisfactory; plugging of the valve occurs, there is difficulty in properly adjusting the valve, and the rate of flow decreases as the tank empties. When such feeders are used, it is advisable to make the installation so that the regulating valve is always flooded and the tank raised as high as possible with respect to the valve (See Figure 40-6).

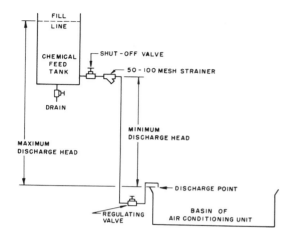

NOTE:

1. THE INSTALLATION SHOULD BE MADE SO THAT THE MINIMUM DISCHARGE HEAD IS AS LARGE AS POSSIBLE COMPARED TO MAXIMUM DISCHARGE HEAD. PLACE THE CHEMICAL FEED TANK AS HIGH AS POSSIBLE ABOVE THE DISCHARGE POINT AND USE A LOW, WIDE TANK WHEN POSSIBLE.

2. THE DISCHARGE CONNECTION OF CHEMICAL FEED TANK IS TO BE A MINIMUM OF 2" ABOVE TANK BOTTOM.

3. THE REGULATING VALVE IS TO BE AT A LEVEL BELOW THE DISCHARGE POINT. USE EITHER A NEEDLE VALVE OR A FLO-CONTROL VALVE.

Figure 40-6 • Drip Feeder Installation

Chemical feed pumps are quite dependable although some types present problems in regulation and maintenance. Piston type pumps are prone to some leakage which can be particularly objectionable when feeding colored materials such as chromate.

A water-motorized proportioning feeder is particularly applicable for the feed of treatment to air conditioning systems. This unit requires no electrical connections whatsoever. The device is merely installed in the makeup water line and adjusted to feed a prescribed rate of chemical in direct proportion to the quantity of makeup.

Up to six pumping heads can be handled by one water-motor base. This feature is advantageous when at least two incompatible materials, such as a corrosion inhibitor and a slimicide, must be fed in a proportional fashion from two tanks.

Compact diaphragm chemical pumps also provide precise and reliable service for the addition of treatment to air conditioning systems. Where a conductivity controller is employed for automatic blowdown control, the electric motor of the diaphragm pump can be connected with the controller to effect automatic chemical feed.

GENERAL CONSIDERATIONS

The importance of properly beginning chemical treatment cannot be overemphasized. New installations will have mill scale on metal surfaces and will contain oil, pipe dope and other miscellaneous debris. Systems which have been operated without protective treatment contain corrosion products which slough-off when protective balances are established. These materials can impede water flow, cause fouling and will increase the corrosion load by cell action. Automatic valves and controls can malfunction and suspended solids can seriously shorten the life of mechanical seals on pumps.

These systems should first be chemically cleaned, drained and then flushed as thoroughly as possible. Cleaning agents are commonly polyphosphates, synthetic detergents or combinations of these materials. It is important to establish the permanent protective treatment immediately after cleaning since the metal surfaces in the system are particularly vulnerable to corrosion.

Air conditioning systems quite often do not operate in winter so that measures should be taken for protection during the idle period. Open cooling water systems should be completely drained if possible. It is good procedure to open condensers at the end of an air conditioning season, not only to inspect conditions, but also to provide for drying of the equipment. When the water cannot be removed from an idle system it is advisable to use a higher concentration of the corrosion inhibitor in order to provide the additional protection necessary when water is not flowing. Basins of cooling towers or air conditioning units should be cleaned of any sediment. The application of protective paints to metal surfaces is generally not satisfactory unless more than one coat is used and a fully continuous film is achieved. The development of holidays can result in serious penetration of the metal through localized corrosion. Whenever ethylene glycol is added to a water system for freeze protection, any chromate treated water should first be drained from the system since these materials are not compatible. Chemical feed systems should be drained and cleaned and the power supply to chemical pumps disconnected to prevent the possibility of inadvertent operation. The packing on piston type pumps should be replaced before start-up.

The eliminator sections of cooling towers are subject to build-up of salts during operation as the result of partial or intermittent wetting. These salts and other dirt and debris also tend to accumulate in the eliminator sections of air washers and evaporative condensers. These areas should be hosed down and where appreciable dirt is present mechanical cleaning may be necessary. These cleaning procedures may also be required several times during the air conditioning season when conditions are particularly severe. Since the treated water does not reach these areas during operation in reasonable amounts, the treatment chemicals added to the water cannot be expected to provide protection.

REFERENCES

S. M. Elonka and Q. W. Minich, "Standard Refrigeration and Air Conditioning Questions and Answers", McGraw-Hill Book Co., Inc., New York, N. Y. (1961).

"Heating Ventilating Air Conditioning Guide 1960" Vol. 38, Am. Soc. of Heating, Refrigerating and Air Conditioning Engineers, Inc., New York, N. Y. (1960)

J. R. Schieber, "Chemical Feed Systems for Air Conditioning", *The Betz Indicator,* Betz Laboratories, Inc., Phila., Pa. (Nov. 1961)

J. R. Schieber, "Water Treatment Control", *Plant Engineering,* Vol. 13, pp. 146, 148, 150 (June 1959)

41

Industrial Waste Treatment

WATER differs from other natural resources, such as fossil fuels and food, in that it is not consumed or destroyed by use. It is a reusable resource.

Water has extraordinary chemical stability, but it also possesses strong solvent powers. Therefore, when used in home and factory, water absorbs substances that can alter its overall quality. Water becomes wastewater and contains unwanted by-products of human activities.

The basic—if oversimplified—concept of wastewater treatment is to remove from wastewater those foreign substances which it contains, thereby returning it along the road toward pure water to be used for the same or other purposes. The extent to which foreign substances are removed depends on practical considerations of the intended uses for the reconditioned water. Man-made wastewater treatment facilities are designed to augment and assist the inherent ability of natural flowing waters to cleanse themselves.

In handling wastewater discharges, industry is faced with a multiplicity and diversity of problems. These problems are largely the outgrowth of technological changes, industrial expansion and urbanization. Industrial waste disposal problems are not only technical in nature, but also have legal and public relations aspects that must be considered.

Since the passage of the Water Quality Act of 1965, there has been increased public concern and activity at all levels of government in matters relating to pollution control and abatement. This Act provides that criteria be established on all interstate waters so as to enhance quality and to protect public health and welfare.

Water quality criteria promulgated for the enhancement of water resources may require increased performance from existing wastewater treatment facilities as well as the removal of constituents which normally pass through these processes. With increasing density of population and industrial expansion, the demands for cleaner water and more stringent water requirements can be antici-

Fig. 41-1
Abridged Classification of Industrial Wastes by Industries

INORGANIC	ORGANIC
Metallurgical	Vegetable Canning
Brass and Copper	Corn Products
Iron and Steel	Alcohol Production
Plating	Slaughterhouse
Sulfur	Dairy and Milk
Sand Washing	Beet Sugar
Acid Manufacturing	Citrus Fruit Canning
Salts	Brewery
Alkalies	Meat Packing
Coal Mines	

MIXED	
Textile	Petroleum
Dyeing	Plastics
Coke and Gas Wastes	Rubber Reclaiming
Paper Board and Allied	Natural and Synthetic Rubber
Laundry	Explosives
Tanning	Vegetable Dehydration
Cutting Oils	Wool Scouring
Dye Manufacturing	

pated. It is reasonable to expect that future demands upon water resources will necessitate more widespread application of present technology, plus the development of new methods to handle new situations.

INDUSTRIAL WATER USE

The general subject of industrial waste is of broad scope. This discussion is primarily directed to liquid or waterborne industrial wastes which are eventually discharged into a watercourse.

Substantially all industries contribute some liquid or waterborne industrial waste to a waterway, either directly or indirectly. Treatment is usually required to prevent the imposition of an excessive pollution load on the receiving stream, lake, river or waste treatment plant.

Certain industries are unaware of enormous losses of valuable by-products in their wastes. Similarly, industries are often not cognizant of the volume and effect of their waste upon the receiving streams or sewers. For these reasons, industrial waste problems may exist and may not be recognized by an industry having such problems.

Most industries use water in their processing operations in such manner that some of the water becomes contaminated. Figure 41-2 indicates the tremendous quantities of water employed by industry. These data are not meant to indicate consumptive use of water, but are illustrative of the large quantities of total water required by various types of industry. Portions of the water, such as that used for cooling purposes, may be uncontaminated. But, substantial portions will require treatment to avoid imposing a pollution load upon the receiving waters.

Fig. 41-2

Abridged List of Industrial Water Requirements

INDUSTRY	GALLONS OF WATER PER UNIT OF PRODUCTION
CHEMICAL INDUSTRIES	
Corn Refinery	333 per ton of starch
Alcohol	20,000 per ton of grain
Ammonium Sulfate	200,000 per ton
Gun Powder	200,000 per ton
Lactose	220,000 per ton
Hydrogen	660,000 per ton
FOOD INDUSTRIES	
Beet Sugar .	20,000-25,000 per ton of sugar
Canning ...	300-25,000 per 100 cases of No. 2 cans
Meat Packing	16,000-55,000 per 100 live units
Milk Products ..	200-250 per 100 lb
Vegetable Dehydration ...	500-2,000 per 100 lb
TEXTILE INDUSTRIES	
Cotton	1,000- 3,800 per 100 lb
Linen	10,000 per 100 lb
Rayon	8,000-10,000 per 100 lb
Wool Scour	2,000-12,000 per 100 lb
MISCELLANEOUS	
Air Conditioning	6,000-15,000 per person, per season
Automotive ...	15,000 per car
Oil Field	18,000 per 100 bbl crude
Oil Refinery ...	77,000 per 100 bbl crude
Steam Power ..	80 per kwh
Steel	20,000-35,000 per ton
Sulfur	3,000 per ton

EFFECTS CAUSED BY WASTE DISCHARGE

In order to measure the effects caused by waste discharges and to ascertain that water quality criteria are being met, the legally designated regulatory agency generally establishes some form of qualitative and/or quantitative specifications for each waste discharge. Where standards are set, they may be 'effluent standards' or 'receiving water standards.' In some instances, both types of standards are simultaneously employed, with one covering general circumstances and the other covering specific aspects.

Effluent standards state precisely what is allowed in a waste discharge as the discharge is introduced into a receiving water. These standards may specify the amount of any particular quality constituent that an effluent may contain, or they may specify the percentage of removal required from the waste treatment facility. Through effluent standards, a portion of the assimilative capacity of the receiving water is, in effect, allocated to each waste discharge so as to insure that the quality criteria set for the receiving water will be met during normal low flow conditions.

Receiving water standards establish quality conditions which must be met after adequate admixture of a waste discharge with the receiving water in order to comply with criteria promulgated for the receiving water. Receiving water standards normally contain no specific limitations on the composition of the waste discharges, provided that the quality of the receiving water is maintained within specified limits. This approach takes advantage of the varying natural flows and assimilative capacities of receiving waters. The receiving water must be examined to ascertain that these standards are being met.

The effect of individual wastes upon the receiving waters will vary, dependent upon the volume, concentration and character of the waste as well as the flow, location and downstream use of the receiving waters. Obviously, the discharge of large volumes of relatively highly concentrated waste into a very large receiving body of water, where appreciable dilution will result, may have a lesser effect than the discharge of a smaller volume into receiving waters where a minimum of dilution can be obtained.

The direct effect on the receiving waters of the discharge of industrial waste is dependent upon the character and specific types of materials present in the waste. Solids may precipitate with the result that all flora growth is killed. Solids which settle out may shroud fish breeding grounds, and minute particles may lodge in fish gills and cause suffocation. Oil waste discharge will float to the surface and may prevent reoxygenation of the water. Toxic metals and salts, acids and alkalies may cause flora and fauna casualties. The wastes may produce taste and odor contamination which can render the water unfit for livestock or for human consumption, even following normal treatment.

The problems of industry due to contamination of its water supplies by industrial waste discharge are numerous. In many cases, treatment of an industrial water supply for process, boiler or cooling water uses is more difficult and costly when a polluted surface supply is used. Frequently, specific corrosion problems in industrial plant water circulating systems or product damage can be traced to contamination of the water supply by upstream discharges of industrial waste.

Fig. 41-3

Average Analyses of Domestic Sewage in Milligrams per Liter

ANALYSIS	WEAK	MEDIUM	STRONG
Total Solids	430	720	1230
Total Volatile Solids	240	420	810
Suspended Solids	98	200	372
Suspended Volatile Solids	72	133	220
Settleable Solids (ml/l)	2.1	3.8	6.4
Biochemical Oxygen Demand	96	212	413
Oxygen Consumed	74	162	267
Total Nitrogen	13	28	40
Ammonia Nitrogen	4.2	12	22
Chlorides	18	38	79
Sulfates	42	22	34
Soaps and Fats	6	13	23
Total Alkalinity	31	40	18
pH	6.9	7.4	7.1

Sewage treatment plants are operated by many cities, some treating a combination of domestic sewage and industrial trade waste. If industrial wastes change in volume or character, serious interference with operation of the sewage treatment plant may result. This operating interference may take many forms, from overloading of solids removal facilities to drastic interference with biological stabilization. Excessive solids, presence of certain toxic metals or oil, or excessive concentrations of organic constituents will cause one or more of the problems indicated.

METHODS OF WASTE TREATMENT

The technology of industrial wastewater treatment practice has not advanced to a point comparable to industrial process and domestic potable water treatment. For the solution of certain waste treatment problems, vast amounts of specialized research are required to devise a practical treatment method. Minor deviations in manufacturing practice among plants in the same type of industry and variations in local conditions may necessitate an entirely different approach to the waste treatment problem. Therefore, generalizations regarding treatment methods for various types of industries cannot be drawn with accuracy. Each problem must receive specific attention, consideration and evaluation for its solution.

Courtesy Link-Belt Company

Figure 41-4 · Straight-line grit chamber for removal of inorganic solids.

The engineer working in the field of industrial waste treatment has available certain tools with which to attack the industrial waste problem. These tools consist of certain unit processes or combination of processes. These processes may be divided generally into mechanical treatment methods, chemical treatment methods and biological treatment methods. Only on very rare occasions is dilution alone an acceptable method for the disposal of industrial waste. In the treatment of some industrial wastes, the need to segregate certain portions is paramount, while with others it is highly desirable to mix the wastes and thereby utilize the beneficial effects of interaction.

Occasionally, there are wastes which can be satisfactorily discharged to large holding lagoons from which evaporation, ground percolation and drying represent all the treatment that is required. In other cases, wastes may be disposed of by field irrigation, resulting in benefits to the soil, and thus avoiding the use of more sophisticated treatment plant facilities.

MECHANICAL METHODS. The simplest form of mechanical treatment for waste involves screening for the separation of the larger solid particles. Screening has its limitations in that the use of fine screens presents mechanical difficulties in operation. Certain wastes contain varied amounts of particulate inorganic solids which can be effectively removed by the use of grit chambers. The debris from screens and grit chambers may differ considerably. The collection from grit chambers is usually inorganic and nonputrescible, and can be taken to dry disposal. Screen residues may be both inorganic and organic in nature and require burning or burial. Suspended solids remaining after screens or grit chambers may be further reduced by sedimentation, either by natural subsidence or by chemical coagulation.

In addition to solids, many wastes contain varied amounts of oil, either in the free state or emulsified form. Preskimming chambers for readily separable oil are quite effective, the skimmed oil being either recovered for use or disposed of by burning or other suitable means. Oil in the emulsified state is much more difficult to remove and may require acid cracking or precoalescence. Occasionally, greater separation of both emulsified and free oil can be accomplished by preaeration.

Aeration, which is highly effective for certain waters, may also be included in mechanical treatment. Air may be satisfactorily applied by spraying the waste through suitable nozzles, adding air through diffuser tubes or cascading the wastes over suitable aerators. There are also other available mechanical aerators which are applicable for certain plant installations.

Flotation is a specialized form of mechanical treatment in which the solid material entraps air and rises to the surface for removal. Flotation may be carried out either under atmospheric pressure or under vacuum. Chemical aids are sometimes employed to assist in this operation.

Courtesy Komline-Sanderson Engineering Co.

Figure 41-5 · Vacuum filter for sludge dewatering.

Filtration of the wastes may be applied either for the clarification of the wastes or for dewatering the separated solids. Centrifuges, either batch or continuous, may be applied for similar purposes, treating either the previously separated sludge or the entire volume of waste as the particular case may require.

Conventional sedimentation is one of the basic waste treatment methods. When natural or mechanical sedimentation does not produce the desired results, or when conditions of the waste are such that the pollution is in a colloidal or soluble form, it is necessary to add chemicals to produce suitable sedimentation. Equipment is commercially available which accomplishes both settling and flotation within the same unit. In such a unit, two layers of solids, one from the surface and one from the bottom, are separately removed, eliminating the necessity of forcing a readily settleable material to float or to settle a difficult settleable component.

Evaporation or drying is applied to certain wastes. Normally, these methods cannot be economically applied unless by-product recovery is realized from the process. However, there are occasions when low flows of particularly difficult wastes are encountered, and drying or evaporation is the only practical known method.

CHEMICAL METHODS. Chemical flocculation and precipitation find application in the treatment of certain industrial wastes, either alone or followed by other treatment. These processes are carried out in a manner similar to the treatment of water and in most cases in similar types of equipment. Chemical treatment is usually effected by means of a suitable mixing apparatus and straight line or upflow type clarifiers. Chemical treatment may be handled in either batch or continuous fashion, or a combination thereof. Chemical precipitation is popular, due largely to its ability to operate unaffected by greatly varying loads of toxic material and to its usually lower capital expenditure in comparison to more involved biological processes.

Flocculation and coagulation are used primarily as aids in sedimentation. The purpose of coagulation is to obtain the removal of suspended and colloidal solids and also to effect precipitation of materials which may be present in solution in the waste. The coagulants used must be selected for the particular waste undergoing treatment, and are usually aluminum sulfate, iron salts, sodium aluminate, calcium chloride or lime.

Certain wastes may be highly acid or highly alkaline, and will require neutralization as part of the treatment. There are times when neutralization may be accomplished by combining the various wastes from a plant. Industrial wastes which contain highly oxidizing or reducing components require neutralization of these factors prior to discharge or further treatment. Chemical conversion of some constituents can be accomplished by strong oxidizing or reducing agents, rendering them unobjectionable. Certain wastes require that adsorptive materials be added for the removal of undesirable characteristics. Some wastes, following preliminary treatment, may be treated through ion exchangers prior to final discharge. Sterilization of the waste may also be necessary and chlorine is usually employed for this purpose.

Fig. 41-6

Reduction Efficiency of Units and Plants on Domestic Sewage

UNITS AND PLANTS	PERCENT SUSPENDED SOLIDS	PERCENT BOD	PERCENT COLIFORM
Sedimentation (2 hours)	45-60	30-45	40-60
Imhoff Tanks (2-3 hours)	45-60	20-45	40-60
Trickling Filters (Standard) ..	10-30	55-75	60-70
Activated Sludge	85-95	80-95	90-96
Chemical Treatment	65-90	45-75	60-90
Sedimentation and Sand Filters	90-98	85-92	85-95
Sedimentation and Trickling Filters	75-85	70-90	80-90

BIOLOGICAL METHODS. Biological treatment may be generally divided into two classifications. Those methods requiring the presence of oxygen are known as aerobic processes. The two aerobic treatment processes most commonly employed are the trickling filter process and the activated sludge process. Both processes are used for the treatment of industrial wastewaters. Proponents of the trickling filter method hold that it is less susceptible to shock resulting from change in rate of flow or characteristics of the waste being treated. It has been shown, however, that well-designed and operated activated sludge plants have effectively handled high proportions of various industrial wastes. In general, both processes have applicability for industrial waste treatment. The choice is determined by circumstances particular to each situation.

The trickling filter and activated sludge

processes are similar in principle in that both depend on biochemical oxidation of complex organic matter in wastes. Soon after a filter is placed in operation, the surface of the filtering media becomes coated with zooglea, a viscous substance containing bacteria and other biota. Under favorable environmental conditions, the zooglea absorb and utilize suspended, colloidal and dissolved organic matter from the wastes which pass in a relatively thin film over its surface. Eventually, a population equilibrium is reached. As biota die, they, together with the more or less partly decomposed organic matter, are discharged from the filter. This sloughing of material may occur periodically or continuously. Generally, secondary settling is provided to retain the settleable solids sloughed from the filter.

The activated sludge process also makes use of biological organism populations. These

Figure 41-7 · Straightline bar screen for removal of large solids.

biota are supplied with oxygen from the air. The activated sludge is similar in character, composition and action to the biological film in trickling filters. When wastes are mixed with a sufficient amount of biologically active sludge, rapid clarification takes place. The finely divided suspended, colloidal and dissolved solids in the wastes are transferred to the surface of the sludge floc, in which large numbers of living organisms have their habitat. These organisms, supplied with oxygen from the air, oxidize the organic material. The floc grows and settles out, leaving a clear, relatively stable liquor. To produce rapid results, the floc must be kept in suspension by agitation and contact with oxygen. A continuous supply of active sludge must be mixed with incoming wastes, hence a portion of the settled sludge is returned to the head of the process. Excess sludge not needed to maintain the process is wasted.

There are possible occasions when natural oxidation ponds may have application for the treatment of some industrial wastes. Usually, industrial wastes are too strong for this approach, and require such large land areas as to make another aerobic treatment method more attractive economically.

The second classification of biological treatment takes place in the absence of air and is designated as anaerobic. This method finds limited use in liquid waste treatment, being normally confined to the treatment of sludge resulting from some of the other processes.

Combination of trickling filters and activated sludge treatment is often required on high organic wastes to effect complete treatment. In biological treatment, as in chemical precipitation, it may be necessary to add chlorine to the final waste prior to discharge.

In those locations where geologic substructures are satisfactory, deep wells have been employed to dispose of difficult to treat industrial wastes.

Courtesy Infilco-Division of Fuller Co.

Figure 41-8 · Trickling filter for biological stabilization.

ADVANCED WASTE TREATMENT

Considerable research is being conducted on advanced waste treatment, or tertiary, methods. One of the objectives of this research is to renovate wastewater for direct and deliberate reuse. Advanced waste treatment is considered to be a two-step process: (1) separating concentrated contaminants from the purified water, and (2) disposing of these contaminants in a way that will render them totally innocuous. The need for advanced waste treatment technology stems largely from the fact that some of the inorganic and organic contaminants now entering receiving waters resist every phase of present day treatment—waste treatment, natural purification in streams and water treatment. There is apprehension over the long range effect that these substances may exert. Some of the processes and principles being studied include: adsorption on activated carbon, elec-

trodialysis, evaporation, freezing, foaming, chemical oxidation, solvent extraction, ion exchange and reverse osmosis.

Approaches under study for the disposal of concentrated impurities include the recovery of usable products from the wastes, dumping of highly concentrated wastes in waste sinks, subsurface disposal through deep-well injection, and converting the refractory contaminants into innocuous material and using them for such purposes as land fill.

SLUDGE DISPOSAL

Practically any waste treatment system will ultimately present the problem of disposal of sludge. This phase of treatment often presents greater problems than are encountered in treating the liquid wastes.

Sludge dewatering schemes have the objective of rendering the sludge suitable for further dewatering or for disposal. Ultimately, the residual sludge product is disposed to the land, to oceans or to the atmosphere. All sludge handling and dewatering procedures are conceived to prepare a product that will be suitable for practical disposal at the point of collection. The form of disposal that is practical at a particular site is dependent upon geographical, political and other considerations.

Various methods have been employed to accomplish sludge disposal. Where adequate ground is available, solar drying of sludge may be accomplished in lagoons or sludge drying beds. Rotary or spray dryers can be applied where space limitations prevent the use of solar drying. Some sludges dewater readily, and this may be accomplished by the above mentioned methods or by vacuum filters or centrifuges. With the recent development of improved dewatering devices, it is now possible to incinerate raw sludge.

Incineration or wet combustion processes dispose of gaseous combustion products to the atmosphere. The ash residue is usually dumped on land or used for fill. Such processes entail high capital outlay, but feature a

Courtesy of Rex Chain Belt Inc.

Figure 41-9 · Sludge flotation clarifier.

minimum of residue to be disposed of to the land. Thickened sludges or partially dewatered sludge cake often have sufficient heat value to support combustion without the addition of auxiliary fuel.

Digestion of sludge has long been recognized as a suitable method of stabilization, if the sludge has the proper characteristics for digestive action. Toxic metals and salts, oils and greases and excessive inert materials interfere with successful digestion. Provided conditions are optimum, digestion produces a readily dewaterable, non-odorous sludge that can be handled without difficulty.

Sludge cake from vacuum filtration or underdrained drying beds is normally suitable for disposal to land by dumping or by burial. In some cases the product is spread on agricultural land. Heat dried sludge product may at times be marketed as a soil conditioner or plant food.

Liquid sludges near coastal areas may be disposed of in the ocean by means of barges or by pumping through long outfall lines. Liquid sludges occasionally have been spread on agricultural land from tank trucks.

PLANT DESIGN

The design of a successfully operating waste treatment plant depends upon the selection of the proper unit processes to accomplish the required degree of treatment and purification of the waste. The degree of purification required is a function of State regulations, which take into account local conditions and requirements. The degree of treatment required is such that the waste discharge will not accomplish degradation of the receiving water nor interfere with its downstream uses. Each waste treatment problem, therefore, re-

Fig. 41-10

**Waste Produced per Employee
of Each Industry
(Domestic Sewage—1.0)**

INDUSTRY	OXYGEN DEMAND	SUSPENDED SOLIDS
Tannery	25.3	12.0
Chemical Manufacturing	22.5	7.4
Organic Waste	2.9	2.4
Mill Pickling	3.6	3.8
Dye Wastes	44.2	5.4
Laundry	22.8	22.2
Distillery	470.0	181.0
Dairy	44.6	5.7
Miscellaneous	13.2	6.8

quires individual attention and study to determine and apply appropriate treatment.

Probable changes in plant processes which would affect the composition of industrial wastes must be taken into account to assure the adequacy of the treatment facilities as installed. Changes in, or additions to, the products manufactured may also affect the industrial wastes. Such manufacturing modifications should be anticipated, if possible, when the treatment plant is designed.

The matter of plant housekeeping is of utmost importance. Vast economies in treatment costs, both for capital and operation, can be realized by the proper practice of adequate industrial housekeeping rules.

In certain cases, a city sewer system can be used as the receiver for industrial waste water. Dependent upon the effect of the industrial waste upon operation of the treatment plant, varying degrees of pretreatment of the waste may be required. In most cases, where wastes are discharged to the city sewers, a charge is assessed for receiving and treating wastes to render them acceptable for ultimate discharge. Many considerations need to be properly evaluated before determining that this will serve as a satisfactory method for waste disposal. The type of waste must be such as to cause no interference, and the city treatment plant must be of proper type and adequate capacity for the added load.

Not every waste contains valuable recoverable by-products; as a matter of fact, most wastes do not contain a sufficient amount of recoverable material to offset the cost of treatment. On the other hand, some industries do waste recoverable products. The economics of waste treatment is not necessarily associated solely with the recovery of reusable or saleable substances. In certain plants, where water is in extremely short supply, treatment of plant waste is economical for salvaging reusable water. In other cases, the cost of the plant water supply is such as to render the recovery of water by treatment of plant wastes attractive. Frequently, a detailed study of plant water uses will reveal that water used in certain operations can be reused in other operations with little or no treatment in the interest of operating economy. Total waste flows requiring treatment may be thereby reduced, resulting in lower treatment cost.

REFERENCES

C. F. Gurnham, "Principles of Industrial Waste Treatment", John Wiley & Sons, Inc. (1955)

R. H. Marks, "Industrial Waste Treatment", *Power,* Vol. 109, pp 185-192 (May, 1965)

R. Neboline and E. J. Donovan, "Treating Methods Available for Industrial Waste Water", *Plant Engineering,* Vol. 20, pp 117-121 (May, 1966)

W. Rudolfs, "Principles of Sewage Treatment", National Lime Association, Fourth Edition (1955)

G. D. Symons, "Industrial Waste Disposal", *Sewage Works Journal,* Vol. XVII (1945)

"Advanced Waste Treatment Research Program", U. S. Public Health Service (1964)

"Water in Industry", National Association of Manufacturers and U. S. Chamber of Commerce (1965)

42

Analytical Methods
and Equipment

I N the conditioning of industrial water, it is necessary that analyses be made to govern the treatment processes. Water treatment without control analyses would be useless and sometimes harmful. For control purposes, a complete analysis of the water usually is not required. For example, in sodium zeolite softening the important determinations are hardness and chloride. The hardness test is employed to determine the end of the softening cycle and the chloride test to determine the end of the rinse cycle. A complete water analysis to control a zeolite softener would be pointless. Similarly, in lime-soda softening the important tests are hardness, phenolphthalein alkalinity and methyl orange alkalinity. These three tests provide proper control of the softener and additional tests are unnecessary under normal circumstances.

When the proper tests have been selected, it is necessary that the analyses be conducted by some responsible person at the plant. The results of the control tests determine the adjustments required in chemical treatment. Treatment methods and practices should be checked by complete analyses at periodic intervals by the supervising laboratory. However, the actual daily control of any treatment process should be in the hands of the plant personnel. The tests must be conducted promptly after sample collection so that any treatment adjustment necessary can be placed into effect without delay. While many processes require more frequent tests and treatment adjustment, the minimum frequency is usually once daily.

RECOMMENDED ANALYTICAL METHODS

In this book, all recommended test methods are those which are the most applicable for control analyses by the plant personnel. The methods have been selected for their simplicity, rapidity and convenience with minimum sacrifice of accuracy. While suitable for use by an experienced chemist, the tests also can be employed by personnel with no formal chemical training.

Methods are given for those tests commonly conducted for the control of various softening processes, internal boiler water treatment and the conditioning of industrial cooling water. Tests made infrequently, or under unusual circumstances, such as sodium, potassium, fluoride, boron, etc. have been omitted. No tests have been included for bacteriological or sanitary purity or for trade wastes.

Referee methods of analysis are contained in such authoritative works as the "Manual on Industrial Water", published by the American Society for Testing Materials and "Standard Methods for the Examination of Water and Wastewater", published jointly by the American Public Health Association, American Water Works Association, and the Water Pollution Control Federation. The referee methods published in these references are intended to be the most precise and accurate known. It is recommended that these publications be consulted where the utmost precision and accuracy are required, such as for research work or where litigation may be involved.

RECOMMENDED ANALYTICAL EQUIPMENT

In titration methods, only common laboratory glassware usually is required. However, in colorimetric work a specific color comparator has been recommended in each case. While color comparisons may be made with the use of Nessler tubes or a photometer, it is more rapid and convenient to use one of the several types of color comparators commercially available. These units are relatively inexpensive and are suitable for most industrial control water analyses.

Therefore, recommendations have been made under the individual analysis for specific commercial analytical equipment when desirable. For example, Taylor color comparators have been recommended for certain tests. These are rugged, practical units that have been found suitable for control work. Other satisfactory units are available from different manufacturers.

COMPOSITION OF REAGENTS

The chemical reagents specified, such as "Sulfuric Acid, Concentrated" under the individual tests should all be reagent grade laboratory chemicals. Where standardized reagents have been specified, the composition of these reagents is shown under the section of this book entitled "Composition of Prepared Reagents". However, standardized reagents should be prepared only in a well-equipped laboratory, under the supervision of an experienced chemist. It is advisable to purchase standardized reagents from a laboratory supply house if complete laboratory facilities are not available for their preparation.

PREPARATION OF SAMPLE

If the results obtained from an analysis are to be of any value, it obviously is necessary to secure a sample that is truly representative of the condition of the water at the point from which the sample was obtained. For example, in sampling from a boiler, the point of sampling should be blown thoroughly before the sample is taken. It is desirable to sample the boiler from the continuous blowdown rather than from the gage column. It is also important to secure the sample with as little flashing of steam as possible, employing a cooling coil for this purpose. In the case of a sample from a tap or valve, the water should be allowed to run for a few minutes before collecting. Sampling points should always be selected so as to secure a representative sample rather than from a "dead spot". The sample should be collected in a clean container, which has been rinsed several times with the water to be sampled.

The sample should be cooled to room temperature (60-80 F) and any suspended matter permitted to settle. Analysis is made on the clear supernatant liquid. Other necessary precautions have been noted under the individual tests.

CARE OF EQUIPMENT

Too much emphasis cannot be placed upon the necessity for keeping the apparatus clean at all times in order to obtain accurate results. Bottles and containers should be cleaned carefully after each using. If dirt or grease accumulate on the glassware, it can be removed by cleaning with a strong solution of chromic acid, made by slowly adding one liter of concentrated sulfuric acid to a 35 ml saturated solution of sodium dichromate.

All measuring apparatus such as pipettes and graduated cylinders should be carefully rinsed before using, preferably with a portion of the water to be tested. Flasks, casseroles and similar vessels in which titrations are made should be rinsed with distilled water, but a portion of the water to be tested may be used if distilled water is not available.

TITRATION METHODS

The most common method of plant control analysis is by titration. This method of testing is based on the use of a burette from which an amount of standard solution is added to the sample until an "endpoint" is reached. The endpoint usually is a color change.

For plant use, automatic burettes should be employed. An automatic burette is constructed so as to start each titration at "zero" reading, thus eliminating any subtraction to determine the amount of standard solution employed.

In using burettes, always employ the same

the bulb to pump air into the bottle until the solution has filled the burette (see Figure 42-1). Release pressure by removing thumb and the excess solution in the burette will return to the reservoir bottle, the solution level in the burette remaining at the "zero" mark. Some types of automatic burettes are equipped with a flexible plastic reservoir bottle instead of an air tube and bulb. This type of burette is filled by squeezing the bottle

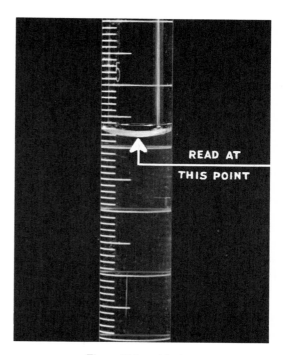

Figure 42-1 • Typical Automatic Burette Design

Figure 42-2 • Meniscus

one for any given standard solution. In the tests decribed, 25 ml automatic burettes have been specified for convenience in handling. Smaller automatic burettes of 15 ml and 10 ml capacity may be used, although usually with less convenience. Always arrange burettes in some standard order to avoid confusion.

If automatic burettes are employed, fill the reservoir with standard solution to be used, first rinsing the reservoir bottle and the burette with a small amount of the solution. Place the thumb on the open glass tube to shut off the air from the reservoir bottle. Use

until the reagent rises above the "zero" mark and then releasing the pressure. In titrating from any burette, be certain that the outlet tip is filled with solution before starting a titration. The reading of the liquid level in either a burette or graduated cylinder should always be made at the bottom of the curved surface, called the "meniscus", as noted in Figure 42-2. This illustration is typical of the appearance of a meniscus in an ordinary burette or graduated cylinder. In most automatic burettes, the center tube slightly affects the curvature of the meniscus.

In using burettes in a plant, they should be protected against breakage and maintained in a position ready for use. Most plants have found the use of a test cabinet containing all of the equipment to be the most satisfactory procedure. However, in protected laboratories, offices, or similar areas, a simple titration stand for holding the burette is satisfactory.

COLORIMETRIC METHODS

Colorimetric tests are particularly useful for plant control because of the simplicity of such methods. These methods are based on the development of a color in the sample which is proportional to the substance to be determined. The concentration present in the sample is determined by comparison with color standards.

The basic method of color comparison is with the use of Nessler tubes. These tubes are available in matched sets made from uniformly drawn tubing. Nessler tubes are used in color comparison work by comparing the color produced by the unknown sample with the color of standard solutions of different concentrations, after treatment with the color-developing reagents. Since standard solutions of known concentration must be prepared for each set of tests, Nessler tubes are not adapted to rapid control analyses.

For color comparison work in control water analyses, it is recommended that one of the several types of commercial color comparators be employed. Color comparators are available in which the color standards are sealed in glass ampoules. Other comparators use colored glass discs as standards. Usually, these instruments carry a nonfading guarantee for the color standards. Units of this type are to be preferred to Nessler tubes for control purposes.

PHOTOMETRIC METHODS

As water treatment problems and the methods for their solution have grown more complex, there has arisen the need for more accurate analytical determinations—not only in laboratory and research analyses — but in

some cases for routine plant control.

One of the most useful tools available to the analyst in this search for more sensitive methods is the filter photometer (sometimes also referred to as photoelectric colorimeter, photoelectric comparator or photoelectric photometer). In general terms, a photometer can distinguish differences in color intensity not apparent to the human eye and can consistently provide a reliable reproducible reading. In addition, a spectrophotometer can measure light absorption in the ultraviolet and infra-red ranges, not visible to the human eye. A flame accessory for the spectrophotometer normally is used in the determination of minute quantities of such elements as sodium, lithium and potassium.

PRINCIPLE OF OPERATION. White light, passing through a solution, is partially absorbed. The unabsorbed portion will produce a sensation of color to the human eye. The strength or depth of this color will vary as the intensity of the unabsorbed light. A photocell can be used to measure the intensity of the unabsorbed light, thus determining the light absorptive capacity of the solution. Consequently, with photometers it is the light absorptive properties of the solution which are measured. The instrument does not measure color, but instead the intensity of light transmitted through the solution.

Photometers operate by responding to the unabsorbed light which is passed through the solution in the absorption cell and which strikes a photocell. The photocell transforms

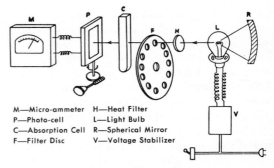

M—Micro-ammeter   H—Heat Filter
P—Photo-cell   L—Light Bulb
C—Absorption Cell   R—Spherical Mirror
F—Filter Disc   V—Voltage Stabilizer

Figure 42-3 • Typical Photometer—
Principle of Operation

Figure 42-4
FILTER DATA

Peak Transmission, millimicrons	Effective Width, millimicrons
415	77
445	54
460	54
490	54
520	57
535	57
550	45
580	44
610	38
640	40

the light into an electric current which is proportional to the intensity of the light. This current is measured by a microammeter, as shown in Figure 42-3 to produce a reading on the dial. For those solutions following Beer's law, the dial reading thus obtained is proportional to the intensity of the color in the solution, which in turn is proportional to the concentration of the ion being measured.

In analytical measurement, it is desirable to measure the light absorptive capacity of the solution at a wave length where there is maximum light absorption by the solution. Instead of passing white light through the solution in the absorption cell, filters are used which absorb all light except that of the desired wave length. By using such a properly selected filter, maximum sensitivity can be obtained. Theoretically, of course, for the most precise work monochromatic light (light of one wave length only) should be employed. Spectrophotometers can produce nearly monochromatic light, but normally are too expensive and fragile for plant control. Filter photometers employ glass filters which pass light in a narrow range of wave length only. Figure 42-4 shows the peak transmission value and effective width at 50% transmission of the ten filters supplied with a typical photometer.

APPLICATION IN WATER ANALYSES. As previously mentioned, the use of photometers is most pertinent where it is desired to secure greater accuracy than is possible with visual color comparators which employ fairly widely spaced standards. For example, if the phosphate content of the boiler water is controlled between 30-60 ppm as PO_4, the use of a conventional color comparator is satisfactory and there is no need for the additional accuracy secured by a photometric method. However, where phosphate may be controlled between 3-6 ppm in some once-through cooling water systems or within narrow limits in some high pressure boiler waters, there is considerable advantage in the use of a photometric method.

Some titration methods for chromate in cooling water systems are subject to interference by various contaminants. The diphenyl-carbohydrazide test is to be preferred because of its freedom from such interference. Comparator methods using fixed standards are unsatisfactory because of the rapid deterioration of the reagent. The photometric method possesses such a high degree of accuracy that, even when high dilutions of the sample are made, no significant error is introduced.

Similarly for those situations where small concentrations of nitrate, copper, iron and sulfate are significant, the use of photometric methods is advisable.

With photometric methods it is important to be aware of the *effect of temperature* on color development. With practically any test there is a definite effect of temperature on color intensity and consequently on the photometer dial reading. To secure reliable results, all samples should be tested at the same temperature used in preparing the calibration curve, namely room temperature. The normal variation in room temperature is not significant in most tests. However, where the utmost accuracy is required, as for example in the silica tests, all standardization and testing should be conducted at exactly the same temperature.

OTHER EQUIPMENT AND METHODS

There are other methods of analyses which are of importance to the water treatment engineer but which are too tedious and complicated to lend themselves to plant control.

Such methods as flame photometry, X-ray diffraction, microscopic and gravimetric analyses can be important in the laboratory. However, there are other special instruments which may be required for plant control for certain tests. The turbidimeter is such an instrument. Where turbidity is an important control, such an instrument is desirable.

Another special instrument, which is important in plant control, is the conductivity meter. This instrument measures electrical conductance which is proportional to dissolved solids. The method of test is particularly important in the control of boiler blowdown and as a check on steam and condensate purity.

Finally, the battery operated or line operated pH meter is sometimes employed where greater accuracy in pH measurements and alkalinity titrations is required.

Figure 42-5 • A Modern Laboratory for Water Analysis

43

Expression of
Analytical Results

I~N~ an analysis of a sample of water, it is necessary to determine the presence of various substances which usually are found in extremely small amounts. It is for this reason that the results of a water analysis usually are expressed in parts per million (ppm) instead of percentage. One part per million equals one ten thousandth of one percent (or 0.0001%). Thus, the expression of results in percentage would require the use of cumbersome figures.

One part per million means one part in a million parts; for example, one ounce in a million ounces of water, or one pound in a million pounds of water. It makes no difference what units are used as long as the relationship between the substance reported and the water is the same. As a further example, one part per million does not equal one pound in a million gallons of water since the units are not similar.

Just as the use of percentage is avoided in favor of parts per million when reporting the results of a water analysis, there are circumstances which may make the use of parts per million somewhat cumbersome. When elements are present in minute or trace quantities, the use of parts per million results in decimal values. It is therefore more convenient to use parts per billion (ppb) in these cases. One part per billion is equal to one thousandth of one part per million (0.001 ppm). For example, in conducting studies of steam purity using a flame spectrophotometer to measure the sodium content, values as low as 0.001 ppm are not uncommon—a result of this type is more conveniently reported as

1.0 ppb.

All methods of water analyses in this book contain the calculations required to obtain results in parts per million (ppm), this being the method accepted by the American Chemical Society, the American Society of Mechanical Engineers, and the American Society for Testing Materials. Test procedures and calculations of results are based on the milliliter (ml) rather than the more common cubic centimeter (cc). The defined distinction between the two terms is so slight that it has no practical significance, but technically the expression milliliter is to be preferred in this work. By definition, a milliliter is the volume occupied by one gram of water at four degrees centigrade in vacuo, whereas a cubic centimeter is the volume enclosed within a cube one centimeter on each side. (1 ml = 1.000028 cc)

EQUIVALENTS PER MILLION

Another unit sometimes employed in ionically reporting water analyses is equivalents per million (epm). This method is closely allied to the use of parts per million and consists in reducing all constituents to a common denominator.

The use of equivalents per million is not recommended for normal plant control. Parts per million is a more simple form of expression of results and is accepted as the common standard basis of reporting a water analysis. However, whenever extensive calculations must be performed the use of equivalents per million greatly simplifies the mathematics since all constituents are on a "chemical equivalent weight" basis. The remainder of this section provides a detailed discussion of parts per million and equivalents per million for those who desire a working knowledge of these means of expression for purposes of calculations.

A part per million (ppm) is a measure of proportion by weight and is equal to a unit weight per million unit weights of solution. Since many different constituents are determined in a water analysis, some of these constituents are reported on a common unit weight basis. For example, calcium is usually expressed in terms of calcium carbonate ($CaCO_3$); in other words, as the unit weight of another substance—calcium carbonate in the example given. When constituents are on the same unit weight basis, they can be directly added or subtracted. For example, ppm total hardness as $CaCO_3$ minus ppm calcium as $CaCO_3$ equals ppm magnesium as $CaCO_3$. In every case, it is necessary to define the unit weight basis of the results such as "ppm alkalinity as $CaCO_3$", "ppm sulfate as SO_4" or "ppm silica as SiO_2". Where the unit weight basis is different, calculations must be based on the use of chemical equations or equivalents per million.

An equivalent per million (epm) is a unit chemical equivalent weight per million unit weights of solution. Concentration in epm is calculated by dividing concentration in ppm by the chemical equivalent weight of the substance or ion. This unit also has been called milliequivalents per liter and milligram equivalents per kilogram.

The following general rules illustrate where epm can be used and where ppm must be used.

(a) The concentration of all dissolved salts may be expressed either in ppm or epm of the individually determined ions.

(b) Two or more ions of similar properties whose joint effect is measured by a single determination may be reported either in ppm or epm. For example, total hardness, acidity, and alkalinity.

(c) The concentration of undissolved or suspended solids should be reported in ppm only.

(d) The concentration of organic matter should be reported in ppm only.

(e) The concentration of dissolved solids (by evaporation) should be expressed as ppm only.

(f) Total dissolved solids by calculation may be expressed both in ppm and epm.

(g) Concentration of individual gases dissolved in water should be reported in ppm. The total concentration of each gas when combined in water may be calculated to its respective ionic concentration in either ppm or epm.

CALCULATION OF DISSOLVED SOLIDS BY EPM

Starting with a reasonably complete water analysis, dissolved solids may be calculated by means of epm. In a complete water analysis, the negative epm will equal the positive epm. Where there is an excess of negative epm, the remaining positive epm usually is assumed to be sodium or potassium or both, and for the sake of convenience generally is considered to be sodium. Where there is an excess of positive epm, the remaining negative epm usually is assumed to be nitrate provided the analysis is rather complete.

To calculate dissolved solids, convert the various constituents from ppm to epm and total the various cations (plus) and anions (minus). The cations should equal the anions. If not, add either sodium (plus) or nitrate (minus) to balance both columns. Convert to ppm as the individual ionic weights and then total to obtain ppm dissolved solids.

In the example shown in Figure 43-1, to convert 150 ppm calcium as $CaCO_3$ to epm, divide by 50 (the equivalent weight of calcium carbonate) and obtain 3.0 epm. To convert 96 ppm sulfate as SO_4 to epm, divide by 48 (the equivalent weight of sulfate) and obtain 2.0 epm. After balancing the cations and anions by the addition of sodium, convert to ionic ppm by multiplying the epm by the particular ionic equivalent weight. For example, to convert 3.0 epm calcium to ppm calcium as Ca, multiply by 20 (the equivalent weight of calcium) and obtain 60 ppm calcium as Ca. To obtain the ppm dissolved solids, total the individual ions.

Figure 43-1

		epm (+) cations	(−) anions	Ionic ppm
		ppm		
Calcium	as $CaCO_3$	150 = 3.0	=	60 as Ca
Magnesium	as $CaCO_3$	50 = 1.0	=	12 as Mg
Sulfate	as SO_4	96 =	2.0 =	96 as SO_4
Chloride	as Cl	18 =	0.5 =	18 as Cl
Bicarbonate	as $CaCO_3$	120 =	2.4 =	146 as HCO_3
Sodium	as Na (difference)	0.9	=	21 as Na
Total Dissolved Solids			353	
		4.9	4.9	

Figure 43-2 — Conversion Table

	Formula	Equivalent Weight		Formula	Equivalent Weight
POSITIVE IONS			Calcium Chloride	$CaCl_2$	55.5
Aluminum	Al^{+++}	9.0	Calcium Hydroxide	$Ca(OH)_2$	37.1
Ammonium	NH_4^+	18.0	Calcium Oxide	CaO	28.0
Calcium	Ca^{++}	20.0	Calcium Sulfate (anhydrous)	$CaSO_4$	68.1
Copper	Cu^{++}	31.8	Calcium Sulfate (gypsum)	$CaSO_4.2H_2O$	86.1
Hydrogen	H^+	1.0	Calcium Phosphate	$Ca_3(PO_4)_2$	51.7
Ferrous Iron	Fe^{++}	27.9	Carbon Dioxide	CO_2	22.0
Ferric Iron	Fe^{+++}	18.6	Chlorine	Cl_2	35.5
Magnesium	Mg^{++}	12.2	Ferrous Sulfate (anhydrous)	$FeSO_4$	76.0
Manganese	Mn^{++}	27.5	Ferric Sulfate	$Fe_2(SO_4)_3$	66.7
Potassium	K^+	39.1	Magnesium Oxide	MgO	20.2
Sodium	Na^+	23.0	Magnesium Bicarbonate	$Mg(HCO_3)_2$	73.2
			Magnesium Carbonate	$MgCO_3$	42.2
NEGATIVE IONS			Magnesium Chloride	$MgCl_2$	47.6
Bicarbonate	HCO_3^-	61.0	Magnesium Hydroxide	$Mg(OH)_2$	29.2
Carbonate	CO_3^{--}	30.0	Magnesium Phosphate	$Mg_3(PO_4)_2$	43.8
Chloride	Cl^-	35.5	Magnesium Sulfate (anhydrous)	$MgSO_4$	60.2
Fluoride	F^-	19.0	Magnesium Sulfate		
Iodide	I^-	126.9	(Epsom Salts)	$MgSO_4.7H_2O$	123.3
Hydroxide	OH^-	17.0	Manganese Hydroxide	$Mn(OH)_2$	44.4
Nitrate	NO_3^-	62.0	Silica	SiO_2	30.0
Phosphate (tribasic)	PO_4^{---}	31.7	Sodium Bicarbonate	$NaHCO_3$	84.0
Phosphate (dibasic)	HPO_4^{--}	48.0	Sodium Carbonate	Na_2CO_3	53.0
Phosphate (monobasic)	$H_2PO_4^-$	97.0	Sodium Chloride	NaCl	58.5
Sulfate	SO_4^{--}	48.0	Sodium Hydroxide	NaOH	40.0
Bisulfate	HSO_4^-	97.1	Sodium Nitrate	$NaNO_3$	85.0
Sulfite	SO_3^-	40.0	Trisodium Phosphate	$Na_3PO_4.12H_2O$	126.7
Bisulfite	HSO_3^-	81.1	Trisodium Phosphate		
Sulfide	S^{--}	16.0	(anhydrous)	Na_3PO_4	54.7
			Disodium Phosphate	$Na_2HPO_4.12H_2O$	119.4
COMPOUNDS			Disodium Phosphate		
Alum	$Al_2(SO_4)_3.18H_2O$	111.0	(anhydrous)	Na_2HPO_4	47.3
Aluminum Sulfate (anhydrous)	$Al_2(SO_4)_3$	57.0	Monosodium Phosphate	$NaH_2PO_4.H_2O$	46.0
Aluminum Hydroxide	$Al(OH)_3$	26.0	Monosodium Phosphate		
Aluminum Oxide	Al_2O_3	17.0	(anhydrous)	NaH_2PO_4	40.0
Ammonia	NH_3	17.0	Sulfuric Acid	H_2SO_4	49.0
Sodium Aluminate	$Na_2Al_2O_4$	27.3	Sodium Metaphosphate	$NaPO_3$	34.0
Calcium Bicarbonate	$Ca(HCO_3)_2$	81.1	Sodium Sulfate	Na_2SO_4	71.0
Calcium Carbonate	$CaCO_3$	50.0	Sodium Sulfite	Na_2SO_3	63.0

44

Acid (Free Mineral)

IT is unusual to encounter a raw water devoid of alkalinity and containing free mineral acid. On some streams subject to acid mine drainage or pickling acid contamination, free mineral acid will be found. Free mineral acidity is due to the presence of acids such as sulfuric, nitric and hydrochloric and does not include carbonic acid formed by the combination of carbon dioxide and water. Naturally, free mineral acid renders a water quite corrosive. Elimination of the corrosive effect of this acidity is secured by neutralization with an alkaline agent, usually lime, caustic soda or soda ash.

Leaks in heating coils in pickling tanks may result in the contamination of boiler feedwater systems with acidic condensate. Where the possibility of such contamination exists, alarm systems should be installed on the returned condensate.

The effluent from a hydrogen zeolite exchange unit will contain free mineral acid in proportion to the anions present in the raw water. This acidity is neutralized by blending either with a sodium zeolite effluent or with raw water. Alkalies, such as caustic soda, may also be used for neutralization. Determination of the free mineral acid content of the hydrogen zeolite effluent serves to control the operating run of these units as well as to indicate when regeneration is required.

FREE MINERAL ACID

THEORY OF TEST. This test is based on the determination of the acidity of a sample by titration with a standard sodium carbonate solution. In this measurement the point of color change of methyl orange indicator (approximately pH 4.3) is taken as the endpoint, representing a definite point to which the acidity of the sample has been reduced by the addition of the standard sodium carbonate solution.

APPARATUS REQUIRED.
1—Burette, automatic, 25 ml
1—Casserole, porcelain, 210 ml
1—Cylinder, graduated, 50 ml
1—Stirring rod, glass

CHEMICALS REQUIRED.
Sodium Carbonate, N/50
Methyl Orange Indicator

PROCEDURE FOR TEST. Measure a clear 50 ml sample of water in the graduated cylinder and transfer to the casserole. Add 4 drops of methyl orange indicator. Titrate from the burette with standard N/50 sodium carbonate until the color changes from pink to yellow. Record the ml of sodium carbonate required.

CALCULATION OF RESULTS.
Formula:

ppm free mineral acid as $CaCO_3$ =

$$\text{ml N/50 sodium carbonate} \times \frac{1000}{\text{ml sample}}$$

Using a 50 ml sample, the free mineral acidity in parts per million as $CaCO_3$ is equal to the ml of N/50 sodium carbonate required multiplied by 20.

LIMITATIONS OF TEST. The procedure outlined is satisfactory for control purposes. Heavy metals can interfere. For most accurate results it is advisable to eliminate the color indicator (methyl orange) and to titrate to a definite pH value using electrometric pH measurement.

45

Alkalinity

THE alkalinity determined by titration with a standard acid may be present due to a large number of different substances. The phenolphthalein and methyl orange alkalinity determinations do not provide a direct measure of any one specific ion present in the water such as is the case with the sulfate and chloride tests. Usually several ions present contribute to the alkalinity. For the sake of simplicity, it is usual to consider alkalinity as due to the presence of bicarbonate, carbonate and hydrate ions although other ions such as phosphate and silicate may partially contribute to the alkalinity.

The points of change in color of phenolphthalein and methyl orange indicators (approximately pH 8.3 and pH 4.3) simply provide standard reference points which can be employed universally to conveniently express the acid neutralizing power of a water.

In natural surface waters, phenolphthalein alkalinity usually is absent and the methyl orange alkalinity is relatively low. Well waters usually contain a higher methyl orange alkalinity than surface waters, but again phenolphthalein alkalinity ordinarily is absent. The alkalinity of a natural water normally consists of calcium and magnesium bicarbonate although, on occasion, some sodium bicarbonate may be present. The origin of the calcium and magnesium bicarbonates lies in the solvent action of carbon dioxide present in rain or surface water reacting with the minerals present in the earth such as calcite and dolomite to form calcium and magnesium bicarbonates.

Carbonate and particularly hydrate ions are rarely encountered in untreated waters although they may be introduced where water is softened by lime or by lime and soda ash.

For drinking purposes the U. S. Public Health Service Drinking Water Standards limit the alkalinity for chemically treated waters only, and in accordance with a scale based on both the total alkalinity and the pH value of the treated water.

Alkalinity may be an undesirable constituent of a water supply used in industrial process work. High methyl orange alkalinity may influence the flavor of carbonated beverages and is to be avoided in this industry. Also, in ice manufacture, waters containing a high methyl orange alkalinity from the presence of calcium and magnesium bicarbonate are undesirable since cloudiness is imparted to the ice and deposits and scum may also be formed.

In boiler feedwater conditioning, the presence of a high methyl orange alkalinity in the boiler feedwater is to be avoided for several reasons, one of which is the resultant carbon dioxide content of the steam. Under the influence of heat in the boiler, bicarbonate will break down producing carbonate and liberating free carbon dioxide with the steam. The carbonate formed undergoes further decomposition, producing hydroxide and liberating additional carbon dioxide with the steam. Carbon dioxide usually is responsible for the corrosion of the steam and return lines. Since the quantity of carbon dioxide evolved with the steam is directly proportional to the feedwater alkalinity, it is desirable from this standpoint to obtain feedwater of as low an alkalinity as possible.

The alkalinity of a boiler water should be sufficiently high to protect the boiler metal against acidic corrosion, but should also be sufficiently low so as not to produce a carryover condition. While subject to variation dependent on individual plant requirements, for relatively low pressure boiler operation a minimum alkalinity of 300 ppm ordinarily is specified. An upper limit for boiler water alkalinity, in order to avoid entrainment of boiler water solids with the steam, is not so easily specified since many factors besides alkalinity are involved. In order to establish the maximum safe alkalinity limits, it is necessary that condensed steam samples be analyzed frequently for purity as boiler water alkalinity concentrations are gradually increased. When contamination of the steam becomes evident from analysis, the maximum permissible boiler water alkalinity has been established. With the development of modern anti-foam agents, it now is possible to tolerate quite high boiler water alkalinities without carryover.

For control purposes a range of boiler water alkalinity is specified which will prevent both acidic corrosion and carryover of solids with the steam and which also will provide the proper environment in the boiler water for the precipitation of the scale forming salts. For example, with phosphate treatment certain minimum alkalinity concentrations must be present in the boiler to insure precipitation of calcium as tricalcium phosphate. If insufficient alkalinity is present, a soluble form of calcium phosphate is produced which will permit the simultaneous presence of both soluble hardness and soluble phosphate. Under such conditions, the proper protection against scale will not be achieved.

High boiler water alkalinities also are undesirable from the standpoint of intercrystalline cracking (caustic metal embrittlement). It has been established that the presence of high hydroxyl ion concentrations is the primary cause of intercrystalline cracking. Even where inhibitors are employed to overcome the embrittling characteristics of a boiler water, it is desirable that excessive alkalinities be avoided since such inhibitors are fed in proportion to the alkalinity content of the boiler water. If boiler water alkalinity is high, a greater quantity of the inhibitor must be fed and both the solids content of the

boiler water and the cost of feedwater conditioning are increased.

In circulating cooling water systems, alkalinity is of major importance since the total alkalinity of a water is one of the factors that must be considered in predicting the tendency for a water to precipitate calcium carbonate scale. The calculation of the Saturation Index by Langelier's Equation requires the use of total alkalinity as one of the factors. With all others factors equal, the higher the alkalinity the greater will be the tendency for the precipitation of calcium carbonate scale. Where acid treatment of the circulating water is employed, alkalinity is an important control test for governing the rate of acid feed.

The lime-soda softening process can effect reduction in the methyl orange alkalinity of a water although in the softening process an increase in the phenolphthalein alkalinity will result. This reduction in total alkalinity by the lime-soda process is a definite advantage not possessed by sodium zeolite softening which neither increases nor decreases the alkalinity of the water being softened. The use of hydrogen zeolite softening completely removes all alkalinity from the water, this property being one of the outstanding features of this process. By the use of a hydrogen zeolite in parallel with the sodium zeolite, the disadvantage of the sodium zeolite can be overcome and the alkalinity of the mixed effluent reduced to any desired value. Dealkalization by chloride-anion exchange is another method of reducing alkalinity.

ALKALINITY, DIRECT TITRATION METHOD

THEORY OF TEST. This test is based on the determination of the alkaline content of a sample by titration with a standard acid solution. In this measurement, the endpoints are taken as points of change in the color of organic indicators; phenolphthalein (approximately pH 8.3) and methyl orange (approximately pH 4.3) represent definite points to which the alkalinity of the sample has been reduced by the addition of the standard acid solution.

APPARATUS REQUIRED.
1—Burette, automatic, 25 ml
1—Casserole, porcelain, 210 ml
1—Cylinder, graduated, 50 ml
1—Stirring rod, glass

CHEMICALS REQUIRED.
Sulfuric Acid, N/50
Phenolphthalein Indicator
Methyl Orange Indicator
Methyl Purple Indicator

PROCEDURE FOR TEST. Measure a clear 50 ml sample of water in the graduate and transfer to the casserole. Add 4 to 5 drops of phenolphthalein indicator. If the sample is an alkaline water, such as usually is the case with boiler water, it will turn red. If the sample is a raw or natural water, it usually will remain colorless. Add the standard N/50 sulfuric acid from the burette drop by drop to the sample in the casserole, stirring constantly until the point is reached where one drop removes the last trace of red color and the sample becomes colorless. Stop and record the total number of ml to this point as the P reading.

Add 4 drops of methyl orange indicator (if no red color develops on the addition of the phenolphthalein indicator to the original sample, the titration may be started with the methyl orange indicator at this point). Continue adding the acid drop by drop until one drop changes the color from a yellow to a salmon-pink. Record the final burette reading as the M reading. This is a more difficult endpoint and some practice may be required. The general tendency is to add too much acid. If too much acid is added, the sample will change from a salmon-pink to a definite red. Record the titration to the P point and the total titration to the M point as the P and M readings respectively. (Note that the M reading will always be greater than the P reading inasmuch as the P reading is included in the M reading.)

If the water sample does not settle clear, the M reading can be determined on a filtered sample. The P reading, however, always should be determined on an unfiltered sample.

If the water sample is colored, such as one containing chromate, methyl purple indicator may be substituted for methyl orange indicator to provide a more definite endpoint. The color change with methyl purple is from green to gray to purple. The endpoint is taken as the first change to a definite purple. This sample cannot be used for the chloride test. A second sample must be used for chloride and neutralized to the P reading as described under Chloride, Mohr Method

CALCULATION OF RESULTS.
Formula:

$$\text{ppm alkalinity as } CaCO_3 =$$
$$\text{ml } N/50 \text{ sulfuric acid} \times \frac{1000}{\text{ml sample}}$$

Using a 50 ml sample, the phenolphthalein alkalinity in parts per million as $CaCO_3$ is equal to the ml of N/50 sulfuric acid required for the P reading multiplied by 20. The methyl orange alkalinity is equal to the ml of N/50 sulfuric acid required for the M reading multiplied by 20.

LIMITATIONS OF TEST. It is preferable to express the results of the alkalinity determination in terms of P and M alkalinity as above. However, results are sometimes calculated in terms of bicarbonate, carbonate and hydrate on the assumption that titration to the P endpoint is equivalent to all the hydrate and one-half the carbonate alkalinity, and that the titration to M is equivalent to the total alkalinity. Many factors such as the presence of phosphate, silica, organic and other buffers affect this titration and the calculation of the form of alkalinity present may be in error. Under normal circumstances in plant control, expression of results as P and M alkalinity is entirely satisfactory and is to be preferred from the standpoint of simplicity.

If an electrometric pH machine is available, the titration may be made without indicators to pH 8.3 and pH 4.3. Particularly where the color of the water sample obscures the indicator endpoint, the electrometric titration method provides greater accuracy. While most authorities on water analyses agree that phenolphthalein changes color at almost exactly pH 8.3, a range is indicated for methyl orange of pH 3.9 to 4.6. The procedure for alkalinity as outlined above presumes the color change of methyl orange to be at pH 4.3 so that a consistent reference point is provided for control purposes.

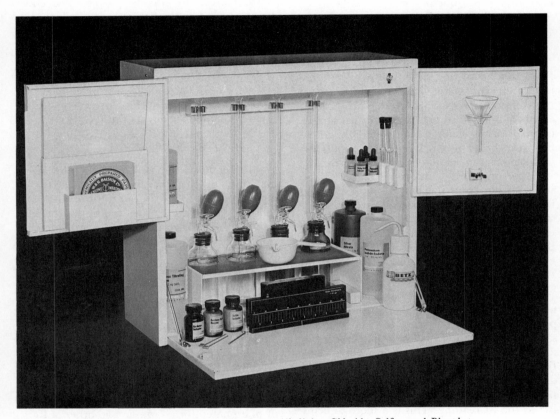

Figure 45–1 • Test Set for Hardness, Alkalinity, Chloride, Sulfite, and Phosphate

46

Alkalinity (Hydrate)

YDRATE alkalinity is that portion of the total alkalinity due to the presence of hydroxyl ions. Hydrate alkalinity is not found in natural waters unless highly contaminated by alkaline trade wastes. The hydrate ion may be introduced to treated waters by the lime-soda softening process or by the introduction of alkaline treatment chemicals such as caustic soda or lime. Even where lime or caustic soda may be added to a water to increase its pH value and overcome its possible corrosive character, it is rare that sufficient treatment is added to produce a definite hydrate alkalinity.

Under ordinary circumstances the control of alkalinity on the basis of phenolphthalein and methyl orange tests is sufficient for control purposes. Direct determination of the hydrate alkalinity is of importance in relatively few instances. However, where interfering substances are present which affect the methyl orange test, a direct determination of the hydrate ion may be of considerable value in controlling lime-soda softening. A definite hydrate alkalinity usually is desired on a lime-soda softener effluent for most efficient hardness removal. While this usually can be accomplished by control of phenolphthalein and methyl orange alkalinity, where organic contamination is present direct measurement of the hydrate alkalinity is to be preferred for best control.

It occasionally is desirable to determine the hydrate alkalinity of a boiler water by direct measurement. This is particularly true in high pressure operation where hydrate alkalinity concentrations may contribute to corrosion and hydrogen evolution or where coordinated pH-phosphate control for embrittlement is maintained.

HYDRATE ALKALINITY, BARIUM CHLORIDE METHOD

THEORY OF TEST. This test is based on the determination of the hydrate alkalinity of a sample by titration with a standard acid solution. Barium chloride is added to remove the carbonate ion from solution thereby permitting direct titration of the hydrate alkalinity. In this measurement, the endpoint is taken as the point of change of color of phenolphthalein indicator (approximately pH 8.3) representing a definite point to which the alkalinity of the sample has been reduced by the addition of a standard acid solution.

APPARATUS REQUIRED.
   1—Burette, automatic, 25 ml
   1—Casserole, porcelain, 210 ml
   1—Cylinder, graduated, 50 ml
   1—Stirring rod, glass
   1—Pipette, delivery, 5 ml

CHEMICALS REQUIRED.
   Hydrochloric Acid, N/50
   Barium Chloride, 10%
   Phenolphthalein Indicator

PROCEDURE FOR TEST. Measure 50 ml of the sample in the graduated cylinder and transfer to the casserole. By means of the pipette add 5 ml barium chloride solution and stir vigorously. Add 4 to 5 drops phenolphthalein indicator and stir. If the sample does not turn red, hydrate alkalinity is not present, the test is discontinued at this point and the hydrate alkalinity is recorded as "zero". If the sample turns red, add N/50 hydrochloric acid continuously from the burette, drop by drop with constant stirring, until one final drop changes the color from red to colorless.

Disregard any reappearance of the red color. Record the ml of N/50 hydrochloric acid required.

CALCULATION OF RESULTS.
Formula:

ppm hydrate alkalinity as CaCO₃ =

$$\text{ml N/50 hydrochloric acid} \times \frac{1000}{\text{ml sample}}$$

Using a 50 ml sample the hydrate alkalinity in parts per million as CaCO₃ is equal to the ml of N/50 hydrochloric acid required multiplied by 20.

LIMITATIONS OF TEST. This method for hydrate alkalinity is considered accurate only to within 10%. High silica, organic matter and aluminates can interfere with the determination. Should the sulfate content of the sample be high, the turbidity produced will tend to mask the endpoint. This method, however, affords a rapid means for checking hydrate alkalinity for routine control and can be of value in the control of lime-soda softening.

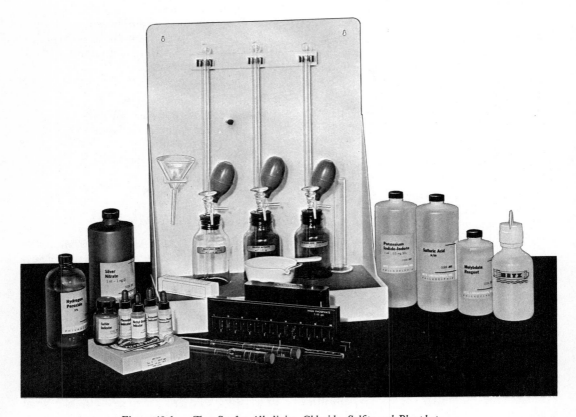

Figure 46-1 • Test Set for Alkalinity, Chloride, Sulfite and Phosphate

47

Ammonia

NITROGEN may be reported in a water analysis in four different forms. These are albumenoid ammonia, free ammonia, nitrite and nitrate.

Free ammonia is determined more frequently than albumenoid ammonia. This latter determination is of significance primarily in the sanitary analysis of water. Direct Nesslerization of steam condensate will determine the free ammonia content.

The presence of free ammonia in the steam condensate is caused by the breakdown of organic nitrogenous compounds under boiler conditions. These compounds enter the boiler system as organic impurities contaminating the makeup water.

Ammonia nitrogen is of importance in connection with the determination of the specific conductance of steam condensate. Ammonia possesses a high specific conductance and where this gas is present in steam condensate, conductance measurements must be corrected for the conductance due to ammonia. Otherwise, erroneously high solids content of the steam would be indicated. Where effective degassing equipment is employed for the removal of ammonia and carbon dioxide prior to the measurement of steam purity, ammonia may be reduced to such a low value in the test sample as to require no correction for its conductance effect.

The determination of ammonia may also be of significance where corrosion of copper or copper bearing alloys is taking place. Ammonia will attack copper, placing it in solution as the copper ammonium ion. Removal of ammonia from a boiler feedwater system may be accomplished by the use of breakpoint chlorination or cation exchange by hydrogen zeolite.

AMMONIA NITROGEN, DIRECT NESSLERIZATION METHOD

THEORY OF TEST. This test is based on the development of a color varying from yellow through amber to red on the addition of Nessler Reagent to water containing the ammonium ion. The color developed is compared with a color standard slide and the ammonia content expressed as N in parts per million is read directly from the slide.

APPARATUS REQUIRED.

1—Taylor Water Analyzer complete (nitrogen slide range 0.0-1.0 ppm)
1—Cylinder, graduated, 50 ml
1—Pipette, Mohr, 1 ml
1—Flask, Erlenmeyer, 250 ml

CHEMICALS REQUIRED.

Nessler Reagent

PROCEDURE FOR TEST. The sample should be freshly obtained with as little contact with air as possible. Measure carefully 50 ml of the sample with the graduate and add to the flask. Add 1 ml of Nessler Reagent. Allow the sample to stand for 10 minutes. Fill one of the comparator tubes to the mark with prepared sample and place it in the middle compartment of the Analyzer. Fill the other two tubes to the mark with the original untreated sample and place them in the outer compartments of the Analyzer.

Place the instrument so that the comparator tubes point toward a source of daylight. Read the instrument by viewing the reflection in the mirror and *not by looking down through the tubes*. Move the slide in front of the test samples until a color match is obtained.

If the ammonia content of the sample exceeds the range of the slide, discard test, take a smaller sample such as 25 ml or 10 ml, dilute to 50 ml with ammonia free distilled water, repeat the test and multiply the reading by the appropriate factor.

CALCULATION OF RESULTS. Using a 50 ml sample, ammonia as N is read directly from the color standard slide in parts per million.

LIMITATIONS OF TEST. The direct Nesslerization of the ammonium ion is applicable to waters of low mineral content such as condensed steam and condensate samples. Results are affected by calcium, magnesium, iron, turbidity and sulfides. Special treatment can be employed for the removal of these interfering substances.

Where the ammonia content is low and greater accuracy is desired than can be obtained from the permanent slide standards, it is necessary to prepare standards for the desired range using standard ammonium chloride in distilled water, employing a Nessler rack and tubes. For most accurate results in the determination of the ammonia the distillation method, which is a laboratory procedure, should be employed.

Figure 47-1 • Taylor Water Analyzer

48

Calcium

THE determination of calcium in a water analysis is closely allied to the determination of hardness, since hardness is caused primarily by the presence of calcium and magnesium.

Under certain circumstances determination of calcium is made so as to subdivide the total hardness into calcium hardness and magnesium hardness. The total hardness minus the calcium hardness equals the magnesium hardness.

The determination of calcium usually is not made as a control test. However, this determination is necessary for making chemical calculations for treatment chemicals. When employing internal boiler water treatment of the phosphate type, the calcium hardness is precipitated by the phosphate whereas the magnesium hardness is precipitated primarily as magnesium hydroxide either by the natural alkalinity of the boiler water or by the use of alkaline materials such as caustic soda or soda ash. This same principle applies to the hot phosphate softener. Therefore, in calculating the quantity of materials required, it is necessary that the hardness be subdivided into calcium hardness and magnesium hardness.

In lime-soda softening, it is necessary to know the calcium hardness in order to calculate the initial quantities of lime and soda ash required. However, once the softener is in operation changes in chemical treatment are usually controlled by analyzing the effluent for total hardness, phenolphthalein and methyl orange alkalinity.

In the treatment of cooling water the determination of calcium as a control test plays a more important part. An important basis for all cooling water treatment is Langelier's Saturation Index which predicts the tendency of a water to form calcium carbonate scale—the scale most easily formed in cooling water systems. In employing the Langelier Index, the determination of calcium is required. On this basis, a plant control can be established.

Most softening processes are primarily concerned with the removal of total hardness (calcium and magnesium hardness). However, under some circumstances the calcium hardness only is removed. The magnesium hardness is allowed to remain in solution. Calcium softening is most applicable where the water is to be employed in heat exchange units. Since calcium hardness is the prime offender in such cases, it may not be necessary to remove the magnesium hardness from the water and a savings in treatment chemicals is obtained by this partial softening for the removal of calcium hardness only.

CALCIUM, TITRATION METHOD

THEORY OF TEST. This test is based on the determination of the calcium content of a sample by titration with a sequestering agent in the presence of an organic dye sensitive to calcium ions and insensitive to magnesium ions under the conditions of test. The endpoint occurs when all the calcium ions are sequestered and the endpoint is a color change from salmon-pink to orchid-purple.

APPARATUS REQUIRED.

1—Burette, automatic, 25 ml
1—Casserole, porcelain, 210 ml
1—Cylinder, graduated, 50 ml
1—Stirring rod, glass
1—Pipette, safety bulb, 2 ml
1—Measuring cup, brass

CHEMICALS REQUIRED.

Calcium Indicator

Hardness Titrating Solution, 1 ml = 1 mg CaCO$_3$

Sodium Hydroxide, 1.0 N

PROCEDURE FOR TEST. Measure 50 ml of sample and transfer to casserole. Add 2 ml of 1.0 N sodium hydroxide to sample and stir. With measuring cup provided, add one level measure (approx. 0.2 g) of calcium indicator and stir. If calcium is present, the sample will turn salmon-pink. Add the hardness titrating solution (same titrating solution as used in hardness test) from the burette with continued stirring. When approaching the endpoint, the sample begins to show a purple tinge. The endpoint is a final change to orchid-purple. Once the endpoint is reached, further addition of hardness titrating solution will not produce any further color change. Always check endpoint by adding one additional drop of hardness titrating solution and observe whether any

further color change occurs.

CALCULATION OF RESULTS.

Formula:

$$\text{ppm calcium as } CaCO_3 = \text{ml titrating solution} \times \frac{1000}{\text{ml sample}}$$

Using a 50 ml sample, the calcium in parts per million as CaCO$_3$ is equal to the ml of titrating solution employed multiplied by 20.

The magnesium hardness can be determined by subtracting the calcium hardness from total hardness.

LIMITATIONS OF TEST. This method is substantially free from ionic interference in the concentrations normally encountered in industrial water conditioning. Orthophosphate above 5 ppm will precipitate calcium at the pH of the test. By dilution of the sample, ionic interference can be minimized. Because of the accuracy possible with both the hardness and calcium methods, a reliable magnesium value can be secured by difference.

49

Carbon Dioxide

FREE carbon dioxide is the term used to designate carbon dioxide gas dissolved in water. The designation "free" carbon dioxide is used to differentiate a solution of carbon dioxide gas from combined carbon dioxide present in the form of bicarbonate and carbonate ions.

Free carbon dioxide in water is caused by the decay of organic matter, solution of carbon dioxide from underground sources and solution from the atmosphere. Since the carbon dioxide content of the normal atmosphere is quite low (less than 0.04%), this is not a source of appreciable carbon dioxide except where flue gases containing a high percentage of carbon dioxide are brought in relatively close contact with the water.

Well waters usually contain an appreciable quantity of free carbon dioxide while surface waters normally are relatively low in free carbon dioxide.

Corrosion is the principal difficulty caused by carbon dioxide. This gas will ionize on solution in water producing carbonic acid. Because of the low pH value and corrosive character contributed to a water by carbon dioxide, this gas is undesirable. Where oxygen also is present, the low pH value due to carbon dioxide enhances the corrosive effect of the oxygen.

Severe corrosion of heat exchangers, piping, valves, etc., can result where appreciable quantities of free carbon dioxide are present and have given the water a corrosive character.

In boiler systems, it is desirable to reduce the free carbon dioxide content of the boiler feedwater as low as possible. This usually is accomplished by the normal deaerating ac-

tion of a feedwater heater unless the free carbon dioxide content of the heater influent is abnormally high. In these cases, such as result from combined sodium-hydrogen zeolite softening, the use of a degasifier is required to reduce the carbon dioxide content of the heater influent to a range suitable to the conventional type feedwater heater.

Corrosion from carbon dioxide in boiler systems is most frequently encountered in steam and return lines. Even though a boiler feedwater contains no free carbon dioxide, appreciable concentrations of this corrosive gas may be present in the steam from the boiler. The source of this carbon dioxide is the bicarbonate and carbonate content of the boiler feedwater. Under the influence of heat in the boiler, the bicarbonates and the carbonates are decomposed, liberating free carbon dioxide with the steam. Sodium hydroxide (caustic soda) is a by-product of this reaction. Normally, the carbon dioxide evolved from the decomposition of the bicarbonate and carbonate of the boiler feedwater is the major source of the carbon dioxide present in the steam, since the free carbon dioxide of the boiler feedwater is usually reduced to a minor value by feedwater deaeration.

Severe corrosion of steam and return lines caused by the carbon dioxide of the steam is to be expected where sodium zeolite softening is used with a raw water of high methyl orange alkalinity. For approximation, the carbon dioxide content of the steam with zeolite softening can be calculated by multiplying the feedwater methyl orange alkalinity by a factor of 0.79 which takes into account 80% sodium carbonate decomposition. For example, if a zeolite softened boiler feedwater possesses a methyl orange alkalinity of

100 ppm as calcium carbonate, a carbon dioxide content of the steam of 79 ppm can be expected. This high carbon dioxide content of the steam would create an extremely corrosive condition particularly in units where accumulation of carbon dioxide can take place, such as unit heaters, jacketed kettles, etc.

Aeration is the most common method employed for the removal of large quantities of free carbon dioxide. Neutralization of the acidic nature of this gas can be accomplished by the feeding of alkaline chemicals such as lime, soda ash and caustic soda. Lime-soda softening effects removal of free carbon dioxide. Free carbon dioxide may be removed from a boiler feedwater by deaeration since the solubility of this gas in water decreases with increased temperature. The filming amines and the neutralizing amines are employed in controlling the problem of corrosion in steam and condensate lines.

FREE CARBON DIOXIDE, DIRECT TITRATION METHOD

THEORY OF TEST. This test is based on the titration of a sample with standard sodium carbonate solution in the presence of phenolphthalein indicator. The carbon dioxide reacts with the sodium carbonate to form sodium bicarbonate, which is colorless to phenolphthalein. As soon as an excess of sodium carbonate is present, a light red color develops and this is taken as the endpoint.

APPARATUS REQUIRED.
1—Burette, automatic, 25 ml
1—Cylinder, graduated, 100 ml
1—Tubing, sulfur free rubber, 10 feet
1—Stirring rod, glass

CHEMICALS REQUIRED.
Sodium Carbonate, N/22
Phenolphthalein Indicator

PROCEDURE FOR TEST. Reliable results in the determination of free carbon dioxide can be secured only on a freshly obtained sample, secured under careful sampling conditions.

Obtain the sample through gum rubber tubing discharging at the bottom of the 100 ml cylinder. Allow the sample to overflow for a few minutes and withdraw tubing while sample is flowing. Flick cylinder to throw off excess sample above the 100 ml mark.

Add 5-10 drops phenolphthalein indicator. If the sample turns red, no free carbon dioxide is present. If the sample remains colorless, titrate rapidly into the cylinder with N/22 sodium carbonate, stirring gently with the stirring rod until a definite pink color develops throughout the sample, permanent for 30 seconds. This color change is the endpoint.

Where the free carbon dioxide of the water sample is high, there may be some loss of carbon dioxide to the atmosphere even with this titration technique. To check this point it is advisable to secure a second sample as before and, after reducing sample to the 100 ml mark, to immediately run in the full amount of N/22 sodium carbonate used in the first titration. Add 5-10 drops of phenolphthalein indicator and if the sample remains colorless, add additional N/22 sodium carbonate to the endpoint, accepting this second test as the more accurate titration.

CALCULATION OF RESULTS.
Formula:

$$\text{ppm free carbon dioxide as } CO_2 = \text{ml N/22 sodium carbonate} \times \frac{1000}{\text{ml sample}}$$

Using a 100 ml sample the free carbon dioxide in parts per million as CO_2 is equal to the ml of N/22 sodium carbonate required multiplied by 10.

LIMITATIONS OF TEST. Free mineral acid, if present, will be measured in this test. Heavy metals such as iron, chromium and aluminum salts interfere. During titration some loss of free carbon dioxide may take place.

Diagrams and nomographs have been proposed for the calculation of the carbon dioxide, bicarbonate, normal carbonate and hydroxide content of natural and treated waters. Knowing the pH, total alkalinity, tempera-

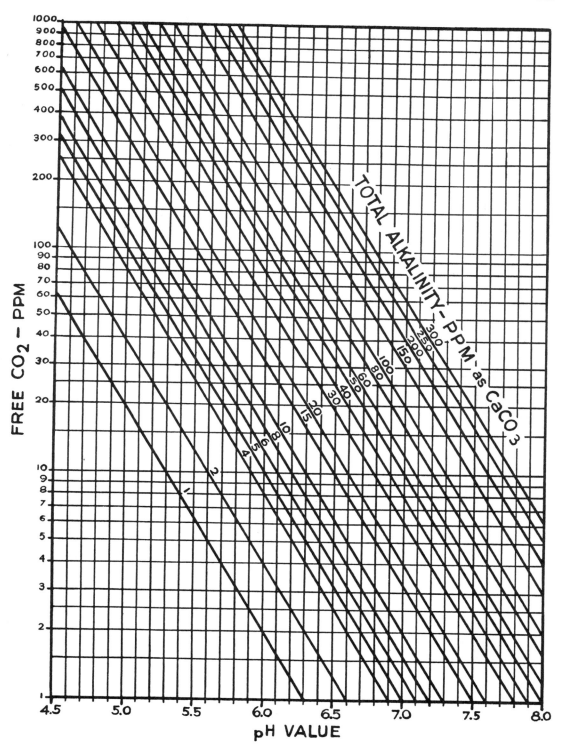

ture and total mineral content of a water any or all of the alkalinity forms and carbon dioxide can be determined. The proper procedures for these calculations are shown in "Standard Methods for the Examination of Water and Wastewater."

Figure 49-1 • Relation of Alkalinity and pH to Free Carbon Dioxide in Raw Waters

This graph indicates approximate relationships between pH, alkalinity and free carbon dioxide and when any two of these three factors are known, the third can be determined. To determine free carbon dioxide, locate the intersection of the vertical line for the pH value, with the slanting line for the total alkalinity (methyl orange) of the water sample and read the free carbon dioxide content of the water at the side of the chart as determined by the horizontal intersection.

CAUTION: The chart should not be depended upon for a high degree of accuracy, but is close enough for average use. For truly accurate results the CO_2 should be actually determined by chemical test.

50

Chloride

THE chlorides of calcium, magnesium, sodium, iron and other cations normally found present in water are extremely soluble. The principal importance of the chloride test in industrial water conditioning is based on the high solubility of the chlorides. Since no precipitation of the chlorides takes place, the chlorides present in boiler water and cooling water are proportional to the concentration of the water.

In natural waters high chloride values sometimes indicate the presence of animal pollution. However, the chloride test is merely an indication and animal pollution should be confirmed by bacteriological and sanitary analyses, as a high chloride value can be due to other reasons such as contamination by oil field brines and industrial wastes. In addition, high chlorides can result simply because the water has passed through a natural salt formation in the earth. The U. S. Public Health Service Drinking Water Standards for potable waters recommend a maximum chloride content of 250 ppm as Cl.

In industrial water conditioning the principal application of the chloride test is in the control of blowdown in boiler and cooling systems. In addition, the chloride test is also suitable for the accurate calculation of the rate of boiler blowdown provided the chloride concentration of the feedwater is of sufficient magnitude for accurate determination. Since chlorides are not subject to precipitation, the determination of the chloride concentration of the feedwater and the boiler water provides an accurate basis for calculating the rate of blowdown using the following formula:

$$\frac{\text{Cl in feedwater}}{\text{Cl in boiler water}} \times 100 = \% \text{ Blowdown}$$

The following facts should be kept in mind when considering blowdown figures based on the above formula:

The feedwater chloride determination must be an average. A spot sample may be misleading, particularly if feedwater chlorides vary to any extent.

Where sodium chloride is used to regenerate an ion exchanger, complete rinsing following regeneration must be employed, otherwise the boiler feedwater chloride will be erroneously high.

The chloride test is unsuitable for blowdown calculation only in those cases where the feedwater chloride is quite low, such as 0.5 ppm or 1.0 ppm. In this range, a slight analytical error in determining feedwater chloride will cause an appreciable error in the calculated rate of blowdown.

Another use for the chloride determination is to estimate the percent makeup present in a boiler feedwater. To make this estimate it is necessary to determine the chloride concentration of the makeup water, the condensate, and the boiler feedwater. The chloride content of pure condensate will be "zero". Assuming a pure condensate, 4 ppm chloride in the boiler feedwater and 10 ppm chloride in the makeup water, then the chloride of the feedwater is 40% of the chloride of the makeup water. Therefore, the feedwater contains 40% makeup and 60% condensate.

In cases where there is a measurable chloride content of the condensate due to carryover or condenser leakage, the percent makeup can still be calculated, employing the Tea Mixers rule or algebraic computations. However, in estimating the percent makeup where the chloride content of the makeup water and feedwater are very low the error introduced by the accuracy of the chloride test itself can be appreciable.

In open recirculating cooling water systems, control of blowdown usually is based on maintaining cycles of concentration within a definite range. The chloride test is employed in determining cycles, using the formula:

$$\frac{\text{Cl in Circulating Water}}{\text{Cl in Makup Water}}$$

$$= \text{Cycles of Concentration}$$

The degree of concentration of the circulating water, as compared with the makeup water, can be determined by the relative chloride content whether blowdown is employed or if natural windage losses are sufficient to restrict cycles.

The chloride test can be of advantage in the control of ion exchange softeners. After the regeneration of a sodium unit, the excess salt must be washed out of the exchanger bed before returning the unit to softening operation. If the salt is not washed out entirely, a sample of softener effluent will possess a high chloride content. In this case, the washing should be continued until the chloride of the softener effluent is reasonably close to the chloride of the raw water entering the softener.

Finally, the chloride test is useful in determining condenser leakage, especially aboard ships or other places where sea water is used for condensing purposes. If leakage is occurring, the condensate will show a material increase in the chloride content.

Generally speaking no attempt is made to remove the chloride ion from water in industrial water conditioning since chlorides are very soluble. However, for certain special industrial uses such as the water employed in the silver plating of mirrors, the chlorides can precipitate silver in the form of silver chloride. In cases such as this, the chloride can be removed by demineralization.

CHLORIDE, MOHR METHOD

THEORY OF TEST. This test is based on the titration of a water containing the chloride ion with a standard silver nitrate solution, using potassium chromate as an indicator. The chloride ion is precipitated by the silver nitrate as silver chloride. As soon as the chloride has been completely precipitated, further additions of silver nitrate will result in a red color due to the reaction of the silver ion with the chromate ion and this change is taken as the endpoint. In the sulfite modification of this test, the hydrogen peroxide oxidizes the sulfite to sulfate which, unlike sulfite, does not interfere with the chloride test.

APPARATUS REQUIRED.
    1—Burette, automatic, 25 ml
    1—Casserole, porcelain, 210 ml
    1—Cylinder, graduated, 50 ml
    1—Bottle, with dropper, 8 oz
    1—Stirring rod, glass
    1—Pipette, Mohr, 5 ml

CHEMICALS REQUIRED.
    Sulfuric Acid, 1 N
    Silver Nitrate, 1 ml = 1 mg Cl
    Phenolphthalein Indicator
    Potassium Chromate Indicator
    Hydrogen Peroxide, 3%

PROCEDURE FOR TEST. If the P or M alkalinity has already been determined, the same sample may be used directly for the chloride test without further neutralization. If the P or M alkalinity has not been determined, the sample must be properly neutralized with sulfuric acid. Take a 50 ml sample of the water to be tested, add 4 to 5 drops of phenolphthalein indicator. By means of a dropper add just sufficient sulfuric acid to neutralize to the colorless side of phenolphthalein as described under alkalinity. In this case, it is not necessary to accurately measure the amount of acid required for neutralization.

Add to the neutralized sample 5 drops of potassium chromate indicator which will turn the solution a bright yellow. Add silver nitrate from the burette slowly to the sample, stirring constantly, until 1 drop produces a permanent reddish color. This reddish color is to be taken as the endpoint and not a brick red color that will develop if additional silver nitrate is added.

A blank of 0.2 ml for this strength silver nitrate solution (1 ml = 1 mg Cl) should be subtracted as this is the quantity of silver nitrate required to produce the endpoint with 50 ml distilled water.

Where brackish waters are encountered, a stronger solution of silver nitrate should be employed (1 ml = 5 mg Cl). No blank is necessary with this stronger solution.

MODIFICATION WHEN SULFITE IS PRESENT. When the sulfite content of the water tested exceeds 10 ppm, the sulfite should be oxidized to sulfate by hydrogen peroxide (3%) to avoid interference with the chloride test. After neutralization to the colorless side of phenolphthalein, add 2.0 ml of hydrogen peroxide (3%) and stir well. Add potassium chromate indicator and titrate as outlined above.

This procedure should not be used on a sample already neutralized to methyl orange. If M alkalinity has been determined, discard the sample and neutralize a fresh sample to the phenolphthalein endpoint only, before adding the hydrogen peroxide.

CALCULATION OF RESULTS.

Formula:

ppm chloride as Cl = (ml silver nitrate − ml blank) × strength AgNO$_3$ mg/ml × $\dfrac{1000}{\text{ml sample}}$

Using a 50 ml sample and silver nitrate of the strength 1 ml = 1 mg Cl, the chloride in parts per million as Cl is equal to the ml of silver nitrate required minus a blank of 0.2 ml, multiplied by 20. When using a 50 ml sample and silver nitrate of the strength 1 ml = 5 mg Cl, the chloride in parts per million as Cl is equal to the ml of silver nitrate required multiplied by 100.

LIMITATIONS OF TEST. This method of chloride determination is unaffected by sulfate, total alkalinity, phosphate, silica, iron and color in the concentrations normally encountered in industrial waters. Sulfite interference can be eliminated as outlined. In the determination of chloride in the low concentrations existing in many natural and boiler feedwaters, however, an error in titration with silver nitrate of 0.1 or 0.2 ml may be an appreciable percentage error. This error is significant if the percentage boiler blowdown is calculated on the relative chloride content of feed and boiler waters. The chloride test is the one used most frequently in calculating and controlling cycles of concentration in recirculating cooling systems. If the chloride content of the makeup water is low and the chloride endpoint is overrun, the cycles of concentration calculated will be erroneously low. The actual cycles may be considerably greater than calculated and thus a scale-forming condition can develop even though cycles apparently are properly restricted. The chloride concentration of the makeup water must be determined accurately to avoid this error.

For greater accuracy in low chloride concentrations, a microburette for silver nitrate is recommended. Accurate determination of chloride above 1000 ppm is not feasible with this method except by dilution of the sample with distilled water so as to lower the chloride concentration below 1000 ppm in the sample to be tested.

51

Chlorine

THE test for chlorine is a test for the hydrolysis products of chlorine gas in water. The chlorine test should not be confused with the test for chloride which is a negative ion. Like other gases, such as carbon dioxide and ammonia, chlorine gas possesses a definite solubility in water forming hypochlorous acid and the hypochlorite ion. It is in the form of hypochlorous acid and the hypochlorite ion that chlorine exerts its disinfecting and oxidizing properties.

Chlorine is not present in natural waters and is found only as a result of chlorination of a water supply. Chlorine gas or hypochlorites are added to potable water supplies for the destruction of harmful bacteria and to render the supply safe for human consumption. In industrial water conditioning, chlorination is employed primarily for the control of slime and algae although chlorine also may be used to assist in coagulation, taste, odor, color and iron removal problems.

Formerly, no differentiation was made between the forms of chlorine residual present in a treated water. In recent years it has been recognized that there is a marked difference in the germicidal properties of a chlorine residual, dependent on the form in which chlorine exists in the treated water.

The free available chlorine residual is defined as that portion of the total residual chlorine which will react chemically and biologically as hypochlorous acid or hypochlorite ion. It is in this form that chlorine exerts the most potent bactericidal effect.

The combined available chlorine residual is defined as that portion of the total residual chlorine which will react chemically and biologically as chloramines, or organic chloramines. In this form, chlorine is a relatively mild bactericide and oxidizing agent.

Because of the significance of the form in which chlorine residual is present, it is becoming increasingly important to determine both the free and combined available chlorine residuals. For example, at a pH of 6.0-8.0, a free available chlorine residual of 0.2 ppm after ten minutes contact will provide excellent bacterial reduction while for the same results a combined available chlorine residual of 1.0 ppm after sixty minutes contact may be required.

CHLORINE, TAYLOR-ENSLOW METHOD

THEORY OF TEST. The determination of residual chlorine in water samples by colorimetric means is based on the fact that such a water, when treated with an acid solution of orthotolidine, will impart a definite coloration to the resulting mixture. Small amounts of chlorine give a yellow color and larger amounts give an orange color.

By comparing the color developed in the sample with that of prepared standards representing certain known concentrations of chlorine, the residual chlorine content of the unknown can be determined. Nitrites, ferric iron and manganic compounds will develop a color with orthotolidine and may yield a false residual chlorine value.

To correct for interference and to determine the free available and combined available portions of the residual chlorine, sodium arsenite is employed, (OTA test). Sodium arsenite reduces free or combined chlorine but does not affect false residuals. A flash reading within ten seconds indicates the free available chlorine residual and a five minute reading yields the total residual of both free and combined available chlorine.

RESIDUAL CHLORINE

APPARATUS REQUIRED.

1—Taylor-Enslow Slide Chlorimeter complete (chlorine slide range 0.0-1.0 ppm or 0.1-4.0 ppm)

CHEMICALS REQUIRED.

Orthotolidine Reagent

PROCEDURE FOR TEST. Rinse the three (3) cells thoroughly with the sample of water to be tested and fill all cells to the mark with the sample.

Place the cells in the three (3) openings in the base of the chlorimeter making certain that the etched side of each cell is next to the rectangular opening in the back of the base.

Add 0.5 ml of the orthotolidine to the middle cell by means of the dropper and mix thoroughly. A yellow color will develop if chlorine is present. The color standard slide should then be placed on the base and moved in front of the test samples until either an exact match is made with one of the standards or the color is determined to be at a point between two adjacent standards. In obtaining a color falling between two standard colors, the resulting concentration should be recorded as the average standard concentrations. As noted, interfering substances may cause the residual chlorine value to register erroneously high. However, if the chlorinated water contains no more than 0.3 ppm iron, 0.01 ppm manganic manganese and/or 0.1 ppm nitrite nitrogen, the characteristic yellow color with orthotolidine may be accepted as being due to chlorine.

Sunlight causes fading of the orthotolidine-chlorine color and tests should never be made in direct sunlight. Exposure of samples to direct sunlight before or during testing is not advisable. A standard artificial light source is best for consistent color comparisons. If not available, North daylight can be used.

If the chlorine content of the sample exceeds the range of the slide, discard test. Take a smaller sample and dilute with chlorine-free distilled water. Multiply results by appropriate factor.

FREE AND COMBINED AVAILABLE RESIDUAL CHLORINE

ADDITIONAL CHEMICALS REQUIRED.

Sodium Arsenite, 0.5%

PROCEDURE FOR TEST. As outlined under the Residual Chlorine Test, place the three (3) cells containing the sample in the base of the chlorimeter. To each of the outside cells add 0.5 ml of sodium arsenite solution. Mix and add 0.5 ml of orthotolidine reagent. To the middle cell add 0.5 ml orthotolidine reagent only and mix quickly. Read the chlorine value within ten seconds. This flash reading yields the free available chlorine residual corrected for interference. After five minutes, again read the chlorine value which will be the total residual chlorine corrected for interference. The difference between the two readings will be the combined available chlorine residual. In the absence of interfering substances, the sodium arsenite may be eliminated and the flash test used to differentiate between the free and combined available chlorine residuals.

CALCULATION OF RESULTS. If a comparison of colors can be accomplished when testing the original sample, the amount of residual chlorine in parts per million can be read directly from the color standard slide.

If the original sample must be diluted, then the final value found for the diluted sample must be multiplied by the dilution factor to give the amount contained in the original sample.

LIMITATIONS OF TEST. In order to obtain accurate results, it is necessary to maintain a pH value of 2.0 or less in the sample treated with orthotolidine. If the pH is above 2.0, reliable colors cannot be obtained. There is sufficient acid in the orthotolidine reagent to give a pH of 1.3 when 0.5 ml is added to 11.5 ml of drinking water or swimming pool water. In the case of sewage or process waters, where alkalinity may be high, it may be necessary to use 1.0 ml of orthotolidine.

Orthotolidine reagent should not be retained for periods longer than three months as an arbitrary precaution against the effect of possible occasional exposure to high temperatures or direct sunlight.

To avoid interferences due to iron, manganese, chromates and nitrates, the amperometric titration method is recommended. This procedure permits an accuracy of ± 0.01 ppm. The required equipment includes a chlorine detecting cell and microammeter. Phenylarsene oxide is used as the titrating solution. Amperometric residual chlorine recorders are also available.

FREE CHLORINE, MICRO-TITRATION METHOD

THEORY OF TEST. This test is based upon the reaction of xylene cyanole with free chlorine to form a stable soluble compound. After the free chlorine residual of the sample has been depleted, further additions of xylene cyanole produce a blue color which is taken as the endpoint.

APPARATUS REQUIRED.
  1—Burette, automatic, 25 ml
  1—Casserole, 210 ml
  1—Cylinder, graduated, 100 ml
  1—Bottle, with dropper
  1—Stirring rod, glass

CHEMICALS REQUIRED.
  Xylene Cyanole, 0.02%
  Hydrochloric Acid, 5 N

PROCEDURE FOR TEST. Measure a 100 ml sample in the graduate and transfer to the casserole. Add 2 or 3 drops of 5 N hydrochloric acid. Add xylene cyanole from the burette drop by drop with constant stirring. In colorless water, the endpoint is taken as the first appearance of a permanent light blue color; in water containing chromate, the endpoint will be green (the shade of green is a function of the amount of chromate present).

CALCULATION OF RESULTS.
Formula:

$$\text{ppm free chlorine as } Cl_2 = \frac{\text{ml xylene cyanole} \times 30}{\text{ml sample}}$$

Using a 100 ml sample, the free chlorine in parts per million as Cl_2 is equal to the ml of xylene cyanole multiplied by 0.30.

LIMITATIONS OF TEST. This method measures only free chlorine and does not measure combined chlorine. Ferric iron and nitrite up to 25 ppm do not cause interference.

Figure 51-1 • Taylor-Enslow Chlorimeter

52

Chromate

CHROMATES are rarely present in untreated water, except as a result of industrial contamination. However, chromates are among the most widely used chemicals for control of corrosion in industrial cooling water systems. The determination of chromate concentration usually is made in order to regulate treatment concentration to the level necessary for satisfactory corrosion inhibition.

The most commonly used chromate salts are sodium and potassium chromate and dichromate. The dichromates are acidic while the chromates are alkaline. It is only in the chromate or hexavalent form that chromium salts function as corrosion inhibitors. Trivalent chromic salts do not inhibit corrosion.

Chromates are anodic inhibitors, and as such, can intensify pitting if used in insufficient concentration to completely stifle corrosive attack. Normally, concentrations of 300-500 ppm chromate are employed for corrosion control in open circulating systems, while it is usual to employ 1000-2000 ppm chromate in closed systems. However, the effect of other ions present may alter the concentration required. High chloride hinders the development of a protective film by chromate and, under some severe conditions, chromate concentrations as high as 10,000 ppm have been required to stifle corrosive attack.

The combination of phosphate and chromate in the proper ratio and under controlled pH conditions in the Dianodic method permits the use of relatively low chromate concentrations. The field of usefulness of chromate corrosion inhibitors has been expanded greatly by the development of the Dianodic method. Inhibition of pitting as well as general corrosion, is secured at relatively low treatment concentrations.

Chromate salts are not suitable for use in potable waters and the U. S. Public Health Drinking Water Standards stipulate a limit for chromium of 0.05 ppm as Cr (hexavalent.

Where it is necessary to remove chromate from plant waste discharge, this removal usually is accomplished by reducing the hexavalent chromate to trivalent chromium and then precipitating chromic hydroxide. Ferrous sulfate and lime commonly are used for this purpose.

CHROMATE, TITRATION METHOD

THEORY OF TEST. This test is based on the oxidizing property of hexavalent chromium to liberate free iodine from potassium iodide in acid solution. The liberated iodine is titrated with sodium thiosulfate solution in the presence of a starch-type indicator. The disappearance of the blue color is taken as the endpoint.

APPARATUS REQUIRED.
   1—Burette, automatic, 25 ml
   1—Flask, Erlenmeyer, 250 ml
   1—Cylinder, graduated, 100 ml
   1—Cylinder, graduated, 10 ml
   1—Measuring dipper (brass)
   1—Measuring dipper (plastic)

CHEMICALS REQUIRED.
   Sodium Thiosulfate, N/10
   Iodide Crystals
   Starfamic Indicator
   Sulfamic Acid

PROCEDURE FOR TEST.
   (Range 10-100 ppm as CrO_4)
The N/100 sodium thiosulfate required to determine chromate in this range is not stable due to absorption of carbon dioxide

from the air. Therefore, this reagent must be freshly prepared (or restandardized) at least every two weeks. To 90 ml of distilled water that has been boiled and cooled to room temperature, add 10 ml of N/10 sodium thiosulfate. Mix thoroughly and store in a tightly stoppered bottle. Avoid unnecessary exposure of the solution to air.

Measure 50 ml of the water sample in the graduated cylinder and transfer to a 250 ml Erlenmeyer flask. Use the *plastic* dipper to add two (2) dipperfuls (approx. 2.0 g) of dry sulfamic acid. Swirl the flask until the acid is completely dissolved. Allow the sample to stand two (2) minutes to eliminate any nitrite interference. Then use the *brass* dipper to add one (1) dipperful (approx. 0.25 g) of iodide crystals. Swirl until the iodide is completely dissolved. Allow the sample to stand for two (2) minutes. Titrate the sample with N/100 sodium thiosulfate until the yellow-brown color of iodine has almost disappeared. Add one (1) *brass* dipperful (approx. 0.15 g) of dry Starfamic Indicator and swirl to dissolve (all of the indicator may not dissolve, creating a slight haze in the sample). Continue to titrate with N/100 sodium thiosulfate until the blue color which developed upon the addition of the indicator first disappears. Disregard any reappearance of the blue color. Record the ml of the sodium thiosulfate used.

CALCULATION OF RESULTS. Using a 50 ml sample, the parts per million of chromate as CrO_4 equals ml N/100 thiosulfate required multiplied by 7.74.

In some cases it may be desirable to use a sample larger than 50 ml. When this modification is required, the quantities of dry reagents and the multiplication factor should be as follows:

Sample Size	Sulfamic Acid	Iodide Crystals
100 ml	4 dippers	2 dippers
200 ml	8 dippers	4 dippers

	Starfamic Indicator	Factor
	1 dipper	3.87
	1 dipper	1.94

(Range 100-1500 ppm as CrO_4)

Measure 50 ml of the water sample in the graduated cylinder and transfer to a 250 ml Erlenmeyer flask. Use the *plastic* dipper to add two (2) dipperfuls (approx. 2.0 g) of dry sulfamic acid. Swirl the flask until the acid is completely dissolved. Allow the sample to stand for two (2) minutes to eliminate any nitrite interference. Then use the *brass* dipper to add two (2) dipperfuls (approx. 0.50 g) of iodide crystals. Swirl until the iodide is completely dissolved. Allow the sample to stand for two (2) minutes. Titrate the sample with N/10 sodium thiosulfate until the yellow-brown color of iodine has almost disappeared. Add one (1) *brass* dipperful (approx. 0.15 g) of Starfamic Indicator and swirl to dissolve (all of the indicator may not dissolve, creating a slight haze in the sample). Continue to titrate with N/10 sodium thiosulfate until the blue color which developed upon the addition of the indicator first disappears. Disregard any reappearance of the blue color. Record the ml of the sodium thiosulfate used.

CALCULATION OF RESULTS. Using a 50 ml sample, the parts per million of chromate as CrO_4 equals ml N/10 sodium thiosulfate required multiplied by 77.4.

(For Brines)

Measure 10 ml of the brine sample in the graduated cylinder. Make up to a total volume of 50 ml with distilled water or tap water and transfer to a 250 ml Erlenmeyer flask.

Use the *plastic* dipper to add two (2) dipperfuls (approx. 2.0 g) of dry sulfamic acid. Swirl the flask until the acid is completely dissolved. Allow the sample to stand for two (2) minutes. Then use the *brass* dipper to add two (2) dipperfuls (approx. 0.50 g) of iodide crystals. Swirl until the iodide is completely dissolved. Allow the sample to stand for two (2) minutes. Titrate the sample with N/10 sodium thiosulfate until the yellow-brown color of iodine has almost disappeared. Add one (1) *brass* dipperful (approx. 0.15 g) of dry Starfamic Indicator and swirl to dissolve (all of the indicator may not dissolve, creating a slight haze in the sample). Continue to titrate with N/10 sodium thiosulfate until the blue color which developed upon the addition of the indicator first disappears. Disregard any reappearance of the blue color. Record the ml of sodium thiosulfate used.

CALCULATION OF RESULTS. Using a 10 ml sample, the parts per million of chromate as CrO_4 equals ml N/10 sodium thiosulfate required multiplied by 387.

LIMITATIONS OF TEST. These tests are not specific for chromate, but rather are a measure of the oxidizing substances present in the water. Ferric iron and organic matter interfere. These procedures are employed when chromate is present over approximately 10 ppm and where sources of appreciable interference are absent.

Where chromate is to be determined in low concentration and also when interfering substances may be present it is preferable to employ the diphenylcarbohydrazide procedure, a Nessler tube or photometric method.

CHROMATE, PHOTOMETRIC METHOD

THEORY OF TEST. This test is based on the development of a reddish color produced by the reaction of hexavalent chromium with diphenylcarbohydrazide. While the color comparison can be made with Nessler tubes, more accurate and satisfactory results can be obtained with the use of a filter photometer or a spectrophotometer.

APPARATUS REQUIRED.
Filter photometer complete with assorted laboratory glassware

CHEMICALS REQUIRED.
Acetone Reagent
Diphenylcarbohydrazide, C. P.
Chromate Standard, 10 ppm CrO_4
Sulfuric Acid Reagent

PROCEDURE FOR TEST. This procedure employs a wave length of 535 mu and a minimum light path of 10 mm. Prepare a calibration curve for the photometer using successive dilutions of the chromate standard to adequately cover the anticipated range of chromate in the samples to be tested. The dilutions of the standard should be treated in exactly the same manner as that shown below for analysis of the water samples.

Each time a determination is made the calibration curve should be checked to establish a correction factor. This procedure is necessary to insure that the results are accurate since reagent age and stability as well as temperature can affect the results. The curve should be checked with chromate-free water and also at a dilution of the chromate standard that approximates the middle of the chromate range covered by the curve. All reagents as well as the "check" samples and the actual sample to be analyzed must be at the same temperature.

Diphenylcarbohydrazide reagent employed in this test must be prepared fresh daily. Add one level measuring cup of diphenylcarbohydrazide (approx. 0.1 g) to 50 ml of acetone reagent. Stir until dissolved. A pink color may develop in this reagent, but is of no significance.

Prepare a "zero" reference blank by adding to a beaker 25 ml sample, 1 ml distilled water and 1 ml sulfuric acid reagent. Use this reference blank to set meter at "zero" immediately prior to test.

To a second beaker add 25 ml sample, 1 ml sulfuric acid reagent and 1 ml of diphenylcarbohydrazide reagent. Allow to stand exactly 1 minute and immediately obtain dial reading.

CALCULATION OF RESULTS. Compare the photometer dial reading with the calibration curve and read the results directly in parts per million of chromate.

LIMITATIONS OF TEST. This procedure is not affected by the ions normally found in water. The test determines only hexavalent (yellow) and not trivalent (green) chromium. Up to 2.5 ppm chromate as CrO_4 can be determined without dilution of the sample. Concentrations above 2.5 ppm can be determined by diluting the original sample with distilled water, following the procedure outlined, and multiplying result by the appropriate factor.

The range covered by this chromate method is only 0-2.5 ppm and the normal procedure is to dilute the sample in order to determine higher chromate contents. However, the accuracy of this chromate method is so high that no appreciable error is introduced even by high dilution factors such as 1 ml of sample diluted to 50 ml.

Figure 52–1 • Filter Photometer-Chromate Analysis

53

Color

THE measurement of the color of a water does not provide any information concerning the nature of the substance producing that color. Instead, similar to the measurement of turbidity, an arbitrary standard scale is used as a means for comparison of color intensity with the water sample. A color of 5 units means that the intensity of the color of the water is equal to the intensity of the color of a sample of distilled water containing 5 milligrams of platinum (as potassium chlorplatinate) per liter.

Waters usually vary from colorless to a deep brown. Color in natural water generally is found to be due to the presence of organics such as tannin from decaying vegetable growth or from various industrial wastes.

The U. S. Public Health Service Drinking Water Standards recommend that the color of potable water should be less than 15 units.

In industrial water, color is most harmful where the water is to be used in process work. For example, in the manufacture of paper, highly colored waters can discolor the paper being manufactured. In boiler feedwater conditioning, the organic can concentrate and reach a point where it makes the analysis of the water most difficult by masking endpoints and color comparisons. The organic materials in solution may aggravate a carryover condition in boiler water, particularly if the organic material is from industrial wastes.

In industrial cooling water, a high color of the makeup water may indicate the presence of organic agents which may reduce corrosion inhibitors such as chromate and nitrite. Organic pollution may also provide an environment favorable to the growth of slime and algae.

The usual methods for color removal involve the use of iron or aluminum coagulants at a low pH value followed by filtration. Activated carbon may also be employed.

COLOR, PLATINUM-COBALT METHOD

THEORY OF TEST. This test is based on the comparison of the color of a water sample with an arbitrary standard color scale. One unit of color is defined as that produced by 1 mg of platinum per liter. The "true" color of a water sample is that due only to the presence of soluble substances. The "apparent" color is that due to the presence of both soluble and suspended substances.

APPARATUS REQUIRED.
  1—Taylor Water Analyzer complete (color slide range 0-70 units)

PROCEDURE FOR TEST. Fill one of the comparator tubes to the mark with sample and place in the middle compartment of the base. Fill the two comparator tubes on either side to the mark with distilled water. Place the standard slide on the base. Place the instrument so that the comparator tubes point toward a source of daylight. Read instrument by viewing the reflection in the mirror and *not by looking down through the tubes*. Move the slide in front of the test sample until a color match is obtained.

CALCULATION OF RESULTS. The color value is read directly from the color standard slide in terms of units of color.

LIMITATIONS OF TEST. The true color of a water sample is due to soluble substances and its accurate determination where suspended matter is present is practically impossible. Filtration should not be used because of the decolorizing action. The best results can be obtained by centrifuging prior to color observation.

Photometers are not recommended for the determination of color, because of interference from turbidity.

Figure 53–1 • Organic Identification by Infrared Spectroscopy

54

Conductance (Specific)

THE specific conductance of a water is a measure of the ability of the water to conduct an electrical current. This property is of no consequence in itself with respect to water treatment. However, from a control standpoint, the conductivity test is important as a direct measure of the total ionizable solids in the water. The conductivity test provides an accurate measurement of steam purity as well as a simple control for boiler water solids. Conductivity also may be used for blowdown control in recirculating cooling water systems.

Specific conductance is inversely proportional to electrical resistance. Pure water is highly resistant to the passage of an electric current and therefore has a low specific conductance. However, if the water contains ions, the water becomes a better conductor of electricity and the specific conductance is increased. Inorganic compounds such as sodium chloride and sodium sulfate dissociate into positive and negative ions, which will conduct electricity in proportion to the amount of ions present. The conductivity test, therefore, is not specific for any one ion, but rather a measure of the total ionic concentration.

The basic unit of electrical resistance is the ohm. Since electrical conductivity is the reciprocal of resistance, the unique term "mho" ("ohm" spelled backwards) was chosen as the basic unit of conductivity. In the conductivity test, small amounts of electrical conductance are measured and the instrument is usually calibrated in micromhos (a micromho is a millionth of a mho). To calibrate a conductivity instrument to read directly in parts per million of dissolved solids (or some specific ion or compound) is not recommended since such a calibration introduces an error into the instrument reading itself. The conversion factor from micromhos of specific conductance to parts per million will vary slightly with different waters. To include a constant conversion factor in the instrument calibration is to introduce an unnecessary source of error.

The conductivity test provides an accurate and simple method of blowdown control. However, certain limitations must be considered. While the conductivity test measures the total ionic concentration, the hydroxide ion has a much higher conductance than the other ions present. Thus, for accurate results the sample must be neutralized before the conductivity test is made.

Conductivity is an exceedingly sensitive test and is accurate down to the level of approximately 0.5-1.0 ppm ionizable solids. Until development of the flame spectrophotometer method for determining low sodium concentrations, conductivity was the most accurate method of determining steam purity. The newer sodium method is preferred where solids in the steam are 1 ppm or less.

CONDUCTANCE OF BOILER WATER, CONDUCTO BRIDGE METHOD

THEORY OF TEST. The ionizable solids in boiler water have the ability to conduct an electric current through a solution. This property of electrical conductance of solids makes it possible to accurately measure the quantity of solids in solution by suitable conductance equipment.

APPARATUS REQUIRED.

1—Conducto Bridge (choice of various ranges)

1—Dip cell (constant 2.0)
1—Cylinder, rimmed glass, not graduated
1—Thermometer, dial type (0-220 F)
1—Measuring cup, brass

CHEMICAL REQUIRED

Gallic Acid, c. p.

PROCEDURE FOR TEST. Pour approximately 50 ml of distilled water or steam condensate into the rimmed glass cylinder and insert the conductivity cell. Move cell up and down several times to wash off any solids present on the cell. Discard the water in the cylinder.

Pour approximately 50 ml of boiler water into the cylinder (use a settled or filtered sample). Add two dippers of gallic acid (approx. 0.2 g) to the sample. (Note—if a small amount of the gallic acid remains undissolved, the conductivity test will not be adversely affected.) Measure temperature of the sample and adjust the temperature correction dial on the Conducto Bridge to the proper temperature. Insert conductivity cell and move up and down several times to insure equilibrium. Measure the specific conductance on the Conducto Bridge by turning the conductivity dial until the electric "eye" is at its widest black angle.

NOTE—Two dippers of gallic acid will neutralize approximately 1300 ppm P alkalinity. On some highly alkaline boiler waters, additional gallic acid may be required. A desirable precaution is to add approximately four drops phenolphthalein indicator to the sample and delay taking the conductivity reading until the pink color has been completely discharged by the addition of gallic acid.

CALCULATION OF RESULTS. The specific conductance in micromhos is read directly from the calibrated scale as indicated by the pointer on the conductivity knob, when the "eye" is at its widest black angle.

The relationship between specific conductance and the dissolved solids content of a boiler water depends on the characteristics of each individual boiler water and therefore may be slightly different for each plant. Using the gallic acid neutralization method,

Figure 54-1 • Determination of Boiler Water Conductivity

an average value determined over a wide range of operating conditions is that one micromho is equivalent to 0.9 ppm dissolved solids. This value is sufficiently accurate for the average industrial plant.

The exact relationship between micromhos and solids can be individually established for each plant by determining both the conductance and solids content of a series of approximately ten samples taken over a two week period.

LIMITATIONS OF TEST. The conductance method affords a rapid means of checking the dissolved solids content of a sample. The effect of hydroxide in causing high conductivity is minimized by the gallic acid neutralization, thereby securing a consistent relationship between solids and conductance. The conductance method does not measure nonelectrolytic solids such as organic matter, and in order to express results in terms of parts per million of boiler water solids it is necessary to use a conversion factor. This conversion factor is described above.

CONDUCTANCE OF STEAM CONDENSATE, CONDUCTO BRIDGE METHOD

THEORY OF TEST. The ionizable solids and gases in condensed steam have the ability to conduct an electric current through a solution. This property of electrical conductance of solids and gases make it possible to detect small quantities of these materials in solution by means of suitable conductance equipment.

APPARATUS REQUIRED.

    1—Conducto Bridge (0-60 micromhos)
    1—Dip cell (constant 0.1)
    1—Cylinder, rimmed glass, not graduated
    1—Thermometer, dial type (0-220 F)

PROCEDURE FOR TEST. Pour approximately 50 ml of the steam condensate into the cylinder. Insert the conductivity cell, moving it up and down several times to wash off any solids present on the cell. Discard the water in the cylinder.

Pour approximately 50 ml of the steam condensate into the cylinder. Measure temperature of the sample and adjust the tem-

Figure 54-2 • Conductivity Test Set

perature correction dial on the Conducto Bridge to the proper temperature. Insert conductivity cell and move up and down several times to insure equilibrium. Measure the specific conductance on the Conducto Bridge by turning the conductivity dial until the electronic "eye" is at its widest angle.

CALCULATION OF RESULTS. With the "eye" at its widest black angle, the scale on the conductivity knob indicates directly the specific conductance in micromhos.

An average value for converting micromhos of conductance to dissolved solids in condensed steam samples is approximately 0.5-0.6 ppm dissolved solids per micromho of conductance. This factor is subject to some slight variation dependent upon the individual steam condensate measured, but for normal work this factor can be employed.

In evaluating the conductance of a condensed steam sample and expressing conductance in terms of dissolved solids through the use of a conversion factor, it is necessary to check the steam condensate for dissolved gases such as ammonia and carbon dioxide which impart conductance. Conductance correction for the presence of these gases may be determined by subtracting from the observed conductance, the conductance due to ammonia and free carbon dioxide as indicated from the curves showing the conductance of these two gases when present together in steam condensate (see Figures 54-3, 54-4 and 54-5). Subtracting the value for conductance due to dissolved gases from the observed conductance will yield the conductance due to solids content of steam condensate.

LIMITATIONS OF TEST. The conductance method is rapid and accurate for determining solids of 1 ppm or more in steam condensate. However, where any appreciable quantity of ammonia or free carbon dioxide is present in the steam, it is necessary to determine the concentration of these gases and make suitable correction, as otherwise the dissolved solids content calculated from the conductance reading would be erroneously high. In many cases for routine control, only negligible amounts of ammonia or free carbon dioxide may be present and a check for these gases need be made only at infrequent intervals. Where a high percentage of contaminated makeup is employed in a plant, it usually is necessary to make frequent checks for the ammonia and free carbon dioxide content of the condensed steam.

CONDUCTANCE CORRECTIONS FOR AMMONIA AND CARBON DIOXIDE

To properly interpret the conductivity of a condensed steam or condensate sample, it is necessary that corrections be made for the conductivity due to any gases present. The purpose of the conductivity determination is to obtain a measure of the solids present in the condensed steam sample as an indication of the degree of carryover of boiler water solids. In many cases, the presence of gases such as ammonia and carbon dioxide will impart a conductivity far greater than that due to the solids present. To interpret the conductivity of the condensed steam sample, it is necessary to determine the ammonia and car-

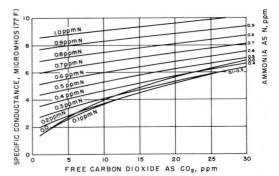

Figure 54-3 • Conductance Correction Curves for Ammonia and Carbon Dioxide

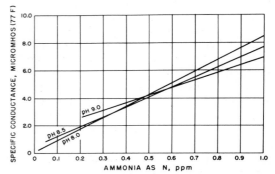

Figure 54-4 • Conductance Correction Curves Based on Ammonia and pH (Low Range)

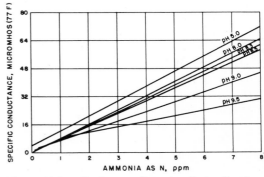

Figure 54-5 • Conductance Correction Curves Based on Ammonia and pH (High Range)

bon dioxide present and to make correction for the conductivity due to these gases.

Figures 54-3, 54-4, and 54-5 are based on the data of R. O. Parker and R. J. Ziobro ("Comments on Corrections to Steam Conductivity Measurements"—Presented at the 1956 National Meeting, American Society for Testing Materials).

Figure 54-3 shows the conductivity correction for ammonia in the range of 0-1.0 ppm and carbon dioxide in the range of 0-30 ppm. For example, if a condensed steam sample contained 10 ppm carbon dioxide and 0.6 ppm ammonia as N, the conductivity correction would be 6.0 micromhos. This correction must be subtracted from the observed conductivity of the sample to obtain the conductivity due to the solids present.

EXAMPLE

Specific conductance = 8.0 micromhos
Ammonia as N = 0.6 ppm

Free carbon dioxide as CO_2 = 10 ppm
Correction due to gases = 6.0 micromhos
Corrected specific conductance: (8.0-6.0) = 2.0 micromhos
Solids content of sample: 2.0 micromhos × 0.5 (average factor) = 1.0 ppm solids

Figure 54-4 is useful in determining the conductivity correction where no free carbon dioxide is found present. The conductivity correction for ammonia is a function both of the ammonia concentration and the pH of the sample. For example, in a sample containing 0.7 ppm ammonia as N, with a pH of 8.0, the correction value would be 6.0 micromhos specific conductance.

Figure 54-5 covers a higher range of ammonia concentration and the same procedure is used to obtain the conductivity correction.

55

Hardness

THE presence of calcium and magnesium salts causes water to be hard, with the degree of hardness being directly proportional to the quantity of these heavy metals that are present. Hardness of natural water will vary considerably, depending upon the source from which it is obtained. Sections that have limestone formations generally have a high hardness content in the water. Since surface waters are diluted by rainfall, well water in the same area will normally have a much higher hardness than surface water since the flow is underground over rock layers and through sand strata.

The terms "temporary hardness" and "permanent hardness" have been superseded by the expressions "carbonate hardness" and "noncarbonate hardness". When the total hardness is greater than the carbonate and bicarbonate alkalinity, the amount of hardness equivalent to the alkalinity is termed carbonate hardness; the remainder of the hardness is noncarbonate hardness. When the sum of carbonate and bicarbonate alkalinity equals or exceeds the total hardness, all hardness is carbonate hardness and there is no noncarbonate hardness.

Hardness will cause numerous detrimental effects domestically, such as excessive soap consumption in the home and laundries, as well as scums and curds formed on equipment; yellowing of fabrics; toughening of vegetables; film formation in tea; and scale formation in hot water heaters, pipes and utensils.

The classification of water supplies as soft, moderately hard, hard and very hard is rather unsatisfactory even where the domestic use of water is concerned. Water with a hardness of 100 ppm may be called a soft water

by one accustomed to using a water with 300 or 400 ppm hardness, whereas, one accustomed to using a water with less than 50 ppm hardness may call waters with a hardness of 100 ppm rather hard. A water with a hardness of 100 ppm is not soft in terms of soap consumption in cleaning, washing and laundering operation. The accompanying table gives a general classification of waters.

Hardness	Classification
Less than 15 ppm	Very Soft Water
15 to 50 ppm	Soft Water
50 to 100 ppm	Medium Hard Water
100 to 200 ppm	Hard Water
Greater than 200 ppm	Very Hard Water

In industry, high hardness is undesirable for laundries, metal finishing, dyeing and textile plants, food processing, pulp and paper, bottle washing, photography, leather goods and many others. Hardness is also the source of scale formation in boiler feedwater heaters, feed lines, and economizers. Boilers also will be heavily scaled due to precipitation of calcium and magnesium salts unless properly treated. In cooling water systems, scale will develop in heat exchange equipment, engine jackets, piping and in general wherever water circulates and is exposed to a temperature change.

Hardness can be removed by lime-soda softening, ion exchange softening, hot lime-hot ion exchange and various combinations of processes. It may be removed in internal boiler water conditioning by employing inorganic salts such as phosphate and carbonate in conjunction with either protective or reactive organic materials, which insure the precipitation of hardness from solution as a fluid nonadherent sludge.

Hardness may be controlled in internal

Fig. 55-1—Range of Recommended Values for Hardness in Industrial Water Supplies

Industry and Process	Limiting or Recommended Values, ppm
Boiler Feedwater	
At 0-150 psi	80
At 150-250 psi	40
At 250-400 psi	10
Over 400 psi	2
Brewing	200-300
Carbonated Beverages	200-250
Cooling	50
Food Canning and Freezing	
General	50-85
Legumes	25-75
Fruits and Vegetables	100-200
Peas	200-400
Food Equipment Washing	10
Food Processing, General	10-250
Laundering	0-50
Pulp and Paper Making	
Groundwood Pulp	200
Soda Pulp	100
Kraft Pulp, Bleached	100
Kraft Pulp, Unbleached	200
Fine Paper Pulp	100
Rayon	
Pulp Production	8
Cloth Manufacture	55
Steel Manufacturing	50
Synthetic Rubber	50
Tanning	
Beam House	513
Tan House	50-135
Textile Manufacturers	0-50

Source—"Water Quality Criteria"
State Water Pollution Control Board
Sacramento, California (1952)

cooling water treatment by employing organic and inorganic surface active agents which frequently are used in conjunction with acidic materials such as sulfuric acid. Here the purpose of the treatment is to retain the hardness in solution and prevent its precipitation as scale.

Hardness in an ion exchange softener effluent should not exceed approximately 5 ppm. When this type of softening is used for makeup to high pressure boiler systems, the effluent hardness should be controlled to much lower values to minimize sludge formation in the boilers. The hardness of the effluent from a lime-soda softener will vary depending upon the temperature at which the process is carried out and the quantity of treatment chemicals employed. However, the hardness usually is within the range of 10 to 30 ppm for a hot lime-soda softener and 25 to 50 ppm for a cold process softener.

HARDNESS, TITRATION METHOD

THEORY OF TEST. This test is based on the determination of the total calcium and magnesium content of a sample by titration with a sequestering agent in the presence of an organic dye sensitive to calcium and magnesium ions. The endpoint occurs when all the calcium and magnesium ions are sequestered and the endpoint is a color change from red to blue.

APPARATUS REQUIRED.
1—Burette, automatic, 25 ml
1—Casserole, porcelain, 210 ml
1—Cylinder, graduated, 50 ml
1—Stirring rod, glass
2—Measuring dippers, brass

CHEMICALS REQUIRED.
Hardness Indicator
Hardness Buffer Reagent
Hardness Titrating Solution, 1 ml = 1 mg $CaCO_3$

PROCEDURE FOR TEST. Measure 50 ml of sample and transfer to the casserole. With the measuring cup provided, add 1 level measure (approx. 0.2 g) of hardness buffer reagent to sample and stir. Add 1 level measure (approx. 0.2 g) of hardness indicator and stir. If hardness is present, the sample will turn red. Add the hardness titrating solution slowly from the burette with constant stirring. When approaching the endpoint, the sample begins to show some blue coloration, but a definite reddish tinge can still be observed. The endpoint is the final discharge of this reddish tinge to produce a definite blue color. Further addition of the hardness titrating solution will not produce any color change.

With the procedure given above the hardness titrating solution must be added slowly since the endpoint is sharp and rapid. For routine hardness determination it is suggested that 50 ml of sample be measured, but only approximately 40-45 ml be added to the casserole at the start of the test. Add the hardness buffer reagent and hardness indicator as described above and rapidly titrate to the endpoint. Then add the remaining portion of the sample. The hardness present in the remainder of the sample will turn the contents of the casserole red. Continue titrating slowly until the final endpoint as indicated above is reached. Record the total number of milliliters of hardness titrating solution employed.

CALCULATION OF RESULTS.
Formula:

ppm hardness as $CaCO_3$ =

$$\text{ml titrating solution} \times \frac{1000}{\text{ml sample}}$$

Using a 50 ml sample, the hardness in parts per million as $CaCO_3$ is equal to the ml of titrating solution employed multiplied by 20.

LOW HARDNESS PROCEDURE. In low hardness waters (0-5 ppm), an accuracy of 0.1 ppm hardness can be obtained by employing the following special procedure.

The same strength chemicals and apparatus given above are used with the exception that a microburette is employed instead of a regular burette.

In the determination of low hardness, 100 ml of sample is taken. Add 2 level measures (approx. 0.4 g) of hardness buffer reagent and stir. Add 1 level measure (approx. 0.2 g) of hardness indicator and stir. The titrating solution is added *very slowly* from the microburette.

The endpoint is the final disappearance of any reddish tinge in the sample and the development of a pure blue color which will not change upon further additions of hardness titrating solution.

Record the number of ml of hardness

titrating solution employed to the second decimal place. Multiply result by 10 to obtain hardness in parts per million as $CaCO_3$.

LIMITATIONS OF TEST. This method of hardness determination is more accurate than the "soap method" and is considerably more rapid. Hardness values up to 1200 ppm can be titrated with an accuracy of 2% without dilution of the sample. In low hardness concentrations (0-5 ppm) an accuracy of 0.1 ppm can be obtained.

Interference results with the presence of sodium hydroxide over 300 ppm, copper over 10 ppm, iron over 20 ppm, manganese over 2 ppm, aluminum over 20 ppm, orthophosphate over 100 ppm and polyphosphate over 25 ppm. Strontium titrates as hardness. Other ions in the concentration normally encountered in industrial water conditioning produce no interference.

The effect of interfering ions can be reduced by dilution of the sample. If interference occurs, measure a 25 ml sample, dilute with 25 ml of distilled water and proceed in the normal fashion. Multiply results by 40 instead of 20 as described under "Calculation of Results". This procedure will reduce any interfering ions, usually enabling a sharp endpoint to be obtained.

When waters contain free mineral acid, such as the effluent of a hydrogen zeolite, the sample should be neutralized with 1 N sodium hydroxide. Litmus paper can be used as the indicator, adding sufficient sodium hydroxide until a blue color is obtained.

In the presence of certain ions, the color change may not be from red to blue. For example, 500 ppm chromate causes no test interference. However, with chromate present the endpoint is from red to green, due to the color of the chromate. The true endpoint in each case in taken as the disappearance of the reddish tinge of the sample, regardless of the final endpoint color.

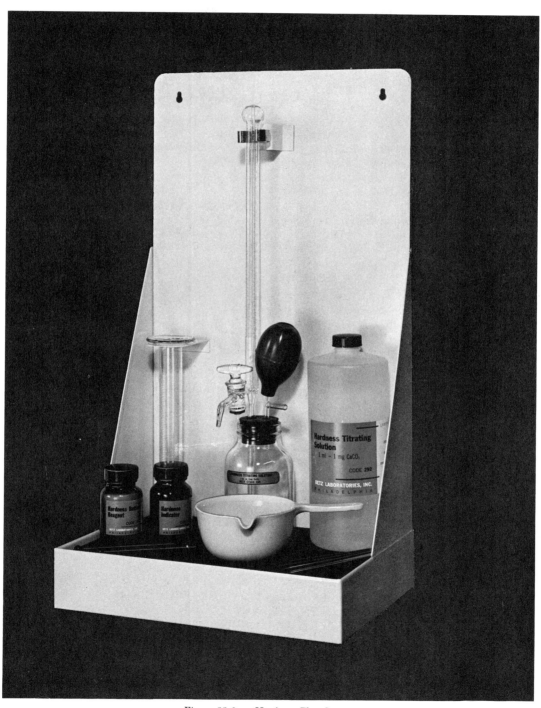

Figure 55-2 • Hardness Test Set

56

Hydrazine

AS boiler operating pressures have increased, two disadvantages have become evident in the use of sodium sulfite as a chemical deaerant. Sodium sulfite reacts with oxygen to produce sodium sulfate which increases the dissolved solids concentration in the boiler water. In addition, there is some tendency for sulfite to decompose at high pressure to produce sulfur dioxide and hydrogen sulfide, both of which are acidic gases and can contribute to corrosion in condensate return systems.

Hydrazine (N_2H_4) reacts with dissolved oxygen to produce nitrogen and water. Therefore, the products of the hydrazine reaction do not add solids to the boiler water. In the event there should be some decomposition of hydrazine, the products of the decomposition reaction are ammonia and nitrogen. Since nitrogen is an inert gas and ammonia is alkaline, there is no attack on ferrous metals. However, if ammonia is present in sufficient quantity, it will attack copper and copper bearing alloys.

Hydrazine is a toxic liquid and must be handled with care. Pure hydrazine has a low flash point so that a 35% aqueous solution usually is employed in water conditioning to avoid fire hazard. Theoretically, 1.0 ppm hydrazine is required to react with 1.0 ppm dissolved oxygen. Therefore, the theoretical quantity of the 35% solution of hydrazine is slightly less than 3.0 ppm to 1.0 ppm dissolved oxygen. In practical applications, hydrazine usually is required in quantities somewhat greater than theoretical. To avoid excessive ammonia concentrations in the steam the residual hydrazine in the boiler water usually is maintained at 0.1 ppm or less. In some cases, a residual of hydrazine as low as 0.01 ppm is employed. The control ranges are

based upon samples of boiler feedwater or boiler water, depending on plant operating conditions.

HYDRAZINE, TAYLOR METHOD

THEORY OF TEST. This test is based on the reaction of paradimethylaminobenzaldehyde with hydrazine to produce a yellow color. The intensity of the yellow color is proportional to the amount of hydrazine present in the sample and follows Beer's law.

APPARATUS REQUIRED.
   1—Taylor Water Analyzer complete (hydrazine slide 0.00-0.30 N_2H_4)
   1—Bottle, amber glass, 4 oz.
   1—Bottle, clear glass, 2 oz, calibrated 50 ml, glass stoppered
   1—Cylinder, graduated, 50 ml
   1—Measuring dipper, plastic
   1—Pipette, graduated, 2.5 ml

CHEMICALS REQUIRED.
   Taylor Hydrazine Reagent A
   Taylor Hydrazine Reagent B

PROCEDURE FOR TEST. The single reagent used in this test is prepared from Hydrazine Reagent A (a powder) and Hydrazine Reagent B (a solvent). Measure 44 ml of Reagent B and transfer to the amber bottle. Add two (2) plastic dipperfuls (approx. 1.6 g) of Reagent A and mix thoroughly. Use the amber bottle for storage; keep tightly closed and avoid unnecessary exposure to air. Due to limited stability prepare fresh reagent every two weeks.

To test for hydrazine fill the 2 oz glass stoppered bottle to the mark (50 ml) with the water sample. Use the pipette to add 2.5 ml of the prepared Hydrazine Reagent to the bottle. Stopper the bottle and shake to mix thoroughly. Allow the treated sample to stand in the stoppered bottle for 30 minutes.

At the expiration of 30 minutes fill one of the tubes with the treated sample and place it in the middle compartment of the Analyzer. Fill the other two tubes with the original untreated sample and place them in the outer compartments of the Analyzer.

Place the instrument so that the comparator tubes point toward a source of daylight. Read the instrument by viewing the reflection in the mirror and *not by looking down through the tubes*. Move the slide in front of the test samples until a color match is obtained.

CALCULATION OF RESULTS. Using a 50 ml sample, hydrazine as N_2H_4 is read directly from the color slide in parts per million.

LIMITATIONS OF TEST. The ions normally present in industrial water do not interfere with this test. If oxidizing agents are collected with the sample or absorbed prior to testing, the hydrazine content may be diminished. This method of analysis is not suitable for water samples that are colored. If color is present, the photometric method should be employed.

HYDRAZINE, PHOTOMETRIC METHOD

THEORY OF TEST. This test is based on the reaction of paradimethylaminobenzaldehyde with hydrazine to produce a yellow color. The intensity of the yellow color is proportional to the amount of hydrazine in the sample and follows Beer's law. The method can be modified to eliminate interference from color.

APPARATUS REQUIRED.
Filter photometer complete with assorted laboratory glassware.

CHEMICALS REQUIRED.
Paradimethylaminobenzaldehyde Powder
Hexyl Alcohol
Hydrazine Standard Solution, 1 ml=0.1 mg N_2H_4
Hydrochloric Acid, Concentrated
Methyl Alcohol (absolute)

PROCEDURE FOR TEST. The following reagents should be prepared for use in this hydrazine test. These reagents and the chemicals used to prepare them should be handled *with care*. When it is necessary to use a pipette, *always* use an aspirator bulb.

Reagent A—Dissolve 4 g of paradimethylaminobenzaldehyde powder in 200 ml of methyl alcohol. When dissolved, add 15 ml of concentrated hydrochloric acid.

Reagent B—Mix 200 ml methyl alcohol and 15 ml concentrated hydrochloric acid.

Reagent C—Dilute 74 ml concentrated hydrochloric acid to one liter with distilled water.

Reagent D—Pipette 10 ml hydrazine standard solution into a one liter volumetric flask. Make up to one liter with Reagent C. One ml of Reagent D is equal to 0.001 mg hydrazine as N_2H_4.

This method for the determination of hydrazine employs a wave length of 460 mu and a light path of 20 mm. Prepare a calibration curve in the following manner. Mix 20 ml of Reagent B and 25 ml of Reagent C; use this mixture to set the photometer at "zero" on the dial. Mix 20 ml of Reagent A and 25 ml of Reagent C; use this mixture to obtain a reference point for hydrazine-free water ("zero" hydrazine).

Reference points for the remainder of the calibration curve are obtained by a series of dilutions of Reagent D to a total volume of 200 ml, using a volumetric flask and Reagent C as the diluent. For example, 1.0 ml Reagent D diluted to 100 ml in a volumetric flask with Reagent C is equivalent to 0.01 ppm hydrazine. Reference points are obtained by treated 25 ml portions of the dilutions with 20 ml Reagent A as shown below.

Each time a determination is made the calibration curve should be checked to establish a correction factor. This procedure is necessary to insure that the results are accurate since reagent age and stability as well as temperature can affect the results. The curve should be checked with Reagent C and also at a dilution of Reagent D that approximates the middle of the hydrazine range covered by the curve. All reagents as well as the "check" samples and the actual sample to be analyzed must be at the same temperature.

To determine hydrazine in a colorless sample—add 15 ml concentrated hydrochloric acid to the sample bottle and collect sample with minimum exposure to air until the 200 ml mark is reached. Measure 25 ml of the sample and add 20 ml of Reagent B. Use this mixture as a blank to set photometer at "zero". Measure a second 25 ml portion of the sample and add 20 ml of Reagent A. Place in the photometer cell and read the dial at the end of one minute.

To determine hydrazine in a colored sample—measure 50 ml of sample (collected as per above) in a graduate and transfer to a separatory funnel. Add 10 ml hexyl alcohol by means of a pipette and shake to mix. Allow the layers to separate and drain bottom layer into a beaker for use as the sample. Proceed as under "colorless sample".

CALCULATION OF RESULTS. The hydrazine content in parts per million as N_2H_4 is obtained by reference to the calibration curve.

LIMITATIONS OF TEST. The ions normally present in industrial water do not interfere with this test. If oxidizing agents are collected with the sample or absorbed prior to testing, the hydrazine content may be diminished.

57

Iron

IRON exists in two states—ferrous iron and ferric iron. In the ferric state, the iron is completely oxidized, whereas in the ferrous state it is only partially oxidized. In the total dissolved iron test, both the ferrous and ferric iron are measured.

Since iron is one of the most common elements in the earth's crust, it frequently is found in natural waters. In surface waters, iron is in the ferric state since it is completely oxidized by the oxygen in the atmosphere. However, in well waters the iron usually is in the ferrous form. Upon removal from the well, exposure to air and release of carbon dioxide, the iron in the water is converted to the ferric state.

Iron is classified as an incrusting solid similar to calcium and magnesium since iron will precipitate out of solution and can form a scale. Iron in water also is objectionable from the standpoint that it will form stains destroying the sanitary appearance of sinks, lavatories, etc. The U. S. Public Health Drinking Water Standards recommend a maximum of 0.3 ppm iron as Fe in potable waters.

In addition to the "natural" iron content of a water, iron is placed into solution when the corrosion of iron and steel surfaces occurs. Thus, the iron test occupies a unique position inasmuch as the interpretation of this test must consider the factors of both scale and corrosion. For example, an iron deposit can occur in a cooling water system as a scale problem (deposition of the natural iron in the water) or as a corrosion problem (wasting away of the metal surfaces).

In industrial water conditioning, the determination of iron can reveal information on corrosive action taking place within a system. However, the natural iron content of the water must be considered in interpreting the results of the test. For example, if a boiler water sample contains appreciable quantities of total iron, it should not be immediately concluded that serious corrosion of the boiler metal is occurring. An examination of the natural iron content of the feedwater should be made since iron will concentrate in a boiler similar to other ions.

Iron removal can be accomplished by aeration, coagulation and filtration, lime and lime-soda softening, cation exchange and contact filtration. Frequently it is more advisable to retain iron in solution rather than to remove it. Iron retention is secured with the use of various surface active agents.

TOTAL IRON, PHENANTHROLINE METHOD

THEORY OF TEST. This test is based on the development of an orange-red complex from the reaction of ferrous iron with phenanthroline. The color developed is matched with that of freshly prepared standards using Nessler tubes to make the comparison. A filter photometer or a spectrophotometer also may be used at a wave length of 510 mu and a minimum light path of 10 mm. When either of these instruments are employed, the values of iron in parts per million are read directly from calibration curves.

APPARATUS REQUIRED.
  1—Nessler tube rack (12 hole)
  12—Nessler tubes (2 matched sets of 6 each), 100 ml
  1—Flask, volumetric, 100 ml
  1—Flask, Erlenmeyer, 250 ml
  1—Pipette, delivery, 100 ml
  1—Pipette, safety, 2 ml
  1—Pipette, delivery, 10 ml

1—Pipette, Mohr, 1 ml

1—Pipette, Mohr, 5 ml

CHEMICALS REQUIRED.

Hydrochloric Acid, Concentrated

Hydrochloric Acid, 10%

Iron Standard Solution, 10 ppm Fe

Hydroxylamine Reagent (modified to eliminate necessity for ammonium acetate buffer)

Orthophenanthroline Reagent

PROCEDURE FOR TEST. All glassware (pipettes, beakers, etc.) must be washed with concentrated hydrochloric acid and rinsed with iron-free distilled water prior to use. Cleaning the equipment in this manner is necessary to remove any iron oxide which may be present as a result of the use of glassware for other analyses. If the hydroxylamine reagent should become cloudy, filter before use.

Preparation of Standards. Prepare a series of standards in increments of 0.1 ppm Fe for use in the Nessler tubes. A typical series would cover the range of 0.0 to 1.0 ppm Fe.

Fill the 100 ml volumetric flask approximately half full of iron-free distilled water. Add the iron standard solution in increments of 1 ml using a graduated Mohr pipette. For example, if only 1 ml is added, then the standard will be equivalent to 0.1 ppm Fe; if 2 ml are added, the standard will be equivalent to 0.2 ppm Fe, etc. Add 2 ml of 10% hydrochloric acid to the flask and fill to the 100 ml mark with distilled water. Stopper and invert several times to mix

Figure 57-1 • Iron Determination—Phenanthroline Method

thoroughly.

Transfer the contents of the volumetric flask to a 250 ml Erlenmeyer flask. Pipette 10 ml hydroxylamine reagent into flask and swirl to mix. Pipette 10 ml orthophenanthroline reagent into the flask and swirl to mix.

Fill Nessler tubes to the 100 ml mark with the series of prepared standards and place in the rack leaving every other hole empty for insertion of the Nessler tube containing the prepared sample. The dilute iron standards should be prepared fresh daily since they are not stable for any appreciable length of time.

To Analyze for Total Iron. Mix the sample thoroughly and pipette 100 ml into a 250 ml Erlenmeyer flask. If the sample contains more than 2 ppm iron, dilute an aliquot portion with distilled water so that the value will be 2 ppm or less. Pipette 2 ml of 10% hydrochloric acid into the sample and boil until the volume is reduced to approximately 20 ml. Cool and transfer the sample to the volumetric flask, using distilled water to rinse from the Erlenmeyer to the volumetric flask. Dilute to the 100 ml mark with distilled water, stopper and invert to mix.

Transfer the contents of the volumetric flask into a clean 250 ml Erlenmeyer flask.

Do not use any rinse water. Pipette 10 ml hydroxylamine reagent into the flask and swirl to mix. Pipette 10 ml orthophenanthroline reagent into the flask and swirl to mix.

Fill a Nessler tube to the 100 ml mark with the prepared sample and place in the rack. Allow 10-15 minutes for color development. Then compare with the iron standards by looking down through the tubes, preferably using daylight as a source of light.

CALCULATION OF RESULTS. When a color match is obtained, record the value as parts per million total iron as Fe. If it was necessary to dilute the sample before starting the analysis, multiply by an appropriate factor.

LIMITATION OF TEST. Phosphates will interfere particularly in the form of polyphosphate. Chromium interferes; zinc in concentrations ten times that of iron; copper and cobalt above 5 ppm; nickel above 2 ppm; bismuth, silver, cadmium, mercury and molybdate are precipitated by phenanthroline.

If much color or organic is present, it may be necessary to evaporate the sample, gently ash, and redissolve in acid. Total iron can be determined in the range of 0.02 to 4.0 ppm. Higher concentrations of iron require the use of aliquots.

58

Manganese

MANGANESE is frequently encountered in iron bearing waters although it usually is present to a lesser extent than iron. The difficulties caused by the presence of each element are very similar and the methods employed for iron removal usually also effect the removal of manganese.

Manganese is encountered most frequently in well waters and usually is not present in excess of 3.0 ppm. Like iron, this element will deposit from solution, clogging piping, valves, etc., with a gray or black deposit of manganese hydroxide. The presence of manganese causes a water to produce undesirable stains in process work. For most industrial purposes, the manganese content of a water supply should not exceed 0.1 ppm and for many purposes, such as the manufacture of fine papers, even this quantity of manganese represents excessive contamination.

The U. S. Public Health Service Drinking Water Standards recommend that the manganese content of a potable water should not exceed 0.05 ppm. as Mn.

The methods used for manganese removal include aeration followed by filtration, contact filtration, lime or lime-soda softening and zeolite softening. As is the case with iron removal, for sodium zeolite softening to operate successfully it is necessary that contact with air be avoided prior to softening. If oxidation of the manganese occurred prior to sodium zeolite softening, the precipitation of manganese hydroxide would take place, clogging the zeolite bed.

TOTAL MANGANESE, PERSULFATE METHOD

THEORY OF TEST. This test is based upon the oxidation of manganous compounds to form permanganate. The oxidation is carried out in the presence of silver nitrate and mercuric sulfate in an acid medium. The color developed is matched with that of freshly prepared standards using Nessler tubes to make the comparison. A filter photometer or a spectrophotometer also may be used at a wave length of 525 mu with a minimum light path of 10 mm. When either of these instruments is employed, the values of manganese are read directly from calibration curves.

APPARATUS REQUIRED.
    1—Nessler tube rack (12 hole)
    12—Nessler tubes (2 matched sets of 6 each), 100 ml
    1—Flask, volumetric, 100 ml
    1—Flask, Erlenmeyer, 250 ml
    1—Pipette, delivery, 100 ml
    1—Pipette, Mohr, 5 ml
    1—Measuring dipper (plastic)
    1—Pipette, Mohr, 1 ml

CHEMICALS REQUIRED.
    Ammonium Persulfate
    Manganese Standard Solution, 10 ppm Mn
    Manganese Special Solution

PROCEDURE FOR TEST. Manganese may exist in a soluble form in a neutral water when a sample is first collected, but readily oxidizes and precipitates from solution or becomes adsorbed on the walls of the container. Manganese should therefore be determined soon after sample collection. Otherwise, the sample should be acidified at the time of collection.

Preparation of Standards. Prepare a series of standards in increments of 0.1 ppm Mn for use in the Nessler tubes. A typical series would cover the range of 0.0 to 1.0 ppm Mn.

Pipette 100 ml distilled water into a 250 ml Erlenmeyer flask. Add the manganese standard solution in increments of 1 ml using a graduated Mohr pipette. For example, if only 1 ml is added, then the standard will be equivalent to 0.1 ppm Mn; if 2 ml are added, the standard will be equivalent to 0.2 ppm Mn, etc. Pipette 5 ml of manganese special solution into the flask. Boil until the volume is reduced to approximately 90 ml. Add one (1) level plastic dipper (approx. 0.8 g) of ammonium persulfate and boil for one (1) minute. Cool and transfer to a 100 ml volumetric flask using a very small amount of distilled water to rinse from the Erlenmeyer flask into the volumetric flask. Fill the volumetric flask to the 100 ml mark with distilled water. Stopper and invert to mix thoroughly.

Fill Nessler tubes to the 100 ml mark with the series of prepared standards and place in the rack leaving every other hole empty for insertion of the Nessler tube containing the prepared sample. The dilute manganese standards should be prepared fresh daily since they are not stable for any appreciable length of time.

To Analyze for Total Manganese. Mix the sample thoroughly and pipette 100 ml into a 250 ml Erlenmeyer flask. If the sample contains more than 1 ppm manganese, dilute an aliquot portion with distilled water so that the value will be 1 ppm or less. Starting with the addition of 5 ml of manganese special solution, prepare the sample in exactly the same manner as that shown in the preparation for manganese standards.

Compare the color of the sample with that of the standards by placing the sample in the rack and looking down through the tubes. It is preferable to use daylight as a source of light.

CALCULATION OF RESULTS. When a color match is obtained, record the value as parts per million total manganese as Mn. If it was necessary to dilute the sample before starting the analysis, multiply by an appropriate factor.

LIMITATIONS OF TEST. The persulfate method is preferred for the determination of manganese in unknown samples because it is less subject to chloride interference and is more rapid for low manganese concentrations. Only minute amounts of bromide or iodide may be present. Small amounts of organic do not interfere if the period of heating and the amount of persulfate is increased. In the absence of interference, manganese may be determined in the range of 0.05-1.5 ppm with an accuracy of 1%.

59

Nitrate

THE nitrate ion is present in natural waters in relatively small quantities. Nitrogenous compounds may be introduced with sewage with the subsequent oxidation of these compounds to nitrate.

The U. S. Public Health Service Drinking Water Standards place no specific limit on the nitrate content of a water. Recently it has been found that high nitrate concentrations (10 ppm and above) appear to be the cause of methemeglobinemia in infants (blue babies). Such high nitrate concentrations seem to be confined to rural dug wells subject to surface influence.

In industrial water conditioning, the nitrate ion does not possess much significance except as affecting the quality of boiler water from the standpoint of embrittlement. Research has shown that the maintenance of certain sodium nitrate-sodium hydroxide ratios in boiler water can inhibit intercrystalline cracking (caustic metal embrittlement). Because of the widespread use of sodium nitrate to control embrittlement, the determination of the nitrate ion in boiler water has assumed increasing importance.

The nitrate concentration of a boiler water necessary to overcome embrittling tendencies will vary with the boiler water alkalinity and with the pressure of operation. It is customary to determine the sodium nitrate-sodium hydroxide ratio required for each individual plant by running tests with an embrittlement detector. Once the proper ratio has been determined, the sodium nitrate feed can be controlled on this basis. Occasionally, it will be found that the natural nitrate content of the raw water is sufficient after concentration in the boiler, to provide the necessary ratio. However, since the nitrate content of natural waters is subject to seasonal variation, it is still necessary to run control tests on the boiler water for nitrate concentrations in order to insure adequate nitrate content for inhibition of embrittlement.

NITRATE IN BOILER WATER, BRUCINE METHOD

THEORY OF TEST. This test is based on the development of a yellow-amber coloration produced by the reaction in sulfuric acid solution, of the brucine reagent with the nitrate content of the water sample. The color developed is matched with nitrate standards and the nitrate content in parts per million is read directly from the slide.

APPARATUS REQUIRED.
    1—Betz-Taylor Nitrate Comparator, complete (nitrate slide range 0-100 ppm)
    1—Beaker, 100 ml
    1—Cylinder, graduated, 10 ml
    1—Dropper, calibrated, 0.5 ml

CHEMICALS REQUIRED.
    Brucine Reagent
    Sulfuric Acid, Concentrated

PROCEDURE FOR TEST. Measure by means of the 10 ml graduate, 5 ml of the sample to be tested and pour into the 100 ml beaker. By means of the dropper add exactly ten drops of brucine reagent. Carefully measure 10 ml of sulfuric acid and slowly add to the contents of the beaker, avoiding spattering.

Swirl the beaker gently to mix, being careful to avoid spilling since the solution is now strongly acid. This solution will become warm following the addition of the acid.

Allow to stand five minutes after the addition of acid (four minutes minimum; six minutes maximum). Then add 10 ml dis-

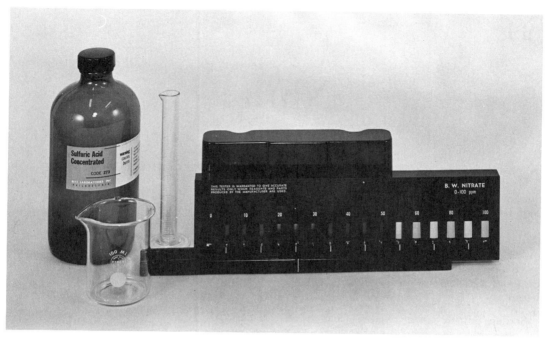

Figure 59-1 • Nitrate Determination—Brucine Method

tilled (or nitrate-free) water. Swirl carefully to mix. The solution may be cooled at this point if desired. Pour into one of the 5ml test tubes. Place this tube in the middle compartment of the comparator base. Fill two of the tubes with distilled water or clear tap water and place on either side of the sample (for most accurate results with highly colored water, prepare the two outside tubes with 5 ml sample, 10 ml sulfuric acid and 10 ml distilled water as outlined above, omitting the brucine reagent).

Place the color slide on the base and holding the instrument toward a source of daylight, move the slide in front of the test samples until a color match is obtained.

If nitrate exceeds 50 ppm, discard test. Take a 1.0 ml sample, dilute to 5 ml with distilled water and proceed as before, multiplying the observed nitrate reading by five to obtain parts per million nitrate as NO_3.

CALCULATION OF RESULTS. When a color match is obtained, the nitrate in parts per million as NO_3 is read directly from the values on the color standard slide.

LIMITATIONS OF TEST. This test is unaffected by ions in the concentrations normally encountered in boiler water. Chloride, sulfite, phosphate, iron, alkalinity, ammonium, calcium, magnesium and silica do not interfere. High tannin concentrations in excess of 800 color units cause interference, but this effect can be eliminated by dilution of the sample.

Although the slide covers the range of 0-100 ppm nitrate, it is difficult to distinguish the color difference above 50 ppm. For this reason, it is recommended that a diluted sample be taken if the observed nitrate value exceeds 50 ppm.

For the most accurate determination of nitrate, a photometer procedure is recommended. The same reagents and essentially the same procedure are employed, but the nitrate concentration is obtained from the photometer dial reading by reference to a calibration curve.

60

Nitrite

Nitrite is present in water as an intermediate compound in an oxidation or reduction process and represents a stage of the nitrogen cycle. In surface supplies, trace amounts of nitrite may indicate the presence of pollution. Nitrite also may be produced in treatment plants, water distribution systems or cooling systems as a result of the action of bacteria or other organisms on ammonia nitrogen.

Sodium nitrite can be used as a corrosion inhibitor in open circulating cooling water systems. While nitrites are sometimes regarded as reducing agents, they do possess oxidizing properties and probably for this reason tend to render metal surfaces passive to corrosive attack in weakly alkaline solutions. In acid solutions, however, nitrites do not render iron passive.

In order to establish a protective iron oxide film, it may be necessary to feed sodium nitrite initially at a greater concentration than normally required. The rate of feed can be reduced to normal once the protective film has been established. For most effective results, sodium nitrite should be fed continuously to the system. Decomposition problems frequently make it difficult to maintain effective nitrite concentrations in the circulating water without excessive feed rates.

Both oxidizing and reducing agents tend to destroy nitrite and certain bacteria also cause its decomposition. Where nitrite concentrations can be continuously maintained at an effective level, satisfactory protection of ferrous metals is secured. Nitrite is not very effective in the prevention of attack on copper or copper alloys.

NITRITE, DIRECT TITRATION METHOD

THEORY OF TEST. This test is based upon the determination of the nitrite content of a sample by titration in an acid medium with a standard oxidizing agent, potassium permanganate. The persistence of a definite pink color for one minute is taken as the endpoint.

APPARATUS REQUIRED.
  1—Burette, automatic, 25 ml
  1—Casserole, 210 ml
  1—Cylinder, graduated, 10 ml
  1—Stirring rod
  1—Timing device

CHEMICALS REQUIRED.
  Potassium Permanganate, N/100
  Sulfuric Acid, 5%

Note—Where facilities are available for accurate dilution, N/10 potassium permanganate may be used. This stronger solution is diluted in the ratio of 100 ml of N/10 potassium permanganate to 900 ml of distilled water, thus preparing 1000 ml of N/100 potassium permanganate solution.

PROCEDURE FOR TEST. Measure a 10 ml sample in the graduate, cool to room temperature and transfer to the casserole. Measure 3 ml of the 5% sulfuric acid in the 10 ml graduate and add the sample in the casserole. Use a 100 watt bulb directly over the casserole for illumination. Add the standard N/100 potassium permanganate from the burette drop by drop to the sample in the casserole, stirring constantly until a pink color starts to persist.

At this point of the determination add the permanganate 1 ml at a time with constant stirring. Continue to add the permanganate at the rate of 1 ml until a definite pink color persists for one minute. The time interval of one minute should be measured with a second hand or a stop watch.

CALCULATION OF RESULTS.

Formula:

$$\text{ppm nitrite as } NO_2 = \text{ml } N/100$$
$$\text{potassium permanganate} \times \frac{230}{\text{ml sample}}$$

Using a 10 ml sample, the nitrite in parts per million as NO_2 is equal to the ml of $N/100$ potassium permanganate multiplied by 23.

LIMITATIONS OF TEST. This method is rapid and adaptable for control purposes where sodium nitrite is used as a corrosion inhibitor. It is affected by any oxidizable substances in the water such as organic matter, sulfides, hydrogen sulfide and mercaptans. The presence of these interfering substances may cause the nitrite obtained from this titration to be shown as a higher value than actually present.

61

Oxygen (Dissolved)

Dissolved oxygen in water is caused by the solubility of atmospheric oxygen. The atmosphere consists essentially of nitrogen and oxygen and while both these gases are soluble to a certain extent in water, nitrogen is an inert gas and of minor importance. The term "dissolved oxygen" represents the amount of oxygen gas actually dissolved in a water and is in no way related to the combined oxygen present in the water molecule, H_2O.

Dissolved oxygen is present in all surface waters and rain waters due to their contact with the atmosphere. If sufficient agitation has taken place in contact with air, the dissolved oxygen content of the water will correspond to the saturation value for the temperature involved. The solubility of oxygen in water follows Henry's law which states that the concentration of dissolved gas in solution is directly proportional to the partial pressure of that gas in the free space above the liquid.

The mineral constituents of the water slightly affect the solubility of oxygen. Distilled water will absorb more oxygen than will waters containing higher solids content. Sea water, because of its high solids content, will dissolve less oxygen than will fresh waters.

Well waters usually contain less dissolved oxygen than surface waters and in deep well supplies, dissolved oxygen may be absent.

In addition to the natural occurrence of oxygen in water supplies, aeration is frequently employed in the removal of other gases such as carbon dioxide and hydrogen sulfide. Efficient aeration results in saturation of the water with dissolved oxygen.

Dissolved oxygen is objectionable in water used for industrial purposes because of the corrosive effect on iron and steel with which the water comes in contact. In cold and hot water lines, failure of piping may occur and the lines may become blocked with the products of corrosion. "Red water" and iron stains in process work may result because of the iron brought into solution by the corrosive attack of dissolved oxygen. Increased temperatures and low pH values accelerate oxygen attack.

In boiler systems, corrosion may result in feed lines, heaters, economizers, boilers, steam and return lines. In cooling water systems, corrosion of heat exchangers, engine jackets, pumps and piping may result.

In the majority of corrosion problems, the dissolved oxygen content of the water is the principal factor influencing corrosion. While corrosion may take place in the absence of oxygen, the usual procedure in the investigation of any corrosion problem is to first obtain data on the dissolved oxygen content throughout the system.

Elimination of the corrosive effect of dissolved oxygen can be accomplished by both direct and indirect means. The direct means involves the actual removal of dissolved oxygen from the water by mechanical or chemical deaeration and such direct action is usually applied to boiler feedwater systems. Indirect means are employed where the removal of oxygen is not feasible either from a technical or economic standpoint such as in recirculating cooling water systems. In such cases, the indirect means employed involves the use of corrosion inhibitors which exhibit a passivating influence on the metal surface. Alkaline chemicals may be used for the development of a protective scale film to prevent contact of the dissolved oxygen with the protected surface.

Removal of dissolved oxygen from water by mechanical deaeration is based on Henry's and Dalton's Laws and involves raising the water to the boiling temperature and continuously venting the mixture of gases and steam from a properly designed heater. This is the method of oxygen removal employed in the preparation of water for boiler feed purposes. Vacuum deaeration may be used on occasions where an increase in water temperature is undesirable.

Chemical deaeration is usually accomplished by the use of sodium sulfite, which reacts with oxygen to form sodium sulfate. At cold water temperatures, catalyzed sodium sulfite is required in order to secure sufficiently rapid reaction between sulfite and oxygen.

The use of a chromate salt is an example of one of the indirect means taken for the elimination of the corrosive effects of oxygen. By formation of a mixed oxide film on the metal surface, that surface is rendered passive to oxygen attack. A continuous supply of passivating agent to the metal surface is required in order to heal any breaks in the film. Because of the high concentration of passivating agent required for the prevention of corrosive attack, this method of treatment is usually only applicable to recirculating cooling water systems. Combination of phosphate with chromate in the Dianodic process permits the use of low treatment concentrations and extends the field of application for corrosion inhibitors.

A principle used for preventing the attack of dissolved oxygen in municipal pipe lines, once through cooling water systems, etc., involves rendering the water supersaturated with respect to calcium carbonate by the addition of alkaline treatment chemicals. Control is usually based on Langelier's Saturation Index. The theory behind this system of treatment relies on the formation of a thin film of calcium carbonate preventing contact of the dissolved oxygen with the surface to be protected. If not carefully controlled, heavy scale may develop. This method of treatment, similar to the use of sodium silicate, is limited

in application and is theoretically satisfactory for only one temperature. Close control is required to maintain the desired protection against corrosion without development of an undesirable formation of heavy scale.

DISSOLVED OXYGEN, WINKLER METHOD

THEORY OF TEST. The determination of dissolved oxygen in water is based on the absorption of oxygen by a flocculent precipitate of manganous sulfate and alkaline potassium iodide. The oxygen reacts with manganous hydroxide to form manganese hydroxide. Following acidification by sulfuric acid, free iodine is released in direct proportion to the amount of oxygen absorbed. The free iodine is then titrated with standard sodium thiosulfate in the presence of starch indicator. The disappearance of the blue color is taken as the endpoint.

APPARATUS REQUIRED.
  1—Bottle, ground-glass stoppered, 10 oz.
  2—Burette clamp
  1—Flask, Erlenmeyer, 250 ml
  1—Burette stand, iron
  1—Thermometer, armored (0-220 F)
  2—Pipette, safety bulb, 1 ml
  1—Pipette, safety bulb, 2 ml
  1—Microburette, self-filling, 2 ml
  1—Cylinder, graduated, 100 ml
  1—Tubing, glass, 10 inches
  1—Cooling coil, copper, 10 feet
  1—Tubing, sulfur free rubber, 10 feet
  1—Stirring rod, glass

CHEMICALS REQUIRED.
  Sulfuric Acid, 50%
  Manganous Sulfate
  Alkaline Potassium Iodide
  Sodium Thiosulfate, N/10
  Starch Indicator

PREPARATION OF N/100 SODIUM THIOSULFATE SOLUTION. Sodium thiosulfate, N/100, is not stable due to absorption of carbon dioxide from the air, and should be freshly prepared (or restandardized) at least every two weeks. To 90 ml distilled water (boiled and cooled to room temperature) add 10 ml N/10 sodium thiosulfate solution. Mix thoroughly and place in tightly stoppered bottle. Avoid unnecessary exposure of the solution to air.

PREPARATION OF SAMPLING EQUIPMENT. If the sample is above 70 F a copper coil should be employed. The inlet side of the cooling coil should be connected to the sampling point by means of a brass nipple, brass valve and suitable length of copper tubing. All of these connections should be of a size equivalent to the size of tubing comprising the coil. Iron should not be used. The discharge side of the cooling coil should be connected to a glass tube with a convenient length of sulfur free rubber tubing. The entire system described above must be air tight. The sample must be secured continuously from a point of the system at which the pressure is greater than atmosphere.

Place the cooling coil in a bucket or similar container into which a regulated flow of cooling water can be discharged and the overflow run to waste.

Secure a clean glass (or metal) container of such proportion that the capacity is approximately 3 or 4 times the volume of the 10 oz glass stoppered bottle used in this test. The height of the container should be at least 1 inch higher than the height of the bottle with the stopper inserted.

SECURING THE SAMPLE. Place the 10 oz bottle in the center of the glass container. Introduce the glass tube into the 10 oz bottle. Place the thermometer in the bottle.

Turn on the sampling line and by means of a valve adjust rate of flow into the bottle so that the bottle overflows approximately once per minute. Make certain no air bubbles are being discharged into the sample. Control the cooling water to the coil in the bucket to reduce and maintain the temperature of the sample to 70 F or less. The cooled sample will overflow the sampling bottle and in turn will continue to fill and overflow the outer container. Remove the glass tube from the bottle and place it in the outside space between the bottle and the outer container. Remove the thermometer in the same fashion. The sample should continue to run and overflow the outside glass container.

PROCEDURE FOR TEST. Fill a 1 ml pipette with manganous sulfate solution. To prevent the introduction of air to the sample be certain a drop of manganous sulfate hangs from the tip of the pipette. Insert the tip of the pipette through the water layer and well into the sample bottle. Permit exactly 1 ml of manganous sulfate to flow into the sample. Slowly withdraw the pipette and immediately repeat this procedure with alkaline potassium-iodide solution, employing a second clean 1 ml pipette.

Wet the glass stopper and gently drop straight into the neck of the sample bottle without removing the sample bottle from the outer container. Allow the stopper to "seat" by its own weight, then press down firmly. Remove the sample bottle from the outer container and mix the contents by gently rotating. Do not shake. Examine for air bubbles and if present the sample is worthless and the entire procedure must be repeated. If no air bubbles are present, replace the tightly stoppered bottle in the glass container and allow to stand three minutes to permit the floc to settle.

Carefully remove the stopper (under water) and add exactly 2 ml of 50% sulfuric acid into the bottle following the procedure for pipetting outlined above. Again replace the stopper. Remove the stoppered bottle and rotate gently to dissolve floc. The sample is now "fixed" and ready to titrate. The titration must be completed within five minutes to minimize errors from any interference.

Measure 200 ml of the fixed sample and pour into a flask. If the sample is colored yellow add N/100 sodium thiosulfate from the microburette with constant swirling, until the yellow color is almost discharged. Add 1 ml (approximately 20 drops) of starch indicator. The sample should turn blue. Continue to add N/100 sodium thiosulfate until one final drop turns the solution from blue to colorless. This is taken as the endpoint. Record to the second decimal the total number of ml of N/100 sodium thiosulfate required. If the 200 ml fixed sample is not colored yellow and does not turn blue upon addition of the starch indicator, the dissolved oxygen is recorded as "zero by the Winkler Method".

CALCULATION OF RESULTS.

Formula:

cc per liter dissolved oxygen =

ml N/100 sodium thiosulfate $\times \dfrac{1000}{\text{ml sample}}$

$\times$ .056

Using a 200 ml sample the dissolved oxygen in cc per liter is equal to the ml of N/100 sodium thiosulfate multiplied by 0.28.

Formula:

ppm dissolved oxygen =

ml N/100 sodium thiosulfate $\times \dfrac{1000}{\text{ml sample}}$

$\times$ .08

Using a 200 ml sample the dissolved oxygen in parts per million is equal to the ml of N/100 sodium thiosulfate multiplied by 0.4.

LIMITATIONS OF TEST. Nitrites, sulfites, ferric iron and certain types of organic matter interfere with this test. The proper securing of the sample, free from contamination by air, and the proper technique in making the determination are of utmost importance.

This method for determining dissolved oxygen is suitable for rapid determinations where the greatest precision and accuracy are not required. An accuracy of approximately 0.05 ppm may be expected. The method is not recommended for dissolved oxygen concentrations below 0.1 ppm and is not suitable for checking performance guarantees of deaerating feedwater heaters.

A colorimetric procedure for the determination of dissolved oxygen in low concentrations, 0 to 100 ppb, is available. This method of testing uses the dissolved oxygen present in the sample to oxidize a reduced solution of indigo carmine. As the reduced indigo carmine is oxidized, the color changes progressively from yellow through various shades of orange, pink and red to purple. When a standard amount of reduced indigo carmine is present in a known volume of sample, the resulting color indicates the amount of dissolved oxygen in parts per billion.

Where more precise methods for dissolved oxygen determinations are required, it is recommended that ASTM Tentative Method D888-49T be consulted.

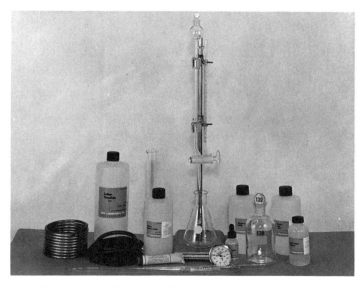

Figure 61-1 • Test Set for Dissolved Oxygen—Winkler Method

62

pH

EXACTLY defined, pH is the logarithm of the reciprocal of the hydrogen ion concentration. A more simple explanation is that the pH is a number between 0 and 14, denoting various degrees of acidity or alkalinity. Neutral water has a pH of 7. Values below 7 and approaching 0 are increasingly acid while values from 7 to 14 are increasingly alkaline.

Pure water ionizes to produce hydrogen or acid ions (H^+) and hydroxyl or alkaline ions (OH^-) as illustrated.

$$H_2O = H^+ + OH^-$$

When pure water ionizes in this manner 0.0000001 grams of hydrogen ion are liberated per liter. This number, which can also be written as 1×10^{-7} is inconvenient to handle, but on the pH scale is written simply as 7.

$$
\begin{array}{ccc}
 & H_2O & \\
H^+ & \longleftarrow | \longrightarrow & OH^- \\
\end{array}
$$

0 1 2 3 4 5 6 7 8 9 10 11 12 13 14

On the pH scale a value of 7 is exactly neutral. Proceeding to the left on the diagram and approaching "zero", indicates an increasing number of hydrogen ions present and increasing acidity. Proceeding to the right on the scale and more closely approaching a pH value of 14 indicates an increasing number of hydroxyl ions and increasing alkalinity.

The further the pH is located from the neutral point of 7, the greater is the concentration of hydrogen or hydroxyl ions, but not in direct arithmetical proportion to the distance between each number. A pH of 7 means 0.0000001 grams of ionizable hydrogen are liberated per liter. A pH of 6 means 0.000001 grams of ionizable hydrogen per

liter are liberated or 10 times the amount of a pH of 7. In a similar manner, a pH of 5 indicates 10 times the number of hydrogen ions liberated as compared to those available at a pH of 6 and 100 times the number as compared to a pH of 7. In short, each number on the pH scale is 10 times the concentration of hydrogen or hydroxyl ions when compared with its adjoining number. The following table will serve to further clarify this point.

H-ion Concentration
(gm Ionizable H^+ per liter)

pH		
0.0	1.0	10^0
1.0	0.1	10^{-1}
2.0	0.01	10^{-2}
3.0	0.001	10^{-3}
4.0	0.0001	10^{-4}
5.0	0.00001	10^{-5}
6.0	0.000001	10^{-6}
7.0	0.0000001	10^{-7}
8.0	0.00000001	10^{-8}
9.0	0.000000001	10^{-9}
10.0	0.0000000001	10^{-10}
11.0	0.00000000001	10^{-11}
12.0	0.000000000001	10^{-12}
13.0	0.0000000000001	10^{-13}
14.0	0.00000000000001	10^{-14}

The pH of most natural waters will fall within the range of 6.0-8.0, although more acid conditions and lower pH will result where the water contains high concentrations of free carbon dioxide or acid mine drainage. A pH above 8.0 is seldom encountered except where pollution by alkaline trade wastes exists or where the water has been chemically treated such as by the lime-soda process.

Since pH is a measure of the relative acidity or alkalinity of a water, it is a most important factor influencing scale forming or corrosive tendencies. A low pH will give rise to corrosion of equipment with which the water comes in contact. High pH values may cause precipitation of calcium carbonate from solution as a scale on the surfaces of pipe lines, heat exchange equipment, condensers, etc. In the calculation of the stability of a water in accordance with Langelier's equation, the determination of pH is required.

In clarification processes, probably the most important determination is pH since the control of coagulation is primarily a matter of pH control, with every coagulant possessing an optimum pH range for most efficient operation. In lime-soda softening, pH is not usually required for control purposes because the proper pH is automatically established with correct control of phenolphthalein and methyl orange alkalinity. In softening for calcium removal, however, pH control is quite important in order to insure proper calcium removal without also precipitating magnesium hydroxide.

For zeolite softening employing siliceous exchange materials, it is generally considered that the pH of the influent water should be in the range of 7.0-8.3 and between 4.3-8.3 where carbonaceous zeolite materials are employed. Some newer ion exchange resins can tolerate high pH and high temperature. Development of exchange materials of this type made possible the use of the hot lime-hot ion exchange process.

Control of pH is an important factor in such processes as iron removal, recarbonation and acid treatment. The pH value of a boiler water is usually adjusted to a minimum of 10.5 to prevent acidic corrosion and to provide a sufficiently high pH for the precipitation of the scale forming salts.

In general, it can be stated that wherever a water analysis is to be interpreted with respect to scale forming or corrosive tendencies, such an analysis is incomplete without a determination of pH. In the control of various treatment processes and in the prevention of scale and corrosion in piping, heat

exchangers, economizers, boilers, turbines, etc., pH is one of the most important control factors.

pH, COLORIMETRIC METHOD

THEORY OF TEST. The numerical expression of pH value denotes the degree of acidity or alkalinity of a sample. A pH of 7.0 represents the neutral point; values below 7.0 indicating acidity and those above 7.0 indicating alkalinity. The colorimetric determination of pH is based on the use of different indicators, each indicator covering a portion of the pH range. Each indicator gives different color reactions from the indicator immediately adjacent to it and gives different shades of color over its own range.

APPARATUS AND CHEMICALS REQUIRED.
1—Taylor pH Comparator
2—Adjustment tubes

Standard Slides and Indicators

pH Range of Slide	Indicator
0.2— 1.8	Acid Cresol Red
1.2— 2.8	Acid Meta Cresol Purple
2.4— 4.0	Benzo Yellow
3.0— 4.6	Bromphenol Blue
3.8— 5.4	Bromcresol Green
4.4— 6.0	Methyl Red
5.2— 6.8	Chlorphenol Red
6.0— 7.6	Bromthymol Blue
6.8— 8.4	Phenol Red
7.2— 8.8	Cresol Red
7.6— 9.2	Meta Cresol Purple
8.0— 9.6	Thymol Blue
8.6—10.2	Phthalein Red
10.0—11.6	Acyl Red
11.0—12.6	Parazo Orange
12.0—13.6	Acyl Blue

PROCEDURE FOR TEST. The determination of pH preferably should be made on a freshly obtained sample, tightly stoppered to prevent contact with air. The sample should not be filtered. If stored, samples should be kept in Pyrex or other resistant glass bottles. Plastic bottles such as polyethylene also are suitable.

Fill three 5.0 ml test tubes to the mark with sample and place in the comparator base. To the middle test tube, add 0.5 ml of indicator by means of the calibrated dropper and mix thoroughly. (Do not place thumb over end of test tube.) Place the color standard slide on the base and holding the instrument toward a source of daylight, move the slide in front of the test samples until a color match is obtained.

CALCULATION OF RESULTS. When a match is obtained, the pH is then read directly from the values on the color standard slide.

PROCEDURE FOR STANDARDIZATION OF INDICATORS. The pH of indicator solutions may change due to direct sunlight, long exposure to air and acid or alkaline fumes. It is possible to check this point and restandardize those indicators in aqueous solution.

The indicators in aqueous solutions are:

Bromphenol Blue	3.0—4.6 pH
Bromcresol Green	3.8—5.4 pH
Chlorphenol Red	5.2—6.8 pH
Bromthymol Blue	6.0—7.6 pH
Phenol Red	6.8—8.4 pH
Cresol Red	7.2—8.8 pH
Meta Cresol Purple	7.6—9.2 pH
Thymol Blue	8.0—9.6 pH

About 0.5 ml of the indicator solution is placed in the larger of the adjustment tubes, the smaller tube filled with distilled water and inserted. A thin layer of indicator is thus formed between the two tubes and the shade and intensity of this layer should correspond to the color standard in the middle of that pH range. As an example, with bromthymol blue indicator, the proper pH is 6.8. The pair of tubes is then placed in the comparator base and compared with the slide. If the pH read is too low, approximately 0.1 N NaOH is added a drop at a time to 100 ml of stock indicator solution, the solution being thoroughly mixed and tested after each addition. If the pH read is too high, the same procedure is applied with approximately 0.1 N HCl.

The other pH indicators, of the alcoholic type, cannot be checked by means of adjustment tubes. Their accuracy can be checked by comparing the indicated pH of a water sample versus the pH obtained electrometrically. Because the alcoholic indicators cannot be adjusted, it is advisable to use the aqueous indicators wherever possible.

LIMITATIONS OF TEST. Particularly with weakly buffered solutions it is essential that the proper indicator be employed as the pH of the indicator may change the pH of the solution under test. Indicators and slides should be chosen so that the pH of the sample is in the middle of the range. A color match with the first or last standard in any slide should never be taken as an accurate determination. Certain specific substances in the water to be tested, such as free chlorine and hypochlorites, affect the color produced by the indicator and may yield erratic results. Under proper conditions the sensitivity of the colorimetric pH method is approximately 0.1 pH.

pH, GLASS ELECTRODE METHOD

THEORY OF TEST. The pH or hydrogen ion concentration of a solution may be measured by determining, with a potentiometer, the voltage developed by two electrodes which are in contact with the solution. The voltage of one electrode known as a calomel half-cell is fixed, while the voltage of the other electrode varies with the pH of the sample. Several types of electrodes may be used, but in general a glass electrode is the most applicable for industrial use. A glass surface of the proper composition separating two solutions gives potentials which are directly proportional to the pH. Due to the high resistance of the circuit, it is necessary to employ some type of electronic device to amplify the current.

APPARATUS REQUIRED.

1—Electrometric pH Meter

PROCEDURE FOR TEST. The exact mechanical procedure for determining pH will vary slightly with the instruments furnished by different manufacturers. However, in general, the instrument is first standardized by using a buffer solution of known pH. The temperature of the sample to be tested is observed and a temperature correction dial on the instrument is adjusted. The electrodes are then inserted in the water sample and the

Figure 62-1 • Taylor pH Comparator

pH is read directly on a dial on the instrument.

LIMITATIONS OF TEST. Glass electrode potentials are not affected by oxidizing or reducing agents, gases, dissolved organic compounds, colloids or suspended matter. The pH of viscous solutions or highly colored solutions may be obtained by this method. Accuracy is superior to colorimetric methods. In high concentrations of sodium ions, an error is introduced which can be corrected by suitable curves, or by standardizing the instrument for that range.

In addition to the determination of pH, an electrometric pH meter can be employed in titrations in place of the various organic indicators. A titration is carried out to the pH value equivalent to the point of color change of the indicator. (Example: Phenolphthalein indicator changes at approximately pH 8.3.) This method of titration is particularly useful where the sample is highly colored, masking color endpoints.

Electrometric pH meters are available either as battery operated or line operated models. In general, the line operated unit will prove most satisfactory.

63

Phosphate

THE phosphate ion rarely occurs naturally in a raw water. The determination of phosphate usually is made in order to control chemical treatment containing phosphate. While the phosphate test is employed most frequently in boiler water conditioning, the determination of ortho and polyphosphate is used also as a control test in the treatment of water in cooling systems, distribution lines, etc. where polyphosphates are employed for scale and corrosion control.

In cooling water systems, the surface active properties of the polyphosphates are employed to advantage in preventing the precipitation of calcium carbonate. By use of these materials and organic surface active agents as well, it is possible to retain calcium carbonate in solution at a positive saturation index which would otherwise result in scale formation. In water distribution lines, municipal systems, etc., the polyphosphates are used for control of tuberculation and some reduction in corrosion. The metal savings through the use of low concentrations of the polyphosphates is not outstanding, but these materials are useful in controlling tuberculation and head losses. Phosphate, in combination with chromate, is widely used in corrosion control in open recirculating cooling water as an essential component of the Dianodic method. This combination of two anodic inhibitors, in the proper ratio and under controlled pH conditions effectively inhibits pitting and tuberculation and provides superior protection compared to the use of either of these inhibitors alone.

In boiler feedwater conditioning, the phosphate test is employed for control of internal conditioning. Under favorable conditions phosphate will react with calcium to form tricalcium phosphate, an insoluble precipitate. However, it is possible to form two soluble forms of calcium phosphate—monocalcium phosphate and dicalcium phosphate. In other words, in order to completely precipitate the calcium hardness, it is necessary to form tricalcium phosphate. Otherwise, part of the hardness will remain in solution as monocalcium and dicalcium phosphate. In order to accomplish this precipitation, it is necessary to maintain a pH value of 9.5 or higher.

The soluble phosphate which is determined by the phosphate test is sometimes referred to as the "excess" phosphate content. The soluble phosphate is that phosphate which is present over and above that required to precipitate the calcium hardness. It is generally desirable to maintain a soluble phosphate content of approximately 30-60 ppm to drive the reaction of calcium and phosphate to completion, and to assure the immediate removal of any calcium hardness entering the boiler in the feedwater. However, operating conditions may alter the concentrations of soluble phosphate which must be maintained in the boiler water. For example, when it is not economically feasible to externally remove high silica concentrations present in the boiler feedwater, the formation of silica scale can be minimized by carrying soluble phosphate concentrations in the boiler water.

The phosphate type internal treatment, while possessing many advantages when properly employed also has the disadvantage of increasing the tendency of a boiler water to carryover. However, it is not the soluble or excess phosphate measured in the phosphate test which increases the tendency to carryover. Instead, it is the small particles of calcium phosphate precipitate which tend to stabilize boiler water foam.

ORTHOPHOSPHATE, COLORIMETRIC METHOD

THEORY OF TEST. This test is based on the formation of phosphomolybdic acid through the reaction of the molybdate reagent with the phosphate present in the water. The phosphomolybdic acid is then reduced by stannous ion to give a blue color, the intensity of which is proportional to the amount of phosphate present.

APPARATUS REQUIRED.
 1—Taylor Phosphate Comparator (slide range 5-100 ppm PO_4)
 1—Funnel, glass, 3″ diameter
 1—Filter paper, Whatman No. 5, 12.5 cm
 1—Mixing tube (5, 15, 17.5 ml, graduated)

CHEMICALS REQUIRED.
 Molybdate Reagent
 Stannous Reagent, Dry (with dipper)

PROCEDURE FOR TEST. The temperature of the sample should be in the range of 70-100 F. Filter the sample through No. 5 Whatman filter paper. Discard the first 10-20 ml of filtrate since there is slight adsorption of phosphate by fresh filter paper. Filter the sample until clear, pouring the filtrate back through the filter paper if necessary to obtain a clear filtrate. *It is important that no suspended matter be present in the filtered sample.*

(Range 5-100 ppm as PO_4)

Use a mixing tube graduated at 5, 15 and 17.5 ml. Fill the mixing tube to the lowest mark (5 ml) with the filtered sample. Add molybdate reagent to the second mark (15 ml). Add distilled or phosphate-free water to the third mark (17.5 ml). Stopper and mix well. Add 1 level brass dipperful of stannous reagent. Stopper and mix well. A blue color will develop, the intensity of which is proportional to the phosphate present. Read the phosphate value in 2 minutes.

Place the mixing tube in the middle compartment in the base. Fill the two test tubes on either side with filtered sample. Place the color slide on the base and holding the instrument toward a source of daylight, move the slide in front of the test samples until a color match is obtained.

If the sample is highly colored, as with organic present, color comparison will be affected. Instead of filling the two side tubes with filtered sample, these blanks should be prepared by mixing 5 ml of filtered sample, 10 ml of molybdate reagent and 2.5 ml of distilled water.

(Range 0-25 ppm as PO_4)

Prepare the filtered sample as described previously. Use a mixing tube graduated at 10 and 14 ml. Fill the mixing tube to the first mark (10 ml) with the filtered sample. Add molybdate to the second mark (14 ml). Stopper and mix well. Add 1 level brass dipperful of stannous reagent. Stopper and mix well. A blue color will develop, the intensity of which is proportional to the phosphate present. Read the phosphate value in 1 minute.

CALCULATION OF RESULTS. When a match is obtained, the phosphate in parts per million as PO_4 is then read directly from the values on the color standard slide.

LIMITATIONS OF TEST. This test is unaffected by most of the ions in the concentrations normally encountered in boiler and cooling water. Up to 150 ppm chromate as CrO_4 can be tolerated. It is essential that the sample taken for test be free of suspended precipitates since calcium phosphate, if present, would be placed in solution by the acidic nature of the reagents. The phosphate value thus obtained would be erroneously high due to the phosphate precipitate dissolved in this manner.

The use of a photometer with essentially the same procedure will provide additional accuracy. Where phosphate in relatively low concentration is to be determined, as in certain cooling water applications, the photometer procedure is preferred for close control.

TOTAL PHOSPHATE, PHOTOMETRIC METHOD

THEORY OF TEST. This test is based on the

formation of phosphomolybdic acid through the reaction of the molybdate reagent with the phosphate present in the sample. The phosphomolybdic acid is then reduced by the stannous ion to yield a blue color which is proportional to the phosphate content of the sample which is measured by comparison of the photometer dial reading with a calibration curve.

APPARATUS REQUIRED.
Filter photometer complete with assorted laboratory glassware.

CHEMICALS REQUIRED.
Hydrochloric Acid, Concentrated, C.P.
Molybdate Reagent
Phenolphthalein Indicator
Stannous Chloride, Crystals
Standard Phosphate Solution, 45 ppm PO_4
Sodium Hydroxide, 7N
Sulfuric Acid, 50%

PROCEDURE FOR TEST. A fresh concentrated stock of solution of stannous chloride should be prepared once each month. For this purpose add 12 gms stannous chloride crystals to 88 gms of C.P. concentrated hydrochloric acid. Store in an amber bottle away from light. Keep container tightly closed.

The dilute stannous chloride reagent used in this test must be prepared fresh daily. The dilute reagent consists of 1.0 ml concentrated stannous chloride diluted to a total volume of 40 ml with distilled water.

This procedure employs a wave length of 610 mu and a light path of 5 mm. Prepare calibration curves for the photometer using successive dilutions of the phosphate standard to adequately cover the range of phosphate in the samples to be tested. Two curves are required—one for orthophosphate and one for total phosphate. The dilutions of the standard should be treated in exactly the same manner as that shown below for analysis of the water samples.

Each time a determination is made the calibration curves should be checked to establish a correction factor. This procedure is necessary to insure that the results are accurate since reagent age and stability as well as temperature can affect the results. Each curve should be checked with phosphate-free water and also at a dilution of the phosphate standard that approximates the middle of the phosphate range covered by the curves. It is very important that the "check" samples are analyzed at the same time, under the same conditions and treated in the same manner as the actual water samples. Do not omit any of the steps such as the conversion procedure, etc.

Phosphate must be determined on a filtered sample, using a filter paper such as Whatman No. 5. Discard the first 10-20 ml of filtrate since there is a slight adsorption of phosphate by fresh filter paper.

To Determine Orthophosphate. Prepare a "zero" reference blank by adding a beaker 5 ml of clear sample, 10 ml molybdate reagent and 2.5 ml distilled water. Use this solution to set the photometer at "zero" immediately prior to test.

To a second beaker add 5 ml clear sample, 10 ml molybdate reagent and 2.5 ml dilute stannous reagent. Allow to stand one (1) minute and then immediately obtain photometer dial reading.

To Determine Total Phosphate. In order to determine total phosphate, it is necessary to convert all polyphosphate in the sample to orthophosphate. Place two 25 ml clear samples in separate 125 ml Erlenmeyer flasks. One sample is to be used as a blank and the other for analysis. To each flask add 2.5 ml 50% sulfuric acid. Boil both the blank and the sample vigorously for at least 30 minutes. Add distilled water periodically so that the volume does not fall below 5 ml. If the volume does fall below 5 ml, the sample must be discarded. If it is not convenient to observe the sample continuously during boiling, reflux condensers may be employed.

Cool the blank and the sample to room temperature. Add 3 drops phenolphthalein indicator to each flask and neutralize with 7N sodium hydroxide (approximately 5 ml will be required) until a faint permanent pink appears. Add 50% sulfuric acid, drop by drop, until the solutions turn colorless.

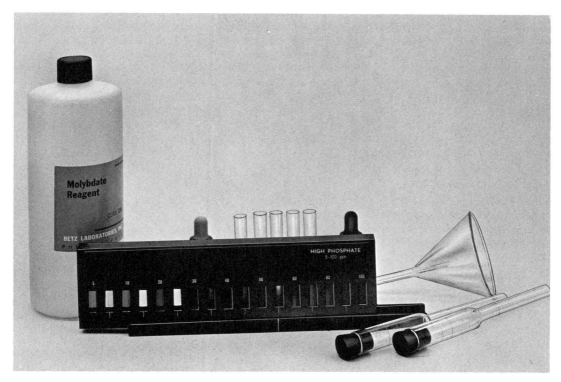

Figure 63-1 • Phosphate Comparator

Since some heat may be generated during neutralization, re-cool and then adjust the volumes to exactly 25 ml with distilled water. A precipitate may form at this point but do not filter.

The total phosphate now can be determined. Measure 5 ml of the blank and 5 ml of the sample after shaking to be sure a representative amount of any precipitate is included. Proceed in exactly the same manner as shown for orthophosphate.

CALCULATION OF RESULTS. The orthophosphate and total phosphate values in parts per million as PO_4 are obtained directly from their respective calibration curves. The polyphosphate concentration is obtained by subtracting the value for orthophosphate from the value for total phosphate.

LIMITATIONS OF TEST. This procedure is not affected by most of the ions normally present in water. Up to 150 ppm chromate at CrO_4 can be tolerated. Up to 40 ppm phosphate can be determined without dilution of the sample. Concentrations above 40 ppm can be determined by diluting *the original sample* with distilled water prior to treatment following the procedure outlined, and multiplying result by the appropriate factor.

64

Silica

SILICA can be present in water in two distinct and separate forms. It is conventionally expressed in a water analysis as silicon dioxide (SiO_2). Actually, silica exists in water in both the crystalloidal and colloidal forms. In the colloidal form, silica is not in solution, but is in suspension in a very finely divided form. This form of silica usually can be removed by proper coagulation and filtration. Silica in the crystalloidal or soluble form, however, is extremely difficult to remove and it is in this form that it occasions the greatest difficulty with scale formation.

Silicon is the second most abundant chemical element found on the earth and, therefore, this element in the form of at least one of its many compounds is found in greater or lesser amounts in all natural waters. The solid crust of the earth is made up of approximately 80 to 90% silicates or other compounds of silicon. Water passing through or over the earth's surface dissolves silica as one of its impurities.

The silica content of natural waters will vary to a considerable extent depending on the locality. There is a general tendency, however, for silica to be higher in waters where the hardness is low and the alkalinity somewhat high. The Pacific Northwest and many Southern states exhibit waters of this character, as do certain sections of New England. Where waters are high in alkalinity, there are a large number of sodium ions present; such ions combine with silicon forming a soluble sodium silicate.

Silica may cause difficulty by forming calcium and magnesium silicate scale where water is used in once through heat exchange processes and in recirculating cooling water systems.

The presence of silica is particularly objectionable in water used for boiler feed purposes as it may lead to the formation of hard dense scales which have unusually high resistance to heat transfer. In boilers operating at relatively low pressures, the silicate scale formed is mostly calcium silicate. In such instances, softening of the water for removal of the calcium ions usually is sufficient to control such incrustation. In higher pressure boilers, the solution to the problem is not so easily obtained. The silica present will combine in such instances with other elements forming a hard scale even though calcium and magnesium are not present in any appreciable amounts in the boiler feedwater. Complex sodium alumino-silicate scales have been identified in high pressure boilers and the formation of these scales may take place in high pressure boiler operation even with a relatively low hardness and silica content of the boiler feedwater.

In addition to the difficulty of boiler scale formation, a very serious problem encountered in high pressure operation is in the deposition of siliceous materials on turbine blades and in superheaters. Serious loss on turbine efficiency results from insoluble silica turbine blade deposits caused by vaporization of silica from the boiler water.

Soluble silica is relatively inert and cannot be precipitated by other chemicals to form insoluble compounds, as can be done with most of the inorganic chemicals present as water impurities. It is this fact which has made the problem of silica removal rather difficult. Successful processes for silica removal involve adsorption of silica from solution. Hot process silica removal by magnesium salts is a process frequently employed. Silica also may be removed by the use of highly basic anion exchange resins in conjunction with demineralization.

SOLUBLE SILICA, TAYLOR COMPARATOR METHOD

THEORY OF TEST. This test is based on the development of the yellow silico-molybdate color produced by the reaction of ammonium molybdate in acidic solution with the silica present in the water sample. The color developed is matched with silica standards and the silica content in ppm is read directly from the slide.

APPARATUS REQUIRED.
1—Taylor Water Analyzer complete (silica slide range 0.0-25.0 ppm)
2—Flasks, Erlenmeyer, 250 ml
1—Cylinder, graduated, 50 ml
1—Pipette, Mohr, 5 ml
2—Pipettes, Mohr, 1 ml

CHEMICALS REQUIRED.
Ammonium Molybdate Reagent
Hydrochloric Acid, 50%
Oxalic Acid, 10%

PROCEDURE FOR TEST. Add 1 ml of hydrochloric acid and 4 ml of ammonium molybdate solution to 100 ml of clear sample. If the sample is not clear before addition of reagents it should be filtered. Stir well and after allowing the sample to stand for 1 minute (do not allow the sample to stand longer than 10 minutes) transfer enough of the sample to one of the comparator tubes to bring the level of the liquid up to the mark on the tube. A yellow color will develop if silica is present. Place this tube in the middle compartment of the Analyzer. The tubes on each side should contain the same water as that being tested to blank out any color present in the sample. In order to compensate for the dilution in volume through addition of reagents, the blank on either side of the sample being tested should be prepared by the addition of 1 ml hydrochloric acid and 4 ml of distilled water per 100 ml sample.

Place the instrument so that the comparator tubes point toward a source of daylight. Read instrument by viewing the reflection in the mirror and *not by looking down through the tubes*. Move the slide in front of the test sample until a color match is obtained.

If the silica exceeds 25.0 ppm, discard test. Take a smaller sample, dilute with distilled water to 100 ml and proceed as before, multiplying observed silica value by the proper factor to obtain parts per million.

The color due to phosphates can be destroyed by oxalic acid. When phosphates are present, proceed as above, permitting the maximum color to develop in the Water Analyzer tube (1-2 minutes). Then, add 1 ml of 10% oxalic acid, mix and read as usual.

CALCULATION OF RESULTS. Using a 100 ml sample, silica as SiO_2 is read directly in parts per million from the slide.

LIMITATIONS OF TEST. This method does not determine suspended silica; tannin and reducing substances interfere. Strong mineral acids will prevent the development of maximum color. Hydrogen sulfide interferes and must be removed by boiling.

SOLUBLE SILICA, PHOTOMETRIC METHOD HIGH RANGE (4-40 ppm)

THEORY OF TEST. This method tests for soluble silica by formation of the yellow silico-molybdate complex followed by reduction to the molybdate blue color. The blue color produced is proportional to the silica content of the sample and is measured by the photometer dial reading.

APPARATUS REQUIRED.
Filter photometer complete with assorted laboratory glassware.

CHEMICALS REQUIRED.*
Hydrochloric Acid Reagent
Ammonium Molybdate Reagent (high range)
Sodium Sulfite Reagent
Silica Standard, 50 ppm SiO_2

*All reagents should be stored in silica-free containers such as polyethylene bottles.

PROCEDURE FOR TEST. This procedure employs a wave length of 690 mu and a cell with a light path of approximately 10 mm. Prepare a calibration curve for the photometer using successive dilutions of the silica standard to adequately cover the anticipated range of silica in the samples to be tested. The dilutions of the standard should be treated in exactly the same manner as that shown below for analysis of the water samples.

Each time a determination is made the calibration curve should be checked to establish a correction factor. This procedure is necessary to insure that the results are accurate since reagent age and stability as well as temperature can affect the results. The curve should be checked with silica-free water and also at a dilution of the silica standard that approximates the middle of the silica range covered by the curve. All reagents as well as the "check" samples and the actual sample to be analyzed must be at the same temperature.

Prepare a "zero" reference blank. To a beaker, add 10 ml of the clear sample, 5 ml hydrochloric acid reagent, 5 ml distilled water and 10 ml sodium sulfite reagent. Use this blank to set the photometer at "zero" immediately prior to the test of a sample.

To a second beaker add 10 ml sample, 5 ml hydrochloric acid reagent and 5 ml of ammonium molybdate reagent. Allow to stand at least one minute, but not more than five minutes. Then add 10 ml of sodium sulfite reagent. Allow to stand exactly one minute and immediately obtain dial reading.

CALCULATION OF RESULTS. The silica in parts per million as SiO_2 is obtained by reference to the silica calibration curve.

LIMITATIONS OF TEST. This procedure is not affected by phosphate, iron, sulfate, chloride and organic matter such as tannins. Alkalinity above 350 ppm as $CaCO_3$ interferes slightly depending on the silica content. Phosphate above 150 ppm gives slightly low results. The effect of high alkalinity and high phosphate can be completely eliminated by testing a diluted sample. This method, by eliminating the interference of tannins and

phosphate, possesses an advantage over comparator and photometric methods employing the yellow silico-molybdate color.

Up to 40 ppm silica can be determined without dilution of the sample. Concentrations above 40 ppm can be determined by diluting the original sample with distilled water, following the procedure outlined, and multiplying result by the appropriate factor.

This method is not sufficiently accurate for the determination of silica in condensed steam samples where silica vaporization may be a problem. The low range silica procedure is required for such samples, covering the range of approximately 0.0-3.0 ppm silica.

SOLUBLE SILICA, PHOTOMETRIC METHOD LOW RANGE (0.0-3.0 ppm)

THEORY OF TEST. The low range silica test also relies on the measurement of the molybdenum blue color from the photometer dial readings. However, amino-naphthol-sulfonic acid is employed as the reducing agent instead of sodium sulfite.

APPARATUS REQUIRED.
Filter photometer complete with assorted laboratory glassware

CHEMICALS REQUIRED.*
Ammonium Molybdate Reagent (low range)
Oxalic Acid, 3%
Amino-Naphthol-Sulfonic Acid
Silica Standard, 50 ppm SiO_2

*All reagents should be stored in silica-free containers such as polyethylene bottles.

PROCEDURE FOR TEST. This procedure employes a wave length of 690 mu and a cell with a light path of 40 mm. Prepare a calibration curve for the photometer using successive dilutions of the silica standard to adequately cover the anticipated range of silica in the samples to be tested. The dilutions of the standard should be treated in exactly the same manner as that shown below for analysis of the water samples.

Each time a determination is made the calibration curve should be checked to establish a correction factor. This procedure is necessary to insure that the results are accurate since reagent age and stability as well as temperature can affect the results. The curve should be checked with silica-free water and also at a dilution of the silica standard that approximates the middle of the silica range covered by the curve. All reagents as well as the "check" samples and the actual sample to be analyzed must be at the same temperature.

The amino-naphthol-sulfonic acid reagent used in this test is not stable and should be prepared once each week. Dissolve 1.0 g of 1-amino, 2-naphthol, 4-sulfonic acid in 4.5 ml of 1N sodium hydroxide. Add with 60 g sodium bisulfite and 2 g sodium sulfite to 900 ml distilled water. Dilute to 1.0 liter with distilled water.

Prepare a "zero" reference blank. To a beaker, add 50 ml of the clear sample, 5 ml oxalic acid, 5 ml sulfonic acid and 5 ml distilled water. Use this blank to set the photometer at "zero" immediately prior to the test of a sample.

To a second beaker, add 50 ml sample, and 5 ml ammonium molybdate reagent. Allow to stand approximately 5 minutes. Add 5 ml oxalic acid reagent. Wait approximately one minute and then add 5 ml sulfonic acid reagent. Allow to stand exactly two minutes and immediately obtain dial reading.

CALCULATION OF RESULTS. The silica concentration in parts per million as SiO_2 is obtained by reference to the prepared silica calibration curve.

LIMITATIONS OF TEST. This procedure is primarily intended for the determination of silica in the low concentrations that may be present in condensed steam samples. The method is not affected by the presence of ions such as phosphate, in the concentrations which would be present in samples of such purity. A precision of approximately 0.02 ppm silica can be secured.

65

Solids
(Total, Dissolved, Suspended)

Suspended solids are those solids which are not in true solution and which can be removed by filtration. Total solids represent the sum of the dissolved and suspended solids. The value for total solids is frequently defined as Total Residue.

The origin of the dissolved solids present in a natural water supply lies in the solvent action of water in contact with the minerals in the earth. Suspended solids are contributed by small particles of insoluble matter, mechanically introduced by turbulent action of the water on the soil. Both suspended and dissolved solids may be introduced by domestic and industrial wastes.

The U. S. Public Health Service Drinking Water Standards recommend that the total solids of a potable supply be limited to 500 ppm for a water of good quality. However, these standards also state if such water is not available, a total solids content of 1000 ppm may be permitted. While the standards are so worded with respect to total solids that no limits are placed directly on dissolved and suspended solids, a practical limit on suspended solids content is covered by the additional restriction that the turbidity of the water should not exceed 10 units.

Suspended solids are objectionable in process work, boiler feed and cooling water conditioning. Since the determination of suspended solids is a gravimetric procedure, it is customary to set up standards of water quality on the basis of the more rapid turbidity test. Since turbidity is caused by the presence of suspended solids, limits on water quality based on the turbidity test effectively limit the suspended solids content.

The dissolved solids of a natural water are usually composed of the sulfate, bicarbonate and chloride of calcium, magnesium and sodium. Each of these individual ions may produce an effect, specific to that ion, dependent on whether the water is employed in process work, or as boiler feed or cooling water.

Limits on the total or dissolved solids content of a water may be imposed where the cumulative effect of various ions may make a water undesirable even where no individual constituent has exceeded a tolerable limit. For example, where water is used in beverage manufacture or ice making, it is customary to stipulate limits on the dissolved solids content of the water. In boiler feedwater conditioning, the American Boiler Manufacturer's Association guarantees on steam purity specify certain maximum total solids content of the boiler water, dependent on the operating pressure. Even though no individual ion may have reached a dangerous concentration, the additive effect of the various boiler water constituents may produce a tendency for carryover.

The removal of suspended solids is accomplished by the processes employed for the removal of turbidity, namely the use of subsidence, coagulation and filtration.

Dissolved solids, depending on their character, may be reduced by various treatment processes. Sodium zeolite softening, which replaces calcium and magnesium ions with sodium ions, does not lower the dissolved solids content. Dependent on the water characteristics, sodium-hydrogen zeolite softening and lime-soda softening may affect a considerable reduction in dissolved solids. For complete removal of dissolved solids from a water however, it is necessary to employ demineralization or distillation.

TOTAL, DISSOLVED AND SUSPENDED SOLIDS, GRAVIMETRIC METHOD

THEORY OF TEST. These tests are based on the evaporation of a water sample to dryness under standard conditions and the weighing of the residue after drying.

APPARATUS REQUIRED. A well equipped laboratory is necessary for these determinations.

PROCEDURE FOR TEST.

Total Solids.

Evaporate to dryness in a weighed platinum dish on a steam or water bath, 100 ml of a thoroughly shaken, unfiltered sample. Dry the residue at 103 C for one hour. The increase in weight of the platinum dish in mg multiplied by 10 equals ppm total solids.

Dissolved Solids.

The sample should be filtered so as to reduce the turbidity of the filtrate to less than 1 unit and then 100 ml of the filtered sample is evaporated to dryness as under the total solids test.

Suspended solids may be calculated as the difference between total and dissolved solids.

Suspended Solids.

Suspended solids may be determined directly by filtering the sample using a Gooch crucible and an asbestos mat. Sufficient sample should be filtered to yield 50-100 mg suspended residue. Dry one hour at 103 C, cool in a desiccator until the weight is constant. This direct determination of suspended solids is to be preferred for accuracy to the calculation of suspended solids.

LIMITATIONS OF TEST. Although a 100 ml sample was specified in the determination of total and dissolved solids, it is necessary to alter the size of the sample taken in order to obtain a weighable residue of sufficient magnitude. The size of the sample taken for test should be such that the residue after evaporation amounts to 50-100 mg. Special precautions are necessary in the determination of the solids content of condensed steam samples. Special apparatus is required and sufficient sample is taken to yield a residue of approximately 25 mg.

66

Sulfate

THE sulfate ion is present in all natural waters due to the solvent action of water on the minerals in the earth. The quantity of sulfates present in natural waters will vary considerably in different sections of the country depending upon the mineral content of the soil in any particular locality. Some industrial wastes such as acid mine drainage and pickling liquors are high in sulfates, contributing to the natural sulfate content of the raw water.

The U. S. Public Health Service Drinking Water Standards recommend that potable water contain less than 250 ppm of sulfate as SO_4.

The principal objection to the sulfate ion in water is its ability to combine with calcium to form calcium sulfate scale. The most common constituent of boiler scale in an untreated boiler is calcium sulfate. While calcium sulfate scale is not as common in cooling water systems, it can occur when high concentrations of calcium and sulfate exist simultaneously.

Sulfate may be either beneficial or detrimental in waters used for manufacturing. In the brewing of beer, calcium sulfate aids in producing desirable flavor. Conversely, in the ice industry calcium sulfate may cause the formation of white butts in the ice core.

In the conditioning of boiler feedwater, it usually is not necessary nor practical to remove sulfate from the water. If the hardness is removed or controlled, the sulfate scale cannot form. In other words, the prevention of calcium sulfate scale is possible by the removal of either the calcium or sulfate. In industrial water conditioning, it is much simpler and more economical to remove the calcium than the sulfate.

In cooling water conditioning, calcium sulfate scale is prevented by maintaining the calcium sulfate in solution by the use of surface active materials and by limitation of concentrations.

In process water where it is sometimes necessary to remove the sulfate ion, this can be accomplished through demineralization.

SULFATE, THQ METHOD

THEORY OF TEST. This method is based on the precipitation of sulfate by barium chloride in alcoholic solution in the presence of THQ indicator. As soon as the sulfate has been completely precipitated, further addition of barium chloride will react with the THQ indicator resulting in a color change from yellow to rose red.

APPARATUS REQUIRED.
- 1—Burette, automatic, 25 ml
- 1—Cylinder, graduated, 50 ml
- 1—Flask, Erlenmeyer, 125 ml
- 1—Measuring cup, brass
- 1—Pipette, delivery, 25 ml
- 2—Bottles, with droppers, 8 oz
- 1—Pipette, Mohr, 5 ml

CHEMICALS REQUIRED.
Barium Chloride, 1 ml = 1 mg SO_4
Barium Chloride, 1 ml = 4 mg SO_4
Hydrochloric Acid, N/10
Phenolphthalein Indicator
Bromcresol Green Indicator
THQ (Tetrahydroxyquinone) Indicator
Isopropyl Alcohol, 99%
Silver Nitrate, 2%
Sodium Hydroxide, N/10

PROCEDURE FOR TEST. Measure 25 ml of clear sample into the Erlenmeyer flask. Add four drops of phenolphthalein indicator and by

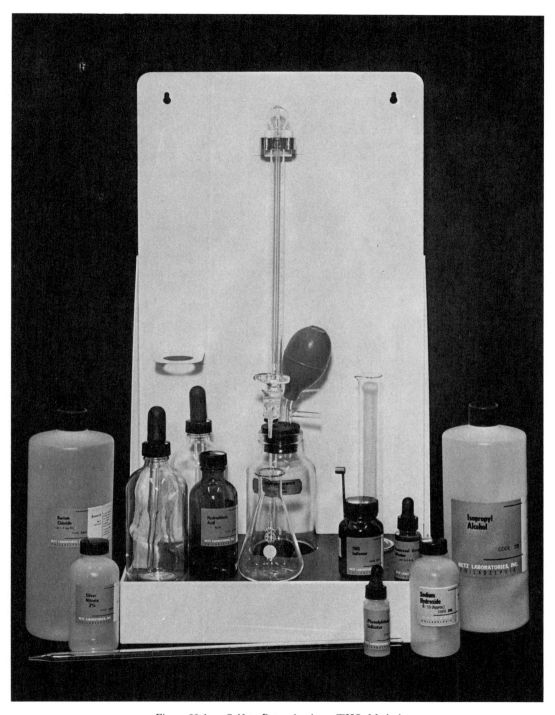

Figure 66-1 • Sulfate Determination—THQ Method

means of the dropper neutralize with N/10 hydrochloric acid until the red color just disappears. If the sample contains less than 50 ppm total alkalinity, a more dilute hydrochloric acid can be employed for greater accuracy in neutralization. If the sample is a natural water containing no phenolphthalein alkalinity, adjust with sodium hydroxide and hydrochloric acid so as to just neutralize to the acid side of phenolphthalein.

After neutralization, add one level measure (approx. 0.2 g) THQ Indicator (for samples containing less than 50 ppm sulfate, only ½ dipper of THQ Indicator should be employed). Swirl flask to dissolve indicator. Then, add 25 ml of isopropyl alcohol (or ethyl alcohol denatured by Formula 3A or 30). Titrate the resulting yellow solution with barium chloride solution, with thorough shaking, until the color changes from a yellow to a rose red.

To Sharpen Endpoint—The sharpness of the endpoint is increased by a small amount of silver nitrate. Use 1.0 ml of 2% silver nitrate solution when chlorides are low and 3.0 ml of silver nitrate solution when the chlorides are high. The silver nitrate is added during the titration.

Caution—If silver nitrate is used in excess of chloride, an intense cherry color will develop. When this color is produced by the introduction of silver nitrate, discard and repeat the titration with less silver nitrate.

For natural waters, use barium chloride solution 1 ml = 1 mg SO_4 and subtract a blank of 0.2 ml from the barium chloride titration. For boiler waters or other waters high in sulfate, use barium chloride solution 1 ml = 4 mg SO_4. Using this strength solution no blank is necessary. For extremely high sulfate concentrations use a 5 or 10 ml sample, diluting to 25 ml with distilled water and multiplying the results by the appropriate factor.

Modification When Phosphate is Present. When soluble phosphate is present in the sample, as is the case with many boiler waters, use bromcresol green indicator in the neutralization in place of phenolphthalein indicator, acidifying with the N/10 hydrochloric acid until the green color is just discharged to a straw color. Then proceed as outlined. By this modification, the titration is carried out at a lower pH at which up to 60 ppm phosphate as PO_4 does not interfere. For samples containing higher concentrations of phosphate, a 5 or 10 ml sample should be diluted to 25 ml with distilled water, neutralized and titrated as indicated above. The results should be multiplied by the appropriate factor.

CALCULATION OF RESULTS.
Formula:

ppm sulfate as SO_4 = (ml barium chloride − ml blank) × strength $BaCl_2$ mg/ml ×

$$\frac{1000}{\text{ml sample}}$$

Using a 25 ml sample and barium chloride of the strength 1 ml = 1 mg SO_4, the sulfate in parts per million is equal to the ml of barium chloride required minus the blank of 0.2 ml, multiplied by 40. When using a 25 ml sample and barium chloride of the strength 1 ml = 4 mg SO_4, sulfate in parts per million as SO_4 is equal to the ml of barium chloride required multiplied by 160.

LIMITATIONS OF TEST. The THQ method for sulfate determination is not affected by chlorides, silica, sulfites, tannins, soluble magnesium, soluble calcium and ferric or ferrous iron. Phosphate up to 60 ppm can be tolerated using the modified method, and above this concentration by dilution and the modified method. It is advisable not to employ the THQ method for sulfates lower than 20 ppm as SO_4. Temperature has little effect below 95 F.

Sulfate also may be measured by the use of a photometer. The analysis is conducted at a 415 mu wave length with a light path of 20 mm. The method is based on the development of turbidity which is proportional to the sulfate content, by precipitation of the sulfate as barium sulfate. This procedure is not affected by the ions normally present in water and sulfate up to 40 ppm can be determined without dilution of the sample.

67

Sulfite

THE determination of sulfite usually is made only on boiler waters or on waters that have been treated with catalyzed sodium sulfite for corrosion prevention. Generally speaking, sulfite is not present in natural waters.

In boiler feedwater conditioning, sodium sulfite is fed to a boiler to remove dissolved oxygen and thus prevent pitting. Under proper conditions sulfite will react with dissolved oxygen to form sulfate, thus removing the dissolved oxygen from the system. In order for this reaction to proceed rapidly and completely, it is necessary to maintain an excess sulfite concentration at an elevated temperature. To assure the rapid and complete removal of any dissolved oxygen entering a boiler in the feedwater, a soluble (or excess) sulfite content of at least 20 ppm is generally maintained in the boiler water.

Theoretically, it requires 7.88 pounds of chemically pure sodium sulfite to remove one pound of oxygen. Sodium sulfite supplied for the purpose of oxygen removal need not be chemically pure unless products such as certain foods are being processed. The average purity of the technical grade usually employed for oxygen removal is about 90% sodium sulfite. The efficiency of the oxygen removal is estimated at 75% to allow for oxidation in contact with air, blowdown losses, etc. Therefore, it is estimated that 10 pounds of commercial sodium sulfite are required for each pound of oxygen removed (or 10 ppm sulfite per 1 ppm dissolved oxygen).

The use of sodium sulfite as a chemical deaerant is economical within certain limitations imposed by the dissolved oxygen content of the feedwater. If appreciable quantities of dissolved oxygen are permitted to enter the boiler, costs will be high when relying entirely upon sodium sulfite as a means of oxygen removal. The safest practice is to remove as much oxygen as possible by mechanical means, through the use of efficient types of boiler feedwater heaters and then to maintain a residual sulfite in the boiler water to react with any oxygen which has not been mechanically removed.

For the prevention of corrosion and pitting in feed lines, closed heaters and economizers, it is desirable that the sodium sulfite be fed continuously to the boiler feedwater rather than direct to the boiler. Reaction between sulfite and dissolved oxygen is not instantaneous and the completion of this reaction is aided by the longer contact period provided by feeding sodium sulfite through the boiler feed line. The preferred point of application of the sodium sulfite is to the storage compartment of the feedwater heater.

The development of catalyzed sodium sulfite has increased considerably the field of usefulness of this material for oxygen removal. Catalyzed sodium sulfite will react almost instantaneously with dissolved oxygen even at cold water temperatures. Because of this property, catalyzed sodium sulfite is finding increased use in the treatment of cooling water, process water, distribution systems, etc., for prevention of oxygen corrosion. In the prevention of economizer corrosion, it frequently is more desirable to employ catalyzed sodium sulfite in order to obtain the advantage of rapid oxygen removal.

SULFITE, POTASSIUM IODIDE-IODATE METHOD

THEORY OF TEST. This test is based on the titration of a water sample containing sulfite by means of a standard potassium iodide-iodate solution. Free iodine is produced when the sulfite has been completely oxidized, resulting in a blue color in the presence of a starch-type indicator. This blue color is taken as the endpoint.

APPARATUS REQUIRED.
    1—Burette, automatic, 25 ml
    1—Casserole, porcelain, 210 ml
    1—Cylinder, graduated, 50 ml
    1—Stirring rod, glass
    1—Measuring dipper (plastic)

CHEMICALS REQUIRED.
    Phenolphthalein Indicator
    Potassium Iodide-Iodate, 1 ml = 0.5 mg
      SO_3
    Sulfite Indicator

PROCEDURE FOR TEST. The water sample should be freshly obtained with as little contact with air as possible. Do not filter. Cool to room temperature (70-80 F).

Measure 50 ml of the water sample with the graduated cylinder and transfer to the casserole. Add 3-4 drops of phenolphthalein indicator to the sample. The sample will turn red. Use the plastic dipper to add one (1) dipperful of sulfite indicator at a time to the sample. Stir thoroughly between each addition of sulfite indicator (all of the indicator may not dissolve creating a slight haze in the sample). Continue to add indicator in this manner until the red color disappears. It is not necessary to *exactly* neutralize the phenolphthalein alkalinity. When the sample is colorless *then add one (1) additional dipperful* of sulfite indicator and stir.

Titrate with potassium iodide-iodate solution until a faint permanent blue color develops in the sample. This color change is taken as the endpoint. Record the ml potassium iodide-iodate solution used.

CALCULATION OF RESULTS.
Formula:

$$\text{ppm sulfite as } SO_3 = \text{ml potassium iodide-iodate} \times \frac{500}{\text{ml sample}}$$

Using a 50 ml sample, the parts per million of sulfite as SO_3 equals ml potassium iodide-iodate required multiplied by 10.

LIMITATIONS OF TEST. This method is rapid and adaptable to field determinations. It is affected by any oxidizable substances in the water such as organic matter, sulfides and nitrites. The presence of these interfering substances may cause the sulfite obtained from this titration to be shown as a higher value than actually present.

68

Turbidity

TURBIDITY can be interpreted as a lack of clearness or brilliance in a water, but should not be confused with color. A water may be dark in color but still clear and not turbid.

Turbidity is due to suspended matter in a finely divided state. Clay, silt, organic matter, microscopic organisms and similar materials are contributing causes of turbidity.

Although the terms "suspended matter" and "turbidity" are closely allied, they are not synonymous. Suspended matter is the quantity of material in a water which can be removed by filtration. Turbidity is a measurement of the optical obstruction of light passed through a water sample.

The standard unit of turbidity formerly was defined as the optical obstruction of light caused by 1 ppm of insoluble silica (diatomaceous earth or Fuller's earth) in distilled water. However, the 10th edition (1955) of "Standard Methods" abandoned the terms "silica scale" and "parts per million" for turbidity. The primary standard for turbidity is the Jackson candle turbidimeter and it is recommended that turbidity readings be expressed as follows:

Turbidities greater than: units	but less than: units	shall be recorded to the nearest: units
0.0	1.0	0.1
1	10	1
10	100	5
100	400	10
400	700	50
700	-	100

Turbidity suspensions standardized by the Jackson candle method may be used in the calibration of other turbidity measuring instruments.

Water taken from a river or turbulent stream usually contains appreciable quantities of turbidity. The water from lakes and ponds generally is less turbid because of the settling action which takes place in these bodies. Springs and wells usually are low in turbidity because of the filtering action of the ground through which the water flows.

The U. S. Public Health Service Drinking Water Standards recommend that the turbidity of potable water be less than 5 units.

The turbidity of industrial water should be as low as possible. This is particularly true of boiler feedwater. The turbidity, which is caused by small particles in suspension, will concentrate in the boiler water and may settle out in the form of a heavy sludge or "mud". This condition can be minimized to some extent by increase in blowdown. The turbidity of the boiler feedwater also limits the cycles of concentration carried in the boiler since one of the factors limiting these concentrations is the suspended solids of the boiler water. Finely divided particles introduced into the boiler water by the turbidity of the boiler feedwater also may be responsible for a foaming and priming condition. Process water, particularly in the food, dyeing and paper industries should have a low turbidity or the quality of the finished products manufactured may be affected.

Turbid makeup water to cooling water systems may cause plugging and overheating where solids settle out on heat exchange surfaces. Corrosive action may be increased under such deposits which hinder penetration of corrosive inhibitors.

Turbidity may be partially removed by

Figure 68-1 • Hellige Turbidimeter

subsidence, but it usually is necessary to employ coagulation and filtration in order to produce a treated water of low turbidity.

TURBIDITY, HELLIGE METHOD

THEORY OF TEST. Turbidity of water results from finely divided suspended matter. Measurement of turbidity is based on the optical obstruction of light rays passed through a sample when compared, under the same conditions, with an arbitrary standard turbidity scale. The Hellige Turbidimeter is based on the comparison of a beam of light with the Tyndall effect produced from the lateral illumination of a specimen by the same light source. As the method involves a comparison of Tyndall effect on the test

sample itself, the use of standard solutions and their preparation is eliminated.

APPARATUS REQUIRED.

    1—Hellige Turbidimeter, complete with calibrated curves for turbidity

PROCEDURE FOR TEST. First thoroughly shake the sample of water and then pour it into one of the glass cells to the mark on the side. Insert the plunger carefully, avoiding formation of bubbles on the under side. Place the cell on the mirror in the slot provided. Close the door of the instrument and then turn on the light.

View turbidity through the ocular, and revolve the dial on the side of the instrument until the black circle matches the surrounding field. The dial reading is noted.

This method covers a turbidity range of 0 to 100 units without dilution of the water sample. This range is covered by use of various size cells and filters, a standard curve being furnished for each set of conditions.

CALCULATION OF RESULTS. The number of units of turbidity are determined by comparison of the dial reading with the calibrated curve.

LIMITATIONS OF TEST. Turbidity varies not only with the nature of the suspended solids present, but with their particle size. Therefore, there is no relation between turbidity and gravimetrically determined suspended solids. For turbidities above 100 units, dilution with "zero" turbid water is necessary. Dial readings should be taken as soon as possible to avoid error introduced by the settling of large particles.

Due to the inability of a photometer to blank out the initial color of a sample, this instrument normally is not recommended for the measurement of turbidity.

69

Composition of Prepared Reagents

REAGENT grade chemicals should be used in the preparation of all solutions. These reagents should be prepared only in a well equipped laboratory, under the supervision of an experienced chemist. It is advisable to purchase these solutions from a laboratory supply house if complete laboratory facilities are not available for their preparation.

ACETONE REAGENT
A 50% by volume solution of acetone in distilled water.

ALKALINE POTASSIUM IODIDE
Dissolve 700 g potassium hydroxide in 700 ml distilled water and cool. Dissolve 150 g potassium iodide in 200 ml distilled water and cool. Mix the two solutions and dilute to 1.0 liter with distilled water.

AMMONIUM MOLYBDATE REAGENT (silica, high range — Taylor and photometer methods)
A 10.2% solution of ammonium molybdate (81% MoO_3) in distilled water. Note— This solution will become cloudy from time to time and any turbidity should be filtered prior to use.

AMMONIUM MOLYBDATE REAGENT (silica, low range—photometer method)
A 4.0% solution of ammonium molybdate (81% MoO_3) in 10% by volume concentrated hydrochloric acid.

BARIUM CHLORIDE, 1 ml = 1 mg SO_4
A solution of approximately 0.255% barium chloride in distilled water, standardized so that 1 ml = 1 mg SO_4.

BARIUM CHLORIDE, 1 ml = 4 mg SO_4
A solution of approximately 1.02% barium chloride in distilled water, standardized so that 1 ml = 4 mg SO_4.

BARIUM CHLORIDE, 10%
A 10.0% solution of barium chloride in distilled water.

BROMCRESOL GREEN INDICATOR
A solution prepared by triturating 0.4 g bromcresol green in 3-5 ml distilled water, then diluting to 25 ml with distilled water. Add 1.6 ml of 1N sodium hydroxide, dilute to 1.0 liter and adjust pH to 4.6±0.1 with electrometric pH meter.

BRUCINE REAGENT
A 5.0% solution of brucine alkaloid ($C_{23}H_{26}N_2O_4 \cdot 4H_2O$) in reagent grade chloroform.

CALCIUM INDICATOR
A dispersion of 0.20 g ammonium purpurate in 100 g c.p. potassium chloride, ground so it will pass through a 30 mesh screen.

CHROMATE STANDARD, 10 ppm as CrO_4
A standardized solution of potassium chromate, 10 ppm as CrO_4.

HARDNESS BUFFER REAGENT
The dry hardness buffer is prepared using special solvents, mixing, evaporation and grinding. Special equipment is necessary.
A liquid buffer reagent, stable for approximately three months, can be prepared by dissolving 10 g sodium hydroxide, 10 g sodium sulfide, 40 g sodium tetraborate ($Na_2B_4O_7 \cdot 10H_2O$) and 10 g sodium potas-

sium tartrate $(NaKC_4H_4O_6 \cdot 4H_2O)$ in a liter of distilled water. In the hardness test, 0.5 ml of the liquid buffer is used.

HARDNESS INDICATOR

The dry hardness indicator is prepared using special solvents, mixing and grinding. Special equipment is necessary.

A liquid hardness indicator, stable for approximately three months, can be prepared by dissolving 10 g Eriochrome Black T in 300 ml of 0.2% sodium carbonate solution. Then dilute to 1.0 liter with isopropyl alcohol (99%), adjusting pH to 9.0 with 0.1 N sodium carbonate. In the hardness test, use 4-6 drops of the liquid indicator.

HARDNESS TITRATING SOLUTION, 1 ml = 1 mg $CaCO_3$

A distilled water solution of 4.0 g disodium ethylenediaminetetracetate dihydrate and 0.86 g sodium hydroxide per liter, standardized so that 1 ml = 1 mg $CaCO_3$.

HYDRAZINE STANDARD SOLUTION, 1 ml = 0.1 mg N_2H_4

A solution of 0.328 g hydrazine hydrochloride $(N_2H_4 \cdot 2HCl)$ in 100 ml distilled water and 74 ml concentrated hydrochloric acid. Dilute to 1.0 liter with distilled water.

HYDROCHLORIC ACID, N/50

A solution of hydrochloric acid in distilled water standardized to 0.02N.

HYDROCHLORIC ACID, N/10

A solution of hydrochloric acid in distilled water standardized to 0.1N.

HYDROCHLORIC ACID, 5 N

A solution of hydrochloric acid in distilled water standardized to 5.0 N.

HYDROCHLORIC ACID 10%

A 10.0% by volume solution of concentrated hydrochloric acid in distilled water.

HYDROCHLORIC ACID, 50%

A 50% by volume solution of concentrated hydrochloric acid in distilled water.

HYDROCHLORIC ACID REAGENT

A 2.0% by volume solution of concentrated hydrochloric acid in distilled water.

HYDROXYLAMINE REAGENT

Dissolve 100 g hydroxylamine hydrochloride in 200 ml distilled water and neutralize to pH 8.0 with 20% sodium hydroxide. Dilute to 600 ml with distilled water and add 100 ml glacial acetic acid. Dissolve 200 g aluminum nitrate $(Al_2(NO_3)_3 \cdot 9H_2O)$ in 150 ml distilled water and add. Dissolve 4 g Sequestrene Na_2 in 50 ml distilled water and add. Dilute to 1.0 liter with distilled water.

IRON STANDARD SOLUTION, 1 ml = 10 ppm Fe

Prepare a concentrated stock solution by dissolving 7.022 g of crystallized ferrous ammonium sulfate $(FeSO_4(NH_4)_2SO_4 \cdot 6H_2O)$ in 500 ml distilled water and 200 ml concentrated sulfuric acid. Completely oxidize with 0.1 N potassium permanganate and dilute to 1.0 liter with distilled water. Dilute this stock solution as required to produce an iron standard solution, 1 ml = 10 ppm Fe.

MANGANESE SPECIAL SOLUTION

Dissolve 75 g mercuric sulfate in 400 ml concentrated nitric acid and 200 ml distilled water. Add 200 ml 85% phosphoric acid and 0.035 g silver nitrate. Cool and dilute to 1.0 liter with distilled water.

MANGANESE STANDARD SOLUTION, 1 ml = 10 ppm Mn

Prepare an aged 0.1 N potassium permanganate solution. Calculate the quantity of this solution required to prepare 1.0 liter so that 1 ml = 10 ppm Mn. Acidify the calculated volume of permanganate with 2-3 ml concentrated sulfuric acid. Add sodium bisulfite solution dropwise (10 g dissolved in 100 ml distilled water) until the permanganate color disappears. Boil to remove SO_2. Cool and dilute to 1.0 liter with distilled water.

MANGANOUS SULFATE SOLUTION

A 48% solution of manganous sulfate $(MnSO_4 \cdot 4H_2O)$ in distilled water.

METHYL ORANGE INDICATOR

A 0.05% solution of methyl orange in distilled water.

METHYL PURPLE INDICATOR

A proprietary dispersion of an organic dye sensitive to essentially the same pH range as methyl orange indicator. (Fleisher

Chemical Co.)

MOLYBDATE REAGENT (for phosphate)

A solution of sodium molybdate in 5.0% by volume sulfuric acid standardized to 0.145 N.

NESSLER REAGENT

Dissolve 100 g of mercuric iodide and 70 g of potassium iodide in a small quantity of ammonia-free water, and add slowly, with stirring, to a cool solution of 160 g sodium hydroxide in 500 ml of ammonia-free water. Dilute to 1.0 liter with ammonia-free water.

ORTHOPHENANTHROLINE REAGENT

Dissolve 1.0 g orthophenanthroline monohydrate in 1.0 liter distilled water.

ORTHOTOLIDINE REAGENT

A solution prepared by adding 50 ml of a 0.270% solution of orthotolidine dihydrochloride in distilled water to 50 ml of a 30% by volume solution of concentrated hydrocholoric acid.

OXALIC ACID, 3%

A 3.0% solution of oxalic acid in distilled water.

OXALIC ACID, 10%

A 10.0% solution of oxalic acid in distilled water.

PHENOLPHTHALEIN INDICATOR

A 0.5% solution of phenolphthalein in 50% ethyl alcohol.

POTASSIUM CHROMATE INDICATOR

A 5.0% solution of neutral potassium chromate in distilled water.

POTASSIUM IODIDE-IODATE, 1 ml = 0.5 mg SO_3

A solution of 0.31 g sodium bicarbonate, 4.35 g potassium iodide and 0.45 g potassium iodate per liter, standardized to 0.0125 N.

POTASSIUM PERMANGANATE, N/100

An aged solution of potassium permanganate in distilled water, standardized to N/100.

SILICA STANDARD, 50 ppm as SiO_2

A standardized solution of sodium silicate, 50 ppm as SiO_2. The sodium silicate is prepared by fusion of pure SiO_2 and Na_2CO_3.

SILVER NITRATE, 1 ml = 1 mg Cl

An approximately 0.03 N solution of silver nitrate in distilled water, standardized so that 1 ml = 1 mg Cl.

SILVER NITRATE, 1 ml = 5 mg Cl

An approximately 0.14 N solution of silver nitrate in distilled water, standardized so that 1 ml = 5 mg Cl.

SILVER NITRATE, 2%

A solution of 2.0% silver nitrate in distilled water.

SODIUM ARSENITE, 0.5%

A 0.5% solution of sodium meta arsenite in distilled water.

SODIUM CARBONATE, N/50

A solution of sodium carbonate in distilled water, standardized to 0.02 N.

SODIUM CARBONATE, N/22

A solution of sodium carbonate in distilled water, standardized to 0.0455 N.

SODIUM HYDROXIDE, 1.0 N

A solution of sodium hydroxide in distilled water, standardized to 1.0 N.

SODIUM HYDROXIDE, 7 N

A solution of sodium hydroxide in distilled water, standardized to 7.0 N.

SODIUM SULFITE REAGENT

A solution of sodium sulfite in distilled water, standardized to 2.7 N.

SODIUM THIOSULFATE, N/10

A solution of sodium thiosulfate in distilled water, standardized to 0.1 N.

STANNOUS REAGENT, Dry

A dispersion of 2.5% stannous sulfate.

STARCH INDICATOR

A 0.5% solution of c.p. starch in distilled water.

STARFAMIC INDICATOR

A proprietary dispersion of cold water soluble starch in a crystalline acid medium. (U.S. Patent No. 2,963,442).

SULFITE INDICATOR

A proprietary dispersion of cold water soluble starch in a crystalline acid medium. (U. S. Patent No. 2,963,442).

SULFURIC ACID, N/50

A solution of sulfuric acid in distilled water standardized to 0.02N.

SULFURIC ACID, 1.0 N

A solution of sulfuric acid in distilled water standardized to 1.0 N.

SULFURIC ACID, 5%

A 5.0% by volume solution of concentrated sulfuric acid in distilled water.

SULFURIC ACID, 50%

A 50% by volume solution of concentrated sulfuric acid in distilled water.

SULFURIC ACID REAGENT

A 15.0% by volume solution of concentrated sulfuric acid in distilled water.

THQ (TETRAHYDROXYQUINONE) INDICATOR

A proprietary dispersion of disodium tetrahydroxyquinone dye.

TAYLOR HYDRAZINE REAGENT A

Paradimethylaminobenzaldehyde powder.

TAYLOR HYDRAZINE REAGENT B

A solution containing 10% concentrated hydrochloric acid and 90% isopropyl alcohol.

XYLENE CYANOLE, 0.02%

A 0.02% solution of xylene cyanole in distilled water.

Conversion Factors

WATER ANALYSIS

		Parts per Million	Parts per 100,000	Grains per U.S. Gallon	Grains per Imp. Gallon
1 part per million	=	1.0	0.10	0.058	0.07
1 part per 100,000	=	10.0	1.00	0.585	0.70
1 grain per U.S. Gal	=	17.1	1.71	1.000	1.20
1 grain per Imp. Gal	=	14.3	1.43	0.835	1.00

HARDNESS

		Parts per Million	Grains per U.S. Gallon	Clark Degrees	French Degrees	German Degrees
1 part per million	=	1.0	0.058	0.07	0.10	0.056
1 grain per U.S. Gal	=	17.1	1.000	1.20	1.71	0.958
1 Clark degree	=	14.3	0.829	1.00	1.43	0.080
1 French degree	=	10.0	0.583	0.70	1.00	0.560
1 German degree	=	17.9	1.044	1.24	1.78	1.000

MISCELLANEOUS

1 U.S. Gallon = 0.1337 cu ft

1 U.S. Gallon = 231 cu in

1 U.S. Gallon = 3.785 liters

1 U.S. Gallon (water) = 8.34 lbs

1 cubic foot = 7.48 U.S. Gallons

1 cubic foot (water) = 62.4 lbs

1 part per millon = 8.33 lbs per million gallons

1 grain per gallon = 143 lbs per million gallons

1 lb per million gallons = 0.12 parts per million

1 lb per million gallons = 0.007 grains per gallon

1 lb per thousand gallons = 120 parts per million

1 cu ft per second = 646,316 gallons per day

1 cu ft per second = 448.83 gallons per minute

1 gal per minute = 0.00144 million gallons per day

1 ft head water = 0.434 psi

1 psi = 2.31 ft head water

$°F = (°C \times 1.8) + 32$

$°C = (°F - 32) \times 0.55$

Index

NOTES

NOTES

NOTES